The Art of
MODELING
in
SCIENCE
and
ENGINEERING

The Art of
MODELING
in
SCIENCE
and
ENGINEERING

Diran Basmadjian

CHAPMAN & HALL/CRC

Boca Raton   London   New York   Washington, D.C.

Acquiring Editor: Bob Stern
Project Editor: Maggie Mogck
Marketing Managers: Barbara Glunn, Jane Lewis,
                          Arline Massey, Jane Stark
Cover Design: Dawn Boyd

Library of Congress Cataloging-in-Publication Data

Basmadjian, Diran
    The art of modeling in science and engineering / Diran Basmadjian.
        p. cm.
    Includes bibliographical references and index.
    ISBN 1-58488-012-0
    1. Mathematical models. 2. Science—Mathematical models. 3. Engineering—
Mathematical models.   I. Title.
QA401.B38   1999
511'.8—dc21

                                                              99-11443
                                                              CIP

Preface

The term *model,* as used in this text, is understood to refer to the ensemble of equations which describe and interrelate the variables and parameters of a physical system or process. The term *modeling* in turn refers to the derivation of appropriate equations that are solved for a set of system or process variables and parameters. These solutions are often referred to as simulations, i.e., they simulate or reproduce the behavior of physical systems and processes.

Modeling is practiced with uncommon frequency in the engineering disciplines and indeed in all physical sciences where it is often known as "Applied Mathematics." It has made its appearance in other disciplines as well which do not involve physical processes per se, such as economics, finance, and banking. The reader will note a chemical engineering slant to the contents of the book, but that discipline now reaches out, some would say with tentacles, far beyond its immediate narrow confines to encompass topics of interest to both scientists and engineers. We address the book in particular to those in the disciplines of chemical, mechanical, civil, and environmental engineering, to applied chemists and physicists in general, and to students of applied mathmatics.

The text covers a wide range of physical processes and phenomena which generally call for the use of mass, energy, and momentum or force balances, together with auxiliary relations drawn from such subdisciplines as thermodynamics and chemical kinetics. Both static and dynamic systems are covered as well as processes which are at a steady state. Thus, transport phenomena play an important but not exclusive role in the subject matter covered. This amalgam of topics is held together by the common thread of applied mathematics.

A plethora of related specialized tests exist. Mass and energy balances which arise from their respective conservation laws have been addressed by Reklaitis (1983), Felder and Rousseau (1986) and Himmelblau (1996). The books by Reklaitis and Himmelblau in particular are written at a high level. Force and momentum balances are best studied in texts on fluid mechanics, among many of which are by Streeter, Wylie, and Bedford (1998) and White (1986) stand out. For a comprehensive and sophisticated treatment of transport phenomena, the text by Bird, Stewart, and Lightfoot (1960) remains unsurpassed. Much can be gleaned on dynamic or unsteady systems from process control texts, foremost among them are those by Stephanopoulos (1984), Luyben (1990) and Ogunnaike and Ray (1996).

In spite of this wealth of information, students and even professionals often experience difficulties in setting up and solving even the simplest models. This can be attributed to the following factors:

- A major stumbling block is the proper choice of model. How complex should it be? One can always choose to work at the highest and most rigorous level of partial differential equations (PDE), but this often leads to models of unmanageable complexity and dimensionality. Physical parameters may be unknown and there is a rapid loss of physical insight caused by the multidimensional nature of the solution. Constraints of time and resources often make it impossible to embark on elaborate exercises of this type, or the answer sought may simply not be worth the effort. It is surprising how often the solution is needed the next day, or not at all. Still, there are many occasions where PDEs are unavoidable or advantage may be taken of existing solutions. This is particularly the case with PDEs of the "classical" type, such as those which describe diffusion or conduction processes. Solutions to such problems are amply documented in the definitive monographs by Carslaw and Jaeger (1959) and by Crank (1978). Even here, however, one often encounters solutions which reduce to PDEs of lower dimensionality, to ordinary differential equations (ODEs) or even algebraic equations (AEs). The motto must therefore be "PDEs if necessary, but not necessarily PDEs."

- The second difficulty lies in the absence of precise solutions, even with the use of the most sophisticated models and computational tools. Some systems are simply too complex to yield exact answers. One must resort here to what we term *bracketing the solution,* i.e., establishing upper or lower bounds to the answer being sought. This is a perfectly respectable exercise, much practiced by mathematicians and theoretical scientists and engineers.

- The third difficulty lies in making suitable simplifying assumptions and approximations. This requires considerable physical insight and engineering skill. Not infrequently, a certain boldness and leap in imagination is called for. These are not easy attributes to satisfy.

Overcoming these three difficulties constitute the core of *The Art of Modeling.* Although we will not make this aspect the exclusive domain of our effort, a large number of examples and illustrations will be presented to provide the reader with some practice in this difficult craft.

Our approach will be to proceed slowly and over various stages from the mathematically simple to the more complex, ultimately looking at some sophisticated models. In other words, we propose to model "from the bottom up" rather than "from the top down," which is the normal approach particularly in treatments of transport phenomena. We found this to be pedagogically more effective although not necessarily in keeping with academic tradition and rigor.

As an introduction, we establish in Chapter 1 a link between the physical system and the mathematical expressions that result. This provides the reader with a sense of the type and degree of mathematical complexity to be expected. Some simple classical models such as the *stirred tank* and what we term the *one-dimensional pipe* and *quenched steel billet* are introduced. We examine as well the types of balances, i.e., the equations which result from the application of various conservation laws to different physical entities and the information to be derived from them.

These introductory remarks lead, in Chapter 2, to a first detailed examination of practical problems and the skills required in the setting up of equations arising from the stirred tank and the 1-d pipe models. Although deceptively simple in retrospect, the application of these models to real problems will lead to a first encounter with the art of modeling. A first glimpse will also be had of the skills needed in setting upper and lower bounds to the solutions. We do this even though more accurate and elaborate solutions may be available. The advantage is that the bounds can be established quickly and it is surprising how often this is all an engineer or scientist needs to do. The examples here and throughout the book are drawn from a variety of disciplines which share a common interest in transport phenomena and the application of mass, energy, and momentum or force balances. From classical chemical engineering we have drawn examples dealing with heat and mass transfer, fluid statics and dynamics, reactor engineering, and the basic unit operations (distillation, gas absorption, adsorption, filtration, drying, and membrane processes, among others). These are also of general interest to other engineering disciplines. Woven into these are illustrations which combine several processes or do not fall into any rigid category.

These early segments are followed, in Chapter 3, by a more detailed exposition of mass, energy and momentum transport, illustrated with classical and modern examples. The reader will find here, as in all other chapters, a rich choice of solved illustrative examples as well as a large number of practice problems. The latter are worth the scrutiny of the reader even if no solution is attempted. The mathematics up to this point is simple, all ODE solutions being obtained by separation of variables.

An intermezzo now occurs in which underlying mathematical topics are taken up. In Chapter 4, an exposition is given of important analytical and numerical solutions of ordinary differential equations in which we consider methods applicable to first and second order ODEs in some detail. Considerable emphasis is given to deducing the qualitative nature of the solutions from the underlying model equations and to linking the mathematics to the physical processes involved. Both linear and nonlinear analysis is applied. Linear systems are examined in more detail in a follow-up chapter on Laplace transformation.

We return to modeling in Chapter 6 by taking up three specialized topics dealing with biomedical engineering and biotechnology, environmental engineering, as well as what we term real-world problems. The purpose here is to apply our modeling skills to specific subject areas of general usefulness and interest. The real-world problems are drawn from industrial sources as well as the consulting practices of the author and his colleagues and require, to a greater degree than before, the skills of simplification, of seeking out upper and lower bounds and of good physical insight. The models are at this stage still at the AE and ODE level.

In the final three chapters, we turn to the difficult topic of partial differential equations. Chapter 7 exposes the reader to a first sight and smell of the beasts and attempts to allay apprehension by presenting some simple solutions arrived at by the often overlooked methods of superposition or by locating solutions in the literature. We term this PDEs PDQ (Pretty Damn Quick). Chapter 8 is more ambitious. It introduces the reader to the dreaded topic of vector calculus which we apply to derive generalized formulations of mass, energy, and momentum balance. The unpalatable subject of Green's functions makes its appearance, but here as elsewhere, we attempt to ease the pain by relating the new concepts to physical reality and by providing numerous illustrations. We conclude, in Chapter 9, with a presentation of the classical solution methods of separation of variables and integral transforms and introduce the reader to the method of characteristics, a powerful tool for the solution of quasilinear PDEs.

A good deal of this material has been presented over the past 3 decades in courses to select fourth year and graduate students in the faculty of Applied Science and Engineering of the University of Toronto. Student comments have been invaluable and several of them were kind enough to share with the author problems from their industrial experience, among them Dr. K. Adham, Dr. S.T. Hsieh, Dr. G. Norval, and Professor C. Yip. I am also grateful to my colleagues, Professor M.V. Sefton, Professor D.E. Cormack, and Professor Emeritus S. Sandler for providing me with problems from their consulting and teaching practices.

Many former students were instrumental in persuading the author to convert classroom notes into a text, among them Dr. K. Gregory, Dr. G.M. Martinez, Dr. M. May, Dr. D. Rosen, and Dr. S. Seyfaie. I owe a special debt of gratitude to S. (VJ) Vijayakumar who never wavered in his support of this project and from whom I drew a good measure of inspiration. A strong prod was also provided by Professor S.A. Baldwin, Professor V.G. Papangelakis, and by Professor Emeritus J. Toguri.

The text is designed for undergraduate and graduate students, as well as practicing professionals in the sciences and in engineering, with an interest in modeling based on mass, energy and momentum or force balances. The first six chapters contain no partial differential equations and are suitable as a basis for a fourth-year course in Modeling or Applied Mathematics, or, with some boldness and omissions, at the third-year level. The book in its entirety, with some of the preliminaries and other extraneous material omitted, can serve as a text in Modeling and Applied Mathematics at the first-year graduate level. Students in the Engineering Sciences in particular, will benefit from it.

It remains for me to express my thanks to Arlene Fillatre who undertook the arduous task of transcribing the hand-written text to readable print, to Linda Staats, University of Toronto Press, who miraculously converted rough sketches into professional drawings, and to Bruce Herrington for his unfailing wit. My wife, Janet, bore the proceedings, sometimes with dismay, but mostly with pride.

REFERENCES

R.B. Bird, W.R. Stewart, and E.N. Lightfoot. *Transport Phenomena,* John Wiley & Sons, New York, 1960.

H.S. Carslaw and J.C. Jaeger. *Conduction of Heat on Solids, 2nd ed.,* Oxford University Press, Oxford, U.K., 1959.

J. Crank. *Mathematics of Diffusion, 2nd ed.,* Oxford University Press, Oxford, U.K., 1978.

R.M. Felder and R.W. Rousseau. *Elementary Principles of Chemical Processes,* John Wiley & Sons, New York, 1986.

D.M. Himmelblau. *Basic Principles and Calculations in Chemical Engineering, 6th ed.,* Prentice-Hall, Upper Saddle River, NJ, 1996.

W.L. Luyben. *Process Modeling, Simulation and Control, 2nd ed.,* McGraw-Hill, New York, 1990.

B. Ogunnaike and W.H. Ray. *Process Dynamics, Modeling and Control,* Oxford University Press, Oxford, U.K., 1996.

G.V. Reklaitis. *Introduction to Material and Energy Balances,* John Wiley & Sons, New York, 1983.

G. Stephanopoulos. *Chemical Process Control,* Prentice-Hall, Upper Saddle River, NJ, 1984.

V.L. Streeter, E.B. Wylie, and K.W. Bedford. *Fluid Mechanics, 9th ed.,* McGraw-Hill, New York, 1998.

F.M. White. *Fluid Mechanics, 2nd ed.,* McGraw-Hill, New York, 1986.

Author

Diran Basmadjian is a graduate of the Swiss Federal Institute of Technology, Zurich, and received his M.A.Sc. and Ph.D. degrees in Chemical Engineering from the University of Toronto. He was appointed Assistant Professor of Chemical Engineering at the University of Ottawa in 1960, moving to the University of Toronto in 1965, where he subsequently became Professor of Chemical Engineering.

He has combined his research interests in the separation sciences, biomedical engineering, and applied mathematics with a keen interest in the craft of teaching. His current activities include writing, consulting, and performing science experiments for children at a local elementary school.

Professor Basmadjian is married and has two daughters.

Nomenclature

The quantities listed are expressed in SI Units. Note the equivalence 1 N = 1 kg m/s^2, 1 Pa = 1 kg/ms^2, 1 J = 1 kg m^2/s^2.

A	Area, m^2
A_C	Cross-sectional area, m^2
A_r	Pre-exponential Arrhenius factor, 1/s
a	Absorptivity, dimensionless
a	Interfacial area, m^2/m^3
B	Magnetic field
Bi	Biot number = hL/k, dimensionless
C	Capacity FC_p, J/SK
C	Mass or molar concentration, kg/m^3 or mole/m^3
C	Speed of light, m/s
c	Speed of sound, m/s
C{ }	Cosine transform operation
C_D	Drag coefficient, dimensionless
C_p	Heat capacity at constant pressure, J/kg K or J/mole K
C_v	Heat capacity at constant volume, J/kg K or J/mole K
D	D-operator = d/dx
D	Diffusivity, m^2/s
D	Dilution Rate, 1/s
D	Distillation or evaporation rate, mole/s
D	Oxygen deficit = $C_{O_2}^* - C_{O_2}$, kg/m^3
D_{eff}	Effective diffusivity in porous medium, m^2/s
d_h	Hydraulic diameter = 4 A_C/P, m
d	Diameter, m
E	Electrical field
(E)	Enzyme concentration, mole/m^3
E	Fin efficiency, dimensionless
E_i	Isothermal catalyst effectiveness factor, dimensionless
E_{ni}	Non-isothermal catalyst effectiveness factor, dimensionless
ETC	Effective therapeutic concentration, kg/m^3
erf(x)	Error function = $(2/\sqrt{\pi}) \int_0^X e^{-\lambda^2} d\lambda$
F	Force, N
F	Mass flow rate, kg/s
Fo	Fourier number = $\alpha t/L^2$, dimensionless
f	Friction factor, dimensionless

f	Self-purification rate = $k_L a/k_r$, dimensionless
G	Mass velocity, kg/m^2s
G*	Limiting mass velocity, kg/m^2s
G_s	Carrier or solvent mass velocity, kg/m^2s
G(P,Q)	Green's function
Gr	Grashof number = $\rho^2 \beta g L^3 \Delta T/\mu^2$, dimensionless
g	Gravitational acceleration = 9.81 m^2/s
H	Enthalpy, J/kg or J/mole
H'	Enthalpy flow rate, J/s
ΔH_f	Enthalpy of freezing or solidification, J/kg or J/mole
ΔH_r	Enthalpy of reaction, J/mole
ΔH_v	Enthalpy of vaporization, J/kg or J/mole
H	Height, m
H	Henry's constant, m^3/m^3
HTU	Height of a transfer unit, m
H{ }	Hankel transform operator
h	Heat transfer coefficient, J/m^2sK
h_f	Friction head, J/kg
$I_k(s)$	Modified Bessel function of the first kind and order k
i	Electrical current, A
J	Current density, A/m^2
$J_k(x)$	Bessel function of first kind and order k
K	Partition coefficient, m^3/m^3
K	Permeability, m/s or m^2
K_D	Dissociation constant = k_r/k_f, dimensionless
K_k	Modified Bessel function of second kind and order k
K_m	Michaelis-Menten constant, $mole/m^3$
K_0	Overall mass transfer coefficient, various units, see Table 3.6
K_s	Monod kinetics constant, $mole/m^3$
k	Thermal conductivity, J/msK
$k_c, k_p, k_x,$ k_y, k_Y	Film mass transfer coefficients, various units
k_e	Elimination rate constant, 1/s
k_r	Reaction rate constant, 1/s (first order)
k_{eff}	Effective thermal conductivity in porous medium, J/msK
L	Length or characteristic length, m
L	Ligand concentration, mol/m^3
L	Liquid flow rate, kg/s or mole/s
L	Pollutant concentration, kg/m^3
L{ }	Laplace transform operator
LMCD	Log-mean concentration difference, kg/m^3, $mole/m^3$ or Pa
LMTD	Log-mean temperature difference, K
M	Molar mass, g/mole
M_n	nth moment = $\int_0^\infty (-t)^n F(t) e^{st} dt$

M_t	Mass sorbed to time t, kg
M_∞	Mass sorbed to time ∞, kg
Ma	Mach number, dimensionless
m	Mass, kg
N	Dimensionless distance = $K_0a\,z/v$
N	Mass transfer rate, kg/s or mole/s
N'	Mass flux, kg/m²s or mole/m²s
N	Pipe number = fL/d, dimensionless
N	Ma^2
N_{av}	Avogadro's number = 6.02×10^{23} 1/mole
Np	Number of theoretical plates or stages
NTU	Number of transfer units, N_T
Nu	Nusselt number = hL/k, dimensionless
n	Number of moles
P	Perimeter, m
P	Power, J/s or W
P^0	Vapor pressure, Pa
Pr	Prandtl number = $C_p\mu/k$, dimensionless
P_T	Total pressure
p	Pressure
p	dy/dx (p-substitution)
Q	Strength of heat source, m³K
Q	Volumetric flow rate, m³/s
q	Amount adsorbed, kg/kg
q	Rate of heat transfer, J/s
q'	Heat flux, J/m²s
q'	Vehicle flux, vehicles/m²s
q_C	Rate of convective heat transfer, J/s
q_m	Amount adsorbed in monolayer, kg/kg
q_r	Rate of radiative heat transfer, J/s
q^+, q^-	Electrical charge, C
R	Gas constant = 8.314 J/mole K
R, r_0	Radius, m
R	Receptor concentration, receptors/cell
R	Thermal resistance, ms/J
Re	Reynolds number = $Lv\rho/\mu$, dimensionless
r	Radial variable, m
r	Reaction rate, mole/m³s
r_{Max}	Maximum reaction rate (Michaelis Menten), mole/m³s
S	Energy source, J/m³s
S	Shape factor, m
(S)	Substrate concentration, mole/m³
S	Steam consumption, kg/s
S{ }	Sine transform operator
Sc	Schmidt number = $\mu/\rho D$, dimensionless
Sh	Sherwood number = kL/D, dimensionless

St	Stanton number = $Nu/RePr$ or $Sh/ReSc$, dimensionless
s	Arc length, m
s	Laplace transform parameter, dimensionless
s	Specific gravity, dimensionless
T	Dimensionless time = $K_0 a(\rho_f/\rho_b)(t/H)$
T	Temperature, K or °C
t	Time, s
U	Internal energy, J/kg or J/mole
U	Outer field velocity, m/s
U	Overall heat transfer coefficient, $J/m^2 sK$
V	Electrostatic potential, V
V	Vapor flow rate, kg/s or mole/s
v	Velocity, m/s
V	Volume, m^3
v_∞	Approach velocity, m/s
W	Moles remaining in a still
W	Width, m
W_m	Minimum bed weight (sorption), kg/kg
w	Rate of work done on surroundings, J/s
w_s	Rate of shaft work, J/s
X	Mass ratio (liquid or solid), kg/kg
x	Liquid mole fraction, dimensionless
x	Rectangular coordinate, m
x*	Dimensionless distance = $x\alpha/vd^2$ or xD/vd^2
Y	Mass ratio (gas), kg/kg
y	Dimensionless radial distance, r/R
y	Rectangular coordinate, m
y	Vapor or gas mole fraction, dimensionless
z	Rectangular coordinate
Z	Flow rate ratio (dialysis) = Q_B/Q_D, dimensionless

GREEK SYMBOLS

α	Separate factor, dimensionless
α	Thermal diffusivity, m^2/s
α	Filter cake resistance = $[K(1-\varepsilon)\rho_s]^{-1}$
β	Compressibility = $\dfrac{1}{V}\dfrac{dV}{dp}$, $1/Pa$
β	Thermal parameter = $(-\Delta H_r D_{eff}/k_{eff} T_s)$
β	Volumetric coefficient of expansion = $\dfrac{1}{V}\dfrac{dV}{dT}$, $1/K$
$\Gamma(n)$	Gamma function = $\displaystyle\int_0^\infty x^{n-1}e^{-x}dx$
γ	Activity coefficient, dimensionless
γ	Ratio of heat capacities = C_p/C_v, dimensionless

γ	Surface tension, N/m
$\dot{\gamma}$	Shear rate, 1/s
∇	Gradient or "del"
$\nabla \cdot$	Divergence or "del dot"
$\nabla \times$	Curl or "del cross"
∇^2	Laplacian or "del square"
δ	Boundary layer thickness, m
δ	Condensate film thickness, m
$\delta(x - x_0)$	Dirac delta function
ε	Emissivity, dimensionless
ε	Heat exchanger efficiency, dimensionless
ε	Void fraction, dimensionless
η	Similarity variable
θ	Angle in cylindrical or spherical coordinate, radians
θ	Dimensionless temperature
λ	Characteristic value, or eigenvalue (linear systems)
λ	Damping coefficient, dimensionless
μ	Characteristic value or eigenvalue (nonlinear systems)
μ	Chemical potential
μ	Viscosity, Pas
μ_{Max}	Maximum monod growth rate, 1/s
ν	Frequency, 1/s
ν	Kinematic viscosity = μ/ρ, m^2/s
ρ	Density, kg/m^3 or C/m^3 (charge)
ρ	Reflectivity, dimensionless
σ	Stefan-Boltzmann constant = 5.767×10^{-8} J/m^{2}sK
τ	Dimensionless time or time constant
τ	Residence time, 1/s
τ_0	Parameter in Bingham model, Pa
Φ	Velocity potential, dimensions depend on coordinate system
Φ	Viscous dissipation function, s^{-2}
ϕ	Angle in spherical coordinates, radians
ψ	Stream function, dimensions depend on coordinate system
ω	Angular velocity, radians/s

OVERLINES

‾	Average
‾	Integral transform of a function
~	Molar

SUBSCRIPTS

A,B	Species in a binary system
a	Ambient
a	Adiabatic

B	Blood
BM	Log-mean partial pressure or concentration of inert component
b	Bulk fluid
b	Bed
c	Cold
D	Dialysate
db	Dry-bulb
e	External
F	Feed
F	Fish
FW	Fish-water
f	Fluid
f	Forward
g	Gas
h	Hot
i	Inside
i	Isothermal
k	Order of Bessel function
L	Liquid
m	Mean
m	Measured
OC	Organic carbon
OW	Octanol-water
o	Initial or inlet
o	Outside
p	Particle
p	Projected
r	Reverse
S	Surface
S	Sediment
s	Shell
s	Solid
t	Terminal
t	Tube
W	Water
wb	Wet-bulb
x,y,z	Component in x, y, z direction
x,y,z	Differentiation with respect to x, y, z

SUPERSCRIPTS

0	Pure component
o	Reference state
*	Equilibrium

Table of Contents

Chapter 1 Introduction...1
1.1 Conservation Laws and Auxiliary Relations......................................2
  1.1.1 Conservation Laws 2
  1.1.2 Auxiliary Relations...3
1.2 Properties and Categories of Balances..3
  1.2.1 Dependent and Independent Variables 5
  1.2.2 Integral and Differential Balances: The Role of Balance Space
         and Geometry 5
  1.2.3 Unsteady-State Balances: The Role of Time 5
  1.2.4 Steady-State Balances...7
  1.2.5 Dependence on Time and Space 7
1.3 Three Physical Configurations 7
  1.3.1 The Stirred Tank...7
  1.3.2 The One-Dimensional Pipe 8
  1.3.3 The Quenched Steel Billet 9
1.4 Types of ODE and AE Mass Balances 9
1.5 Information Obtained from Model Solutions 10
  1.5.1 Steady-State Integral Balances...10
  1.5.2 Steady-State One-Dimensional Differential Balances 11
  1.5.3 Unsteady Instantaneous Integral Balances............................11
  1.5.4 Unsteady Cumulative Integral Balances 11
  1.5.5 Unsteady Differential Balances...12
  1.5.6 Steady Multidimensional Differential Balances 12
         Illustration 1.1 Design of a Gas Scrubber............................13
         Illustration 1.2 Flow Rate to a Heat Exchanger....................14
         Illustration 1.3 Fluidization of a Particle.............................14
         Illustration 1.4 Evaporation of Water from an Open
            Trough 15
         Illustration 1.5 Sealing of Two Plastic Sheets......................15
         Illustration 1.6 Pressure Drop in a Rectangular Duct.................16
    Practice Problems 16
References...17

Chapter 2 The Setting Up of Balances 19
         Illustration 2.1 The Surge Tank......................................19
         Illustration 2.2 The Steam-Heated Tube..............................22
         Illustration 2.3 Design of a Gas Scrubber Revisited....................24
         Illustration 2.4 An Example from Industry: Decontamination
            of a Nuclear Reactor Coolant 26

Illustration 2.5 Thermal Treatment of Steel Strapping 29
Illustration 2.6 Batch Filtration: The Ruth Equations.................32
Illustration 2.7 Drying of a Nonporous Plastic Sheet................35
Practice Problems 38
References...42

Chapter 3   More About Mass, Energy, and Momentum Balances................45
3.1   The Terms in the Various Balances...45
3.2   Mass Balances 46
    3.2.1   Molar Mass Flow in Binary Mixtures 46
    3.2.2   Transport Coefficients...48
        Illustration 3.2.1 Drying of a Plastic Sheet Revisited:
        Estimation of the Mass Transfer Coefficient k_y 52
        Illustration 3.2.2 Measurement of Diffusivities by the
        Two-Bulb Method: The Quasi-Steady State...........................55
    3.2.3   Chemical Reaction Mass Balance.....................................57
        Illustration 3.2.3 CSTR with Second Order Homogeneous
        Reaction A + B → P..57
        Illustration 3.2.4 Isothermal Tubular Reactor with First
        Order Homogeneous Reaction...59
        Illustration 3.2.5 Isothermal Diffusion and First Order
        Reaction in a Spherical, Porous Catalyst Pellet:
        The Effectiveness Factor E 60
    3.2.4   Tank Mass Balance..62
        Illustration 3.2.6 Waste-Disposal Holding Tank 63
        Illustration 3.2.7 Holding Tank with Variable Holdup................64
    3.2.5   Tubular Mass Balances..65
        Illustration 3.2.8 Distillation in a Packed Column: The Case
        of Total Reflux and Constant α 66
        Illustration 3.2.9 Tubular Flow with Solute Release from
        the Wall 68
    Practice Problems 69
3.3   Energy Balances 71
    3.3.1   Energy Flux 71
    3.3.2   Transport Coefficients...72
        Illustration 3.3.1 Heat Transfer Coefficient in a Packed Bed
        of Metallic Particles 75
        Illustration 3.3.2 The Counter-Current Single Pass Shell
        and Tube Heat Exchanger..76
        Illustration 3.3.3 Response of a Thermocouple to a
        Temperature Change 82
        Illustration 3.3.4 The Longitudinal, Rectangular Heat
        Exchanger Fin 83
        Illustration 3.3.5 A Moving Bed Solid-Gas Heat
        Exchanger..86

Illustration 3.3.6 Conduction Through a Hollow Cylinder: Optimum Insulation Thickness 89
Illustration 3.3.7 Heat-Up Time of an Unstirred Tank 92
Illustration 3.3.8 The Boiling Pot 94
Illustration 3.3.9 Melting of a Silver Sample: Radiation 96
Illustration 3.3.10 Adiabatic Compression of an Ideal Gas: Energy Balance for Closed Systems: First Law of Thermodynamics 99
Illustration 3.3.11 The Steady-State Energy Balance for Flowing (Open) Systems 101
Illustration 3.3.12 A Moving Boundary Problem: Freeze-Drying of Food 102
Practice Problems 105
3.4   Force and Momentum Balances 110
      3.4.1   Momentum Flux and Equivalent Forces 110
      3.4.2   Transport Coefficients 110
      Illustration 3.4.1 Forces on Submerged Surfaces: Archimides' Law 114
      Illustration 3.4.2 Forces Acting on a Pressurized Container: The Hoop-Stress Formula 116
      Illustration 3.4.3 The Effects of Surface Tension: Laplace's Equation; Capillary Rise 117
      Illustration 3.4.4 The Hypsometric Formulae 120
      Illustration 3.4.5 Momentum Changes in a Flowing Fluid: Forces on a Stationary Vane 121
      Illustration 3.4.6 Particle Movement in a Fluid 123
      Illustration 3.4.7 The Bernoulli Equation: Some Simple Applications 128
      Illustration 3.4.8 The Mechanical Energy Balance 132
      Illustration 3.4.9 Viscous Flow in a Parallel Plate Channel: Velocity Distribution and Flow Rate — Pressure Drop Relation 135
      Illustration 3.4.10 Non-Newtonian Fluids 136
      Practice Problems 139
3.5   Combined Mass and Energy Balances 142
      Illustration 3.5.1 Nonisothermal CSTR with Second Order Homogeneous Reaction $A + B \rightarrow P$ 142
      Illustration 3.5.2 Nonisothermal Tubular Reactors: The Adiabatic Case 143
      Illustration 3.5.3 Heat Effects in a Catalyst Pellet: Maximum Pellet Temperature 145
      Illustration 3.5.4 The Wet-Bulb Temperature 149
      Illustration 3.5.5 Humidity Charts: The Psychrometric Ratio ... 151
      Illustration 3.5.6 Operation of a Water Cooling Tower 157
      Illustration 3.5.7 Design of a Gas Scrubber Revisited: The Adiabatic Case 160

Illustration 3.5.8 Flash Vaporization..162
Illustration 3.5.9 Steam Distillation..165
Practice Problems 167
3.6 Combined Mass, Energy, and Momentum Balances......................172
Illustration 3.6.1 Isothermal Compressible Flow in a Pipe 173
Illustration 3.6.2 Propagation of a Pressure Wave, Velocity
of Sound, Mach Number 174
Illustration 3.6.3 Adiabatic Compressible Flow in a Pipe........177
Illustration 3.6.4 Compressible Flow Charts...........................179
Illustration 3.6.5 Compressible Flow in Variable Area
Ducts with Friction and Heat Transfer................181
Illustration 3.6.6 The Converging-Diverging Nozzle.................183
Illustration 3.6.7 Forced Convection Boiling: Vaporizers
and Evaporators..184
Illustration 3.6.8 Film Condensation on a Vertical Plate..........188
Illustration 3.6.9 The Nonisothermal, Nonisobaric Tubular
Gas Flow Reactor..191
Practice Problems 196
References..198

Chapter 4 Ordinary Differential Equations............................203
4.1 Definitions and Classifications 203
4.1.1 Order of an ODE 203
4.1.2 Linear and Nonlinear ODEs.....................................205
4.1.3 ODEs with Variable Coefficients 206
4.1.4 Homogeneous and Nonhomogeneous ODEs.................207
4.1.5 Autonomous ODEs...208
Illustration 4.1.1 Classification of Model ODEs......................208
4.2 Boundary and Initial Conditions 209
4.2.1 Some Useful Hints on Boundary Conditions 211
Illustration 4.2.1 Boundary Conditions in a Conduction
Problem: Heat Losses from a Metallic Furnace Insert.........212
4.3 Analytical Solutions of ODEs...213
4.3.1 Separation of Variables..216
Illustration 4.3.1 Solution of Complex ODEs by Separation of
Variables..217
Illustration 4.3.2 Repeated Separation of Variables: The
Burning Fuel Droplet as a Moving Boundary Problem.........218
4.3.2 The D-Operator Method: Solution of Linear nth Order ODEs with
Constant Coefficients...221
Illustration 4.3.3 The Longitudinal Heat Exchanger Fin
Revisited...223
Illustration 4.3.4 Polymer Sheet Extrusion: The Uniformity
Index...225
4.3.3 Nonhomogeneous Linear Second Order ODEs with Constant
Coefficients 230

Illustration 4.3.5 Vibrating Spring with a Forcing Function 230
4.3.4 Series Solutions of Linear ODEs with Variable Coefficients 232
Illustration 4.3.6 Solution of a Linear ODE with Constant
Coefficients by a Power Series Expansion 233
Illustration 4.3.7 Evaluation of a Bessel Function 235
Illustration 4.3.8 Solution of a Second Order ODE with
Variable Coefficients by the Generalized Formula 238
Illustration 4.3.9 Concentration Profile and Effectiveness
Factor of a Cylindrical Catalyst Pellet 239
4.3.5 Other Methods 240
Illustration 4.3.10 Product Distribution in Reactions in
Series: Use of the Substitution y = vx 241
Illustration 4.3.11 Path of Pursuit 243
Illustration 4.3.12 Design of a Parabolic Mirror 244
4.4 Numerical Methods 245
4.4.1 Boundary Value Problems 246
4.4.2 Initial Value Problems 246
4.4.3 Sets of Simultaneous Initial Value ODEs 249
4.4.4 Potential Difficulties: Stability 249
Illustration 4.4.1 Example of a Solution by Euler's
Method 250
Illustration 4.4.2 Solution of Two Simultaneous ODEs by
the Runge-Kutta Method 251
4.5 Nonlinear Analysis 252
4.5.1 Phase Plane Analysis: Critical Points 253
Illustration 4.5.1 Analysis of the Pendulum 255
4.5.2 Analysis in Parameter Space: Bifurcations, Multiplicities, and
Catastrophe 258
Illustration 4.5.2 Bifurcation Points in a System of Nonlinear
Algebraic Equations 262
Illustration 4.5.3 A System with a Hopf Bifurcation 263
4.5.3 Chaos 265
Practice Problems 268
References 270

Chapter 5 The Laplace Transformation 273
5.1 General Properties of the Laplace Transform 274
Illustration 5.1.1 Inversion of Various Transforms 278
5.2 Application to Differential Equations 280
Illustration 5.2.1 The Mass Spring System Revisited:
Resonance 282
Illustration 5.2.2 Equivalence of Mechanical Systems and
Electrical Circuits 284
Illustration 5.2.3 Response of First Order Systems 286
Illustration 5.2.4 Response of Second Order Systems 290
Illustration 5.2.5 The Horizontal Beam Revisited 296

5.3 Block Diagrams: A Simple Control System 298
    5.3.1 Water Heater 301
    5.3.2 Measuring Element 301
    5.3.3 Controller and Control Element 302
5.4 Overall Transfer Function; Stability Criterion; Laplace Domain
    Analysis 302
        Illustration 5.4.1 Laplace Domain Stability Analysis 305
    Practice Problems 307
References 310

Chapter 6 Special Topics 313
6.1 Biomedical Engineering, Biology, and Biotechnology 314
        Illustration 6.1.1 One-Compartment Pharmacokinetics 314
        Illustration 6.1.2 Blood–Tissue Interaction as a Pseudo
        One-Compartment Model 319
        Illustration 6.1.3 A Distributed Model: Transport Between
        Flowing Blood and Muscle Tissue 321
        Illustration 6.1.4 Another Distributed Model: The Krogh
        Cylinder 322
        Illustration 6.1.5 Membrane Processes: Blood Dialysis 324
        Illustration 6.1.6 Release or Consumption of Substances
        at the Blood Vessel Wall 330
        Illustration 6.1.7 A Simple Cellular Process 333
        Illustration 6.1.8 Turing's Paper on Morphogenesis 338
        Illustration 6.1.9 Biotechnology: Enzyme Kinetics 341
        Illustration 6.1.10 Cell Growth, Monod Kinetics, Steady-State
        Analysis of Bioreactors 344
    Practice Problems 348
6.2 A Visit to the Environment 351
        Illustration 6.2.1 Mercury Volatilization from Water 353
        Illustration 6.2.2 Rates of Volatilization of Solutes from
        Aqueous Solutions 356
        Illustration 6.2.3 Bioconcentration in Fish 357
        Illustration 6.2.4 Cleansing of a Lake Bottom Sediment 359
        Illustration 6.2.5 The Streeter-Phelps River Pollution Model:
        The Oxygen Sag Curve 361
        Illustration 6.2.6 Contamination of a River Bed
        (Equilibrium) 364
        Illustration 6.2.7 Clearance of a Contaminated River Bed
        (Equilibrium) 366
        Illustration 6.2.8 Minimum Bed Requirements for Adsorptive
        Water Purification (Equilibrium) 367
        Illustration 6.2.9 Actual Bed Requirements for Adsorptive
        Water Purification (Nonequilibrium) 368
    Practice Problems 371

6.3   Welcome to the Real World 373
                Illustration 6.3.1 Production of Heavy Water by Methane
                Distillation 373
                Illustration 6.3.2 Clumping of Coal Transported in Freight377
                Cars 377
                Illustration 6.3.3 Pop Goes the Vessel 378
                Illustration 6.3.4 Debugging of a Vinyl Chloride Recovery
                Unit 379
                Illustration 6.3.5 Pop Goes the Vessel (Again) 383
                Illustration 6.3.6 Potential Freezing of a Water Pipeline 385
                Illustration 6.3.7 Failure of Heat Pipes 387
                Illustration 6.3.8 Coating of a Pipe 389
                Illustration 6.3.9 Release of Potentially Harmful Chemicals
                to the Atmosphere 392
                Illustration 6.3.10 Design of a Marker Particle (Revisited) 396
        Practice Problems 398
References 404

Chapter 7   **Partial Differential Equations: Classification, Types, and**
           Properties; Some Simple Transformations and Solutions 407
7.1   Properties and Classes of PDEs 409
    7.1.1   Order of a PDE 409
        7.1.1.1   First Order PDEs 409
        7.1.1.2   Second Order PDEs 410
        7.1.1.3   Higher Order PDEs 410
    7.1.2   Homogeneous PDEs and BCs 410
    7.1.3   PDEs with Variable Coefficients 411
    7.1.4   Linear and Nonlinear PDEs: A New Category — Quasilinear
        PDEs 411
    7.1.5   Another New Category: Elliptic, Parabolic, and Hyperbolic
        PDEs 412
    7.1.6   Boundary and Initial Conditions 413
            Illustration 7.1.1 Classification of PDEs 415
            Illustration 7.1.2 Derivation of Boundary and Initial
            Condition 416
7.2   PDEs of Major Importance 418
    7.2.1   First Order Partial Differential Equations 419
        7.2.1.1   Unsteady Tubular Operations (Turbulent Flow) 419
        7.2.1.2   The Chromatographic Equations 419
        7.2.1.3   Stochastic Processes 421
        7.2.1.4   Movement of Traffic 421
        7.2.1.5   Sedimentation of Particles 422
    7.2.2   Second Order Partial Differential Equations 422
        7.2.2.1   Laplace's Equation 422
        7.2.2.2   Poisson's Equation 426

		7.2.2.3	Helmholtz Equation	427
		7.2.2.4	Biharmonic Equation	427
		7.2.2.5	Fourier's Equation	428
		7.2.2.6	Fick's Equation	428
		7.2.2.7	The Wave Equation	428
		7.2.2.8	The Navier-Stokes Equations	429
		7.2.2.9	The Prandtl Boundary Layer Equations	430
		7.2.2.10	The Graetz Problem	431

Illustration 7.2.1 Derivation of Some Simple PDEs 431

7.3 Useful Simplifications and Transformations 435

    7.3.1 Elimination of Independent Variables: Reduction to ODEs...........435

        7.3.1.1 Separation of Variables......................................436

        7.3.1.2 Laplace Transform 437

        7.3.1.3 Similarity or Boltzmann Transformation: Combination of Variables 437

        Illustration 7.3.1 Heat Transfer in Boundary Layer Flow over a Flat Plate: Similarity Transformation 438

    7.3.2 Elimination of Dependent Variables: Reduction of Number of Equations 443

        Illustration 7.3.2 Use of the Stream Function in Boundary Layer Theory: Velocity Profiles Along a Flat Plate 443

    7.3.3 Elimination of Nonhomogeneous Terms...............................445

        Illustration 7.3.3 Conversion of a PDE to Homogeneous Form 445

    7.3.4 Change in Independent Variables: Reduction to Canonical Form ..447

        Illustration 7.3.4 Reduction of ODEs to Canonical Form 450

    7.3.5 Simplification of Geometry 454

        7.3.5.1 Reduction of a Radial Spherical Configuration into a Planar One 456

        7.3.5.2 Reduction of a Radial Circular or Cylindrical Configuration into a Planar One...456

        7.3.5.3 Reduction of a Radial Circular or Cylindrical Configuration to a Semi-Infinite One 457

        7.3.5.4 Reduction of a Planar Configuration to a Semi-Infinite One..457

    7.3.6 Nondimensionalization 457

        Illustration 7.3.5 Nondimensionalization of Fourier's Equation 457

7.4 PDEs PDQ: Locating Solutions in Related Disciplines; Solution by Simple Superposition Methods 459

    7.4.1 In Search of a Literature Solution...460

        Illustration 7.4.1 Pressure Transients in a Semi-Infinite Porous Medium 460

        Illustration 7.4.2 Use of Electrostatic Potentials in the Solution of Conduction Problems 463

7.4.2   Simple Solutions by Superposition 464

       7.4.2.1   Superposition by Simple Flows: Solutions in Search of a Problem 464

       Illustration 7.4.3 Superposition of Uniform Flow and a Doublet: Flow Around an Infinite Cylinder or a Circle 468

       7.4.2.2   Superposition by Multiplication: Product Solutions 470

       7.4.2.3   Solution of Source Problems: Superposition by Integration 472

       Illustration 7.4.4 The Instantaneous Infinite Plane Source 474

       Illustration 7.4.5 Concentration Distributions from a Finite and Instantaneous Plane Pollutant Source in Three-Dimensional Semi-Infinite Space 479

       7.4.2.4   More Superposition by Integration: Duhamel's Integral and the Superposition of Danckwerts 482

       Illustration 7.4.6 A Problem with the Design of Xerox Machines 483

   Practice Problems 488

References 492

Chapter 8   Vector Calculus: Generalized Transport Equations 495

8.1   Vector Notation and Vector Calculus 496

   8.1.1   Synopsis of Vector Algebra 496

       Illustration 8.1.1 Two Geometry Problems 501

   8.1.2   Differential Operators and Vector Calculus 503

       8.1.2.1   The Gradient ∇ 505

       8.1.2.2   The Divergence $\nabla \cdot$ 506

       8.1.2.3   The Curl $\nabla \times$ 507

       8.1.2.4   The Laplacian ∇^2 508

       Illustration 8.1.2 Derivation of the Divergence 510

       Illustration 8.1.3 Derivation of Some Relations Involving ∇, $\nabla \cdot$, and $\nabla \times$ 511

   8.1.3   Integral Theorems of Vector Calculus 512

       Illustration 8.1.4 Derivation of the Continuity Equation 513

       Illustration 8.1.5 Derivation of Fick's Equation 514

       Illustration 8.1.6 Superposition Revisited: Green's Functions and the Solution of PDEs by Green's Functions 515

       Illustration 8.1.7 The Use of Green's Functions in Solving Fourier's Equation 520

   Practice Problems 523

8.2   Transport of Mass 526

       Illustration 8.2.1 Catalytic Conversion in a Coated Tubular Reactor: Locating Equivalent Solutions in the Literature 527

       Illustration 8.2.2 Diffusion and Reaction in a Semi-Infinite Medium: Another Literature Solution 532

       Illustration 8.2.3 The Graetz–Lévêque Problem in Mass Transfer: Transport Coefficients in the Entry Region 533

Illustration 8.2.4 Unsteady Diffusion in a Sphere: Sorption and Desorption Curves..538
Illustration 8.2.5 The Sphere in a Well-Stirred Solution: Leaching of a Slurry 540
Illustration 8.2.6 Steady-State Diffusion in Several Dimensions..542
Practice Problems 543
8.3 Transport of Energy..545
Illustration 8.3.1 The Graetz-Lévêque Problem (Yet Again!) ...546
Illustration 8.3.2 A Moving Boundary Problem: Freezing in a Semi-Infinite Solid 549
Illustration 8.3.3 Heat Transfer in a Packed Bed: Heat Regenerators...551
Illustration 8.3.4 Unsteady Conduction....................................554
Illustration 8.3.5 Steady-State Temperatures and Heat Flux in Multidimensional Geometries: The Shape Factor.................556
Practice Problems 556
8.4 Transport of Momentum..560
Illustration 8.4.1 Steady, Fully Developed Incompressible Duct Flow..562
Illustration 8.4.2 Creeping Flow...564
Illustration 8.4.3 The Prandtl Boundary Layer Equations 565
Illustration 8.4.4 Inviscid Flow: Euler's Equations of Motion 567
Illustration 8.4.5 Irrotational (Potential) Flow: Bernoulli's Equation 568
Practice Problems 569
References..571

Chapter 9 Solution Methods for Partial Differential Equations 575
9.1 Separation of Variables..575
9.1.1 Orthogonal Functions and Fourier Series 575
9.1.1.1 Orthogonal and Orthonormal Functions 580
Illustration 9.1.1 The Cosine Set...582
9.1.1.2 The Sturm-Liouville Theorem..583
9.1.1.3 Fourier Series...583
Illustration 9.1.2 Fourier Series Expansion of a Function f(x)..585
Illustration 9.1.3 The Quenched Steel Billet Revisited.............586
Illustration 9.1.4 Conduction in a Cylinder with External Resistance: Arbitrary Initial Distribution 591
Illustration 9.1.5 Steady-State Conduction in a Hollow Cylinder..593
Practice Problems 597
9.2 Laplace Transformation and Other Integral Transforms 599
9.2.1 General Properties 599

9.2.2 The Role of the Kernel 601

9.2.3 Pros and Cons of Integral Transforms 604

    9.2.3.1 Advantages 604

    9.2.3.2 Disadvantages 605

9.2.4 The Laplace Transformation of PDEs 605

    Illustration 9.2.1 Inversion of a Ratio of Hyperbolic
    Functions 606

    Illustration 9.2.2 Conduction in a Semi-Infinite Medium 607

    Illustration 9.2.3 Conduction in a Slab: Solution for
    Small Time Constants 609

    Illustration 9.2.4 Conduction in a Cylinder Revisited: Use
    of Hankel Transforms 611

    Illustration 9.2.5 Analysis in the Laplace Domain: The Method
    of Moments 614

Practice Problems 617

9.3 The Method of Characteristics 620

9.3.1 General Properties 620

9.3.2 The Characteristics 622

    Illustration 9.3.1 The Heat Exchanger with a Time-Varying
    Fluid Velocity 625

    Illustration 9.3.2 Saturation of a Chromatographic Column 627

    Illustration 9.3.3 Elution of a Chromatographic Column 630

    Illustration 9.3.4 Development of a Chromatographic Pulse 632

    Illustration 9.3.5 A Traffic Problem 634

Practice Problems 636

References 637

Index 639

1 Introduction

Il est aisé à voir ...

Pierre Simon Marquis de Laplace
(Preamble to his theorems)

*When using a mathematical model, careful attention must be
given to the uncertainties in the model.*

Richard P. Feynman
(On the reliability of the Challenger space shuttle)

Our opening remarks in this preamble are intended to acquaint the reader with some
general features of the mathematical models we shall be encountering. In particular,
we wish to address the following questions:

- What are the underlying laws and relations on which the model is based?
- What type of equations result from the application of these laws and
  relations?
- What is the role of time, distance, and geometry in the formulation of the
  model?
- Is there a relation between the type of physical process considered and
  the equations that result?
- What type of information can be derived from their solution?

These seemingly complex and sweeping questions have, in fact, well-defined
and surprisingly simple answers.

The underlying laws for the processes considered here are three in number and
the *principal* additional relations required no more than about two dozen. Equations
are generally limited to three types: algebraic equations (AEs), ordinary differential
equations (ODEs), and partial differential equations (PDEs) in which time and
distance enter as independent variables, geometry as either a differential element,
or an entity of finite size. There is a distinct relation between the type of process
and equation which depends principally on geometry and the nature of transport
(convective or diffusive). Thus, convective processes which take place in and around
a well-mixed tank lead to algebraic or *first order* differential equations; likewise
those which occur in "one-dimensional pipes." This holds irrespective of whether
the events involve transport of mass, energy, momentum, or indeed chemical reac-

tions. Diffusive transport, whether of mass, energy, or momentum, yields, with few exceptions, *second order* differential equations. The information derived from the solution of these equations generally falls into the following three broad categories: (1) distributions in time or distance of the state variables (i.e., temperature, concentration, etc.), (2) size of equipment, and (3) values of system parameters. We can, thus, without setting up the model equations or proceeding with their solution, make some fairly precise statements about the tools we shall require, the mathematical nature of the model equations, and the uses to which the solutions can be put.

We now turn to a more detailed consideration of these items.

1.1 CONSERVATION LAWS AND AUXILIARY RELATIONS

The physical relations underlying the models considered here are, as we had indicated, conveniently broken up into two categories, the so-called *basic laws* that consist of the relevant *conservation laws,* and additional expressions which we term *auxiliary relations.* Together these two sets of physical laws and expressions provide us with the tools for establishing a mathematical model.

1.1.1 CONSERVATION LAWS

For systems that involve transport and chemical reactions, the required conservation laws are those of mass, energy, and momentum. Use of these laws is widespread and not confined to chemical engineering systems. Fluid mechanics draws heavily on the law of conservation of mass (known there as the *continuity equation*) and the law of conservation of momentum which in its most general form leads to the celebrated Navier-Stokes equations. In nuclear processes, conservation of mass is applied to neutrons and includes diffusive transport as well as a form of reaction when these particles are produced by nuclear fission or absorbed in the reactor matrix. The law of conservation of energy appears in various forms in the description of mechanical, metallurgical, nuclear, and other systems and in different areas of applied physics in general.

We note that conservation laws other than those mentioned are invoked in various engineering disciplines: conservation of charge in electrical engineering (Kirchhoff's law) and conservation of moment, momentum and moment of momentum in mechanical and civil engineering.

Application of the laws we have chosen to a system or process under consideration leads to equations which are termed *balances.* Thus, the law of conservation of mass leads to the mass balance of a species, e.g., a water balance or a neutron balance. Energy balances arise from the law of conservation of energy and are termed *heat balances* when consideration is restricted to thermal energy forms. They are also referred to as the *first law of thermodynamics,* particularly when dealing with closed systems (no convective flow). Momentum balances, drawn from the corresponding conservation law, have a dual nature: the rate of change of momentum is equivalent to a force, hence they may be termed *force balances* or Newton's law. We have summarized these concepts for convenience in Table 1.1.

TABLE 1.1
Basic Conservation Laws

Conservation of	Balance	Alternative Terms
Mass	Mass balance	Continuity equation
Energy	Energy balance	First law of thermodynamics
		Heat balance (limited to thermal energy forms)
Momentum	Momentum balance	Force balance
		Newton's law
		Navier-Stokes equation

1.1.2 AUXILIARY RELATIONS

Once the basic balances have been established, it is necessary to express the primary quantities they contain in terms of more convenient secondary state variables and parameters. Thus, an energy term which originally appears as an enthalpy H is usually converted to temperature T and specific heat C_p, reaction rate r to concentration C and rate constant k_r, and so on. This is done by using what we call auxiliary relations which are drawn from subdisciplines such as thermodynamics, kinetics, transport theory, and fluid mechanics. Parameters which these relations contain are often determined experimentally. Thus, for convective interphase mass transfer N_A, such as evaporation of water into flowing air, we use the auxiliary relation $N_A = k_G A \Delta p_A$ where Δp_A is the partial pressure driving force and k_G a measured mass transfer coefficient. When transport is diffusive, Fick's law $N_A = -DA(dC_A/dz)$ is invoked.

Similar considerations apply to the transport of heat. Individual coefficients h are usually measured experimentally and can be super-posed to obtain overall coefficients U, which have their counterpart in the overall mass transfer coefficient K_0. When transport is by conduction, Fourier's law $(q = -kA(dT/dz))$ is needed. Chemical reaction rate constants such as k_r (first and second order) or r_{Max} and K_m (Michaelis-Menten kinetics) likewise are determined experimentally (see Table 1.2). We note that some parameters can be derived from appropriate theory and are themselves based on conservation laws. For viscous flow around and in various geometries, for example, drag coefficients C_D, friction factors f and various transport coefficients can be derived directly from appropriate balances. Among other parameters which have to be obtained by measurement, we mention in particular those pertaining to physical equilibria such as Henry's constants H and activity coefficients γ.

Some of the more commonly encountered auxiliary relations have been grouped together and are displayed for convenience in Table 1.2.

1.2 PROPERTIES AND CATEGORIES OF BALANCES

Having outlined the major types of balances and the underlying physical laws, we now wish to acquaint the reader with some of the mathematical properties of those balances and draw attention to several important subcategories that arise in the modeling of processes.

TABLE 1.2
Important Auxiliary Relations

1. Transport Rates

Mass Transport

Molecular

$$N_A = -DA\frac{dC_A}{dz}$$

Fick's Law

Convective Interphase

$$N_A = k_C A(C^* - C)$$
$$N_A = K_{OC} A(C^* - C)$$

Energy Transport

$$q = -kA\frac{dT}{dz}$$

Fourier's Law

$$q = hA\Delta T$$
$$q = UA\Delta T$$

Momentum Transport

$$\tau = -\mu\frac{dv}{dz}$$ $$v = -\frac{K}{\mu}\frac{dp}{dz}$$ $$\tau_w = f\frac{\rho v^2}{2}$$

Newton's Viscosity Law   Darcy's Law   Shear Stress at Pipe Wall

2. Chemical Reaction Rates

First Order
$$r = k_r C_A$$

Second Order
$$r = k_r C_A{}^2 = k_r C_A C_B$$

3. Drag and Friction in Viscous Flow

Sphere

$$C_D = \frac{24}{Re}$$

$$F_D = C_D A_c \frac{\rho v^2}{2}$$

Pipe

$$f = \frac{16}{Re}$$

$$\Delta p = 4f\rho \frac{v^2}{2}\frac{L}{D}$$

4. Equations of State for Gases

Ideal Gas
$$pV = nRT$$

Real Gas
$$pV = z(T_r, p_r)RT$$

5. Physical Equilibria

Henry's Law
$$y = Hx$$

Vapor-Liquid Equilibrium
$$yP_T = \gamma \times P^o$$

6. Thermodynamics

Enthalpy
$$\Delta H = Cp\Delta T$$

1.2.1 Dependent and Independent Variables

An important mathematical consideration is the dependent and independent variables associated with various balances.

Dependent variables, often referred to as state variables, arise in a variety of forms and dimensions dictated by the particular process to be modeled. Thus, if the system involves reaction terms, molar concentration C is usually the dependent variable of choice since reaction rates are often expressed in terms of this quantity. Phase equilibria, on the other hand, call for the use of mole fractions x, y or ratios X, Y, or partial pressures p, for similar reasons. Humidification operations which rely on the use of psychrometric concepts will be most conveniently treated using the absolute humidity Y (kg water/kg air) as the dependent variable. We had already mentioned temperature as the preferred variable in energy balances over the primary energy quantity of enthalpy or internal energy. Similarly, shear stress is converted to its associated velocity components which then enter the momentum balance as new dependent variables. We remind the reader that it is the dependent variables which determine the number of equations required. Thus, the aforementioned velocity components which are three in number — v_x, v_y, v_z for Cartesian coordinates, for example — require three equations, represented by force or momentum balances in each of the three coordinate directions.

Consideration of the independent variable is eased by the common occurrence, in all balances, of time t and the three coordinate directions as independent variables. We have summarized these, as well as the relevant dependent variables in Table 1.3.

1.2.2 Integral and Differential Balances: The Role of Balance Space and Geometry

Spatial and geometrical considerations arise when deciding whether a balance is to be made over a differential element that generally results in a differential equation, or whether to extend it over a finite entity such as a tank or a column in which case we can obtain algebraic as well as differential equations.

In the former case we speak of "differential," "microscopic" or "shell" balances and the underlying model is often termed a *distributed parameter model* (see Table 1.4). Such balances lead, upon solution, to distributions or "profiles" of the state variables in space, or in time and space. Thus, a one-dimensional energy balance taken over a differential element of a tube-and-shell heat exchanger will, upon integration, yield the longitudinal temperature profiles in both the shell and the tubes.

When the balance is taken over a finite entity, we speak of "integral" or "macroscopic" balances, and the underlying models are frequently referred to as "compartmental" or "lumped parameter" models (see Table 1.4). Solutions of these equations usually yield relations between input to the finite space and its output.

1.2.3 Unsteady-State Balances: The Role of Time

Time considerations arise when the process is time dependent, in which case we speak of unsteady, unsteady-state, or dynamic systems and balances. Both macroscopic and microscopic balances may show time dependence. A further distinction

TABLE 1.3
Typical Variables for Various Balances

Balance	Dependent Variable	Independent Variable
Mass	Molar flux N	Time t
	Mass flux W	Coordinate distances
	Mole and mass fraction x, y	x, y, z Cartesian
	Mole and mass ratio X, Y	r, θ, z cylindrical
	Molar concentration C	r, θ, φ spherical
	Partial pressure p	
Energy	Internal energy U	Time t
	Enthalpy H	Coordinate distances
	Temperature T	x, y, z Cartesian
		r, θ, z cylindrical
		r, θ, φ spherical
Momentum	Velocity $\overset{r}{v}$	Time t
	Shear stress $\underset{\sim}{\tau}$	Coordinate distances
	Pressure p	x, y, z Cartesian
		r, θ, z cylindrical
		r, θ, φ spherical

is made between processes which are instantaneous in time, leading to differential equations, and those which are cumulative in time, usually yielding algebraic equations (Table 1.4). The rate of change of the mass in a tank being filled with water, for example, is given by the instantaneous rate of inflow and leads to a differential equation. On the other hand, the actual mass of water in the tank at a given moment equals the cumulative amount introduced to that point and yields an algebraic

TABLE 1.4
Categories of Balances and Resulting Equations

Names and Model Types	Equations
A. Integral or macroscopic balances	
Compartmental or lumped parameter models	
1. Steady-state balance	AE
2. Unsteady-state or dynamic balance	
– Instantaneous in time	ODE
– Cumulative in time	AE
B. Differential, microscopic, or shell balances	
Distributed parameter models	
1. Steady-state one-dimensional balance	ODE
2. Unsteady-state one-dimensional balance	PDE
3. Steady-state multidimensional balance	PDE
4. Unsteady-state multidimensional balance	PDE

equation. The difference is a subtle but important one and will be illustrated by examples throughout the text.

1.2.4 STEADY-STATE BALANCES

Both macroscopic and microscopic balances can result in steady-state behavior, giving rise to either algebraic or differential equations (Table 1.4). A stirred-tank reactor, for example, which is operating at constant input and output will, after an initial time-dependent "start-up" period, subside to a constant steady-state in which incoming and outgoing concentrations are related by algebraic equations. The shell-and-tube heat exchanger mentioned previously will, if left undisturbed and operating at constant input and output, produce a steady, time-invariant temperature distribution which can be derived from the appropriate differential (microscopic) energy balances. An integral energy balance taken over the entire exchanger on the other hand will yield a steady-state relation between incoming and outgoing temperatures.

1.2.5 DEPENDENCE ON TIME AND SPACE

Systems which are both time and space dependent yield partial differential equations. The same applies when the state variables are dependent on more than one dimension and are either at steady or unsteady state. Diffusion into a thin porous slab, for example where no significant flux occurs into the edges, is described by a PDE with time and one dimension as independent variables. When the geometry is that of a cube, a PDE in three dimensions and time results.

We draw the reader's attention to both Tables 1.3 and 1.4 as useful tabulations of basic mathematical properties of the balances. Table 1.4 in particular is designed to help in assessing the degree of mathematical difficulty to be expected and in devising strategies for possible simplifications.

1.3 THREE PHYSICAL CONFIGURATIONS

We present in this section three simple physical devices designed to illustrate the genesis of various types of balances and equations. The *stirred tank*, frequently encountered in models, demonstrates the occurrence of integral balances (ODEs and AEs). Steady-state differential balances arise in what we call the one-dimensional pipe which is principally concerned with changes in the longitudinal direction (ODEs). The genesis of PDEs, finally, is considered in the somewhat whimsically termed *quenched steel billet*. Figure 1.1 illustrates the three devices.

1.3.1 THE STIRRED TANK (FIGURE 1.1A)

In this configuration, streams generally enter and/or leave a tank, frequently accompanied by chemical reactions, phase changes, or by an exchange of mass and energy with the surroundings. As noted before, the device results in integral unsteady balances (ODEs), or integral steady-state balances (AEs) and assumes uniform distributions of the state variables (concentration, temperature, etc.) in the tank. Uniformity is achieved by thoroughly mixing the contents by means of a stirrer, or by conceptually deducing from the physical model that distribution of the state

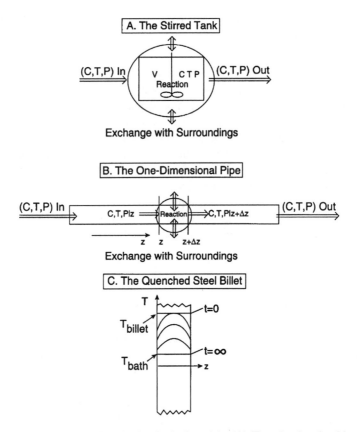

FIGURE 1.1 Diagrams of three basic physical models: (A) The stirred tank with uniform, space-independent properties, (B) the one-dimensional pipe with property distribution in the longitudinal direction and at the wall, (C) the quenched steel billet with variations of temperature in both time and space.

variable is uniform. The latter situation arises in entities of small dimensions and/or high transport and reaction rates. A thin cylindrical thermocouple subjected to a temperature change, for example, will have negligible temperature gradients in the radial direction due to the high thermal conductivity of the metal, much as if the metal had been "stirred." The temperature variation with time can then be deduced from a simple unsteady energy balance (ODE).

An important subcategory of the stirred tank is the so-called continuous stirred tank reactor (CSTR). In this device reactants are continuously introduced and products withdrawn while the contents are thoroughly mixed by stirring. In crystallization processes, the configuration is referred to as a mixed-suspension mixed-product removal crystallizer (MSMPRC).

1.3.2 THE ONE-DIMENSIONAL PIPE (FIGURE 1.1B)

This term is used to describe a tubular device in which the principal changes in the state variables take place in the longitudinal direction. Radial variations are either neglected or lumped into a transport "film resistance" at the tubular wall, termed *exchange with surroundings* in Figure 1.1B. Devices which can be treated in this fashion include the tube-and-shell heat exchanger, packed columns for gas absorption, distillation and extraction, tubular membranes, and the tubular reactor. The model has the advantage of yielding ordinary differential or algebraic equations and avoids the PDEs which would be required to account for variations in more than one direction.

1.3.3 THE QUENCHED STEEL BILLET (FIGURE 1.1C)

The operation conveyed by this term involves the immersion of a thin, hot steel plate in a bath of cold liquid. Conduction through the edges of the plate can be neglected so that temperature variations are limited to one direction, z. This results in a PDE in two independent variables whose solution yields the time-variant temperature distributions shown in Figure 1.1C.

1.4 TYPES OF ODE AND AE MASS BALANCES

As a further illustration of the balances and equations used in modeling, we display in Figure 1.2 four examples of standard processes and equipment which require

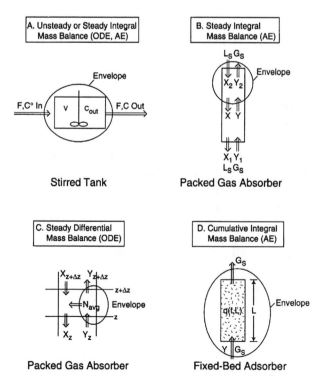

FIGURE 1.2 Types of mass balances leading to algebraic and ordinary differential equations.

simple mass balances at the ordinary differential and algebraic level. We consider both steady and unsteady processes and indicate by an "envelope" the domain over which the balances are to be taken.

Figure 1.2A shows a standard stirred tank which takes a feed of concentration $C°$ and flow rate F. The concentration undergoes a change to C within the tank brought about by some process such as dilution by solvent, precipitation or crystallization, evaporation of solvent, or chemical reaction. After an initial unsteady period which leads to an ODE, such processes often settle down to a steady state leading to an algebraic equation (AE).

Figures 1.2B and 1.2C consider steady-state mass balances which describe the operation of a gas scrubber. The balance is an integral one in Figure 1.2B taken over a finite portion of the column. A liquid stream of concentration X and flow rate L_s enters the envelope at the top and comes in contact with a gas stream of concentration Y and flow rate G_s until the bottom of the column is reached where the roles are reversed. In Figure 1.2C on the other hand, the balance is taken over a differential element and involves the gas phase only. The mass transfer rate N enters into the picture and dictates the change in concentration which occurs in the element.

In Figure 1.2D, finally, we show an example which calls for the use of a cumulative balance. The operation is that of fixed-bed adsorber in which a gas stream of solute concentration Y and carrier flow rate G_s enters the bed and ultimately saturates it at time t. If transport resistance is neglected, that time can be calculated by a cumulative balance in which the total amount of solute introduced up to time t is equated to the accumulated amount of solute retained by the bed.

1.5 INFORMATION OBTAINED FROM MODEL SOLUTIONS

It is of some importance and comfort to know, even prior to setting up the model equations, the type of information which the solutions will yield. This will depend on the type of balance performed and the resulting solutions. Thus, unsteady integral balances lead to time-dependent solutions, or distributions in time, while steady-state differential balances yield distributions in space. When both time and distance vary, distributions in time and space are obtained.

Often these distributions are not of direct interest to the analyst and one wishes instead to extract from them a particular parameter such as flow rate or a transport coefficient. On other occasions it will be convenient to differentiate or integrate the primary distributions to arrive at results of greater practical usefulness. We term this type of information *derived information*, and its source *primary information*. The summary which follows lists the results obtained from various balances.

1.5.1 STEADY-STATE INTEGRAL BALANCES

These balances are taken over a finite entity. Algebraic relations result that provide the following information:

Primary information: Interrelation between input and output.

Derived information: Output concentrations, purities, temperatures, etc., for different inputs and vice versa. Effect of various recycle schemes, stream splits, number of processing units.

Such balances arise with great frequency in plant design. The large number of algebraic equations that result are usually solved with special simulation packages.

1.5.2 STEADY-STATE ONE-DIMENSIONAL DIFFERENTIAL BALANCES

Here the balance is taken over the differential element of a "one-dimensional pipe" and yields the following information:

Primary information: Profiles or distributions of the state variables in one dimension; temperature, concentration, velocity, or pressure distributions as a function of distance.
Derived information:
  – Design length or height.
  – Parameter estimation from experimental distributions (transport coefficients, reaction rate constants).
  – Equipment performance for different flow rates, feed conditions, lengths or heights.
  – Differential quantities: Heat flux from temperature gradients, mass flux from concentration gradients, shear stress from velocity gradients.
  – Integral quantities: Flow rate from integrated velocity profiles, energy content, or cumulative energy flux from integrated temperature profiles.

1.5.3 UNSTEADY INSTANTANEOUS INTEGRAL BALANCES

We have seen that these balances are taken over finite entities in space and yield ODEs. The solutions provide the following information:

Primary information: Distribution of state variables in time; temperature, concentration, pressure, etc., as a function of time; transient or dynamic behavior.
Derived information:
  – Design volume or size.
  – Parameter estimation from experiment (transport coefficients, reaction rate constants).
  – Equipment performance for different inputs, flow rates, sizes.
  – Sensitivity to disturbances.
  – Effect of controller modes.
  – Choice of controller.

1.5.4 UNSTEADY CUMULATIVE INTEGRAL BALANCES

The algebraic equation which result here provide the following information:

Primary information: Interrelation between cumulative input or output and amount accumulated or depleted within the envelope.

Derived information:
- Time required to attain prescribed accumulation/depletion, cumulative input or output.
- Amount accumulated/depleted in prescribed time interval.

1.5.5   UNSTEADY DIFFERENTIAL BALANCES

We are dealing with more than one independent variable resulting in a PDE which provides the following information:

Primary information: Distributions of state variables in time and in one-to-three dimensions; temperature, concentration, velocity, etc., profiles as a function of time.

Derived information:
- Geometry or size required for a given performance.
- Parameter estimation from measured distributions (transport coefficients, reaction rate constants).
- Performance for time varying inputs.
- Differential quantities: Time varying heat flux from temperature gradients, mass flux from concentration gradients, shear stress from velocity gradients.
- Integrated quantities: Accumulated or depleted mass and energy within a given time interval and geometry; time varying drag on a particle from shear stress distributions.

1.5.6   STEADY MULTIDIMENSIONAL DIFFERENTIAL BALANCES

Primary information: Steady state distributions of state variables in two or three dimensions; temperature, concentration, velocity, etc., profiles in two- or three-dimensional space.

Derived information:
- Geometry or size required for a given performance.
- Differential quantities: Heat flux from temperature distributions, mass flux from concentration gradients, shear stress from velocity gradients.
- Integrated quantities: Total heat or mass flux over entire surface from gradient distributions; total flow rate from velocity distributions; drag force on a particle from shear stress and pressure distributions.

In the illustrations which follow, a number of physical processes are presented, and an attempt is made to identify the type and number of balances and auxiliary relations required to arrive at a solution. This is the second major stumbling block encountered by the analyst, the first one being the task of making some sense of the physical process under consideration. This may appear to many to be a formidable undertaking, and our excuse for introducing it at this early stage is the stark fact that no modeling can take place unless one has some notion of the balances or equations involved. To ease the passage over this obstacle, we offer the following guidelines:

- Sketch the process and identify the known and unknown variables; draw an "envelope" around the space to be considered.
- Establish whether the process is at steady-state, or can be assumed to be nearly steady, or whether the variations with time are such that an unsteady balance is called for.
- Investigate the possibility of modeling the process or parts of it, as a stirred tank or one-dimensional pipe. These two simple devices, previously shown in Figure 1.1, must be regarded as mainstays in any early attempts at modeling.
- Determine whether a differential or integral balance is called for. Stirred tanks always require integral balances, but in the case of the one-dimensional pipe, both integral and differential balances can be implemented. Which of the latter two is to be chosen is usually revealed only in the course of the solution. Several trials may then become necessary, a not unusual feature of modeling.
- Start with the simplest balance, which is usually the mass balance. Remember that it is possible to make instantaneous or cumulative balances in time. Introduce additional balances until the number of equations equals the number of unknowns, or state variables. The model is then complete.
- Carefully consider whether the stirred tank or one-dimensional pipe have to be replaced by a PDE model. Avoid PDEs if possible but face up to them when they become necessary. They are not always the ogres they are made out to be (see Chapters 7 to 9).
- Use Table 1.2 as an initial guide as to which auxiliary relations may be required.
- Remember that the primary information often comes in the form of *distributions* in time or space of the state variable which may have to be processed further, for example, by differentiation or integration, to arrive at the information sought.

Illustration 1.1   Design of a Gas Scrubber

Suppose we wish to establish the height of a packed gas absorber that will reduce the feed concentration of incoming gas to a prescribed value by countercurrent scrubbing with a liquid solvent. What are the required relations and the information derived from them?

Balances Required — This system calls for the use of one-dimensional steady-state mass balances in a one-dimensional pipe. Since two phases and two concentrations X and Y are involved, two such balances are required in principle and two ODEs result. Alternatively, a differential steady-state balance may be used for the gas phase (see Figure 1.2C), the second relation being provided by an *integral* steady-state balance over both phases (see Figure 1.2B). These equations are analyzed in greater detail in Illustration 2.3.

Auxiliary Relations — An expression for the mass transfer rate N has to be provided which is comprised of a mass transfer coefficient K_ya and a linear concentration driving force ΔY. The latter contains the equilibrium concentration Y^* which is to be obtained from an appropriate equilibrium relation $Y^* = f(X)$. We now have three equations in the three state variables: X, Y, Y^*.

Primary Information — Gas and liquid phase concentration profiles arise from the ODEs. The algebraic integral balance relates concentrations X, Y to concentrations X_2, Y_2 at the top of the column.

Derived Information — Integration of the ODEs yields the height at which the concentration of the feed stream Y_1 reaches the prescribed value Y_2.

Illustration 1.2   Flow Rate to a Heat Exchanger

The flow rate of the heating medium to an existing countercurrent single-pass heat exchanger is to be established such that a cold fluid of flow rate F_c and inlet temperature T_1 will be heated to a prescribed exit temperature T_2.

Balances Required — This calls again for the use of the one-dimensional pipe model and its application to the two streams entering the heat exchanger. In principle, two steady-state differential energy balances need to be applied to the tube and shell side fluids, resulting in two ODEs. These equations will be discussed in greater detail in Chapter 3, Illustration 3.3.2.

Auxiliary Relations — An expression for the heat transfer rate q between shell and tube is required. This is customarily expressed as the product of a heat transfer coefficient U, area A, and the temperature driving force ΔT. In contrast to the analogous case of the countercurrent gas scrubber, no equilibrium relation needs to be invoked to establish the driving force. The convective energy terms or enthalpies H arising from flow into and out of the element are related to the temperature state variable and specific heat of the fluids by means of an appropriate thermodynamic relation.

Primary Information — Solution of the ODE energy balances yields the longitudinal temperature distributions for the shell and tube side fluids.

Derived Information — The required flow rate resides as a parameter in the solution of the model equation.

Illustration 1.3   Fluidization of a Particle

It is required to establish the air velocity necessary to fluidize a solid particle of a given diameter, i.e., to maintain it in a state of suspension in the air stream.

Balances Required — Fluidization of a particle occurs when the forces acting on it are in balance. These forces are comprised of buoyancy, gravity, and friction (drag). A steady state integral force balance, therefore, is called for.

Auxiliary Relations — Buoyancy and gravity need to be expressed as functions of particle diameter, the drag force as a function of both diameter, and air velocity using empirical drag coefficients.

Primary Information — The force balance directly yields a functional relation between particle diameter and air velocity. No derived information, therefore, needs to be considered.

Illustration 1.4 Evaporation of Water from an Open Trough

Here the evaporation of water from a shallow trough to flowing air, and the attendant evaporation rate and loss of mass, is to be considered.

Balances Required — This is a seemingly complex process involving both mass transfer and the transport of energy required to provide the necessary latent heat of evaporation. That heat initially comes both from the surrounding air and through evaporative cooling of the water surface. Ultimately, the water surface reaches the so-called wet-bulb temperature that signals the fact that the entire energy is supplied by the surrounding air. At this point, which is reached very quickly, the process can be modeled by a simple differential mass balance over the flowing air, which leads to an ODE in the humidity change in the direction of the air flow. See Illustration 2.7 Drying of a nonporous plastic sheet.

Auxiliary Relation — Convective transport of the moisture from the trough to the bulk air is expressed as the product of a humidity driving force ΔY, differential area ΔA ($\rightarrow dA$), and a mass transfer coefficient k_Y obtained from standard correlations (see Illustration 3.2.1). The required saturation humidity at the water surface Y^* is read from psychometric or humidity charts at the appropriate wet-bulb temperature. A discussion of these charts will be given in Illustration 3.5.5.

Primary Information — Solution of the ODE yields the humidity profile in the air, $Y = f(z)$.

Derived Information — The total amount of water evaporated in a given time interval t is obtained from a cumulative balance for air humidity, i.e., from the total quantity of moisture in the effluent air at $z = L$ and over time t.

Illustration 1.5 Sealing of Two Plastic Sheets

Two plastic sheets of equal thickness are to be sealed together by applying two heated plates of temperature T_p to the surface of each sheet. One wishes to calculate the time required for the sealing surface to attain a prescribed sealing temperature T_s.

Balances Required — The temperature within and at the surface of the sheets is related to time via an unsteady differential energy balance. This calls for the use of the unsteady, one-dimensional conduction equation which leads to a PDE.

Auxiliary Relations — Energy flux in and out of the differential element is described by Fourier's law which is composed of the product of the thermal conductivity k, area A, and temperature gradient dT/dz. Accumulation of energy within the element is initially given by the enthalpy H, which is then converted to temperature T and specific heat by means of an appropriate thermodynamic relation.

Primary Information — Solution of the PDE yields the time-dependent temperature profiles within the plastic sheet. Solutions of this type for various geometries are given in both analytical and convenient graphical form in standard texts.

Derived Information — The required time is read from the temperature profiles at the value $T = T_s$.

Illustration 1.6   Pressure Drop in a Rectangular Duct

We consider steady laminar flow of a liquid in a rectangular duct and wish to obtain the pressure drop for a given flow rate and length of conduit.

Balances Required — A force balance will be needed here to relate pressure p to the viscous forces τ which arise in laminar flow. The situation is not as simple as the case of a circular duct since shear stress now varies in two directions x and y rather than a single radial variable r. The force balance is taken over a difference element Δx, Δy, which in the limit yields a PDE in two independent variables x, y. We recognize that shear stress does not vary in the direction of flow and that pressure drop is likewise constant so that we can write $\partial P/\partial z = \Delta P/L$.

Auxiliary Relations — Since pressure will ultimately have to be related to flow rate, shear stress must, in the first instance, be expressed in terms of the local velocity. This is done using Newton's viscosity law which relates shear stress to viscosity and velocity gradients.

Primary Information — Integration of the PDE leads to the velocity distributions in the lateral directions, i.e., $v = f(x, y, \Delta p/L)$.

Derived Information — The velocity distributions are integrated over the cross-sectional area of the duct to yield the volumetric flow rate Q. The resulting expression contains pressure drop $\Delta P/L$ as a parameter which can be extracted as a function of Q.

Practice Problems

1.1 Flushing-out of a contaminant — A contained body of water with in- and out-flow of F_{in} and F_{out} (kg/s) has been contaminated with an undesirable impurity. Indicate the balances required to calculate the time needed to reduce the impurity concentration to a prescribed level after contamination has ceased. (*Hint: assume the water to be well-stirred.*)

1.2 Design of a marker particle — A marker particle is to be designed that has the property of rising through water with a prescribed velocity v. Both geometry and density of the particle are to be established. State the balances and auxiliary relations required. If one assumes that a steady terminal velocity is quickly attained, what type of balances would result?

1.3 Heating-up of a tank — An internal steam coil is to be used to heat the contents of a tank from T_1 to T_2 in a prescribed time interval. The cumulative steam requirement F(kg) to achieve this is to be calculated. What are the requisite balances and auxiliary relations, and what is the primary information that results from their solution?

1.4 Batch distillation of a binary mixture — A solution of two volatile liquids is to be distilled in a batch still. One wishes to calculate the time required to achieve a prescribed enrichment in the less volatile component. Vapor and liquid are assumed to be in equilibrium at all times. How many balances are required and what are the auxiliary relations? (*Hint: assume still contents to be well-stirred.*)

1.5 Batch distillation again — Suppose that in the preceding example one were to monitor the composition and total mass in the distillate receiver. Can one infer from this information the composition in the boiler at any instant? If so, what balances are required?

1.6 Moving-bed ore heater — Crushed ore is to be heated in a moving bed where it is contacted countercurrently with a stream of hot gas. The bed height necessary for the ore to attain a given exit temperature is to be calculated. Identify a set of two balances which would provide this information. What are the auxiliary relations and the primary information obtained from the solution? Identify another operation which leads to identical balances and auxiliary relations.

1.7 Blood dialysis — Patients suffering from kidney failure have their blood periodically purified by passage through a tubular semi-permeable membrane immersed in a bath. Toxic and other undesirable substances pass from the blood through the tubular wall into the bath. Consider the following two cases:

1. Blood in laminar flow, membrane wall thickness: small compared to tubular diameter.
2. Blood in laminar flow and diameter: small compared to tubular wall thickness.

What are the balances and auxiliary relations required to model the device for the two cases? *(Hint: consider under what conditions concentration changes in the radial direction can be neglected or must be taken into account. This determines the dimensionality of the model.)*

1.8 Heat losses from a buried steam pipe — Heat is lost from a buried isothermal steam pipe to the surrounding soil and ultimately to the ground surface. Discuss in some detail the balance required to calculate the heat loss sustained by the pipe, the primary information obtained from the solution as well as the way in which heat loss is inferred from derived information. *(Hint: a PDE in at least two dimensions is involved.)*

REFERENCES

Models of the type discussed in this chapter can be found in a host of texts. An early text by Franks describes many of these models and the numerical techniques required to solve them.

R.G.E. Franks. *Modeling and Simulation in Chemical Engineering*, John Wiley & Sons, New York, 1972.

A more comprehensive and up-to-date treatment is given in the following reference.

S.M. Walas. *Modeling with Differential Equations in Chemical Engineering*, Butterworth, Boston, 1991.

The modeling of other specific systems can be found, for example, in:

E. Beltrami. *Mathematics for Dynamic Modeling, 2nd ed.,* Academic Press, 1997.

P. Zannetti (Ed.). *Environmental Modeling, Vol. I and II,* Elsevier, New York, 1993.

Books on transport phenomena are a rich source of models of concern here. In addition to the text by Bird, Stewart, and Lightfoot, the following recommend themselves.

J.R. Welty, C.E. Wicks, and R.E. Wilson. *Fundamentals of Momentum, Heat and Mass Transfer, 2nd ed.,* McGraw-Hill, New York, 1976.

C.O. Bennett and J.E. Myers. *Momentum, Heat and Mass Transfer, 3rd ed.,* McGraw-Hill, New York, 1987.

2 The Setting Up of Balances

The study of mathematics is apt to commence in disappointment.

Alfred North Whitehead

The reader will have noted that the previous chapter, meant to be an introductory one, nevertheless made some fairly heavy demands. One was asked to extrapolate the knowledge gained in elementary courses in transport and reaction theory plus certain skills in applied mathematics to make some fairly sweeping predictions about the type of balances required in a model and the information to be extracted from them. We tried to alleviate the severity of the task by a careful listing of the balances and equations to be expected in a given physical process and to relate them to the resulting solutions. No actual balances were presented or required.

The aim of the present chapter is to introduce the reader to the craft of setting up such balances, the art of choosing the correct ones, and to generalize the results wherever possible into comprehensive tools. The main focus will be on the more demanding task of setting up ordinary differential equations, although algebraic equations also frequently will make their appearance. The basic procedures will be amply supplemented with illustrations drawn from various disciplines. The more intricate task of setting up partial differential equations is left to later chapters.

We start by considering two simple devices, shown in Figures 2.1 and 2.2, which typify ODE balances. The surge tank illustrates the genesis of unsteady integral balances; the steam-heated tube that of steady-state differential balances. These equations can be generalized to cover more complex situations.

Illustration 2.1 The Surge Tank

In this simple device time varying flows of water, $F_1(t)$ and $F_2(t)$ enter and leave a tank whose contents $W(t)$ also vary with time (Figure 2.1). To ensure proper setting up of the balance we start by considering a finite time interval Δt, and then proceed to the limit, $\Delta t \to 0$. This is a somewhat elaborate procedure which the skilled practitioner will ultimately be able to dispense with. It pinpoints, however, some pitfalls whose existence are best illustrated in this way.

Elementary application of the law of conservation of mass leads to the following relation:

Mass in over Δt – Mass out over Δt = Change in contents over Δt

$$[F_1(t)]_{avg} \, \Delta t - [F_2(t)]_{avg} \, \Delta t = \Delta W(t) \tag{2.1}$$

FIGURE 2.1   Diagram of a surge tank with time-varying inflow, outflow, and contents.

We note that since we chose a finite time interval Δt, the flow rates by necessity have to be average quantities. They can be represented, if one wishes to do so, by time-averaged integral quantities of the type $\int_{t_1}^{t_2} F(t)dt / \Delta t$. Evidently this leads to a complex integral equation which would be difficult to solve. We circumvent this by dividing by Δt and letting $\Delta t \to 0$. The flow rates then become instantaneous values and we obtain:

Instantaneous mass in − Instantaneous mass out = Rate of change in contents

$$F_1(t) - F_2(t) = \frac{dW}{dt} \tag{2.2}$$

It is important to note that the flow rates have now become algebraic quantities which are instantaneous at a point t in time, while the contents are represented by a rate of change derivative. It is often tempting for the uninitiated to proceed directly to differential forms of the following type.

$$dF_1 - dF_2 = dW \tag{2.3}$$

or

$$dF_1 - dF_2 = \frac{dW}{dt} \tag{2.4}$$

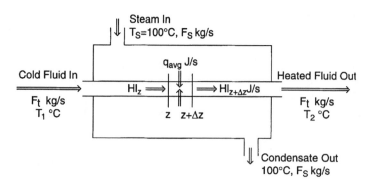

FIGURE 2.2   Energy transport in a steam-heated shell and tube heat exchanger.

The differential Form 2.3 can at best be divided by dt, leading to an incorrect result. The Form 2.4 is incorrect by virtue of the fact that it contains both finite and infinitesimally small quantities. These are precisely the type of pitfalls we wished to draw to the reader's attention by following a more elaborate procedure. Once it is clearly understood, however, that the flow rates become instantaneous algebraic quantities while the contents of the tank lead to a derivative, it becomes possible to proceed to more generalized formulations. To make these easier to set up, we make a point of putting all algebraic quantities on the left side and the derivative on the right. In abbreviated form we obtain the following formulation:

$$\text{Rate in} - \text{Rate out} = \text{Rate of change in contents} \qquad (2.5)$$

It being understood that the terms on the left side are instantaneous algebraic quantities, the ones on the right derivatives.

Suppose now, that in addition to the flows entering and leaving, we have convective evaporation at a rate N from the tank to the surroundings. One must recognize that this is a process instantaneous in time, identical in behavior to the outflow of water, and must therefore be placed in the "rate out" category. We obtain:

$$\text{Rate of mass in} - \text{Rate of mass out} = \text{Rate of change in mass contents}$$

$$F_1(t) - [F_2(t) + N] = \frac{dW}{dt} \qquad (2.6)$$

or, using a linear driving force mass transfer law:

$$F_1(t) - F_2(t) - k_G A (p^*_{H_2O} - p_a) = \frac{dW}{dt} \qquad (2.7)$$

where $p^*_{H_2O}$ = vapor pressure of water

p_a = partial pressure of water in the ambient air

A = surface area of water

What happens when a chemical reaction occurs in the tank? Consider for simplicity a batch reactor with no inflow or outflow, and a first order reaction of rate r = kC_A. Here it must be recognized that the reaction represents an instantaneous removal of the species A and must therefore be placed in the "rate out" category, while the change in concentration yields a derivative which is placed on the right side of the balance. We obtain:

$$\text{Rate of A in} - \text{Rate of A out} = \text{Rate of change in content of A}$$

$$0 - kC_A = V \frac{dC}{dt} \qquad (2.8)$$

where V = volume of reactor.

We are now in a position to generalize these results to encompass all forms of transport and reaction. We do this as follows:

$$\begin{matrix} \text{Rate of mass, energy,} \\ \text{momentum in} \end{matrix} - \begin{matrix} \text{Rate of mass, energy,} \\ \text{momentum out} \end{matrix} = \begin{matrix} \text{Rate of change} \\ \text{of contents} \end{matrix}$$

$$\begin{bmatrix} \text{by flow} \\ \text{by convective transport} \\ \text{by reaction} \end{bmatrix} - \begin{bmatrix} \text{by flow} \\ \text{by convective transport} \\ \text{by reaction} \end{bmatrix} = \frac{d}{dt}\text{contents} \qquad (2.9)$$

When the right side becomes $= 0$, steady-state integral balances result which are algebraic equations. Many processes involving tanks lapse into a steady state after an initial unsteady period unless disturbances occur in input or output. For the momentum balance we note a special case which draws on the equivalence of force and rate of momentum change and results in Newton's law, where force and velocity are now vector quantities.

$$\sum \mathbf{F} = \frac{d(m\mathbf{v})}{dt} \qquad (2.10)$$

Here the forces or their components are given positive and negative signs depending on their direction, corresponding to the *in* and *out* terms in Equation 2.9.

We repeat for emphasis that all terms appearing on the left side are of an instantaneous, algebraic type, while all derivatives appear on the right side as $\frac{d}{dt}$ (contents). We now turn to the consideration of steady-state differential balances.

Illustration 2.2   The Steam-Heated Tube

In this device, a cold liquid flows at a flow rate F_t and temperature T_{t1} into a tube where it is heated by isothermally condensing steam of temperature T_s, exiting at a higher temperature T_{t2} (Figure 2.2). It is instructive here, as it was in the case of the surge tank, to start the balance with an increment Δz, and then generalize the results. Flow enters and leaves the difference element with an enthalpy H which increases in the direction of flow due to the heat q_{avg} transferred from the steam. We obtain, in the first instance, the following balance:

$$\text{Rate of energy in} - \text{Rate of energy out} = 0$$

$$[H_z + q_{avg}] - H\,|_{z+\Delta z} = 0 \qquad (2.11)$$

where q_{avg} is the average, or mean integral heat flow from shell to tube over the increment Δz. Before going to the limit it will be convenient to express q_{avg} and H in terms of the independent and state variables z and T. To do this we draw on appropriate auxiliary relations. From thermodynamics we obtain (see Table 1.2):

$$\Delta H' \text{ (J/kg)} = C_p \text{ (J/kg K)} \Delta T \text{ (K)} \tag{2.12}$$

which is converted to enthalpy flow H(J/s) by multiplication by the flow rate. Thus,

$$\Delta H \text{ (J/s)} = F_c \text{ (kg/s)} C_p \text{ (J/kg°C)} [T - T°] \text{ (°C)} \tag{2.13}$$

For convective heat transfer, we use the usual product of heat transfer coefficient U, area (here $\pi D\Delta z$), and the linear temperature driving force ΔT (here $T_s - T_t$). Hence,

$$q_{avg} = U\pi d\Delta z(T_s - T_t)_{avg} \tag{2.14}$$

where D = diameter of the tube, T_t = tube-side temperature. It is to be noted that the average heat flow has now been replaced by an average temperature driving force. Upon dividing by Δz and letting $\Delta z \to 0$, ΔT becomes a point quantity at the distance z, much as the average flow rates to the surge tank became, upon going to the limit, point quantities in time. We obtain:

$$F_t C_{pt} \frac{dT_t}{dz} - U\pi d(T_s - T_t) = 0 \tag{2.15}$$

It is tempting for the uninitiated to proceed directly to the differential form. This often results in the following formulation:

$$F_t C_{pt} \frac{dT_t}{dz} - U\pi dd(T_s - T_t) = 0 \tag{2.16}$$

This is an incorrect result since it contains both infinitesimally small and finite quantities and demonstrates the pitfalls in directly proceeding to a differential equation. For this and other reasons it has become customary to retain the difference formulation Δz as a starting point, introduce auxiliary relations when appropriate, divide by Δz, and only then proceed to the limit $\Delta z \to 0$. This requirement is not necessary in the case of unsteady integral balance since the ODE Formulations 2.2 and 2.7 to 2.9 are free of pitfalls provided the relevant terms are recognized as instantaneous algebraic quantities and placed on the left side of the balance equation.

We are now in a position to provide a general formulation of one-dimensional steady-state differential balances in much the same way as was done in Equation 2.9 for unsteady integral balances. It takes the following form:

$$
\begin{matrix}
\text{Rate of mass, energy} & & \text{Rate of mass, energy} \\
\text{momentum in at z} & - & \text{momentum out at z} + \Delta z = 0 \\
\text{and over } \Delta z & & \text{and over } \Delta z
\end{matrix}
$$

$$
\begin{bmatrix}
\text{by flow} \\
\text{by convective transport} \\
\text{by reaction}
\end{bmatrix}
\begin{bmatrix}
\text{by flow} \\
\text{by convective transport} \\
\text{by reaction}
\end{bmatrix}
\tag{2.17}
$$

We note that for the special case $\Delta z = L$ (finite length), the differential balance reverts to a steady-state integral balance.

We now present a number of additional illustrations drawn from various disciplines and from industrial practice. Some of these are of an unusual or otherwise challenging character. The reader may at this stage feel unprepared to meet the challenge but, hopefully, will ultimately benefit from the experience. The exercise is at any rate not meant as premature punishment — much of that follows later — but to provide an early glimpse of the complexities of modeling.

Illustration 2.3   Design of a Gas Scrubber Revisited

We had used this example in Illustration 1.1 to coach the reader in anticipating the types of balances required for this process and the information to be derived from the solutions. It was seen that the height of scrubber required to reduce the feed gas concentration to a prescribed value required either two steady-state differential balances or one differential and one integral balance.

The differential balances are taken over each phase and yield the following results (see Figure 1.2C).

$$\begin{matrix} \text{Rate of solute in} \\ \text{at z and over } \Delta z \end{matrix} - \begin{matrix} \text{Rate of solute out} \\ \text{at z} + \Delta z \text{ and over } \Delta z \end{matrix} = 0$$

$$G_s Y \mid_z - [G s Y \mid_{z+\Delta z} + N_{avg}] = 0 \tag{2.18}$$

where Y = kg solute/kg carrier

$\quad G_s$ = kg carrier/m²s

Carrier units are chosen in order to obtain a constant gas flow rate and, thus, reduce the number of variables. We now introduce the auxiliary relation for N_{avg} which takes the form of the product of a mass transfer coefficient K_Y, surface area in the element, $a\Delta z$, and a solute driving force $(Y - Y^*)_{avg}$:

$$N_{avg} = K_Y a \, \Delta z \, (Y - Y^*)_{avg} \tag{2.19}$$

Here the surface area "a" is conveniently taken in volumetric units (m²/m³ packing) and Y^* is the gas phase solute mole ratio in equilibrium with the liquid phase concentration X at that point. Upon dividing by Δz and letting $\Delta z \to 0$, we obtain:

$$G_s \frac{dY}{dz} + K_Y a(Y - Y^*) = 0 \tag{2.20}$$

The liquid phase balance is obtained in similar fashion and yields:

$$L_s \frac{dX}{dz} + K_Y a(Y - Y^*) = 0 \tag{2.21}$$

We note again that the driving force $(Y - Y^*)$ has now become a point quantity at the position z, i.e., it is not to be differentiated.

Since we now have three state variables X, Y and Y^* to deal with, it follows that a third equation will be required which is given by the equilibrium relation.

$$Y^* = f(X) \tag{2.22}$$

Thus, the most general model consists of two differential and one algebraic equation and yields the profiles of X, Y and Y^* in the longitudinal direction. It yields the most general solution that can be used for design, parameter estimation, as well as performance analysis. For design purposes, it is often more convenient to replace the liquid phase ODE by an integral algebraic balance (see Figure 1.2B).

$$\text{Rate of solute in} - \text{Rate of solute out} = 0$$
$$(G_s Y + L_s X_2) - (G_s Y_2 = L_s X) = 0 \tag{2.23}$$

This expression is conveniently regrouped to yield the so-called operating line with slope L_s/G_s:

$$\frac{Y - Y_2}{X - X_2} = \frac{L_s}{G_s} \tag{2.24}$$

To solve the Equations 2.20, 2.22, and 2.23 in the variables X, Y and Y^*, we start by formally integrating Equation 2.20. One obtains by separation of variables,

$$H = \int_{z_1}^{z_2} dz = \frac{G_s}{K_Y a} \int_{Y_2}^{Y_1} \frac{dY}{Y - Y^*} \tag{2.25}$$

It has become the convention to separate the integral from its coefficient and express the right side as the product of the so-called height of a transfer unit = HTU $= \dfrac{G_s}{K_Y a}$ and the number of transfer units = NTU $= \displaystyle\int_{Y_2}^{Y_1} \frac{dY}{Y - Y^*}$. Thus, the height H of packed column required to achieve the prescribed purification is given by the expression:

$$H = \frac{G_s}{K_Y a} \int_{Y_2}^{Y_1} \frac{dY}{Y - Y^*} = \text{HTU} \times \text{NTU} \tag{2.26}$$

The Relations 2.24 and 2.26 are conveniently plotted on an "operating diagram" shown in Figure 2.3. In this diagram, prescribed solvent and carrier gas flow rates L_s and G_s are used to establish the slope of the operating line which passes through the point (X_2, Y_2), i.e., solute concentration in the solvent entering the top of the column

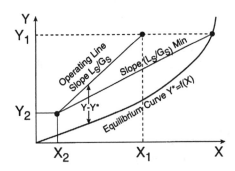

FIGURE 2.3   Operating diagram for an isothermal packed gas scrubber.

and the prescribed exit concentration of the gas, Y_2. The vertical distance between operating line and equilibrium curve establishes the driving force $Y - Y^*$ which is used for the graphical or numerical evaluation of the NTU integral. Together with the value for HTU based on experimental values of $K_Y a$, this yields the desired height of the column, H. The operating diagram can also be used for a quick assessment of the effect of a change in variables. A reduction in solvent flow rate L_s, for example, lowers the slope of the operating line, resulting in an increase in the NTU and hence height H of the column. Ultimately, the operating line intersects the equilibrium curve. The driving force there converges to zero; thus, NTU and H become infinite. The value of L_s at which this occurs represents the *minimum* solvent flow rate that will achieve the required separation and results in a *column of infinite height*.

We note in addition that the Relation 2.26 is only suited for design or for estimation of the parameter $K_Y a$ from measured values of Y_2. Analysis of the performance of an existing column would require a trial and error procedure. This can be avoided by using the solutions to the two ODEs 2.20 and 2.21 which are quite general and suited for all tasks.

Illustration 2.4   An Example from Industry: Decontamination of a Nuclear Reactor Coolant

Organic coolants of nuclear reactors have to be purified periodically by passage through an adsorbent bed to remove degradation products and other impurities which reduce the efficiency of the coolant. Since it is desirable to maintain continuous operation of the reactor, the coolant cannot be removed to a separate facility for treatment. It is customary instead to circulate it continuously through a purifier and return the decontaminated coolant to the reactor (Figure 2.4). Twenty four h are to be allowed for completion of the operation which requires reduction in impurity concentration from 2500 ppb to 75 ppb.

To size the required recirculation pump, both flow rate F and head $H = \Delta p/\rho$ to be generated by the pump have to be known. Head is calculated from the pressure drop through the piping and the adsorbent by means of appropriate correlations for flow through a packed bed (see Chapter 3, Section 3.4). Flow rate comes from a mass balance taken over a chosen unit of the loop. It is this latter problem which is addressed here.

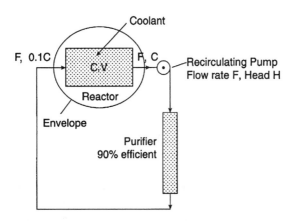

FIGURE 2.4   Flow diagram for the purification of an organic coolant for a nuclear reactor.

Analysis — We have the choice of performing a contaminant balance over the tank or the adsorbent bed. It we choose the tank, it has to be assumed to be "well-stirred," since the actual flow pattern within it is usually too complex to ascertain the precise exit concentration of contaminant at a given instant. That concentration will be lower than that emerging from a well-stirred tank and the model will, therefore, underestimate or provide a lower bound of the required flow rate and size of pump. Since centrifugal pumps of the type contemplated are capable of accommodating a fairly wide range of flow rates for a given head, this is not a serious drawback.

Performing the balance over the purifier poses other problems. Since contaminant contents vary with both time and distance, a PDE balance is in principle called for. If we resort to an integral balance instead, the unsteady term dm/dt, where m represents the bed loading, has to be established by separate measurement. In principle this can be achieved in the same experiment used to establish purified efficiency, but an escalation in both effort and model complexity results. It is, therefore, more convenient to perform the balance around the tank.

The Model — The instantaneous and algebraic "in" and "out" terms for the contaminant balance are indicated in the accompanying diagram, Figure 2.4. For the unsteady term, the industrial data specify a volume $V = 141$ m^3 and coolant density of $\rho = 1200$ kg/m^3. We obtain:

$$\text{Rate in of contaminant} - \text{Rate out of contaminant} = \begin{array}{c}\text{Rate of change}\\\text{in contaminant}\\\text{content}\end{array}$$

$$(2.27)$$

$$F(0.1C) - FC = \frac{d}{dt}V\rho C$$

Collecting terms and integrating by separation of variables there results:

$$-\frac{0.9F}{V\rho}\int_0^t dt = \int_{C_i}^{C_f}\frac{dC}{C} \qquad (2.28)$$

and

$$F = \frac{V\rho}{0.9t} \ln \frac{C_i}{C_f} = \frac{(141)(1200)}{(0.9)(24)} \ln \frac{2500}{75} \qquad (2.29)$$

or

$$F = 27,470 \text{ kg/h}$$

Comments:

The process involved is a seemingly highly complex one; in fact, baffling the engineers assigned to the problem. It is customary in such situations to pass it to a higher level, for example R&D, with instructions to come up with an immediate solution. Alternatively, all attempts to obtain an answer by analysis are abandoned and the required unit is chosen in more or less arbitrary fashion or on what passes as expert advice in the circles involved. It is not known to the writer which route was chosen.

We do not minimize the initially baffling complexity of the process. The coolant contacts the reactor moderator, heavy water, in a heat exchanger whose geometry is not accurately reflected by the simple tank shown in Figure 2.4. Contaminant concentrations vary, during recirculation, with both time and distance, often in an unpredictable fashion. We had already noted that the purifier also has to be modeled by a PDE in time and distance. An additional difficulty arises from the fact that not every engineer or scientist will recognize the relation between pump size and system variables. Setting up an elaborate research program on the other hand is not justified by the importance of the problem or founders on constraints of time and resources. Small wonder that the analysis of such problems is quickly relegated to the dustbin.

The example was chosen to serve two purposes. First, it introduces the reader to the complexity of industrial problems. These are not textbook problems which adhere to well-defined, often artificially simplified processes and lend themselves to the direct application of well-defined models. Such "real-life" problems appear, in fact, to be completely intractable. Second, we hope with this example to provide the reader with a first introduction to the art of modeling. That deceptively simple phrase hides a number of hard and harsh requirements. Basic skills in elementary transport and reactor theory as well as applied mathematics up to perhaps the fourth-year level are a prerequisite. Added to those are the skills of a seasoned engineer capable of recognizing the complexities of a process and applying simplifications that do not lose touch with the realities of the system. As often as not this will require a leap of faith when the validity of the approach cannot be established with certainty and instinct as well as experience are thrown in the balance. Physical insight is an additional ingredient which is indispensable.

Finally, the analyst must be willing to accept and be content with approximate answers. One is not dealing here with academic questions to be answered with precision to several significant figures. Lower or upper bounds, or both, are often the only answers attainable. We have referred to this as "bracketing the solution"

A. Lead Bath

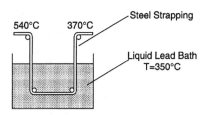

B. Difference Element

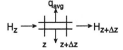

FIGURE 2.5   Annealing of steel strapping in a molten lead bath.

and note its widespread use in respectable scientific disciplines such as mathematics. On other occasions one has to content oneself with order of magnitude estimates without knowing if they represent lower or upper bounds, or with qualitative trends, i.e., whether a quantity of interest increases or decreases.

The art of modeling comprises all of the above tools, skills, and attributes, and more. The discerning reader will have noted that this will call for a marked departure from the tools, skills, and attributes acquired in the usual academic program, and hence a change in attitude. The above example and those that follow show not only that this can be done, but also that the solutions are elegant in their simplicity and Spartan in their use of time and their execution. More problems of this variety will be given in Chapter 6, Section 6.3: Welcome to the Real World.

Illustration 2.5   Thermal Treatment of Steel Strapping

In this example, also drawn from industry, one is asked to establish the dimensions of a liquid lead bath used in the annealing of steel strapping (Figure 2.5A). Such thermal treatments of newly cast or drawn metal forms are designed to relieve stresses created during the forming process and in general to improve the physical properties of the material. They often involve a slow, controlled cooling over a prescribed temperature interval or prolonged exposure to a fixed temperature. Such procedures are common in the metallurgical industries.

Analysis — The strapping of width 6.4×10^{-3} m (1/4 in.) enters at a flow rate of 0.189 kg/s and temperature of 540°C and is required to be cooled to a temperature of 370°C during its passage through the bath. The dimensions of that bath will be determined by the submerged length or what one might term the residence length of the strapping, and it is this length that will have to be established.

An examination of the physics of the problem will quickly reveal that one is here dealing with the heating of a flowing medium by an isothermal fluid, akin to the steam-heated exchanger discussed previously, with the steel strapping taking the place of the tubular fluid, the lead bath that of the condensing steam. The model will consequently be of the form given by Equation 2.15. The challenge here, in fact, lies not so much in the setting up of the balance but in the proper choice of a heat transfer coefficient h for what is clearly an unconventional system with unusual physical properties. We note that heat transfer here is by free convection from a moving solid to a molten metal. Correlations for precisely this type of energy transport do not appear to exist and one is forced instead to draw on expressions for natural convection heat transfer from a *stationary* solid (usually an electrically heated wire). For water and common organic liquids, the heat transfer coefficient is correlated by the expression:

$$\frac{hd}{k} = 0.53 \left[\frac{d^3 \rho^2 g \beta \Delta T}{\mu^2} \right]^{1/4} \left[\frac{C_p \mu}{k} \right]^{1/4}$$

or

$$Nu = 0.53 \, (GrPr)^{1/4} \tag{2.30}$$

where C_p, μ, ρ, k, β are the heat capacity, viscosity, density, thermal conductivity, and coefficient of thermal expansion of the liquid; d the diameter of the wire; Nu, Gr, Pr the so-called Nusselt, Grashof, and Prandtl numbers respectively. We note in addition a weak dependence of h (Nu) on the temperature driving force ΔT which is often approximated by the arithmetic average of the end temperature differences.

For liquid metals, the Prandtl numbers are unusually low, of the order 10^{-2}, because of the high values of thermal conductivity k. Conduction contributes quite substantially to the overall transfer of heat, with the result that the Prandtl number now has a stronger influence than that expressed in Equation 2.30 for conventional fluids. This is accounted for by the following modification of the correlation:

$$Nu = 0.53 \, (GrPr^2)^{1/4} \tag{2.31}$$

An additional problem which needs to be resolved is the proper determination of the physical properties of molten lead for use in Equation 2.31. These are not usually found in conventional science or engineering handbooks and one must instead draw on the specialized metallurgical literature (see References at end of chapter). From these sources, one obtains the following values for molten lead:

Density	$\rho = 10.7 \text{ g/cm}^3$
Heat capacity	$C_p = 0.15 \text{ J/gK}$
Thermal conductivity	$k = 15.4 \text{ J/msK}$
Viscosity	$\mu = 2.65 \text{ mPas}$
Thermal expansion	$\dfrac{d\rho}{dT} = -1.317 \text{ mg/cm}^3\text{K}$

From the density and its variation with temperature one obtains the coefficient of thermal expansion β as follows:

$$\beta = -\frac{d\rho / dT}{\rho} = \frac{1.317}{10.7 \times 10^3} = 1.23 \times 10^{-4}\ K^{-1}$$

The temperature driving force is taken as the arithmetic average of the end temperature differences, so that:

$$\Delta T = \frac{(540 - 350) + (370 - 350)}{2} = 105\ K$$

With these values in hand and using the definitions of Equation 2.30, one obtains

$$Gr = \frac{(6.4 \times 10^{-3})^3 (10.7 \times 1000)^2 (9.81)(1.23 \times 10^{-4})(105)}{(2.65 \times 10^{-3})^2} = 5.4 \times 10^5$$

$$Pr = \frac{(0.15)(2.65 \times 10^{-3})}{1.54 \times 10^{-3}} = 0.026$$

Hence,

$$h = 0.53\, Gr^{1/4}\, Pr^{1/2}\, (k / d)$$

$$h = 0.53 (5.4 \times 10^5)^{1/4} (0.025)^{1/2} (15.4 \times 10^{-3} / 6.4 \times 10^{-3})$$

$$h = 5.56\ kJ / m^2 sK$$

The actual value of the coefficient is likely to be somewhat higher because of the movement of the strapping.

The Model — The difference element to be used is indicated in the accompanying diagram, Figure 2.5B. The strapping carries enthalpy H in and out of the element and releases heat q_{avg} to the lead bath. We obtain, in the first instance:

$$\text{Rate in} - \text{Rate out} = 0$$

$$H_z - (H_{z+\Delta z} + q_{avg}) = 0 \tag{2.32}$$

Introducing the same auxiliary relations used for the steam-heated exchanger, Equations 2.13 and 2.14, converted to the appropriate transfer area $2d\Delta z$, we obtain, after division by Δz and letting $\Delta z \to 0$:

$$FC_p \frac{dT_s}{dz} + h2d(T_s - T_b) = 0 \tag{2.33}$$

where the derivative can also be written as $d(T_s - T_b)/dz$. Integrating by separation of variables between the limits $(0, L)$ and $[(T_s — T_b)_L, (T_s — T_b)_0]$ and solving for length L yields:

$$L = \frac{FC_p}{h2d} \ln \frac{(T_s - T_b)_0}{(T_s - T_b)_L} \qquad (2.34)$$

or

$$L = \frac{(0.189)(0.545)}{(5.56)(2)(6.35 \times 10^{-3})} \ln \frac{190}{20} = 3.3\,\text{m}$$

where $C_p = 0.545$ kJ/kg K = Heat capacity of steel strapping.

Comments:

A number of lessons can be drawn from this example. Setting up the model equations or obtaining a solution to them need not be the most difficult part of the task. Often the principal difficulty, as was the case here, resides in obtaining appropriate rate constants or other parameters.

One has to know where to look for the required information. Reference to the metallurgical literature appears to be a natural path to follow but is not one which is always adopted. On other occasions it may be fruitful to cast a wider net in the search for information. This often requires considerable background knowledge of other engineering disciplines. In the case of the example at hand, such knowledge may lead us to consult texts dealing with nuclear reactors of early vintage, where the use of molten metals as a heat transfer medium was fairly common (see References). These items, too, are part of the Art of Modeling. Heat transfer by natural convection is a fairly common occurrence. We shall encounter it again in Illustrations 3.37 and 6.3.6.

Illustration 2.6   Batch Filtration: The Ruth Equations

The example considered in this illustration deals with the batch filtration of a slurry and aims to relate the time of filtration to the area of the filter, the pressure drop driving the process, and the physical properties of both filtrate and filter cake. The accompanying diagram (Figure 2.6) provides some details.

Analysis — The fact that a time dependence is sought leads us naturally to the choice of unsteady balances around the filter. An initial analysis also reveals two facts: (1) the cumulative filtrate volume V is a more convenient choice of dependent variable than the volume or thickness of filter cake, since the latter is not readily accessible to intermittent measurement. (2) an auxiliary expression will be required which relates the flow rate Q to the desired pressure drop driving force $\Delta P/L$ and filter area A. This is done by means of what is known as D'Arcy's law (see Chapter 1, Table 1.2), which here takes the form:

$$Q = \frac{K}{\mu} A \frac{\Delta P}{z} \qquad (2.35)$$

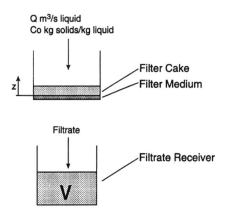

FIGURE 2.6   Diagram of batch filter and filtrate receiver.

where K = permeability of the filter cake obtained from experimental measurement. It is not clear at this stage what the balance envelopes should be but it seems natural to start with an unsteady integral balance around the filter cake and proceed to introduce the desired variables by means of additional balances and auxiliary relations.

The Model — The unsteady integral balance about the cake takes the following form:

$$\text{Rate in of solids} - \text{Rate out of solids} = \text{Rate of change in contents}$$

$$QC_o - 0 = \frac{d}{dt} Az(1-\varepsilon)\rho_s \tag{2.36}$$

where ε and ρ_s are the porosity and density of the filter cake, respectively.

We now proceed to eliminate the unwanted quantities Q and z. The former is related to the desired pressure drop and filter area by D'Arcy's law, Equation 2.35. To relate z to cumulative volume V, two avenues present themselves: (1) a cumulative integral balance about the filter cake or (2) an unsteady integral balance about the receiver. We choose the former, which is algebraic, for convenience, and obtain:

$$\begin{array}{c} \text{Solids previously in} \\ \text{filtrate volume V} \end{array} = \begin{array}{c} \text{Solids retained} \\ \text{in cake} \end{array}$$

$$C_0 V = zA(1-\varepsilon)\rho_s \tag{2.37}$$

Upon elimination of Q and z, the following expression results, also known as the Ruth equation:

$$\frac{KA^2(1-\varepsilon)\rho_s}{\mu C_0} \Delta p = V \frac{dV}{dt} \tag{2.38}$$

where the inverse of $K(1 - \varepsilon)\rho_s$ is termed the cake resistance α, a quantity which is determined experimentally. Thus,

$$\frac{A^2 \Delta p}{\alpha \mu C_0} = V \frac{dV}{dt} \tag{2.39}$$

Note that the resistance of the filter medium has been neglected.

It is customary to distinguish between constant rate filtration (dV/dt = constant) and constant pressure filtration (ΔP = constant). In the former case we obtain:

$$V(t) = \frac{A^2 \Delta p(t)}{\alpha \mu C_0 dV / dt} \tag{2.40}$$

where α can be determined from an experimental plot of cumulative filtrate volume V vs. the varying pressure drop ΔP. For constant pressure filtration, integration yields the expression:

$$\frac{V^2}{2} = \frac{A^2 \Delta p}{\alpha \mu C_0} t \tag{2.41}$$

where α can now be obtained from the slope of a plot of V^2 vs. time. As a point of practical interest we note that constant rate filtration requires the use of positive displacement pumps, while in constant pressure filtration one employs centrifugal pumps capable of providing a near constant head (i.e., pressure drop) over a range of flow rates.

Comments:

The choice of variables proved to be of some importance and not immediately obvious to the uninitiated. It was clear, however, that the cake resistance plays a crucial role in determining time of filtration and had to be brought into the model in some fashion. This was done through the use of D'Arcy's law, Equation 2.35 which led to the replacement of the flow rate Q by the pressure driving force ΔP.

The equations obtained, 2.40 and 2.41, known as Ruth's equations, are quite general, i.e., can be used for design (filter area A), parameter estimation from experiment (cake resistance α), or prediction of performance of an existing filter. The functional relationships displayed by these equations are worth some scrutiny. We note in particular that the amount filtered in a given time interval, represented by the cumulative volume V, varies with the square of filter area in constant rate filtration, but only linearly in constant pressure filtration. This could not have been immediately anticipated on the basis of the physics of the process and shows the power of models to reveal the unexpected. It is these unexpected features, not mere confirmation of conventional wisdom, that the analyst should look for and exploit.

In this illustration, as in the previous ones, it was not always possible to arrive at an *a priori* choice of balances, envelopes, or auxiliary relations. A preliminary analysis is of some help, but in more complex situations it is often not possible to establish the form and number of equations in advance. In these cases it is best to

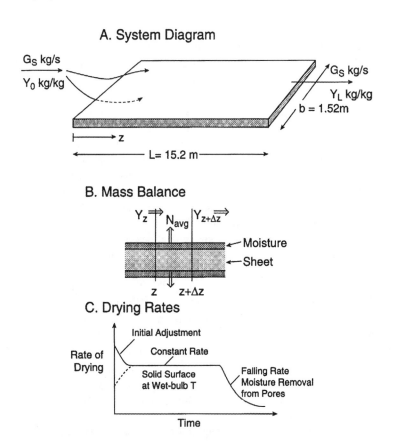

FIGURE 2.7 Drying of a nonporous plastic sheet with air: (A) system and dimensions, (B) diagram of the differential mass balance, (C) the various drying periods.

start with the simplest or most obvious balance and proceed to add, step by step, further relations until the number of equations equals the number of state variables. The model then can be said to be complete.

Illustration 2.7   Drying of a Nonporous Plastic Sheet

Moist plastic sheets are to be dried by passing a stream of air over and under them. It is desired to calculate the time necessary to remove 90% of the initial moisture (Figure 2.7).

Analysis — The drying of solids in general is a highly complex process involving both heat and mass transfer. If the solid is porous, the moisture content will ultimately vary in both the longitudinal and lateral directions as well as with time. Thus, we could be dealing with two coupled partial differential equations (mass and energy balances) in time and two dimensions.

Early studies of drying processes had revealed that considerable simplifications result by recognizing three distinct drying periods, shown in the accompanying diagram (Figure 2.7C). During an initial adjustment period, the surface moisture quickly drops to the so-called wet-bulb temperature due to evaporative cooling which signals the fact that the drying process is now entirely driven by energy supplied from the air. The drying rate at this stage has become constant and remains so until the surface moisture has evaporated. During this constant rate period, the process can be modeled algebraically if we assume negligible change in air humidity, or by an ODE if the latter varies. Thereafter the process becomes more complex as moisture removal now has to take place from the *interior* porous structure and a continually receding water interface. A lengthy drying period results as the moisture becomes increasingly inaccessible, and it is this period that results in the aforementioned partial differential equations. By restricting ourselves to nonporous plastic sheets we eliminate the falling rate period. If, in addition, the initial adjustment period is neglected and the sheets are assumed to remain uniformly moist, the process becomes accessible to simple modeling.

An additional point needs to be addressed. Since time of drying is to be determined, it is tempting to assume that the process is an unsteady one. In fact, the constant rate period leads to a steady-state humidity profile in the flowing air, with evaporation being driven by the difference of the constant wet-bulb humidity Y^* and the humidity Y of the air as a particular point. Thus, air leaves the sheets at a constant humidity Y_L throughout the constant rate drying period (see Figure 2.7). How, then, is the drying time to be determined? Some reflection will show that this calls for the use of an integral cumulative balance in which the total amount to be evaporated (here 90% of the initial moisture) is equated to the cumulative amount of moisture which has left the sheet at a steady humidity Y_L over a period t. We first must calculate Y_L from a differential balance over the sheet and then make use of the integral balance to calculate t.

The mass transfer coefficient k_Y required to express the drying rate N is drawn from standard correlations for mass transfer from a flat plate parallel to a flowing fluid. Derivation of its value is discussed in detail in Chapter 3, Illustration 3.2.1: Drying of Plastic Sheets Revisited. In industrial practice one often dispenses with the use of a mass transfer coefficient and calculates drying time based on the assumption that the exiting air is fully saturated at Y^*. This evidently represents a lower bound to the value of time sought. Both the full model and the asymptotic one are discussed below.

The Models — We start with a steady-state differential balance for the air, see Figure 2.7B. The data provided are as follows:

Air flow rate	$G_s = 1$ kg dry air/s
Air velocity	$v = 15$ m/s
Inlet air humidity	$Y_0 = 0$
Initial moisture content	$M_0 = 6.0$ kg/sheet
Wet-bulb temperature	$T_w = 21°C$
Wet-bulb humidity	$Y^* = 0.016$ kg H_2O/kg air
Mass transfer coefficient	$k_Y = 0.0479$ kg/sm$^2\Delta Y$

We obtain, in the first instance:

Rate in of moisture − Rate out of moisture = 0

$$(G_s Y_z + N_{avg}) - G_s Y_{z+\Delta z} = 0 \tag{2.42}$$

or, after introduction of the auxiliary relation for N_{avg},

$$G_s \Delta Y - 2 k_Y b \Delta z (Y^* - Y)_{avg} = 0 \tag{2.43}$$

Dividing by Δz and going to the limit $\Delta z \to 0$ yields:

$$G_s \frac{dY}{dz} - 2 k_Y b (Y^* - Y) = 0 \tag{2.44}$$

where dY/dz can also be expressed as $d(Y^* - Y)/dz$. Separation of variables then results in the expression:

$$\int_0^{Y_L} \frac{dY}{Y^* - Y} = \int_0^L \frac{2 k_Y b}{G_s} dz \tag{2.45}$$

$$Y_L = Y^* \left[1 - \exp\left(-\frac{2 L k_Y b}{G_s} \right) \right] \tag{2.46}$$

and

$$Y_L = 0.016 \left[1 - \exp\left(-\frac{(2)(15.2)(0.0313)(1.52)}{1} \right) \right]$$

Hence,

$$Y_L = 0.0122 \text{ kg H}_2\text{O/kg air}$$

We now introduce the cumulative balance, the need for which was established in the analysis:

Mass H_2O removed to time t = 90% of initial moisture

$$G_s Y_L t = 0.9 M_o \tag{2.47}$$

Hence,

$$t = \frac{0.9 M_o}{G_s Y_L} = \frac{(0.9)(6)}{(1)(0.0122)} = 7.4 \text{ min} \tag{2.48}$$

For the asymptotic case of saturated air leaving the sheet, we set $Y_L = Y^*$ in Equation 2.48 and obtain:

$$t = \frac{0.9\,M_o}{G_s Y^*} = \frac{(0.9)(6)}{(1)(0.016)} = 5.6\,\text{min} \qquad (2.49)$$

Comments:
The principal point to emerge from this illustration is that a highly complex process has been reduced to manageable form. It is somewhat far-fetched to assume that the three drying periods could have been identified by physical reasoning alone. They were, in fact, established by experimentation in the early stages of drying studies. Thus, the importance of experimental measurements should not be underestimated and the analyst should be prepared to draw on them and, more importantly, interpret them so as to arrive at suitable simplifications.

The second point to note is that the required time of drying does not imply that we are dealing with an unsteady process. It takes experience and steadiness not to be tempted into reaching for an unsteady balance.

Finally, asymptotic solutions should not be disdained simply because a more complete model is available and easily solved. Remember that it takes time to obtain the necessary information (i.e., the mass transfer coefficient k_Y) and the knowledge of where to look for it. Neither may be available to the industrial practitioner.

Practice Problems

Note: Most of the problems given here are of a fairly challenging nature and the reader may wish to defer their solution until after Chapter 3 has been covered. The author's own recommendation is that they be studied, nevertheless, and an attempt be made to address them. The comments added to each problem are designed to provide some aid in that direction.

2.1 Discharge of a Ladle of Molten Steel — In a continuous vacuum degassing operation, molten steel is to be discharged from a ladle open to the atmosphere into a vacuum chamber maintained at essentially zero pressure. The ladle is 2.44 m (8 ft) in height and internal diameter. Attached to the bottom of the tank and extending into the vacuum chamber is a nozzle, 0.45 m (18 in.) in length and 0.051 m (2 in.) in inside diameter. Calculate the time of discharge. Data:

Steel density ρ = 7,300 kg/m³
Steel viscosity μ = 0.15 Ns/m²
Friction factor in nozzle f = 0.00094
Entrance and exit losses and friction within the ladle are neglected

Comments:
Since the level and mass of the steel diminishes with time, an unsteady mass balance over the tank is called for. That mass balance contains the level height z and exit velocity v as dependent variables. A second equation, therefore, is required which is given by the mechanical energy balance (see Chapter 3, Illustration 3.4.8).

Note that in that equation, changes in pressure, velocity, and elevation, as well as friction in the nozzle, will have to be taken into account. Velocity at the steel surface itself can be neglected.

Answer: 14.2 min

2.2 A Simplified Leaching Process — A water-soluble material is to be leached from a mass of solid particles in a well-stirred tank. This is in principle a time dependent process in which the rate of leaching also varies with distance since the solute front continually recedes into the interior of the particle and the diffusion path consequently lengthens. A PDE model of Fick's law would, therefore, appear to be called for (see Illustration 8.2.5). A simplification can be effected, however, by approximating the leaching process in terms of a mass transfer coefficient $k_L = \dfrac{D_{eff}}{\Delta x}$ and a driving force $(C^* - C_{ext})$, where D_{eff} = diffusivity in the solid matrix, Δx can be expressed in terms of the solute mass m remaining in the matrix. Assume the particles to be rectangular flakes of area A and thickness 2L, with negligible transport through the edges. Derive an ODE mass balance which upon solution will yield the time dependence of solute mass m remaining in the solids and hence the time of leaching required. Do not solve the ODE.

Answer:
$$\frac{D_{eff}A}{L(1 - m/m_o)}\left[C^* - \frac{(m_o - m)}{V}\right] = V\frac{d\left(\dfrac{m_o - m}{V}\right)}{dt}$$

2.3 Isotope Separation Factors by Rayleigh Distillation — Low abundance isotopes such as deuterium D and C^{13} are often separated from their more abundant partners by distillation of liquid compounds such as HDO/H_2O and $C^{13}O/C^{12}O$. Vapor–liquid equilibria required for the design of such distillation units are characterized by a separation factor α which is very close to unity, and the relation $y = \alpha x$, where y and x are the vapor and liquid mole fractions of the isotope respectively. The value of α, which is crucial to the design of the units, can be determined in a variety of ways.

1. Precise measurements of pure component vapor pressures p_1^0, p_2^0, related to α through the expression: $\alpha - 1 = p_1^0/p_2^0$
2. By column distillation using high efficiency packing.
3. By single stage equilibration of vapor and liquid.
4. By Rayleigh distillation.

Of the four methods, the so-called Rayleigh distillation recommends itself for its simplicity and the high degree of enrichment attainable which surpasses by far the separation obtained in single-stage equilibration and avoids the need for high precision analytical determinations of isotopic content, or those of pure component vapor pressures. It also avoids the uncertainties and complexities inherent in column separations.

Rayleigh distillation consists of the slow, controlled batch distillation of a liquid solution in which the well-mixed contents are assumed to have attained phase

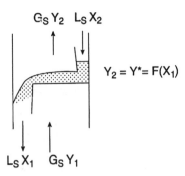

$$G_S Y_2 \quad L_S X_2$$

$$Y_2 = Y^* = F(X_1)$$

$$L_S X_1 \quad G_S Y_1$$

FIGURE 2.8   Flow diagram for a theoretical plate.

equilibrium. Typically in this operation, some 90 to 95% of the initial charge is boiled off and the residue analyzed for isotopic content that is combined with the known composition of the initial charge to reflect the enrichment obtained. This quantity is then related to the separation factor α through an appropriate model.

Identify the balances required and show that by elimination of the time variable one obtains the following relation between separation factor α, initial to final ratio of moles n_f/n_i and mole fractions x_f/x_i:

$$\alpha - 1 = \frac{\ln(x_f x_i)}{\ln(n_f n_i)} \tag{2.50}$$

(Hint: Make component and total mole balances over the still and divide the equations to eliminate dt.)

2.4 Response of a Theoretical Tray to Disturbances — The concept of a theoretical tray is widely used in the design and analysis of plate distillation and absorption columns. The principal assumption inherent in this concept is that both phases in contact with the tray are well-mixed, i.e., uniform in concentration, and that the effluent concentrations are in equilibrium with each other, $Y^* = f(X)$ (see Figure 2.8).

Consider a single theoretical plate in a gas absorber which has its gas feed composition suddenly raised from 0.02 to 0.03 kg solute/kg carrier gas. Calculate the time necessary for the liquid outlet concentration to attain 95% of the new steady-state value, indicating type of balance and auxiliary relation used.

Data: G_s = 80 kg carrier gas/h
        L_s = 15 kg solvent/h
        H = 3 kg solvent hold up on plate
        $m = Y^*/X = 0.125$ (Henry's constant)

(Hint: Prior to setting up the principal unsteady balances, both the initial and ultimate steady-state liquid effluent concentrations must be established by means of appropriate integral balances.)

Answer: t = 13.7 min

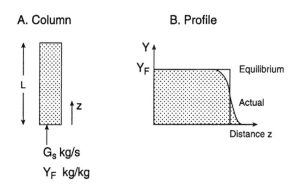

FIGURE 2.9 Adsorber column and profile.

2.5 Propagation of a Rectangular Pulse in an Adsorber — A column packed with granular adsorbent is to be used to purify an incoming gas stream of flow rate G_s kg carrier/s and feed concentration Y_F kg solute/kg carrier. Concentration fronts are known to stabilize ultimately to an S-shaped form when mass transfer effects are taken into account (Figure 2.9). Much useful information may be gained, however, by assuming the two phases everywhere to be in equilibrium with each other: $Y^* = f(q)$, where q is in units kg solute/kg bed. This leads to the formation of a rectangular front which coincides with the mid-point of the actual S-shaped profile (Figure 2.9B). You are asked to address the following questions:

1. What type of balance and auxiliary relations are needed in principle to establish the solute profile in the adsorber?
2. How can this model be simplified to treat the case of a rectangular front?
3. Use the simplified approach to establish the time required to saturate a bed of length L with a rectangular pulse.

(Hint: Use a cumulative balance neglecting fluid phase content of solute.)

Answer: $t = \dfrac{\rho_b (q/Y)_F}{\rho_f v} L$

2.6 Ground Penetration from Oil Spills — In connection with oil spill studies, it is desirable to develop a mathematical model which will yield the depth of oil penetration into the ground as a function of time. The basis for the model is D'Arcy's law, which was encountered in connection with the filtration problem (Illustration 2.6) and relates the flow rate Q through a porous medium to the total head h and other physical parameters:

$$Q = K \frac{Ah\rho g}{\mu z}$$

where h = total height of oil column
    A = total cross-sectional area of medium

z = thickness of medium filled with oil

K = "permeability" of medium

and   hρg takes the place of Δp in Equation 2.35.

It is desired to use the model to calculate the time it takes for the oil to penetrate 4 cm into the ground.

Data: Initial height of oil level h_0 = 6 cm
        Porosity of ground = 0.7 cc/cc
        Permeability of ground K = 10^{-6} cm^2
        Oil viscosity μ = 0.02 Ns/m^2
        Oil density = 800 kg/m^3

(Hint: Use a cumulative balance to express amount of oil remaining on the surface as a function of time.)

Answer: t = 210 sec

2.7 Diffusion Through the Wall of a High-Pressure Hydrogenation Vessel — Hydrogen is capable of dissolving in and diffusing through metals. The rate of diffusion is represented by Fick's law:

One is asked to set up an appropriate balance and by simple integration obtain an expression for the concentration profile of hydrogen in the metal.

(Hint: Consult Chapter 3, Illustration 3.3.6.)

Answer: $\dfrac{C - C_2}{C_1 - C_2} = \dfrac{\ln r / r_2}{\ln r_1 / r_2}$

REFERENCES

Treatments of shell and tube heat exchanger and packed gas scrubbers can be found in standard heat and mass transfer texts; among them are:

F. Kreith and M.S. Bohn. *Principles of Heat Transfer, 4th ed.,* Harper & Row, 1986.

J.P. Holman. *Heat Transfer, 8th ed.,* McGraw-Hill, New York, 1997.

R.E. Treybal. *Mass Transfer Operations, 3rd ed.,* McGraw-Hill, New York, 1979.

See also:

R.F. Strigle. *Packed Tower Design and Applications: Random and Structured Packings,* Gulf Publishing, Houston, 1994.

The authoritative compilation of metal properties and metallurgical information is:

E.A. Brandes and G.A. Brook (Eds.). *Smithell's Metals Reference Book, 7th ed.,* Butterworths-Heinemann, London, 1992.

Early treatments of liquid metal heat transfer appear in:

S. Glasstone and A. Sesonske. *Nuclear Reactor Engineering,* Van Nostrand, Princeton, NJ, 1963.

R.P. Stern. Liquid Metal Heat Transfer, in *Adv. Heat Transfer, vol. 3,* Academic Press, 1966.

More up-to-date coverage of metallurgical processes is given in:
N.J. Themelis. *Transport and Chemical Rate Processes in Metallurgy,* Gordon and Breach,
    New York, 1995.

*The correlation Equation 2.31 is taken from Kreith and Bohn, previously cited, who also
cover natural convection in general.*

The topic of filtration is treated in:
M.J. Matteson and C. Orr. *Filtration. Principles and Practice,* 2nd ed., Marcel Dekker, New
    York, 1987.
C.J. Dickenson. *Filters and Filtration Handbook,* 3rd ed., Elsevier, 1992.

A more specialized text of interest to environmental engineers is:
C. Tien. *Granular Filtration of Aerosols and Hydrosols,* Butterworths, 1989.

*Drying operations are covered in individual chapters of most mass transfer texts, including
that by Treybal cited previously, as well as in:*
T.K. Sherwood, R.L. Pigford, and C.R. Wilke. *Mass Transfer,* McGraw-Hill, New York, 1975.
A.H.P. Skelland. *Diffusional Mass Transfer,* John Wiley & Sons, New York, 1985.

Among texts on drying per se, that by Keey deserves mention:
R.B. Keey. *Introduction to Industrial Drying,* Pergamon, New York, 1975.

Recent developments in drying are well covered in the serial:
Advances in Drying. Hemisphere, Washington.

Practice Problems 2.1 and 2.7 were adapted from similar illustrations given in:
G.H. Geiger and D.R. Poirier. *Transport Phenomena in Metallurgy,* Addison-Wesley, Reading,
    MA, 1973.

An up-to-date version of this text is:
D.R. Poirier and G.H. Geiger. *Transport Phenomena in Materials Processing,* TMS, Warren-
    dale, PA, 1994.

*Isotope distillation (Practice Problem 2.3) and other isotope separation and enrichment
processes are well covered in the monograph:*
H. London, Ed. *Separation of Isotopes,* George Newnes, London, 1961.

*Practice Problem 2.5, drawn from the field of adsorption, is dealt with in a monograph by
the author:*
D. Basmadjian. *The Little Adsorption Book,* CRC Press, Boca Raton, FL, 1996.

3 More About Mass, Energy, and Momentum Balances

Ah, but this is not the end. It is not even the beginning of the end. But it may well be the end of the beginning.

Winston Spencer Churchill
(Speech after the Battle of El Alamein, 1942)

The purpose of this chapter is to delve in considerably greater detail into the makeup of mass, energy, and momentum balances then had hitherto been the case. We start by considering various terms that appear in the balances, and follow this up with five separate and major sections on the following topics:

1. Mass balances (3.2)
2. Energy balances (3.3)
3. Momentum/force balances (3.4)
4. Simultaneous mass and energy balances (3.5)
5. Simultaneous mass, energy, and momentum balances (3.6)

Sections 1 to 3 start by considering transport and transport coefficients associated with both convective and diffusive mechanisms. Tabulations of their values and correlations applicable to the major geometries of interest (flat plate, sphere, cylinder, tube, packed bed) are presented. This is followed by illustrations and practice problems usually drawn from a wide variety of subdisciplines and are mostly kept at the level of single units although many model equations show an enhanced degree of sophistication. They are typically supplemented with charts and graphs which allow system variables to be read off with ease and rapidity. References to all six subsections appear at the end of the chapter.

3.1 THE TERMS IN THE VARIOUS BALANCES

It is of some use as a guide in modeling to be aware of the types of terms which may appear in various balances. They are conveniently tabulated for mass and energy balances in Table 3.1. A distinction is made among terms which arise due to bulk flow, convective interphase, and diffusive transport, as well as reaction and unsteady behavior. Both the basic stirred tank and the one-dimensional (steady-state) pipe are considered. One notes the similarity in terms which are due to a particular mode of

TABLE 3.1
Contributing Terms Used in Mass and Energy Balances

	Stirred Tank	1-D Pipe
A. Mass Balances		
1. Bulk or convective flow	FC	$FC\vert_z - FC\vert_{z+\Delta z}$
2. Convective interphase transport	$kA(C - C^*)$	$k(C - C^*)\Delta A$
3. Molecular or diffusive transport	—	$-DA\dfrac{dC}{dz}\Big\vert_z - DA\dfrac{dC}{dz}\Big\vert_{z+\Delta z}$
4. Reaction	rV	$r\Delta V$
5. Unsteady term	$\dfrac{d}{dt}(VC)$	—
B. Energy Balances		
1. Bulk or convective flow	FH	$FH\vert_z - FH\vert_{z+\Delta z}$
2. Convective interphase transport	$hA\Delta T$	$(h\Delta T)\Delta A$
3. Molecular or conductive transport	—	$kA\dfrac{dT}{dz}\Big\vert_z - kA\dfrac{dT}{dz}\Big\vert_{z+\Delta z}$
4. Reaction	$rV\,\Delta H_r$	$(r\,\Delta H_r)\Delta V$
5. Unsteady term	$\dfrac{d}{dt}VH$	—

transport. Thus, interphase heat and mass transfer are both proportional to the product of transport coefficients and driving force, diffusive transfer to the gradients of temperature and concentration. Reaction enters the balances through the reaction rate r. Note that neither r nor the driving forces ΔC and ΔT are differentiated over the increment A, as was shown in Chapter 2.

For momentum or force balances, not included in Table 3.1, the important operative terms are

$$\text{For convective or bulk flow: } \rho Qv \qquad (3.1.1)$$

$$\text{For diffusive or molecular transport: } \tau = -\mu\frac{dv}{dx} \qquad (3.1.2)$$

We note that for bulk flow, velocity has to be expressed in vectorial form since momentum depends on both magnitude and direction of v. The term for molecular transport, also known as Newton's viscosity law, is expressed in terms of the shear stress τ (Pa) acting on adjacent fluid lamellae.

3.2 MASS BALANCES

3.2.1 MOLAR MASS FLOW IN BINARY MIXTURES

In this Introductory Section we consider expressions for the combined flux due to bulk and molecular motion. This requirement is unique to mass transfer processes since diffusive transport may itself give rise to a bulk motion of fluid and, therefore, must be considered in conjunction with it. Such linked mechanisms do not arise in either energy or momentum transport and need not be taken up there.

We start with what is commonly known as Fick's law or Fick's first law which relates molar flux of a species N_A' (moles/m^{2}s) to the molar concentration gradient dC_A/dz.

$$N_A' = -D_{AB}\frac{dC_A}{dz} = -CD_{AB}\frac{dx_A}{dz} \qquad (3.2.1)$$

and

$$N_A' = D_{AB}(C_{A1} - C_{A2})/(z_2 - z_1) = CD_{AB}(x_{A1} - x_{A2})/(z_2 - z_1) \qquad (3.2.2)$$

where x_A = mole fraction of A, C = molar density of the fluid (moles/m^3).

When bulk flow $N_A' + N_B'$ takes place in conjunction with or superposed on diffusive flow, a corresponding compensating term must be added to Fickian diffusion. This is done as follows. For fluids in general:

$$N_A' = -CD_{AB}\frac{dx_A}{dz} + x_A(N_A' + N_B') \qquad (3.2.3)$$

Flux of A   Diffusive Flux   Bulk Flow

and for ideal gases in particular:

$$N_A' = -\frac{D_{AB}}{RT}\frac{dp_A}{dz} + \frac{p_A}{P_T}(N_A' + N_B') \qquad (3.2.4)$$

Two special cases are of particular importance:

1. Equimolar Counterdiffusion — For this case we have:

$$N_A' = -N_B' \qquad (3.2.5)$$

i.e., Equation 3.2.3 is reduced to Fick's law, Equation 3.2.1. The case arises with great frequency in the interdiffusion of pure fluids and in adiabatic distillation processes. Fick's law also is approximately valid when dealing with trace quantities of A, i.e., when the bulk flow term is essentially zero.

2. Diffusion Through a Stagnant Film — Here the flux of the species B is zero:

$$N_B' = 0 \qquad (3.2.6)$$

so that Equation 3.2.3 is reduced to the form:

$$N_A' = -\frac{CD_{AB}}{1-x_A}\frac{dx_A}{dz} = -\frac{CD_{AB}}{x_B}\frac{dx_B}{dz} \tag{3.2.7}$$

It can be shown that integration of the two segments within Equation 3.2.7 by separation of variables leads, after some manipulation, to the final expression:

$$N_A' = \frac{CD_{AB}}{(z_2 - z_1)(x_B)_M}(x_{A1} - x_{A2}) \tag{3.2.8}$$

where $(x_B)_M$ is the designation commonly used for the average, or so-called log-mean concentration difference of the stagnant component:

$$(x_B)_{avg} = x_{BM} = \frac{x_{B2} - x_{B1}}{\ln\dfrac{x_{B2}}{x_{B1}}} \tag{3.2.9}$$

For ideal gases, the analogous expression is given by:

$$N_A' = \frac{P_T D_{AB}/RT}{(z_2 - z_1)(p_B)_M}(p_{A1} - p_{A2}) \tag{3.2.10}$$

One notes again that for trace quantities of the solute A, Equations 3.2.8 and 3.2.10 reduce to the integrated form of Fick's law, Equation 3.2.2, since we then have $p_{BM} = x_{BM} \approx 1$. The two expressions appear frequently in the description of the evaporation of a liquid or dissolution of a solid into a flowing or well-stirred medium. The reverse processes of condensation and crystallization and other similar events are described in the same fashion.

The discerning reader will have noted that all three expressions (3.2.2, 3.2.8, and 3.2.10) relate the flux to a driving force ΔC, Δx, or Δp, preceded by a coefficient. We shall see in the next section how this leads, under certain simplifying assumptions, to the formulation of a transport coefficient or its inverse, the transport resistance.

3.2.2 TRANSPORT COEFFICIENTS

We start this section by considering binary molecular or diffusive coefficients D_{AB} which appear in Fick's law and the various flux equations presented in the preceding section. We have displayed typical values for both binary gaseous and liquid mixtures in Tables 3.2 and 3.3. While experimental measurements are to be preferred, gaseous diffusivities can be predicted to a fair degree of accuracy, particularly at low pressures, from theoretical expressions. Of note in these relations is the simple dependence on total pressure P_T and temperature T, given by:

TABLE 3.2
Diffusivities of Gases at 1 atm

System	Temp., °C	Diffusivity, cm²/s	Sc
O_2–N_2	0	0.181	—
Air–H_2	0	0.611	0.218
Air–H_2O	0	0.220	0.606
Air–NH_3	0	0.198	0.610
Air–ethanol	0	0.102	1.31
Air–benzene	25	0.0962	1.48

$$D_{AB} \propto \frac{T^{3/2}}{P_T} \tag{3.2.11}$$

For liquid mixtures, particularly those involving dissociating solutes, predictions are more difficult.

Also listed in Tables 3.2 and 3.3 are values of the dimensionless group known as the Schmidt number $Sc = \mu/\rho\, D_{AB}$. This parameter is one of the three defining dimensionless groups that appear in correlations of mass transfer coefficients, to be taken up below. Some simple statements can be made as to the order of magnitude of both diffusivities and Schmidt numbers, which are useful for quick engineering estimates. These are summarized in Table 3.4.

When dealing with transport in a turbulent or well-stirred medium, diffusivities are no longer applicable since they are restricted to stagnant systems or systems in laminar flow. Of the many theories which have been proposed, the so-called *film*

TABLE 3.3
Liquid Diffusivities

System	Temp., °C	Solute Conclusion mol/L	Diffusivity cm²/s · 10^5	Sc
CO_2–H_2O	10	~0	1.46	856
	20	~0	1.77	910
NH_3–H_2O	5	3.5	1.24	863
	15	1.0	1.77	808
NaCl–H_2O	18	0.05	1.26	1220
	18	5.4	1.54	1000
Ethanol–H_2O	10	0.05	0.83	1510
		3.75	0.50	2500
CO_2–ethanol	17	~0	3.2	472
Chloroform–ethanol	20	2.0	1.25	1290
Proteins–blood	37	—	~0.01–0.1	~30,000
				–300,000

TABLE 3.4
Approximate Values of Diffusivities and Schmidt Numbers

System	D_{AB}, cm²/s	Sc
Hydrogen and helium in gases (1 atm)	~1	~0.1
Binary gaseous mixtures in general (1 atm)	~10^{-1}	~1
Gases in porous solids (1 atm)	~$10^{-3} - 10^{-2}$	—
Simple binary liquid-phase systems	~10^{-5}	10^3
Proteins and polymeric solutes in different solvents	~$10^{-7} - 10^{-6}$	$10^4 - 10^5$
Simple binary liquid systems in porous solids	~$10^{-7} - 10^{-6}$	—

theory remains, because of its simplicity, the most widely used description of transport in these situations. Its genesis is illustrated in Figure 3.1.

Figure 3.1A shows an actual mean concentration profile as well as the one which evolves from film theory for turbulent flow past an evaporating or dissolving surface. Mirror images apply to condensing and crystallizing or precipitating solutes. Film theory proposes that the actual transport mechanism be replaced by diffusion through a fictitious or effective stagnant film of thickness z_F. Fick's law, Equation 3.2.2, can then be written in the form:

A. The Single Film

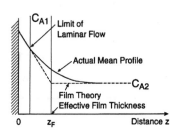

B. Two-Film Theory

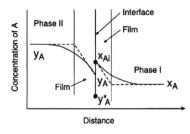

FIGURE 3.1   Diagram illustrating single and two-film theories.

$$N_A' = k_C(C_{A1} - C_{A2}) = Ck_C(x_{A1} - x_{A2}) \tag{3.2.12}$$

where the mass transfer coefficient k_C is defined by the relation:

$$k_C = \frac{D_{AB}}{z_f} \tag{3.2.13}$$

Similar expressions apply to the flux Equations 3.2.8 and 3.2.10.

When both phases in contact with each other are in turbulent flow, two effective films or resistances are postulated, as shown in Figure 3.1B. Transport takes place from a high concentration y_A through the effective film associated with Phase II to the interface. Here the Phase II concentration y^*_{Ai} is assumed to be in equilibrium with the Phase I interfacial concentration x_{Ai} so that:

$$y^*_{Ai} = m \, x_{Ai} \tag{3.2.14}$$

where m is the local slope of the equilibrium curve. Transport then continues from the interface to the bulk of Phase I of concentration x_A.

The entire process can be regarded as proceeding through two resistances in series represented by the two films. If we define these resistances as $1/k_y$ and m/k_x respectively, addition of the two terms will yield an overall resistance $1/K_{oy}$ given by:

$$\frac{1}{K_{oy}} = \frac{1}{k_y} + \frac{m}{k_x} \tag{3.2.15}$$

where K_{oy} is termed the overall mass transfer coefficient. It can be shown that with these definitions in hand, the mass transfer flux takes the form:

$$N_A = K_{oy}(y_A - y^*_A) \tag{3.2.16}$$

where y^*_A is the fictitious concentration in equilibrium with x_A:

$$y^*_A = m \, x_A \tag{3.2.17}$$

Overall coefficients are widely used to describe transport between two phases in contact with each other. They are determined experimentally or computed from Equation 3.2.15.

To aid in the computation of both film and overall mass transfer coefficients we have compiled correlations of the former for flow in and around various common geometries (Table 3.5). The film coefficients appear in the form of dimensionless Stanton or Sherwood numbers, defined in the table. Both of these groups depend solely on the dimensionless Reynolds and Schmidt numbers, so that one can write:

$$St, Sh = f(Re, Sc) \tag{3.2.18}$$

TABLE 3.5
Correlations for Mass Transfer Coefficients

Range	Equation
(1) Flat Plate	
Re < 10⁵	$St = 0.66 \ (Re)^{-1/2} \ (Sc)^{-2/3}$
Re > 10⁶	$St = 0.036 \ (Re)^{-0.2} \ (Sc)^{-2/3}$
(2) Sphere	
Unlimited	$Sh = 2.0 + 0.60 \ (Re)^{1/2} \ (Sc)^{1/3}$
(3) Cylinder	
1 < Re < 4000	$Sh = 0.43 + 0.53 \ Re^{0.5} \ (Sc)^{0.31}$
(4) Inside pipes (μ = const.)	
Re < 2100	$Sh = 1.86 \ (ReSc \ d/L)^{1/3}$
Re > 20,000	$Sh = 0.026 \ (Re)^{0.8} \ (Sc)^{1/3}$
(5) Packed Bed of Spheres	
Re < 50	$St = 0.91 \ (Re)^{-0.51} \ (Sc)^{-2/3}$
Re > 50	$St = 0.61 \ (Re)^{-0.41} \ (Sc)^{-2/3}$

Note: Re = Reynolds number = $\dfrac{Lv\rho}{\mu}$, Sh = Sherwood number = $\dfrac{k_{c,l}L}{D}$

St = Stanton number = $\dfrac{k_{c,l}}{v}$, Sc = Schmidt number = $\dfrac{\mu}{\rho D}$

L = Length of plate, diameter of sphere, cylinder, or pipe

We conclude this section by drawing attention to Table 3.6 which lists mass transfer fluxes in terms of different modes (stagnant film and equimolar counterdiffusion), driving forces, as well as conversion factors for the various mass transfer coefficients. Since correlations in Table 3.5 are given in terms of k_c or k_L, conversions become necessary whenever it proves convenient to use driving forces other than ΔC. An example of the use of the correlations and conversion factors is given in Illustration 3.2.1 below.

Illustration 3.2.1 Drying of Plastic Sheets Revisited: Estimation of the Mass Transfer Coefficient k_Y

In Illustration 2.7 (Chapter 2) we had considered the problem of drying nonporous plastic sheets to 10% of their original moisture content by passing air at 44°C over the sheets at a velocity of 15 m/s. We now wish to calculate the mass transfer coefficient k_Y which was given there without mention of its origin. To do this, we draw on Table 3.5 for correlations of k_c (m/s) and on Table 3.6 for conversion of k_c to k_Y. For flow over a flat plate, the suggested correlations are

TABLE 3.6
Relations Among Mass Transfer Coefficients

Rate Equation		
Equimolar Counterdiffusion	Diffusion of A Through Stagnant B	Units of Mass Transfer Coefficient
Gases		
$N_A' = k_G' \Delta p_A$	$N_A' = k_G \Delta p_A$	Moles/time area pressure
$N_A' = k_y' \Delta y_A$	$N_A' = k_y \Delta y_A$	Moles/time area mole fraction
$N_A' = k_C' \Delta C_A$	$N_A' = k_C \Delta C_A$	Moles/time area (moles/vol.)
	$W_A = k_Y \Delta Y_A$	Mass/time area (mass A/mass B)
Liquids		
$N_A' = k_L' \Delta C_A$	$N_A' = k_L \Delta C_A$	Moles/time area (moles/vol.)
$N_A' = k_x' \Delta x_A$	$N_A' = k_x \Delta x_A$	Moles/time area mole fraction

Conversion for Gases

$$k_G P_{BM} = k_y \frac{P_{BM}}{P_T} = k_C \frac{P_{BM}}{RT} = \frac{k_Y}{M_B} = k_G' P_T = k_Y' = k_C' C$$

Conversion for Liquids
$$k_L x_{BM} C = k_x x_{BM} = k_L' C = k_x'$$

For Re < 10^5 St = 0.66 (Re)$^{-1/2}$ (Sc)$^{-2/3}$

For Re > 10^6 St = 0.036 (Re)$^{-0.2}$ (Sc)$^{-2/3}$

We establish the proper choice by first computing the Reynolds number. Using Table 3.8 of the properties of air, interpolated for a temperature of 44°C, we obtain:

$$Re = \frac{Lv\rho}{\mu} = \frac{(15.2)(1.5)(1.12)}{1.93 \times 10^{-5}} = 1.32 \times 10^7$$

TABLE 3.7
Properties of Liquid Water

T°C	ρ (kg/m³)	C_p (kJ/kg K)	μ(Pas × 10³) or (kg/ms × 10³)	k (W/mK)	Pr
0	1000	4.23	1.79	0.569	13.7
25	997	4.18	0.89	0.590	6.10
100	958	4.21	0.28	0.681	1.75

Note: Latent heat of vaporization (100°C) ΔH_v = 2446.9 kJ/kg. Latent heat of fusion (0°C) ΔH_f = 334.1 kJ/kg.

TABLE 3.8
Properties of Air

T°C	ρ (kg/m³)	C_p (kJ/kg K)	μ(Pas $\times$ 10⁵) or (kg/ms $\times$ 10⁵)	k (W/mK) 10²	Pr
0	1.29	1.005	1.72	2.42	0.715
25	1.18	1.005	1.84	2.60	0.709
100	0.94	1.01	2.19	3.20	0.691

leading to the choice of the second correlation. Thus, we use the expression:

$$\frac{k_c}{v} = 0.036\left(\frac{Lv\rho}{\mu}\right)^{-0.2}\left(\frac{\mu}{\rho D}\right)^{-2/3}$$

For the Schmidt number $\mu/\rho D$, we draw on Table 3.2 for diffusivities in gases and use the value of Sc = 0.606 given there for T = 0°C. This is justified since the necessary temperature corrections to compute physical properties at 44°C are minor and very nearly cancel out. This yields:

$$\frac{k_C}{15} = 0.036\left(\frac{(1.32\times10^7)}{1.93\times10^{-3}}\right)^{-0.2}(0.606)^{-2/3}$$

or

$$k_C = 0.0284 \text{ m/s}$$

Conversion to k_Y requires the following relation given in Table 3.6:

$$k_Y = k_C\frac{M_B P_{BM}}{RT} = 0.0445\frac{29\times10^{-3}}{(8.31)(317)}P_{BM}$$

For the computation of

$$P_{BM} = \frac{p_{B1} - p_{B2}}{\ln\dfrac{p_{B1}}{p_{B2}}}$$

we note that the vapor pressure of water at the interface temperature T_{wb} = 21°C is p_A = 2487 Pa so that p_{B1} = 101300 − 2487 = 98813 Pa and p_{B2} = 101300 Pa. We obtain

$$k_Y = 0.0284\frac{29\times10^{-3}}{(8.31)(317)}\frac{98813-101300}{\ln\dfrac{98813}{101300}} = 0.0313\,\text{kg}\,H_2O\,/\,s\,m^2\Delta Y$$

which is the value used in Chapter 2's Illustration 2.7.

Comments:

We note here that this exercise assumes some knowledge of appropriate sources of information. In this case the information is conveniently tabulated in the text (see Tables 3.5, 3.6, and 3.8). This will evidently not be possible for all parameter values one has to deal with, and the analyst must therefore be prepared at an early stage to accumulate a storehouse of source material and to draw on it when necessary. Alternatively, one can consult colleagues with expertise in a particular area. This is perfectly respectable and widely practiced.

We note again the wide diversity of mass transfer coefficients that exist and the necessity to interconvert them. k_Y was needed here because the humidity driving force ΔY was a convenient quantity to use. The correlations given in Table 3.5, on the other hand, are as already mentioned expressed in terms of k_c (m/s) and must be converted to k_Y via the relations listed in Table 3.6.

Illustration 3.2.2 Measurement of Diffusivities by the Two-Bulb Method: The Quasi-Steady State

Diffusion coefficients in gases and liquids can be measured in a variety of ways, an important one being the so-called two-bulb method. We draw attention to the details of the experimental configuration, shown in Figure 3.2. The two bulbs containing the species A and B at the same total pressure and temperature are connected by a long capillary of small cross-sectional area A. The purpose of the arrangement is to ensure that transport through the capillary becomes the rate-determining step and that consequently the contents of the bulbs may at any instant be assumed to have a uniform composition as if stirred. This is referred to as the quasi steady-state assumption and allows us to express the transport of A in terms of an instantaneous driving force $C_{A1} - C_{A2}$. We apply a mass balance for A around the reservoir 2 and obtain the following expression:

$$\text{Rate of A in} - \text{Rate of A out} = \frac{\text{Change in}}{\text{A content}}$$

$$D_{AB}A\frac{C_{A1} - C_{A2}}{L} - 0 = V_2\frac{dC_{A2}}{dt} \qquad (3.2.19)$$

Since we have two state variables C_{A1} and C_{A2}, an additional relation is required. We can use a second unsteady balance around reservoir 1 which leads to an ODE, or more conveniently, an algebraic cumulative balance to time t. Thus,

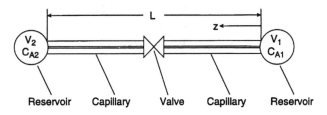

FIGURE 3.2 Measurement of diffusivities by the two-bulb method.

$$\begin{array}{c} \text{Initial amount} \\ \text{of A at t} = 0 \end{array} = \begin{array}{c} \text{Total amount of A} \\ \text{at time t} \end{array} \tag{3.2.20}$$

$$V_1 C^0_{A1} + V_2 C^0_{A2} = V_1 C_{A1} + V_2 C_{A2}$$

Substitution of C_{A1} from this equation into Equation 3.2.19 yields after rearrangement:

$$\frac{D_{AB}A(V_1 + V_2)}{V_1 V_2}\left[\frac{V_1 C_{A1}{}^0 + V_2 C_{A2}{}^0}{V_1 + V_2} - C_{A2}\right] = \frac{dC_{A2}}{dt} \tag{3.2.21}$$

We note that the fraction in the bracket equals the average concentration $(C_A)_{avg}$ in the two bulbs:

$$C_{Aavg} = \frac{V_1 C_{A1}{}^0 + V_2 C_{A2}{}^0}{V_1 + V_2} \tag{3.2.22}$$

so that upon integration by separation of variables one obtains:

$$\frac{C_{Aavg} - C_{A2}}{C_{Aavg} - C_{A2}{}^0} = \exp\left[-\frac{D_{AB}(V_1 + V_2)}{(L/A)(V_1 V_2)}t\right] \tag{3.2.23}$$

Values for D_{AB} are then obtained from the slope of a semilogarithmic plot of measures values of C_2 as a function of time t.

Comments:

The experimental apparatus deserves some attention. A first point to note is that the capillary has to be uniform and its cross-sectional area known to a high degree of accuracy to ensure precision in the value of D_{AB} obtained. Second, while the ratio of bulb to capillary diameter must be kept large to ensure validity of the quasi-steady state assumption, the volume of the bulbs must on the other hand, be kept reasonably small so that noticeable concentration changes can be brought about in a reasonable time period. For the same reason, capillary length should not be excessive. Proper values for these parameters can be established from Equation 3.2.23 using order of magnitude estimates for D_{AB} (see Table 3.4).

The quasi-steady state assumption introduced in this example is widely used to simplify model equations. Note that without it, the "stirred tank" assumption could not be made and one would have to resort to partial differential equations for a description of the process. These equations would be quite complex because of the mixed geometry of the apparatus.

It follows that successful experimentation requires an understanding of the underlying physics of the process as well as considerable skill in modeling. The reader is invited to add these items to the arsenal that comprises the Art of Modeling.

3.2.3 CHEMICAL REACTION MASS BALANCE

The following three illustrations deal with classical problems which arise in chemical reactor engineering practice. All three assume isothermal operation so that no energy balances need to be invoked. In the first example the model mass balance for a continuous flow stirred tank reactor under transient conditions is addressed. The steady-state mass balance for a tubular reactor is taken up next and leads, as expected, to a first order ODE in the independent distance variable. Finally, we consider the mass balance which applies to diffusion and reaction in a catalyst pellet. We show that the primary result, which consists of the concentration profiles within the pellet can be integrated to obtain the so-called effectiveness factor E, which is a measure of the reaction efficiency of the pellet. This factor can be directly incorporated in a mass balance which describes the behavior of a tubular fixed-bed catalytic reactor.

The rate of reaction r in these and subsequent examples is defined as

$$r \equiv -\frac{1}{V}\frac{dN_A}{dt} \equiv \frac{1}{V}\frac{dN_P}{dt} \qquad (3.2.24)$$

where A and P are the designations for a typical reactant and product respectively, V is volume, and N_A, N_P are the moles consumed and produced. These definitions are to be distinguished from experimentally determined rate laws which are expressed in terms of molar concentrations C and involve the *order* of a reaction and the reaction rate constant k. Thus,

$$r_A = k\,C_A \qquad \text{First order reaction}$$

$$r_A = k\,C_A^2 \qquad \text{Second order reaction} \qquad (3.2.25)$$

$$r_A = kC_A^a\,C_B^b\,...\,C_K^k \quad a + b + ... + k = n$$

The latter is quite general and is of order a with respect to A, of order b with respect to B, and nth order overall.

Illustration 3.2.3 CSTR With Second Order Homogeneous Reaction A + B → P

The simple example considered here and shown in Figure 3.3A involves a second order reaction taking place in a continuous flow stirred tank reactor operating at constant hold-up (V = constant). Reactant A enters at a volumetric flow rate Q and molar concentration C_{Af}. A component balance for the species A then leads to:

$$\text{Rate of A in} - \text{Rate of A out} = \frac{\text{Rate of change}}{\text{in A content}}$$

$$QC_{Af} - \left[\begin{array}{c} QC_A \\ +k_r\,C_A C_B\,V \end{array}\right] = V\frac{dC_A}{dt} \qquad (3.2.26)$$

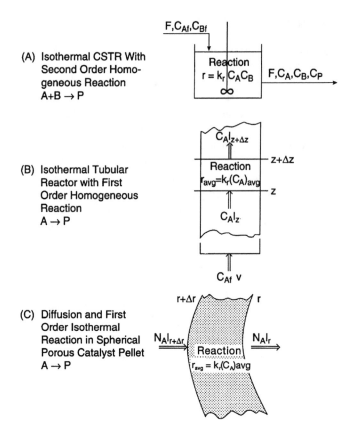

(A) Isothermal CSTR With Second Order Homogeneous Reaction A+B → P

(B) Isothermal Tubular Reactor with First Order Homogeneous Reaction A → P

(C) Diffusion and First Order Isothermal Reaction in Spherical Porous Catalyst Pellet A → P

FIGURE 3.3 Diagrams of various isothermal reactor models: (A) the continuous stirred tank reactor (CSTR), (B) the tubular plug flow reactor, (C) reaction within a catalyst pellet.

Similar balances for the B and P species yields:

$$\text{Rate of B in} - \text{Rate of B out} = \frac{\text{Rate of change}}{\text{in B content}}$$

$$QC_{Bf} - \left[\begin{matrix} QC_{AB} \\ +k_r C_A C_B V \end{matrix}\right] = V\frac{dC_B}{dt} \tag{3.2.27}$$

$$\text{Rate of P in} - \text{Rate of P out} = \frac{\text{Rate of change}}{\text{in P content}}$$

$$k_r C_A C_B V - QC_p = V\frac{dC_p}{dt} \tag{3.2.28}$$

We note again that production and consumption rates of the various species *by reaction* are grouped under input and output terms respectively and represent instantaneous algebraic quantities. The transient or rate of change terms do not contain reaction rate expressions and are placed on the right side of the equations.

The system of Equations 3.2.25 to 3.2.28 is composed of a set of simultaneous coupled ODEs and would ordinarily have to be solved numerically. This can be circumvented by introducing a new variable, the conversion X, which is defined as follows:

$$X = \frac{\text{Initial moles} - \text{Moles at time t}}{\text{Initial moles}} \qquad (3.2.29)$$

Thus, for the reactant species A, since V = constant, we have:

$$X = \frac{N_{Af} - N_A}{N_{Af}} = \frac{C_{Af} - C_A}{C_{Af}} \quad \text{or} \quad C_A = C_{Af}(1 - X) \qquad (3.2.30)$$

and in similar fashion for the other species,

$$C_B = C_{Bf}(1 - X) \qquad (3.2.31)$$

$$C_p = C_{Af} X \qquad (3.2.32)$$

The advantage of this procedure is that the set of three equations is reduced to a single ODE which can, if desired, be integrated analytically by separation of variables. Thus, the species A balance becomes, upon substitution of Equations 3.2.30 to 3.2.32, and simplification

$$-k_r C_{Af} C_{Bf} \tau (1 - X)^2 + C_{Af} X \equiv \tau \frac{dX}{dt} \qquad (3.2.33)$$

where $\tau = V/Q$ is the so-called residence time.

Illustration 3.2.4 Isothermal Tubular Reactor with First Order Homogeneous Reaction

The mass balance is in this case taken over a difference element Δz and yields, upon going to the limit $\Delta z \to 0$, a first order differential equation in the reactant concentration C_A (see Figure 3.3B). For a first order reaction with no volume changes, i.e., at constant flow velocity v and steady state, we obtain:

$$\text{Rate of A in} - \text{Rate of A out} = 0$$

$$vAC_A \big|_z - \left[\begin{array}{c} vAC_A \big|_{z+\Delta z} \\ + k_r (C_A)_{avg} A \Delta z \end{array} \right] = 0 \qquad (3.2.34)$$

and after division by $A\Delta z$ and letting $\Delta z \to 0$,

$$v\frac{dC_A}{dz} + k_r C_A = 0 \qquad (3.2.35)$$

Note that here again, as in the case of the gas absorber, $(C_A)_{avg} \to C_A$ in the limit so that this quantity does not get to be differentiated. Integration by separation of variables yields

$$\ln\frac{C_A}{C_{Af}} = -\frac{k_r}{v}z = -\frac{k_r zA}{vA} = -k_r\tau$$

$$C_A = C_{Af} \exp(-k_r\tau) \qquad (3.2.36a)$$

where $\tau = zA/vA = V/Q$ = residence time, as in the previous case of the CSTR. Alternatively, we can use conversion X in lieu of C_A (see Equation 3.2.30), and obtain

$$X = 1 - \exp(-k_r\tau) \qquad (3.2.36b)$$

One notes that conversion increases with residence time, as would be expected on physical grounds.

Illustration 3.2.5 Isothermal Diffusion and First Order Reaction in a Spherical, Porous Catalyst Pellet: The Effectiveness Factor E

In this classical problem we demonstrate the combined use of Fick's law and chemical reaction rate in setting up a steady-state differential mass balance (Figure 3.3C). Because of the form of Fick's law which contains a derivative as well as an area term that varies with distance, a second order ODE with variable coefficients is obtained. This yields, in the first instance,

$$\text{Rate of A in} - \text{Rate of A out} = 0$$

$$N_A\big|_{r+\Delta r} - \left[\begin{array}{c} N_A\big|_r \\ +(r_A)_{avg}\Delta V \end{array}\right] = 0 \qquad (3.2.37)$$

or in the limit

$$dN_A - (r_A)_{avg}\, dV = 0 \qquad (3.2.38)$$

Note that N_A equals the previously used flux N_A' times the area A.

The auxiliary Fick's law is now introduced but since flux is in the negative r-direction, it takes a double negative sign, i.e., becomes positive. Thus,

$$N_A = -\left(-D_{eff} A \cdot \frac{dC_A}{dr}\right) = D_{eff} A \frac{dC_A}{dr} \qquad (3.2.39)$$

Using expressions for area and differential volume of a sphere and a first order reaction, we obtain:

$$d\left(D_{eff} 4\pi r^2 \frac{dC_A}{dr}\right) - k_r C_A 4\pi r^2 dr = 0 \qquad (3.2.40)$$

Note that the diffusion term is a product of two functions of r and has to be differentiated accordingly. Subsequent division by $4\pi r^2$ dr finally yields:

$$\frac{d^2C_A}{dr^2} + \frac{2}{r}\frac{dC_A}{dr} - k_r C_A / D_{eff} = 0 \qquad (3.2.41)$$

Comments:

The first two terms of Equation 3.2.41 are characteristic of *diffusive* transport in spherical geometries and, therefore, can be expected to arise in conduction, diffusion, and viscous flow in and around spheres. For radial flux in cylindrical geometries, the coefficient of the first derivative is halved, while in rectangular or planar configurations (slab) that quantity is unity. The characteristic terms for diffusive transport are thus,

For planar or rectangular geometries	$\dfrac{d^2u}{dx^2}$
For cylindrical geometries	$\dfrac{d^2u}{dr^2} + \dfrac{1}{r}\dfrac{du}{dr}$
For spherical geometries	$\dfrac{d^2u}{dr^2} + \dfrac{2}{r}\dfrac{du}{dr}$

We note that the expression for spherical geometries can be reduced to the planar case by making the substitution v = ur. This results in a considerable simplification of the differential equation involved.

The solution methods for second order ODEs with constant coefficients differ, as will be discussed in Chapter 4, from those with coefficients which are functions of the independent variable. In the former case, the classical D-operator method or equivalent matrix operations can be applied to arrive at a solution which generally leads to exponential or trigonometric forms. Second order ODEs with variable coefficients which arise whenever the diffusive flux area varies with distance usually require series solutions that lead to a different class of functions (Bessel functions, Legendre functions).

The solution of Equation 3.2.41 and the corresponding expressions for reactions of arbitrary order yield, as primary information, the concentration profiles of the reactants within the catalyst pellet. The question then arises as to how this initial result can be used to describe the behavior of a tubular catalytic reactor packed with catalyst pellets. To do this, use is made of the so-called (isothermal) effectiveness factor E_i of the pellet, defined as the ratio of the overall reaction rate within the pellet with and without diffusional hindrance. Thus,

$$E_i = \frac{\text{Reaction rate with diffusion } r_p}{\text{Reaction rate without diffusion } r_p'} = \frac{\int_0^V r_p dV}{r_p' V} \qquad (3.2.42)$$

where V is the pellet volume and r_p is evaluated from the concentration profile previously obtained from Equation 3.2.41. r_p' on the other hand represents the intrinsic reaction rate on the catalyst material and can be obtained in principle from experimental conversion measurements on finely powdered catalysts in which diffusional resistance can be considered negligible. We note that the effectiveness factor is in essence a measure of the extent to which r_p' is *reduced* due to the effect of diffusional resistance. Thus, E can be regarded as a *correction factor* to the intrinsic rate r_p' and can as such be directly incorporated in the appropriate model. Thus, for a first order reaction the equation applicable to a tubular reactor with an intrinsic rate constant k_r' is simply replaced by the corresponding expression incorporating the correction factor E:

$$v \frac{dC_A}{dz} - E_i k_r' C_A = 0 \qquad (3.2.43)$$

Extensive tabulations of E_i can be found in the literature and are usually given as plots of effectiveness factor vs. the so-called Thiele modulus $mL = (L^2 k_r/D_{eff})^{1/2}$. The latter is a measure of the relative effect of diffusional resistance (D_{eff}), reaction rate (k_r), and pellet dimension (L). A typical plot, applicable to first order reactions in various geometries, and for different reaction volume changes is shown in Figure 3.4. Low values of E_i occur at high values of mL, i.e., in large pellets or at high reaction rates and low diffusivities. Under these conditions the reactant is consumed rapidly and this, together with low diffusion rates and a substantial particle size, makes for a high transport resistance. As mL is reduced, an increase in E_i occurs which ultimately converges to unity. At this value of E_i, the reactant concentration within the pellet has become uniform and equals that prevailing at the surface. The catalyst is then at its maximum effectiveness.

3.2.4 TANK MASS BALANCES

In this section we present further examples of mass balances taken around a stirred tank which we had seen lead to first order ODEs in the unsteady state and algebraic equations when the system has attained a steady state. Illustration 3.2.3 considered a stirred-tank reactor under transient conditions. Here, we limit ourselves to nonre-

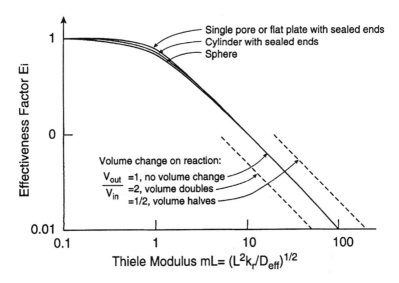

FIGURE 3.4 Isothermal catalyst pellet effectiveness factor E_i as a function of the Thiele modulus mL for various geometries and reaction volume changes. (R. Aris. *Chem. Eng. Sci.,* 6:262, 1957. With permission.)

acting systems in which the amount of the species in the tank increases, decreases, or remains constant due solely to the influence of the inflow and outflow terms. Such models arise routinely in problems involving a dilution or concentration of tank contents, evaporation, distillation, extraction, and crystallization processes carried out in tanks and a host of natural systems which can be approximated by a stirred-tank configuration. The classical example of a surge tank given in Section 2.1 also falls in this category.

Illustration 3.2.6   Waste-Disposal Holding Tank

A holding tank containing solid waste suspended in water or in settled form is to be flushed with a constant inflow of water at $Q = 100$ m³/h. Volume of tank contents is constant at $V = 200$ m³ and initial solids content 1000 kg. It is desired to calculate the remaining solids contents S after 4 h of flushing. The volume of solids is negligible compared to the tank volume V.

We compose a mass balance with respect to the solids and obtain

$$\text{Rate in} - \text{Rate out} = \text{Rate of change of contents}$$

$$0 - XQ = V\frac{dX}{dt} \tag{3.2.44}$$

where X = kg solids/m³ water.

Integrating by separation of variables yields:

$$-\frac{Q}{V}t = \ln\frac{X_2}{X_1} \qquad (3.2.45)$$

or

$$X_2 = X_1 \exp(-t/\tau)$$

where $\tau = V/Q$ = residence time or "holding time."
  Substituting numerical values we obtain:

$$X_2 = \frac{1000}{200}\exp[-4/(200/100)] = 0.677 \text{ kg solids / kg water}$$

and

$$S = (0.677)(200) = 135 \text{ kg solids}$$

Illustration 3.2.7   Holding-Tank with Variable Holdup

Here we consider, without injecting numerical values, the general case of a holding tank with variable holdup, i.e., with different in- and outflow terms, Q_1 and Q_2. Since two dependent variables are now involved, volume of the tank contents V and the solids concentration X, we have to use two mass balances, one for the solids and one for the water.

Water mass balance:

$$\text{Rate of water in} - \text{Rate of water out} = \frac{\text{Rate of change}}{\text{in water content}}$$

$$\qquad (3.2.46)$$

$$Q_1 - Q_2 = \frac{dV}{dt}$$

Solids mass balance:

$$\text{Rate of solids in} - \text{Rate of solids out} = \frac{\text{Rate of change}}{\text{in solids content}}$$

$$\qquad (3.2.47)$$

$$0 - XQ_2 = \frac{d}{dt}XV$$

  The system can be solved by first integrating Equation 3.2.46, substituting the solution $V = f(t)$ into Equation 3.2.47, and performing a second integration to obtain $X = g(t)$. Another approach, which is used extensively when the independent variable t is not required, is to divide the two equations, thus eliminating dt and integrating the result to obtain a relation between the two dependent variables, $X = f(V)$ (see in this connection Practice Problem 2.3: Rayleigh Distillation). This is a useful intermediate result, but we shall go a step further and solve for $S = F(t)$. The procedure is demonstrated below.

Dividing Equation 3.2.47 by Equation 3.2.46, we obtain:

$$X \frac{Q_2}{Q_2 - Q_1} = \frac{d}{dt} XV = X + V \frac{dX}{dV} \tag{3.2.48}$$

Collecting variables and integrating by separation of variables yields:

$$\frac{Q_1}{Q_2 - Q_1} \ln\left(\frac{V_2}{V_1}\right) = \ln \frac{X_2}{X_1} \tag{3.2.49}$$

or, equivalently,

$$\left(\frac{V_2}{V_1}\right)^{Q_1/(Q_1 - Q_2)} = \frac{X_1}{X_2} = \frac{S_1}{S_2}$$

where $S = $ kg solids. This is the intermediate relation between solid content X or S and water volume in the tank V.

To obtain an expression for $S = F(t)$, we first integrate Equation 3.2.46, again by separation of variables, obtaining:

$$V_2 - V_1 = (Q_1 - Q_2)t \tag{3.2.50}$$

Substituting V_2 into Equation 3.2.49 and solving for S_2 finally yields:

$$S_2 = S_1 \left[\frac{(Q_1 - Q_2)t + V_1}{V_1}\right]^{Q_1/(Q_2 - Q_1)} \tag{3.2.51}$$

This expression allows the calculation of the solids remaining, S_2, after a water purge of duration t. Alternatively it can be used to calculate the time required to achieve a desired reduction in solids content or to set incoming flow rate Q_1 to achieve that result in a prescribed time interval.

3.2.5 TUBULAR MASS BALANCES

We have previously seen, in the section on chemical reaction mass balances, that tubular mass balances arise in models of various types of tubular reactors (homogeneous, heterogeneous, or catalytic, etc.). In this section we limit ourselves to mass transport in a tubular device devoid of chemical reactions and present as examples

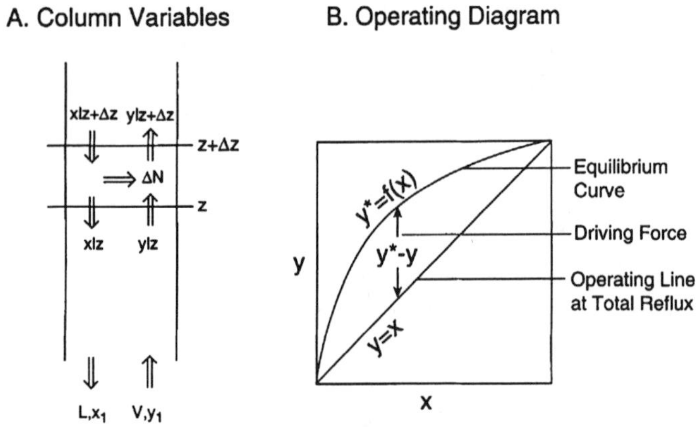

A. Column Variables   B. Operating Diagram

FIGURE 3.5 Column variables and operating diagram for a packed distillation of column at total reflux.

the column distillation of a binary mixture and the release of a solute from a tubular wall into a flowing medium.

Illustration 3.2.8   Distillation in a Packed Column:
The Case of Total Reflux and Constant α

This example again requires some background knowledge in chemical processing or unit operations and is primarily addressed to chemical engineers.

The mass balance here takes a form similar to that obtained in the case of the gas scrubber; the balance is taken with respect to the more volatile component in one phase and over a difference element which yields, upon going to the limit, a first order differential equation in distance z. Since the conventional distillation analysis assumes constant molar flow rates above and below the feed point (molar evaporation rate L and molar condensation rate V are each constant), mole fraction concentration units can be used without the attendant complications of a variable flow rate. This leads to the use of mass transfer coefficients K_x, K_y based on a mole fraction driving force which shows greater constancy than the mole ratio based coefficients K_X, K_Y employed for the scrubber to ensure constant (carrier) flow rates. We obtain, for a component balance over the vapor phase of the element (see Figure 3.5A) —

Differential component balance:

$$\text{Rate in} - \text{Rate out} = 0$$

$$\left[\begin{array}{c} V y \,|_z \\ +K_y a(y^* - y)\Delta z \end{array} \right] = V y \,|_{z+\Delta z} = 0 \qquad (3.2.52)$$

which yields upon dividing by Δz and going to the limit:

$$V\frac{dy}{dz} - K_y a(y* - y) = 0 \qquad (3.2.53)$$

Separating variables and integrating results in

$$H = \frac{V}{K_y a}\int \frac{dy}{y* - y} - \text{HTU NTU} \qquad (3.2.54)$$

in complete analogy to the Expression 2.26 obtained for the gas scrubber. As was done there, the expression has to be supplemented by an integral component balance (which leads to the so-called operating line) and an appropriate equilibrium relation. Thus,

Integral component balance:

$$\text{Rate in} - \text{Rate out} = 0$$
$$(L_1 x_1 - Vy) - (Lx + Vy_1) = 0 \qquad (3.2.55)$$

Equilibrium relation:

$$y* = f(x) \qquad (3.2.56)$$

The Relations 3.2.55 and 3.2.56 are then conveniently plotted on the so-called operating diagram (Figure 3.5B) and the NTU Integral 3.2.54 evaluated by graphical or numerical integration as was done in the case of the scrubber.

The special case of total reflux and constant relative volatility α (Raoult's law) — A particular simple evaluation of the NTU integral becomes possible when the column is at total reflux and one is dealing with ideal solutions (Raoult's law). The equilibrium relation then takes the simple form:

$$y* = \frac{\alpha x}{1 + (\alpha - 1)x} \qquad (3.2.57)$$

where α is the so-called relative volatility. Furthermore, at total reflux liquid and vapor compositions are equal: $y = x$, i.e., the operating line becomes the diagonal in the operating diagram (Figure 3.5B). Substituting these relations into the NTU integral, one obtains:

$$\text{NTU} = \int_{y_1}^{y_2} \frac{dy}{y* - y} - \int_{y_1}^{y_2} \frac{dy}{\dfrac{\alpha y}{1 + (\alpha - 1)y} - y} = \int_{y_1}^{y_2} \frac{1 + (\alpha - 1)y \, dy}{y(\alpha - 1)(1 - y)} \qquad (3.2.58)$$

Using the integration formula

$$\int \frac{dx}{x(a+bx)} = -\frac{1}{a} \ln \frac{a+bx}{x}$$

evaluation of the integral yields:

$$NTU = \frac{1}{\alpha - 1} \ln \frac{y_2(1-y_1)}{y_1(1-y_2)} + \ln \frac{1-y_1}{1-y_2} \qquad (3.2.59)$$

This expression is frequently used in the experimental evaluation of HTU or $K_y a$ values for packed columns that are for this purpose operated at total reflux.

Illustration 3.2.9   Tubular Flow with Solute Release from the Wall

In the device considered here, solute is released from the tubular wall into a fluid in turbulent flow which is usually a liquid. Applications of this configuration occur in medicine as controlled release devices, in the determination of mass transfer coefficients, and in other areas. The reverse process in which solute is transported to the wall and is deposited there and/or undergoes reaction is also of interest, e.g., in the fouling of tubes and in reactors in which the tubular wall is coated with a catalyst.

We examine two cases, one in which the solute is released at a constant rate $N'(kg/sm^2)$, while the other considers the tubular wall to be at the saturation concentration C^* so that transport is driven by the driving force $C^* - C_{bulk}$.

In the former case we obtain by mass balance over a difference element:

$$\text{Rate of solute in} - \text{Rate of solute out} = 0$$

$$\begin{bmatrix} C_{1z} \\ +N'\Delta z \end{bmatrix} - C_{1z+\Delta z} = 0 \qquad (3.2.60)$$

where P = perimeter.

Dividing by Δz and going to the limit as usual yields:

$$\frac{dC}{dz} - N'P = 0 \qquad (3.2.61)$$

whence by separation of variables and integration:

$$C = N'Pz \qquad (3.2.62)$$

i.e., the concentration profile is a linear one.

In the second case, a similar procedure leads to

$$\text{Rate of solute in} - \text{Rate of solute out} = 0$$

$$\left[\begin{matrix} C_z \\ +k_L(C*-C)P\Delta z \end{matrix}\right] - C_{1z+\Delta z} = 0 \tag{3.2.63}$$

which, after going through the same procedures as before, yields as the end result:

$$\frac{C*-C}{C*} = \exp(-k_L Pz) \tag{3.2.64}$$

This expression was frequently used in the past for the experimental determination of mass transfer coefficients. In these experiments, a pipe coated with, or cast from a solute such as sugar, benzoic acid, etc., would be exposed to a flow of solvent and the concentrations monitored at various distance z. k_L could then be extracted from a semilog plot of Equation 3.2.64. We underline that the simple expressions derived here apply to release into *turbulent* flow. Release to a fluid in *laminar* flow is a more complex problem that is taken up in Chapter 6, Illustration 6.1.6, and in Chapter 8.

Practice Problems

3.2.1 Diffusion Through a Stagnant Spherical Gas Film — Diffusion is taking place from the surface of a sphere, radius r_1, into a stagnant gas film with outer radius r_2. Corresponding partial pressures of the diffusing solute at these locations are p_{A1} and p_{A2}, with total pressure P_{tot} invariant. Derive an expression for the flux N_A of the diffusing species.

(Hint: Convert Equation 3.2.7 to partial pressure units, make a mass balance over a spherical shell, and integrate.)

Answer: $N_A = \dfrac{4\pi r_1 r_2}{r_2 - r_1} \dfrac{D_{AB} P_{Tot}}{RT} \ln \dfrac{P_{Tot} - p_{A2}}{P_{Tot} - p_{A1}}$

3.2.2 Evaporation of Water — Water evaporates from a 1 m² shallow square trough into air flowing at $v = 10$ m/s. The water is at its wet bulb temperature of 32°C with a vapor pressure of 0.0475 atm. Air is at 60°C and has a partial water vapor pressure of 0.0315 atm. Calculate the rate of evaporation of water using the correlation given in Table 3.5. The properties of air may be estimated from Table 3.8.

3.2.3 Irreversible Second Order Reaction — Show that for a constant volume batch reactor and the irreversible bimolecular reaction

$$A + B \rightarrow \text{Products}$$

$$r = k\, C_A C_B$$

integration of the rate expression leads to the result

$$\ln\frac{1-X_B}{1-X_A} = C_{A0}(M-1)kt$$

where X = conversion and M = ratio of initial concentrations = C_{B0}/C_{A0}.

3.2.4 Tubular Reactor with Axial Diffusion — Derive the ODE which will yield the concentration profile $C_A = f(z)$ for a reactant A with arbitrary reaction kinetics in a reactor with diffusion superimposed on bulk flow. Note that because of the additional diffusional process, expressed through Fick's law $NA = -DA\dfrac{dC_A}{dz}$, the model now consists of a second order ODE. Integration of the ODE will be addressed in Practice Problem 4.2.

3.2.5 Half-Life for a nth Order Reaction — Show that for an nth order reaction

$$r = k\,C_A^n$$

carried out in a constant volume batch reactor, the half-life $t_{1/2}$, i.e., the time needed for the concentration of reactant to drop to one-half the original value, is given by

$$t_{1/2} = \frac{2^{n-1}-1}{k(n-1)}C_{A0}^{1-n}$$

3.2.6 Diffusion and Reaction in a Flat Plate Catalyst — (a) Set up the model equation (but do not solve) for diffusion and reaction with arbitrary kinetics in a flat plate with the dimensions $L \geq x \geq 0$. (b) For the first order reaction in the same geometry, the reactant concentration profile is given by

$$\frac{C}{C_e} = \frac{\cosh\left(\dfrac{k_r}{Deff}\right)^{1/2}x}{\cosh\left(\dfrac{k_r}{Deff}\right)^2 L}$$

where k = rate constant, D_{eff} = diffusivity and $\cosh x = \dfrac{1}{2}(e^x + e^{-x})$.

Derive an expression for the effectiveness factor E for this pellet. (Hint: Use Table 4.6.)

Answer: (b) $E = \dfrac{1}{L}\left(\dfrac{Deff}{k_r}\right)^{1/2}\tan k\left(\dfrac{k_r}{Deff}\right)^{1/2}L$

3.2.7 Dilution of a Solute in a "Stirred Tank" — A stream containing a dissolved solute of concentration C_1 enters a well-mixed body of water of initial volume V_0

at a flow rate Q_1 and leaves with a flow rate of Q_2. Derive an expression for the exit concentration as a function of time.

(Hint: Study Illustration 3.2.7.)

3.2.8 Surge Tank Revisited — Flow into a surge tank undergoes a step increase in inflow. Derive an expression that gives the time dependence of the level in the tank. Assume outflow varies with the square root of tank level.

3.2.9 Evaporation of Solvent Vapor in a Factory Enclosure — A drum of trichloroethylene with the bung off is left in a factory room of dimension 4 m × 4 m × 2.55 m. Over a period of a week, the weight of the drum has decreased by 1 kg. The ventilation rate is about 0.5 air volume changes per hour.

(a) Estimate the steady-state concentration, assuming perfect mixing.
(b) What is the instantaneous exposure of a worker who enters the room two and one-half days after the drum was placed there?

Answers: (a) 298 mg/m^3

3.2.10 Tubular Reactor with Catalyst-Coated Wall — Derive the model equation that would yield the concentration profile of reactant in the longitudinal direction of a tubular reactor coated with a thin layer of catalyst. Assume arbitrary kinetics at the wall and turbulent flow.

3.3   ENERGY BALANCES

3.3.1   ENERGY FLUX

The complications we had encountered in the case of mass flux where bulk flow could be triggered by diffusive transport do not arise here. No distinction needs to be made between transport through a stagnant film and equimolar counter diffusion, and single expressions are sufficient for either molecular or convective transfer. Thus, conductive heat flux is described simply by Fourier's law:

$$q = -kA \frac{dT}{dz} \qquad (3.3.1)$$

and convective heat transport in turbulent flow by the linear driving force law

$$q = hA \, \Delta T \qquad (3.3.2)$$

We had indicated this to some extent in Table 3.1. A further simplification arises from the fact that we need not deal with various definitions and units of the state variable as was the case in mass transport where different forms of concentration (molar concentration, mass and mole fractions, mass and mole ratios, partial pressures) had to be considered. A single state variable, temperature, suffices here. As a consequence, only a single form of the heat transfer coefficient which is taken up below applies, and the various forms of transport coefficients that had to be invoked in the case of mass transport (see Table 3.6) can be dispensed with.

3.3.2 Transport Coefficients

We start this section, as we did in the case of mass transport, with the consideration of the molecular transport coefficients, i.e., the thermal conductivities, k. Values of k for representative gases, liquid, metals, and other solids are compiled in Table 3.9. Not much variation is seen in the values for liquids and nonmetallic solids. They lie in the range 10^{-1} to 1 J/msK. Values, for gases are an order of magnitude lower, ~ 10^{-2} J/m²sK. The latter are at low densities independent of pressure and vary with the square root of temperature:

$$k_{gas} \propto \sqrt{T} \neq f(P) \tag{3.3.3}$$

Thermal conductivities of metals are, as expected, much higher, in the range 10 to 400 J/m sK. Silver, copper, and, somewhat surprisingly, aluminum stand out as the metals with the highest conductivities.

The dimensionless group that corresponds to the Schmidt number $Sc = \mu/\rho D$ and appears in correlation for heat transfer coefficients is the so-called Prandtl number $Pr = C_p\mu/k$. Values for Pr for air and liquid water appear in Tables 3.6 and 3.7 in Section 3.2 and for other subtances in Table 3.9. For gases at low densities in general, the Prandtl number is of the order 1, those for nonviscous, nonmetallic liquids, of the order 10. For liquid metals, the Prandtl numbers are quite low, of the order 10^{-2}, because of the much higher thermal conductivity.

When dealing with transport in a turbulent or well-stirred medium, the thermal conductivities are replaced by heat transfer coefficients U which are based on the same film or linear driving force concept as in the case of mass transfer. The resistance additivity rule for films in series also applies. Thus, for the frequently encountered case where two films, outside (o) and inside (i) are separated by a solid wall (w); additivity of resistances leads to the relation:

$$\frac{1}{U} = \frac{1}{h_o} + \frac{1}{h_i} + \frac{L}{k_w} \tag{3.3.4}$$

where U is the overall heat transfer coefficient and k_w, and L is the thermal conductivity and thickness of the wall, respectively.

Correlations of heat transfer coefficients are given in terms of the dimensionless Nusselt number $Nu = hL/k$ as a function of Reynolds and Prandtl numbers. Thus,

$$Nu = f(Re, Pr) \tag{3.3.5}$$

TABLE 3.9
Thermal Conductivities and Prandtl Numbers at 25°C

Substance	Thermal Conductivity J/sm°C	Prandtl Number
Metals		
Silver	430	
Copper	390	
Aluminum	240	
Brass	110	
Steel	46	
Lead	35	
Gases		
Water vapor (373 K)	2.5×10^{-2}	1.96
Nitrogen	2.6×10^{-2}	0.715
Hydrogen	1.8×10^{-1}	0.706
Oxygen	2.7×10^{-2}	0.709
Liquids		
Water	5.9×10^{-1}	11.4
Ethyl alcohol	1.8×10^{-1}	16.3
Benzene	1.6×10^{-1}	6.5
Glycerol	2.8×10^{-1}	10^4
Sulfuric acid	3.6×10^{-1}	—
Mercury	9.0	2.5×10^{-2}
Others		
Asbestos	0.15	
Concrete	0.13	
Cork	0.04	
Glass	0.5–1	
Ice	2.2	
Wood	0.15–0.20	

Table 3.10 lists a compilation of heat transfer coefficient correlations which corresponds to that compiled for mass transfer coefficients in Table 3.5. One notes a direct correspondence between the two sets of correlations that arises from the analogous mechanisms that apply to heat and mass transfer. Thus, by replacing Sherwood number Sh by Nusselt number Nu, and Schmidt number Sc by Prandtl number Pr, the two sets of correlations become identical.

We have supplemented this table by two additional compilations, Tables 3.11 and 3.12, that list ranges and typical values of heat transfer coefficients encountered in various applications. These are film coefficients which allow an immediate estimate to be made of h values likely to be encountered in practice. One notes in particular the high values of condensing steam, 5700 to 28,000 J/m²sK, compared to those of other substances. As a consequence, the film resistance on the steam side can, for most practical cases, be neglected. Low values apply to gases, typically of

TABLE 3.10
Correlations for Heat Transfer Coefficients

Range	Equations
(1) Flat plate	
Re < 10^5	$St = 0.66 \, (Re)^{-1/2} \, (Pr)^{-2/3}$
Re > 10^6	$St = 0.036 \, (Re)^{-0.2} \, (Pr)^{-2/3}$
(2) Sphere	
Unlimited	$Nu = 2.0 + 0.60 \, (Re)^{1/2} \, (Pr)^{1/3}$
(3) Cylinder	
1 < Re < 4000	$Nu = 0.43 + 0.53 \, Re^{0.5} \, Pr^{0.31}$
(4) Inside pipes (μ = const.)	
Re < 2100	$Nu = 1.86 \, (Re \cdot Pr \cdot d/L)^{1/3}$
Re > 20,000	$Nu = 0.026 \, (Re)^{0.8} \, (Pr)^{1/3}$
(5) Packed beds of spheres	
Re < 50	$St = 0.91 \, (Re)^{-0.51} \, (Pr)^{-2/3}$
Re > 50	$St = 0.61 \, (Re)^{-0.41} \, (Pr)^{-2/3}$

Note: Re = Reynolds number = $\dfrac{Lv\rho}{\mu}$, Nu = Nusselt number = $\dfrac{hL}{k}$

St = Stanton number = $\dfrac{h}{C_p v\rho}$, Pr = Prandtl number = $\dfrac{C_p\mu}{k}$

L = Length of plate, diameter of sphere, cylinder, or pipe = volume of bed/surface area of spheres

TABLE 3.11
Approximate Values of Some Heat Transfer Coefficients

Mechanism	Range of Values of h, J/m²sK
Condensing steam	5700–28,000
Condensing organics	1100–2800
Boiling liquids	1700–28,000
Moving water	280–17,000
Moving hydrocarbons	55–1700
Still air	2.8–23
Moving air	11.3–55

Source: From C.J. Geankoplis. *Transport Processes and Unit Operations,* Allyn and Bacon, Boston, 1978. With permission.

TABLE 3.12
Typical Overall Heat Transfer
Coefficients in Steam-Heated
Jacketed Vessels

Fluid in Vessel	Agitation	U, J/m²sK
Water	None	852
Water	Simple stirring	1420
Boiling water	None	1420
Paste	Double scrapers	710
Milk	None	1135
Milk	Stirring	1700
Tomato purée	Stirring	170

Source: From C.J. Geankoplis. *Transport Processes and Unit Operations,* Allyn and Bacon, Boston, 1978. With permission.

the order 10 when in movement, while h values for moving liquids range from about 100 to several thousand J/m²sK. In steam-heated vessels, the overall coefficients U are all of the order 10^3 J/m²sK, with the exception of particularly viscous media.

Illustration 3.3.1 Heat Transfer Coefficient in a Packed Bed of Metallic Particles

A bed packed with irregular metallic particles with an equivalent diameter of 2.0 cm is to be heated with air at 100°C and a velocity of 10 m/s. We wish to estimate the heat transfer coefficient. Since the particles have a thermal conductivity roughly two to three orders of magnitudes larger than that of air (see Table 3.9) and are relatively small in size, it will be assumed that the heat transfer resistance resides entirely in the air. To use the correlations for film coefficients given in Table 3.10, we first compute the Reynolds number using air properties from Table 3.7:

$$Re = \frac{Dv\rho}{\mu} = \frac{(0.02)(10)(0.94)}{2.19 \times 10^{-5}} = 8585$$

Thus, the correlation applicable to Re > 50 applies, and we obtain:

$$h = C_p v\rho \ 0.61 \ (Re)^{-0.41} \ (Pr)^{-2/3} = 1.01 \times 10^3 \ (10)(0.94)(0.61)(8585)^{-0.41}(0.69)^{-2/3}$$

$$h = 181 \ J/sm^2K$$

We now demonstrate the setting up of energy balances with a number of illustrations. We start with what have by now become three classical examples. The first one deals with the single-pass countercurrent shell-and-tube heat exchanger. We had already, in Chapter 2, Section 2.2, dealt with a similar device, the steam-heated tube, in which the shell-side medium was isothermal. Here we allow the shell-side temperature to vary which leads to a more complete model of the exchanger. The resulting model may be viewed as consisting of two coupled "one-dimensional pipes."

In the second illustration, we examine the case of a thermocouple which is exposed to a temperature disturbance. This may be considered an example of a "well-stirred" tank with constant or time varying "inflow" but no "outflow."

The third example considers heat transfer by convection and conduction in a finned heat exchanger. Finned exchangers, also known as extended surface heat exchangers, use attachments to the tubes and similar devices to enhance the heat transfer area. The reader is introduced to the concept of fin efficiency E, which, like the catalyst effectiveness factor defines the degree to which conduction in the fin is effective in transferring heat in the exchangers.

Several additional problems follow which are drawn from various applications. Systems which involve *simultaneous* heat and mass balances, such as nonisothermal reactors and packed columns, humidification and dehumidification, and the like are deferred to Section 3.5.

Illustration 3.3.2   The Counter-Current Single Pass Shell and Tube Heat Exchanger

A sketch of the device with its pertinent variables is shown in Figure 3.6. We note that since two state variables are involved, the shell and tube side temperatures, at least two balances will be required. We choose to make two differential balances, one over each of the two phases. This not only yields the most general solution, but can also, by various combinations and manipulations, be reduced to yield solutions obtained from integral balances. We assume that the heating medium is located in the shell, and obtain the following.

Tube Side Balance:

$$\text{Rate of energy in} - \text{Rate of energy out} = 0$$

$$H_t|_z + q_{avg} - H_t|_{z+\Delta z} = 0$$

or, replacing the total enthalpies by flow rate F x specific enthalpy $\overline{H}$:

$$F_t \Delta \overline{H}_t - q_{avg} = 0 \tag{3.3.6}$$

Expressing $\overline{H}$ in terms of temperature and heat capacity and introducing the auxiliary relation for overall convective heat transfer, we obtain:

$$F_t C_{pt} \Delta T_t - U \pi d \Delta z (T_s - T_t)_{avg} = 0 \tag{3.3.7}$$

A. Flow Diagram

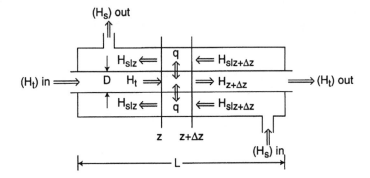

B. Effectiveness Chart

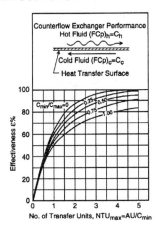

FIGURE 3.6 The countercurrent single-pass shell-and-tube heat exchanger: (A) flow diagram showing difference element for the energy balance, (B) plot of exchanger effectiveness ε vs. number of transfer units NTU. (Figure 3.6B: F. Kreith and M.S. Bohn, *Heat Transfer*, *4th ed.*, Harper and Row, New York, 1986. With permission.)

Dividing by Δz and letting $\Delta z \rightarrow 0$ yields:

$$F_t C_{pt} \frac{dT_t}{dz} - U\pi d(T_s - T_t)_{avg} = 0 \qquad (3.3.8)$$

where the subscripts $_t$ and $_s$ refer to tube and shell side variables, respectively.

Shell Side Balance:
Using the same procedure, we obtain the result

$$F_t C_{ps} \frac{dT_s}{dz} - U\pi d(T_s - T_t) = 0 \qquad (3.3.9)$$

which is of *exactly* the same form as the tube side balance. This may at first be surprising, but is due to the fact that both the flow and heat transfer change direction so that no changes in sign occurs.

We now proceed to manipulate these differential balances to arrive at various results of interest.

1. Subtracting the two balances leads to cancellation of the heat transfer terms as well as dz, and yields:

$$F_s C_{ps}\, dT_s - F_t C_{pt} dT_t = 0 \qquad (3.3.10)$$

which upon integration over *part* of the exchanger yields:

$$F_s C_{ps}\, (T_s - T_{s\,out}) = F_t C_{pt}\, (T_t - T_{t\,in}) \qquad (3.3.11)$$

and over the *entire* exchanger

$$q_{Total} = F_s C_{ps}\, (T_{s\,in} - T_{s\,out}) = F_t C_{pt}\, (T_{t\,out} - T_{t\,in}) \qquad (3.3.12)$$

It is immediately seen that the same results could have been obtained by algebraic integral energy balances taken over both phases. Since z disappeared, they tell us nothing about the *profiles* or the size of the heat exchanger required but are, as we shall see, used to supplement other model equations.

2. In a second manipulation, we first divide each differential balance by FC_p and *then* subtract. This is a clever device to reduce T_s and T_t to a *single* variable $(T_s - T_t)$. We obtain

$$\frac{d(T_s - T_t)}{dz} - U\pi d \left[\frac{1}{F_s C_{ps}} - \frac{1}{F_t C_{pt}} \right] \qquad (3.3.13)$$

which when integrated by separation of variables over the entire exchanger yields:

$$\ln \frac{(T_s - T_t)_L}{(T_s - T_t)_0} - U\pi dL \left[\frac{1}{F_s C_{ps}} - \frac{1}{F_t C_{pt}} \right] \qquad (3.3.14)$$

with $\pi dL = A$ = total heat transfer area.

The equation does not provide us with individual temperature profiles, but, if one replaces L with z (integration over part of the exchanger), it yields the profile of the temperature *difference*. This turns out to be sufficient for design purposes. It is conventional in this case to replace the FC_p terms by corresponding temperature differences using Equation 3.3.9 which after rearrangement yields the expression:

$$q = UA \frac{(T_s - T_t)_L - (T_s - T_t)_0}{\ln \frac{(T_s - T_s)_L}{(T_s - T_t)_0}} \qquad (3.3.15)$$

The fraction in this expression is commonly known as the *log mean temperature difference* (LMTD):

$$LMTD = \frac{(T_s - T_t)_L - (T_s - T_t)_0}{\ln \frac{(T_s - T_t)_L}{(T_s - T_t)_0}} \qquad (3.3.16)$$

Equation 3.3.12 then becomes in abbreviated form:

$$q = UA(LMTD) \qquad (3.3.17)$$

This is a frequently used design equation. It is a design equation because knowing the inlet temperatures $T_{t\,in}$ and $T_{s\,in}$, and *specifying* the desired outlet temperature $T_{t\,out}$, the fourth end temperature can be calculated from the integral balance (Equation 3.3.12). Both q and LMTD can then be evaluated, thus allowing the design area A to be obtained. U is assumed to have been estimated *a priori* from Equation 3.3.4 and the relevant film coefficient correlations. The equation cannot be used in problems where only the inlet temperatures are known and the third temperature remains unspecified. This occurs, for example, if for an *existing* heat exchanger (A known), one wishes to calculate the effect of a change in inlet conditions on the outlet temperatures. Similarly, one cannot predict the effect of changes in heat exchanger length or area on outlet conditions.

3. To handle problems not amenable to solution by Equation 3.3.17, one has to solve the differential balances (Equations 3.3.8 and 3.3.9) to obtain full profiles.

The complete solution is posed as a Practice Problem in Chapter 4 and we give here an outline of the method and the final result obtained. We note that the equations are coupled so that a simultaneous solution seems to be indicated. This can, however, be avoided by the use of a small "trick." We solve Equation 3.3.8 *algebraically* for T_s and substitute the result in Equation 3.3.9. The penalty we pay is that the result is a *second order* ODE which is of the form:

$$\frac{d^2 T_t}{dz^2} + K \frac{dT_t}{dz} = 0 \qquad (3.3.18)$$

This equation can then be solved by simple separation of variables by first making the substitution $u = dT/dz$.

One would, at this point, expect to have obtained the full tube-side temperature profile. This is, however, not the case: One of the two required boundary conditions is given in terms of $T_{s\,in}$, which cannot be applied in the evaluation of the integration constant since the solution is in terms of T_t, not T_s. Evaluation can only be obtained by solving the second differential balance in T_s. We are now in a position to do this by substituting the solution to Equation 3.3.18 into the differential balance (Equation 3.2.9) and integrating. The final result is given by:

$$\frac{T_t - T_{tin}}{T_{sin} - T_{tin}} = \frac{F_s C_{ps}}{F_t C_{pt}} \cdot \frac{\exp U\pi dz \left(\dfrac{1}{F_s C_{ps}} - \dfrac{1}{F_t C_{pt}} \right) - 1}{\exp U\pi dL \left(\dfrac{1}{F_x C_{px}} - \dfrac{1}{F_t C_{pt}} \right) - \dfrac{F_s C_{ps}}{F_t C_{pE}}} \qquad (3.3.19)$$

A similar expression applies to the shell side profile $T_s = f(z)$.

These are fairly formidable equations but they carry the advantage of having much greater versatility than the previous LMTD expression, Equation 3.3.17. Thus, to calculate the outlet temperature for an existing heat exchanger taking flow rates F_s and F_t, one simply sets z equal to tube length L and solves for T_t. The equation can also be used to obtain a "profile" of the parameter U by measuring tube side temperatures T_t at various positions. Design problems are accommodated by setting T_t equal to the desired or specified outlet temperature and z equal to L, and solving for length L or heat exchanger area $U\pi dL = A$.

To make these equations easier to use, plots of them have been constructed in terms of convenient nondimensional quantities that encompass temperature flow parameters, transport resistance, and exchanger area. These quantities are

Capacity Ratio C_{Min}/C_{Max} — This is the ratio of flow rate times heat capacity, $C = FC_p$, of the two streams being considered. C_{Min} is the smaller of the two products, C_{Max} the larger.

Number of Transfer Units NTU —

$$NTU = \frac{UA}{C_{Min}} \qquad (3.3.20)$$

This is a measure of the exchanger performance; high performance being associated with large transfer areas A and high heat transfer coefficients. The quantity has similarities to the corresponding quantity encountered in packed column mass transfer operations (Equations 2.26 and 3.2.54). These equations are all of the form:

$$NTU = \frac{\text{Transport Coefficient} \times \text{Transfer Area}}{\text{Flow Rate}} \qquad (3.3.21)$$

Thus, for the three cases in question,

Gas absorption $\qquad NTU = \dfrac{H}{HTU} = \dfrac{K_G aH}{G_s} \qquad (3.3.22)$

Distillation $\qquad NTU = \dfrac{H}{HTU} = \dfrac{K_y aH}{V} \qquad (3.3.23)$

Heat exchanger $\qquad NTU = \dfrac{UA}{(FC_p)_{Min}} \qquad (3.3.24)$

This correspondence was, of course, to be expected because of the similarities in the operations involved. Each of the variables in one operation has a direct counterpart in the other. A minor exception is the flow rate term of the heat exchanger which has to be multiplied by the heat capacity C_p. Note that G_s and V are the superficial gas flow rates in kg (or moles)/m²s which upon inversion and multiplication by H yield the total column volume. Further multiplication by the specific area a (m²/m³) finally gives the total transfer area.

Exchanger Effectiveness ε —

$$\varepsilon = \frac{C_h[(T_h)-(T_h)_{out}]}{C_{min}[(T_h)_{in}-(T_c)_{in}]} = \frac{C_c[(T_c)-(T_c)_{in}]}{C_{Min}[(T_h)_{in}-(T_c)_{in}]} \qquad (3.3.25)$$

is the third quantity where the subscripts c and h correspond to the cold and hot streams, respectively. ε, like NTU, is a measure of the performance of the exchanger which is here expressed in terms of the temperature changes effected, a large ΔT between inlet and outlet corresponding to high performance. Two alternative expressions are given which allow calculation of either the hot stream temperature T_h or the cold stream temperature T_c. A representative plot of ε vs. NTU, with the capacity ratio as parameter, is shown in Figure 3.6B. Extensive compilations of such charts, applicable to co-current, countercurrent, cross flow, and extended surface exchangers are available in the open literature (see the references at the end of this chapter).

The plots can be used for a variety of computations. For design purposes, for example, ε for the desired (design) outlet temperature $(T_c)_{out}$ is first calculated, a horizontal line drawn to intersect the curve with the prescribed C_{Min}/C_{Max} values, a vertical line dropped from the intersection to the abscissa, and the NTU value read off. From its value, and the known or previously calculated values of C_{Min} and U, the design area A is then calculated. Similarly, for a heat exchanger of given area A, NTU and C_{Min}/C_{Max} are established after first having calculated the heat transfer coefficient U from appropriate film coefficient correlations. The corresponding ε value is then read off on the ordinate from which the desired outlet temperature (usually $(T_c)_{out}$) can be immediately calculated.

A point to be noted is that these plots also can be used for other operations, including co-current and countercurrent packed-bed mass transfer operations with linear isotherms, moving bed processes (see in this connection Illustration 3.3.5), dialysis, permeation, and ultrafiltration, and similar processes. The only requirement is that the operation involve streams separated by a wall or barrier across which an exchange of mass or energy takes place.

Illustration 3.3.3 Response of a Thermocouple to a Temperature Change

We consider here a thermocouple suspended in flowing air which undergoes a step change in temperature from an initial value T_i to a new value T_a. It is composed of two cylindrical wires of two different materials whose heat capacities differ slightly but can for the purposes of the problem be averaged to a value of $C_p = 0.419$ kJ/kgK. For density, we similarly use an average value of $\rho = 8800$ kg/m³. The film heat transfer coefficient for the flowing air is estimated at 0.455 kJ/m²sK (see correlation for flow around a cylinder, Table 3.10). We wish to use a thermocouple whose response time is such that a 15°C change in the air temperature will be registered within 0.5°C of the final value in no more than 4 sec.

This can be considered as a design problem in which the desired dimension, the diameter of the thermocouple, is extracted from the primary information consisting of the time dependence of the thermocouple temperature, or its "response."

Since the conductivity of the metal wires is several orders of magnitude higher than that of air and the wires are very thin, resistance to heat transfer within the wires can be neglected. Thus, the thermocouple becomes in a sense a "well-stirred tank" of uniform temperature.

The model equation consists of an energy balance around the thermocouple. Thus,

$$\text{Rate of energy in} - \text{Rate of energy out} = \frac{\text{Rate of change of}}{\text{energy content}} \tag{3.3.26}$$

$$q - 0 = \frac{d}{dt}H$$

which, after introduction of the relevant auxiliary relations becomes:

$$hA(T - T_a) = \frac{d}{dt}m\overline{H} = \rho V C_p \frac{dT}{dt} \tag{3.3.27}$$

Integration by separation of variables yields, in the first instance:

$$t = \frac{\rho C_p V}{hA} \ln \frac{T_a - T_i}{T_a - T} = \frac{\rho C_p d}{4h} \ln \frac{T_a - T_i}{T_a - T_f} \tag{3.3.28}$$

from which

$$d = \frac{4ht}{\rho C_p \ln \dfrac{T_a - T_i}{T_a - T_f}} = \frac{(4)(0.455)(4)}{(8800)(0.419)\ln \dfrac{15}{0.5}} \qquad (3.3.26)$$

$$d = 5.8 \times 10^{-4} \text{ m} = 0.58 \text{ mm}$$

Comments:

The particular simplicity of the model was due to the fact that we were able to assume uniform temperature within the system at any given moment. Had this not been the case, we would have been forced to solve a time-variant PDE in at least one dimension. Similarly, the thinness of the wires enabled us to neglect heat losses along them which would have complicated the model further and which would at any rate have been difficult to estimate. Radiation losses were similarly and for the same reasons also neglected.

The step change considered here is a special case of a more general, time varying input, also termed *forcing functions.* Such forcing functions give rise to some interesting responses. In the case of a sinusoidal input, for example, the response shows an attenuation in the amplitude as well as a lag, or phase shift in the oscillation. Frequency remains unchanged. No such unusual features arise in the step response which shows a smooth asymptotic rise to the new temperatures. Both these responses are typical of so-called first order systems, i.e., those arising from first order differential equation. Second order systems, i.e., those arising from second order ODEs, show still more diverse behavior. The whole intriguing topic of system responses, which is cardinal to process control, is best treated — in the case of linear systems — by the method of Laplace transformation. Detailed consideration of such responses is, therefore, left to the section dealing with this technique (see Chapter 5).

Some readers may feel uncomfortable with the notion that the internal resistance to heat transfer can be neglected based on what are essentially qualitative arguments. A more quantitative criterion is available. It stipulates that for internal resistance to be negligible, the dimensionless group known as the Biot number $Bi = hL/k$ must be less than 0.1. Let us see whether this criterion is satisfied in the present case. We set the thermal conductivity $k = 390$ J/m^{2}sK (copper, see Table 3.9) and the linear dimension L equal to the diameter of the thermocouple wire. This yields $Bi = (455)(5.8 \times 10^{-3}/390 = 6.8 \times 10^{-4} < 0.1$. We were consequently justified in assuming that the thermocouple can be treated as a well-stirred tank.

Illustration 3.3.4   The Longitudinal, Rectangular Heat Exchanger Fin

Finned tubular heat exchangers are used extensively for the purpose of enhancing the heat transfer area. The fins are usually attached externally to the exchanger tubes and are typically mounted in a longitudinal, rectangular, or circular radial mode. Transport of heat is, in the first instance, from the external (and assumed hot) fluid to the fin by convection, radially through the fin to the fin base and tube wall, from which the heat is transferred by further convective transport to the internal (and colder) tubular fluid.

The question which arises in the design and analysis of these devices is the extent to which the heat transfer area is enhanced. If conduction within the fin was infinitely fast, the effective transfer area would be simply the sum of the fin and tubular areas: $A_{eff} = A_{fin} + A_{tube}$, and temperature throughout the fin would be equal that of the tubular wall. This corresponds to a catalyst pellet effectiveness factor E = 1 which arises when there is no diffusional resistance and concentration throughout the pellet is equal to the external concentration. Because of the finite conduction rate, however, a temperature gradient develops within the fin, reducing the local heat transfer driving force associated with the external fluid. To assess its effect, one must first derive the temperature profile within the fin and compute the total heat transfer rate from the external fluid by integration of the local rates over the entire fin. This is the actual rate that can then be compared with the ideal rate that prevails if the entire fin were at the tube wall temperature. From the ratio of the two then springs the concept of the fin efficiency E which is completely analogous to that of the catalyst pellet effectiveness factor E and is a measure of the degree to which one is able to approach the ideal case. A value of E = 0.8, or 80%, for example, means that the effective heat transfer area now becomes $A_{eff} = 0.8\ A_{fin} + A_{tube}$. Thus, E can be incorporated in simple fashion into heat exchanger model equations or their solutions as a mere correction factor. The fact that we are able to do this constitutes a major simplification of a system of considerable complexity. Note that temperatures vary in both radial and axial directions. Even if one were to invoke a PDE model, the discontinuous nature of the geometry and the associated boundary conditions would make this a difficult problem to solve. The reader will note that we avoided this by cleverly decoupling the effect of the fin from the remainder of the heat exchange process. Not only is this simple and elegant, but it is also legitimate and completely rigorous within the constraints of film theory.

The fin we consider here is a rectangular, longitudinal one which extends along the entire external length of the tube. To avoid the complication of varying external and internal fluid temperatures, we limit consideration to a small finite length Δz along which the temperature variations can be neglected. This is a legitimate procedure since the final result, the fin efficiency, is independent of the temperature driving force.

The model fin we use is depicted in Figure 3.7A. The energy balance is taken over the vertical increment Δx. Convective transport enters the element over Δz, while conductive heat enters and leaves at positions x and x + Δx. We obtain:

$$\text{Rate of energy in} - \text{Rate of energy out} = 0$$

$$\left[\begin{array}{c} 2h_f \Delta z \Delta x (T_h - T_f) \\ -kW\Delta z \dfrac{dT_f}{dx}\bigg|_x \end{array} \right] - \left[-kW\Delta z \dfrac{dT_f}{dz}\bigg|_{x+\Delta x} \right] = 0 \tag{3.3.30}$$

A. Longitudinal Fin

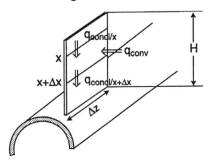

B. Radial Fin

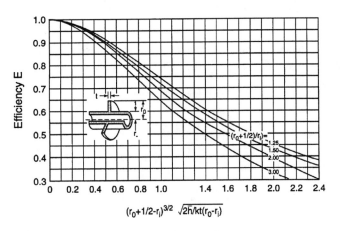

FIGURE 3.7 Extended surface heat exchangers: (A) diagram of a longitudinal fin with difference element for the energy balance, (B) efficiency plot for a radial fin. (Figure 3.7B: F. Kreith and M.S. Bohn, *Heat Transfer, 4th ed.,* Harper and Row, New York, 1986. With permission.)

Dividing by $kW\Delta x\Delta z$ and going to the limit yields:

$$\frac{d^2}{dx^2}(T_h - T_f) - \frac{2h_f}{kW}(T_h - T_f) = 0 \tag{3.3.31}$$

This is a second order linear ODE with constant coefficients in the fin temperature T_f and can be solved by standard methods, to be taken up in Chapter 4 (see Illustration 4.3.3). The two boundary conditions (BCs) we need require some consideration. Formulation at one end, $X = L$, is straight-forward: fin temperature equals the tubular wall temperature $T_{f/L} = T_t$. At the other end, the formulation is somewhat more uncertain. It is best to argue that, because of the small thickness of the wedge, heat transfer from the hot fluid at this point is negligible, i.e., the fin is effectively insulated at this position so that $\dfrac{dT_f}{dx}\bigg|_0 = 0$. These two boundary conditions are used in the evaluation of the two integration constants of Equation 3.3.31.

The fin efficiency E is computed by evaluating the ratio:

$$E = \frac{\text{Actual heat transfer } q_a}{\text{Ideal heat transfer } q_i} = \frac{\displaystyle\int_0^L h(T_h - T_f)2\Delta z dx}{h(T_h - T_t)2\Delta z L} \tag{3.3.32}$$

Alternatively, one can use the fact that the total actual heat transfer must equal the rate at which heat leaves the base of the fin. Thus,

$$\text{Actual heat transfer } q_a = -kW\Delta z\frac{dT_f}{dx}\bigg|_L \tag{3.3.33}$$

With E evaluated by either formulation, it can be inserted directly into appropriate model equations. Thus, insertion into the tubular energy balance (Equation 3.3.7) yields:

$$F_t C_{pt}\frac{dT_t}{dz} - U(EL + \pi d)(T_s - T_f) = 0 \tag{3.3.34}$$

and into the design Equation 3.3.17:

$$q = U(EA_{fin} + A_{tube})\, LMTD \tag{3.3.35}$$

Extensive compilations of fin efficiencies as a function of system parameters are available in the literature (see References). A representative plot appears in Figure 3.7B.

Illustration 3.3.5   A Moving Bed Solid-Gas Heat Exchanger

In the metallurgical industry it is a frequent practice to preheat the primary raw materials, such as ores, prior to further processing. We consider here the preheating of scrap steel with nitrogen gas entering at 1500°F (816°C) in a countercurrent moving bed shaft in preparation for melting in an electric arc furnace. The steel is to be heated from 70°C to 1200°F (21.1°C to 646°C). The novelty here is that the nitrogen flow rate cannot be fixed *a priori* and is instead specified as $G = 1.2\, G_{min}$. This is common practice in countercurrent operations when the flow rate of one stream cannot be specified. In gas absorption, for example, one usually sets the unknown solvent flow rate at $(1.2$ to $1.5)\, L_{Min}$; L_{Min} being the flow rate required for an infinitely long column, i.e., under conditions where entering solvent and exiting gas are in equilibrium. Similarly, G_{Min} corresponds to an infinitely long shaft with an exiting nitrogen temperature equal that of the entering steel (21°C). The factors

1.2 or 1.2 to 1.5 ensure that there is a near optimum balance between increased solvent or gas costs and the saving which comes about from the reduction in column height. In distillation similar considerations lead us to specify the initially unknown reflux ratio R at $R = (1.2 \text{ to } 1.5)R_{min}$.

G_{min} can be established from an algebraic integral energy balance over an infinitely long shaft, with the appropriate temperatures inserted. Having thus obtained the actual gas flow rate, we can then proceed to set up the energy balances for the finite length exchanger. This is shown below. Additional data required are as follows:

Steel flow rate	$S = 6.78$ kg/m^{2}s
Nitrogen heat capacity	$C_{pg} = 1$ kJ/kg K
Steel heat capacity	$C_{ps} = 0.69$ kJ/kg K
Gas-solid heat transfer coefficient	$h = 114$ J/m^{2}sK
Interfacial area	$a = 65.6$ m^2/m^3

We are required to calculate the height of the shaft.

Integral steady-state energy balance for infinitely long shaft:

$$\text{Rate of energy in} - \text{Rate of energy out} = 0$$
$$\left[\begin{matrix} C_{Min}C_{pg}T_{g\,in} \\ +SC_{ps}T_{s\,in} \end{matrix}\right] - \left[\begin{matrix} G_{Min}C_{pg}T_{g\,out} \\ +SC_{ps}T_{s\,out} \end{matrix}\right] = 0 \tag{3.3.36}$$

or

$$G_{Min} = \frac{SC_{ps}}{C_{pg}}\frac{\bar{T}_{s\,out} - \bar{T}_{s\,in}}{\bar{T}_{g\,in} - \bar{T}_{s\,in}} = \frac{(6.78)(0.69)}{1}\frac{646 - \bar{2}1}{816 - 21} = 3.68\,\text{kg}/\text{m}^2$$

and

$$G = 1.2\,G_{Min} = (1.2)(3.68) = 4.4\,\text{kg}/\text{m}^2$$

Since this is a design problem, we can follow the procedure given for this case in Illustration 3.3.2 for the shell-and-tube heat exchanger, i.e., after division by the flow terms we subtract the two differential energy balances and invoke an integral balance over the shaft to calculate $T_{g\,out}$.

Differential energy balance over solid phase:

$$SC_{ps}\frac{dT_s}{dz} + ha(T_g - T_s) = 0 \tag{3.3.37}$$

Differential energy balance over gas phase:

$$GC_{pg}\frac{dT_g}{cz} + ha(T_g - T_s) = 0 \tag{3.3.38}$$

Dividing by the flow terms and subtracting yields:

$$\frac{d}{dz}(T_g - T_s) + \left(\frac{ha}{GC_{pg}} - \frac{ha}{SC_{ps}}\right)(T_g - T_s) = 0 \qquad (3.3.39)$$

and after integration by separation of variables:

$$\ln\frac{T_{gout} - T_{sin}}{T_{gin} - T_{sout}} = -\left(\frac{ha}{GC_{pg}} - \frac{ha}{SC_{ps}}\right)L \qquad (3.3.40)$$

Integral energy balance over finite shaft:

$$\text{Rate of energy in} - \text{Rate of energy out} = 0$$

$$\begin{bmatrix} GC_{pg}T_{gin} \\ +SC_{ps}T_{sin} \end{bmatrix} - \begin{bmatrix} GC_{pg}T_{gout} \\ +SC_{ps}T_{sout} \end{bmatrix} = 0 \qquad (3.3.41)$$

whence,

$$T_{gout} = T_{gin} - \frac{SC_{ps}}{GC_{pg}}[T_{sout} - T_{sin}]$$

$$\qquad\qquad\qquad\qquad (3.3.42)$$

$$T_{gout} = 816 - \frac{(6.78)(0.69)}{(4.4)(1)}[646 - 21] = 151°C$$

Hence, from Equation 3.3.37,

$$L = \left[\frac{ha}{GC_{pg}} - \frac{ha}{SC_{ps}}\right]^{-1} \ln\frac{T_{gin} - T_{sout}}{T_{gout} - T_{sin}}$$

$$= \left[(0.114)(65.6)\left(\frac{1}{(4.4)(1)} - \frac{1}{(6.78)(0.69)}\right)\right]^{-1} \ln\frac{816 - 646}{151 - 21}$$

$$L = 2.6\,m$$

Evaluation from generalized plot, Figure 3.6B:
   Capacity Ratio

$$C_s = SC_{ps} = (6.78)(0.69) = 4.68 = C_{Max} = C_c$$

$$C_g = GC_{pg} = (4.4)(1) = 4.4 = C_{Min} = C_h$$

where subscripts $_h$ and $_c$ denote hot and cold fluids. We obtain:

$$C_{Min}/C_{Max} = 4.4/4.68 = 0.94$$

Effectiveness ε

$$\varepsilon = \frac{C_h}{C_{Min}} \frac{[T_{hin} - T_{hout}]}{[T_{hin} - T_{cin}]} = \frac{1}{1} \frac{[816 - 151]}{[816 - 21]} = 0.836$$

NTU
This is read off the abscissa of Figure 3.6B and yields:

$$NTU = \frac{UA}{C_{Min}} = \frac{haL}{C_{Min}} \cong 4.5$$

Solving for L, we obtain:

$$L = NTU(C_{Min})/(ha) = (4.5)(4.4)/(0.114)(65.6)$$

$$L = 2.65 \text{ m}$$

in close agreement with the analytical value of 2.60 m.

Comments:
We note that use of the charts does not entirely dispense with the use of model equations. Integral balances over the shaft are still required to calculate the fourth end temperature and the actual nitrogen flow rate.

The calculated height L = 2.65 m seems somewhat short for an industrial application. It could easily be doubled for a marginally lower nitrogen flow rate. Remember that part of the purpose of the exercise is to ensure that one does not require an unduly high shaft (say 100 m).

Estimation of the heat transfer coefficient causes some difficulty because of the varying and irregular size of the scrap iron and the possibility of a dual heat transfer resistance. If we assume negligible solid phase resistance because of the much higher thermal conductivity of the metal and define an equivalent spherical diameter, use can be made of the correlation listed in Table 3.10, which is, however, for stationary beds. Alternatively, an experimental determination could be carried out on a short bed, and h values obtained from measured gas outlet temperatures and the use of Equation 3.3.15.

Illustration 3.3.6 Conduction Through a Hollow Cylinder: Optimum Insulation Thickness

Temperature profiles and conductive heat fluxes in a thick-walled hollow cylinder, either metallic or of some other material, is of importance in assessing the conductive resistance of such configurations. In the case of insulating materials, the question arises as to what the optimum thickness is, since the larger external surface and accompanying heat losses ultimately overtake the benefits of increased insulation thickness.

Heat flux q:

We start by first deriving the heat flux in terms of known temperatures T_i and T_o and cylinder radii r_i and r_o since the temperature *distribution* is best derived from that quantity. This is done by direct integration of Fourier's law, $q = -k 2\pi r L \, dT/dr$, so that no energy balance is required. We obtain, by integrating by separation of variables:

$$q = 2\pi k L \frac{(T_i - T_o)}{\ln(r_o / r_i)} \tag{3.3.43}$$

where o and i denote outer and inner conditions.

By multiplying numerator and denominator by $(r_o - r_i)$ this can be cast into the frequently used alternate form:

$$q = k A_m \frac{(T_i - T_o)}{r_o - r_i} = \frac{T_i - T_o}{R} \tag{3.3.44}$$

where A_m is the log mean of the outer and inner areas:

$$A_m = \frac{A_o - A_i}{\ln(A_o / A_i)} \tag{3.3.45}$$

and

$$\text{Resistance } R = (r_o - r_i)/k A_m \tag{3.3.46}$$

The introduction of the resistance has the advantage that one can, in the case of a composite cylinder made up of different materials, simply add the resistances. For a cylinder composed of three different materials, for example, one obtains:

$$q = \frac{T_o - T_i}{R_1 + R_2 + R_3} \tag{3.3.47}$$

where the resistances can be expressed respectively as:

$$R_1 = \frac{r_1 - r_i}{k_1 A_{m1}} \quad R_2 = \frac{r_2 - r_1}{k_2 A_{m2}} \quad R_3 = \frac{r_o - r_2}{k_3 A_{m3}} \tag{3.3.48}$$

Composite cylinder with internal and external film resistance:

For a film resistance, the heat flux is given by $q = 2\pi r L h \, \Delta T$, with a corresponding resistance of $R = 1/2\pi r L h$. Using the concept expressed in Equations 3.3.47 and 3.3.48, the heat flux for a cylindrical wall with internal and external resistances becomes:

$$q = \frac{T_i - T_o}{\dfrac{1}{2\pi r_i L h_i} + \dfrac{\ln r_2 / r_1}{2\pi k L} + \dfrac{1}{2\pi r_o L h_o}} = \frac{\Delta T}{\Sigma R} \qquad (3.3.49)$$

Temperature profile:

With the heat flux expression (Equation 3.3.43) in hand, we can now proceed to derive the temperature profile. This is done by again integrating Fourier's equation, but this time only up to an arbitrary radius r and the temperature T at that position. We obtain:

$$\int_{r_i}^{r} \frac{q}{k 2\pi L} \frac{dr}{r} = -\int_{T_i}^{T} dT \qquad (3.3.50)$$

or, since q is a constant given by Equation 3.3.43,

$$T(r) = T_i - \frac{T_i - T_o}{\ln(r_o / r_i)} \ln(r / r_i) \qquad (3.3.51)$$

Critical radius; optimum insulation thickness:

Optimum insulation thickness is equivalent to minimum heat flux which in turn leads to the definition of a critical radius. We draw for this purpose on Equation 3.3.49, neglect for simplicity the internal film resistance which is usually minor, and differentiate the heat flux q with respect to the outer radius r_o. We obtain:

$$\frac{dq}{dr_o} = \frac{-2\pi k L (T_i - T_o)[1/r_c - (k/h_o r_c^2)]}{[\ln(r_c / r_i) + k/h_o r_c]^2} = 0 \qquad (3.3.52)$$

This yields, for the critical radius,

$$r_c = k/h_o \qquad (3.3.53)$$

which is seen to equal the ratio of thermal conductivity to external film coefficient.

Comments:

Of the various Equations 3.3.43 to 3.3.51, the ones most frequently used in engineering applications are the Equation 3.3.43 and its extension, Equation 3.3.47. They allow the direct calculation of the heat flux q which is the quantity of greatest practical interest. The temperature profile (Equation 3.3.51) is not of immediate use, but reveals the surprising fact that T(r) is independent of thermal conductivity. It is these unexpected results that are the most rewarding feature of modeling. One should never set a model aside without scrutinizing it first for unusual features of this type.

Equation 3.3.53 for the critical radius, r_c, is as it turns out largely of academic interest. We show this by substituting some typical numerical values for h_o and k, $h \cong 10$ J/m²sK (air) and $k \cong 10^{-1}$ J/msK (asbestos). We obtain $r_c = 10^{-2}$ m, i.e., the critical radius is far too small to be used in practical applications and one is forced to accept suboptimal insulation thicknesses. This is yet another example of an unexpected feature revealed by the model.

Illustration 3.3.7   Heat-Up Time of an Unstirred Tank

We turn next to the problem of calculating the time required to heat a steam-jacketed, unstirred tank containing water to its (normal) boiling point prior to further operations. (The development evidently holds for other liquids as well, but water was chosen because of the easy availability of physical property data.)

The heat transfer process is one of free or natural convection from the tank bottom and walls to the water. Although an approximate value of the overall heat transfer coefficient for such a system appears in Table 3.11, we wish to undertake a more detailed analysis. The results of the two approaches differ considerably, in large part because the dependence of the free convection heat transfer coefficient h_c on the temperature driving force itself is neglected in the tabulated value.

Natural convection heat transfer occurs because of the volumetric expansion of the heated fluid and its consequent movement in the upward direction. Upon cooling, the liquid packet contracts and reverses direction, thus setting in motion a circulatory transfer of thermal energy. As we had seen in Chapter 2, Illustration 2.5, correlations take this mechanism into account by introducing the volumetric coefficient of expansion β(1/K) and incorporating it in the relevant dimensionless group termed the Grashof number Gr:

$$Gr = \frac{L^3\rho^2 g\beta\Delta T}{\mu^2} \qquad (3.3.54)$$

where g = gravitational constant = 9.81 m²/s.

The complete correlation of h_c is in terms of Nusselt, Grashof, and Prandtl numbers and takes the form:

$$Nu = a(GrPr)^n \qquad (3.3.55)$$

For convection from vertical cylinders and horizontal plates, applicable to the system under consideration, a = 0.13, and n = 1/3, provided GrPr > ~ 10^6. This is, as we shall see, the case here.

To evaluate the heat-up time, an integral unsteady energy balance about the tank contents is required. Thus,

$$\text{Rate of energy in} - \text{Rate of energy out} = \begin{array}{c}\text{Rate of change}\\ \text{in energy content}\end{array}$$

(3.3.56)

$$h_c A(T_s - T) - 0 = \frac{d}{dt} H = \rho V C_p \frac{dT}{dt}$$

which upon integration by separation of variable yields:

$$t = -\frac{\rho V C_p}{A} \int \frac{dT}{h_c(T_s - T)}$$

(3.3.57)

where h_c has been placed under the integral sign to account for the $(T_s - T)^{1/3}$ factor and the variation with temperature of the physical properties, in particular viscosity. We do not wish to attempt a graphical or numerical evaluation of the full expression (Equation 3.3.57) and will instead use physical properties at a temperature of 60°C which is the average of the initial and final water temperatures set at 20°C and 100°C, respectively. The factor $(T_s - T)^{1/3}$ is retained under the integral since its analytical evaluation poses no problem. Steam temperature T_s is at 120°C.

We now turn to the evaluation of h_c using the following average physical properties:

$$C_p = 4.2 \text{ kJ/kgK}, \ \rho = 984 \text{ kg/m}^3, \ \mu = 0.50 \times 10^{-3} \text{ kg/ms},$$
$$\beta = 4.8 \times 10^{-4} \text{ K}^{-1}, \ k = 0.65 \text{ J/msK}, \ Pr = 3.0$$

The dimensions of the tank are

$$\text{Height: } L = 3 \text{ m}, \quad \text{Diameter: } D = 1.5 \text{ m}$$

Using the expression for h_c, Equation 3.3.51, we obtain:

$$h_c = 0.13 \frac{k}{L} \left(\frac{L^3 \rho^2 g \beta \Delta T}{\mu^2} \right)^{1/3} \left(\frac{C_p \mu}{k} \right)^{1/3}$$

$$h_c = \frac{(0.13)(0.65)}{3} \left[\frac{3^3 (984)^2 (9.81)(4.8 \times 10^{-4}) \Delta T}{(0.50 \times 10^{-3})^2} \right]^{1/3} (3.0)^{1/3}$$

The Grashof number is seen to be of the order 10^{11}, thus satisfying the condition for the use of the correlation. We obtain:

$$h_c = 321 \ \Delta T^{1/3} \text{ J/m}^2 \text{sK}$$

Surface area and volume of the tank are, from the given dimensions:

$$A = 14.1 \text{ m}^2, \quad V = 5.30 \text{ m}^3$$

Introducing these values into Equation 3.3.57 and noting that

$$\int_{T_i}^{T_f} \frac{dT}{(T_s - T)^{4/3}} - \int_{T_i}^{T_v} \frac{d(T_s - T)}{(T_s - T)^{4/3}} = 3\left[\frac{1}{(T_s - T)_f^{1/3}} - \frac{1}{(T_s - T)_i^{1/3}}\right]$$

we obtain:

$$t = \frac{(1000)(5.3)(4.2 \times 10^3)}{(321)(14.2)} 3\left[\frac{1}{20^{1/3}} - \frac{1}{(100)^{1/3}}\right]$$

$$t = 1700\,s\,(i.e.,\,nearly\,40\,min.)$$

Comments:

The effect of the dependence of the heat transfer coefficient on $(T_s - T)^{1/3}$, seemingly a weak one, is in fact not trivial. During the initial heat-up period, with $\Delta T \sim 100°C$, its inclusion increases the heat transfer rate by $100^{1/3}$, i.e. a factor of nearly 5. Even near the termination of the heat-up process the increase is by a factor of $20^{1/3}$ to 2.7. This evidently brings about a fairly radical change in the results of the model.

The effect of the temperature dependence of the physical properties on the other hand, is considerably milder if we choose values midway between the initial and final process temperatures. Choosing μ^2 as the most severe case, we have for the ratio $(\mu_{20}/\mu_{60})^{2/3} \sim (0.95/0.50)^{2/3} \cong 1.5$ (see Table 3.7). This is, however, nearly compensated at the high temperature end where the relevant ratio is $(0.28/0.50)^{2/3} \cong 0.68$, whence $1.5 \times 0.68 = 1.01$. This compensating effect evidently does not exist in the case of the factor $(T_s - T)^{1/3}$ which causes an *increase* in heat transfer during the entire heat-up period.

Illustration 3.3.8   The Boiling Pot

We use this simple example of a pot boiling on a stove or hot plate to introduce the reader to what is termed *boiling heat transfer*, i.e. the heat transfer rate, flux, and coefficients that are associated with boiling. Imagine, then, a pot brought to a boil on a hot element whose power input can be adjusted so that the pot bottom assumes various surface temperatures T_s. The boiling heat transfer is then driven by the temperature difference $\Delta T_b = T_s - T_b$, where T_b is the (constant) temperature of the boiling liquid. Let us examine what happens when this driving force is changed by adjusting the power input to the element. It turns out that the boiling mechanism undergoes various complex transitions as ΔT_b is increased, and that the heat transfer coefficient h_b not only depends on ΔT_b, as was the case in convective heat transfer (considered in Illustration 3.3.7), but does so in a complex manner.

At low values of ΔT_b of less than $\sim 5°C$, the mechanism is one of natural convection with very few bubbles formed to disturb the normal natural convection. The dependence of h_b on ΔT_b is then roughly with the power 1/3, i.e., $h_b \propto (\Delta T_b)^{1/3}$, and we speak of *convective boiling*.

When ΔT_b is raised to the range 5 to 25°C, bubble production increases and with it there is an increase in the degree of turbulence and liquid circulation. This causes a dramatic increase in the temperature dependence of h_b to $h_b \propto (\Delta T_b)^2 - (\Delta T_b)^3$. We speak of the process being in the *nucleate boiling* range.

This trend does not continue indefinitely, however. A stage is reached where evaporation is so fast that there is insufficient time for the bubbles to detach themselves. The pot bottom is then blanketed with a layer of steam which causes a sharp decline in the dependence of h_b on ΔT_b and the associated heat transfer because of the lower conductivity of the gas.

This situation persists until a driving force of $\Delta T_b \sim 100°C$ is reached. The steam bubbles are now able to detach themselves as fast as they are formed so that heat transfer takes place through a thin liquid film adjacent to the metal surface to a region that is well mixed and of uniform temperature because of the action of the bubbles. This stage is referred to as the region of *film boiling*. Further increases in ΔT bring an additional contribution due to radiation heat transfer.

The values of h for boiling are quite high. At the beginning of the nucleate boiling region it ranges from 6000 to approximately 11,000 J/m^2sK (for water). At the peak of nucleate boiling, before the decline due to blanketing sets in, it reaches a maximum value of approximately 60,000 J/m^2sK.

Let us next examine, by actual numerical example, how this affects the evaporation rate of water. Extensive analysis of boiling rate data have led to the following two correlations for convective and nucleate boiling, respectively.

Convective Boiling: $h = 1043 \, (\Delta T, K)^{1/3}$; $q/A < 16 \, kJ/m^2$ (3.3.58)

Nucleate Boiling: $h = 5.56 \, (\Delta T, K)^3$; $16 < q/A < 240$ (3.3.59)

We first choose a $\Delta T = 5$, characteristic of the convective boiling region. Thus,

$$h = 1043 \, (5)^{1/3} = 1.78 \, kJ/m^2sK; \, q/A = (1.78)(5) = 8.99 \, kJ/m^2$$

which places it within the range of validity of the correlation, Equation 3.3.58.

Using a latent heat of evaporation at the boiling point of $\Delta H = 2460 \, kJ/kg$ (Table 3.7), and assuming a pot surface $A = 0.02 \, m^2$, we obtain:

$$Q = \frac{q}{\Delta H} = \frac{hA\Delta T}{\Delta H} = \frac{(1.78)(0.02)(5)}{2460} \, 3600 = 0.28 \, kg \, steam \, produced \, / \, h$$

Choosing next a $\Delta T = 12$, the rounder figures of $\Delta T = 15$ or $\Delta T = 20$ being out of reach of the correlation, Equation 3.3.59, we obtain:

$$h = 5.56 \, (12)^3 = 9.61 \, kJ/m^2sK; \, q/A = (9.61)(12) = 115 \, kJ/m^2$$

which is within the range of the correlation, Equation 3.3.59. The corresponding evaporation rate becomes:

$$Q = \frac{hA\Delta T}{\Delta H} = \frac{(9.61)(0.02)(12)}{2260} \, 3600 = 3.7 \, \text{kg steam produced} \, / \, h$$

These startling results indicate that by raising the pot bottom temperature by only 7°C, i.e., from a ΔT_b of 5 to a ΔT_b of 12, a nearly 18-fold increase in evaporation rate is achieved. This is an indication of the powerful influence of the cubic dependence of h on ΔT.

Illustration 3.3.9   Melting of a Silver Sample: Radiation

We use this example of the melting of a silver sample in a high temperature furnace to introduce the reader to some simple concepts of radiation.

Thermal radiation is an important mode of heat transfer, especially so when large temperature differences occur as, for example in furnaces, driers, metallurgical processes, and other high-temperature operations. It is a form of electromagnetic radiation and its rate of transfer depends on the temperature of the emitting and receiving objects. Part of the radiation transmitted is absorbed by the receiving body and part of it reflected, so that:

$$\alpha + \rho = 1 \qquad\qquad (3.3.60)$$

where α = absorptivity, the fraction absorbed
and ρ = reflectivity, the fraction reflected.

Bodies, whether they are the source or the receiver of radiation, emit radiation of their own, which depends on the temperature of the body. To provide a measure of emission radiation in general, we use that of a so-called black body as a reference, and define:

$$\text{Emissivity}\,\varepsilon = \frac{\text{Emission radiation of an arbitrary object}}{\text{Emission radiation of a black body}} \qquad (3.3.61)$$

where the black body refers to an entity with an absorptivity $\alpha = 1$, i.e., one which reflects none of the incident radiation. It can be approximated by blackening the surface of an object with charcoal. All real bodies have an emissivity $\varepsilon < 1$ and are referred to as gray bodies.

Emissivity is high for dull surfaces, $\varepsilon \approx 0.6$ to 0.95, low for highly reflective or polished surfaces, $\varepsilon \approx 0.01$ to 0.2. Water and oil paints of all colors, for example, have emissivities $\varepsilon = 0.92$ to 0.96. For highly polished iron, ε rises to 0.74, but if dulled by oxidation, dramatically drops to a value of $\varepsilon = 0.052$.

The rate of radiation heat emission is given by the Stefan-Boltzmann law:

$$q_r = \varepsilon \sigma A T^4 \qquad\qquad (3.3.62)$$

where σ = Stefan-Boltzmann constant = 5.767×10^{-8} J/m²sK and T is in K. Note the strong fourth power dependence on temperature compared to the linear dependence on the driving force in the case of convective and conductive heat transfer.

To derive the radiative heat transmission rate between two bodies, one argues that the radiative emission from the hot body, T_2, reaching the colder body, T_1 and area A, is given by

$$q_{21} = \varepsilon\sigma A T_2^4 \qquad (3.3.63)$$

This amount has to be diminished by the amount emitted by the cold body, again with area A and absorbed by the hot body:

$$q_{12} = \alpha\sigma A T_1^4 \qquad (3.3.64)$$

Since absorptivity is usually very nearly equal to emissivity, $\alpha \approx \varepsilon$, the net heat flow received by the cold body is the difference of the two, i.e.,

$$q_r = \varepsilon\sigma A(T_2^4 - T_1^4) \qquad (3.3.65)$$

To calculate the time required to melt the silver sample under consideration, we neglect for the time being the heat-up time and use the following data:

Latent heat of fusion of silver ΔH_s = 89 J/g
Specific heat of silver C_p = 0.24 J/gK
Melting point of silver T_1 = 1230 K
Furnace temperature T_2 = 1500 K
Crucible charge m = 1000 g silver
Crucible surface area A = 10^{-2} m²
Furnace emissivity ε = 0.6

We then have, for the time of melting:

$$t = \frac{\Delta H_s m}{q_r} = \frac{\Delta H_s m}{A\varepsilon\sigma(T_2^4 - T_1^4)}$$

$$t = \frac{(89)(1000)}{(10^{-2})(0.6)(5.8 \times 10^{-8})(1500^4 - 1230^4)}$$

$$t = 93\,\text{sec}$$

The process is seen to be extremely fast, about a minute and a half in duration after the melting point is reached. This is due to the extremely low heat of fusion of silver which is about one-quarter that of ice.

An estimate of the heat-up time can be arrived at by first neglecting the T_1^4 term. This is valid up to temperatures of about 800 K. We have, for the energy balance about the crucible:

$$\text{Rate of energy in} - \text{Rate of energy out} = \frac{\text{Rate of change of}}{\text{energy contents}}$$

(3.3.66)

$$hAT_2^4 - 0 = mC_p \frac{dT_1}{dt}$$

Integrating by separation of variables and solving the result for time t we obtain:

$$t = \frac{mC_p}{A\varepsilon\sigma T_2^4}(T_{1f} - T_{1i}) = \frac{(1000)(0.24)}{10^{-2}(0.65)(5.8 \times 10^{-8})1500^4}(800 - 298)$$

$$t = 63 \text{ sec}$$

which is of the same order as the time of melting. The total heat-up time to roughly double the temperature of 800 K is likely to be of the order of 6 to 7 min., much longer than the time required to melt the charge. This makes immediate sense since the sensible heat requirements $mC_p\Delta T = (1000)(0.24)(1200)$ exceed the latent heat requirement $m\Delta H_s = (1000)(89)$ by a factor of about 5.

Comments:

It is of some interest to examine at what point radiative heat transfer becomes significant. This occurs at much lower temperatures than one might think. It certainly need not be as high as the temperatures usually associated with furnaces. To show this, we consider both still air and circulating air within the furnace, with convective heat transfer coefficients set at 10 and 100 J/m²sK, respectively, and compare heat transfer to a body at 300 K by both convection and radiation. For parity to be reached between the two mechanisms, we must have, assuming an emissivity of unity,

$$\frac{h}{\sigma} \frac{(T_2 - T_1)}{T_2^4 - T_1^4)} = \frac{h}{5.8 \times 10^{-8}} \frac{(T_2 - 300)}{(T_2^4 - 300^4)} = 1$$

(3.3.67)

Solving for T_2 for the two cases, we obtain:

For still air: $T_2 \sim 400 \text{ K} = 127°C$
For moving air: $T_2 \sim 650 \text{ K} = 277°C$

Though respectably high, these temperatures are a far cry from the levels usually seen in high temperature operations. The numbers also show that radiation need not be considered in the steam heating of moving air but does become the predominant mode of heat transfer when electrical heating is used.

Illustration 3.3.10 Adiabatic Compression of an Ideal Gas: Energy Balance for Closed Systems First Law of Thermodynamics

In this example we consider an ideal gas in a closed system, i.e., under conditions of no flow which undergoes a compression or expansion process. The system is considered to be perfectly insulated and no heat exchange takes place between it and the surroundings.

Given the initial conditions temperature T_1, pressure p_1 and molar volume V_1, and a change by compression of expansion to V_2, we wish to establish the relations among the final values of these variables, T_2, p_2, and V_2.

For a closed system with only thermal energy q and work w exchanged with the surroundings, the energy balance is expressed as the first law of thermodynamics:

$$\Delta U = \pm q \pm w \qquad (3.3.68)$$

where U = internal energy of the system. The positive signs signify energy transfer *to the system*, the negative sign transfer *to the surroundings*. To avoid the cumbersome dual notation, it is customary to choose the special case of heat transfer *to the* system and work done *by* the system, so that:

$$\Delta U = q - w \qquad (3.3.69)$$

or in differential form:

$$dU = dq - dw \qquad (3.3.70)$$

We now make use of two further relations. We first note that for compressive work,

$$-dw = -pdV \qquad (3.3.71)$$

We next introduce the definition of enthalpy H in differential form:

$$dH = dU + d(pV) \qquad (3.3.72)$$

which for one mole of an ideal gas becomes:

$$\frac{dH}{dT} = \frac{dU}{dT} + \frac{d(RT)}{dT} \qquad (3.3.73)$$

We note that dH is associated with heat transfer at constant pressure, dU with heat transfer at constant volume, so that the respective temperature derivatives in Equation 3.3.73 become the corresponding heat capacities at constant pressure and volume: $dq_p/dT = dH/dT = C_p$, and $dq_v/dT = dU/dT = C_v$. Introducing these relations into Equation 3.3.69 we finally obtain:

$$C_p = C_v - R \tag{3.3.74}$$

where the heat capacities are in units of J/mol K. With these expressions in hand, we return to Equations 3.3.70 and 3.3.71, and obtain, for dq = 0 (adiabatic case),

$$dU = C_v dT = -dw = -pdV = -RT\frac{dV}{V} \tag{3.3.75}$$

or

$$\frac{C_v}{T}dT = R\frac{dV}{V} = (C_p - C_v)\frac{dV}{V} \tag{3.3.76}$$

Integration of Equation 3.3.76 between initial and final states yields:

$$\frac{T_2}{T_1} = \left(\frac{V_1}{V_2}\right)^{\gamma-1} = \left(\frac{p_2}{p_1}\right)^{(\gamma-1)/\gamma} \tag{3.3.77}$$

where γ = Heat capacity ratio = C_p/C_v which has a value of 1.4 for air. This expression is cast in the alternative form:

Adiabatic:

$$p_1 V_1^{\gamma} = p_2 V_2^{\gamma} = pV^{\gamma} = \text{constant} \tag{3.3.78}$$

which can be compared with the corresponding isothermal P-V relation (Boyle's law).

Isothermal:

$$p_1 V_1 = p_2 V_2 = pV = \text{constant} \tag{3.3.79}$$

The work associated with adiabatic compression can be evaluated from the expressions of Equation 3.3.75, i.e.,

$$w = -C_v\Delta T = \frac{-R}{\gamma-1}\Delta T = \frac{p_1 V_1 - p_2 V_2}{\gamma-1} \tag{3.3.80}$$

If V_2 is not known, which is usually the case, it can be eliminated using Equation 3.3.78 and we obtain:

Adiabatic compression work:

$$w_a = \frac{p_1 V_1}{\gamma - 1}\left[1 - \left(\frac{p_2}{p_1}\right)^{(\gamma-1)/\gamma}\right] = \frac{RT_1}{\gamma - 1}\left[1 - \left(\frac{p_2}{p_1}\right)^{(\gamma-1)/\gamma}\right] \quad (3.3.81)$$

The corresponding expression for isothermal compression, obtained by integration of the expression $W = -pdV = -RT\dfrac{dV}{V}$ is given by:

Isothermal compression work:

$$w_i = RT \ln \frac{V_1}{V_2} = RT \ln \frac{p_2}{p_1} \quad (3.3.82)$$

For a given compression ratio p_2/p_1, w_a is always greater than w_i. In practical compression processes, cooling is, therefore, provided to bring the process as near as possible to isothermal conditions and, thus, reduce the work load.

Illustration 3.3.11 The Steady-State Energy Balance for Flowing (Open) Systems

The energy balance for closed systems, enshrined in the first law of thermodynamics, Equations 3.3.68 to 3.3.70, did not and was not required to consider energy forms other than work and thermal energy.

When the system is opened up and flow occurs, additional energy terms have to be included. They comprise kinetic and potential energy changes, ΔE_K and ΔE_p, the so-called shaft work w_s, i.e., work done by a pump or on a turbine, and the so-called flow work w_f, which is associated with the energy required to introduce the fluid at the upstream end and to extract it at the downstream end. We obtain, in the first instance:

$$\Delta U + \Delta E_K + \Delta E_P = q - w_s - w_f \quad (3.3.83)$$

Figure 3.8 shows a diagram of the system under consideration. Kinetic and potential energy are given by their customary expression $E_K = mv^2/2$ and $E_P = mg.z$. For the flow work, we write w_f = Force × Distance = Pressure × Area (Volume/Area) = pV. For a unit mass of fluid, Equation 3.3.83 then becomes:

$$\Delta U + \Delta \frac{v^2}{2} + g\Delta z + \Delta(pV) = q - w_s \quad (3.3.84)$$

or by virtue of Equation 3.3.72:

$$\Delta H + \Delta \frac{v^2}{2} + g\Delta z = q - w_s \quad (3.3.85)$$

This equation applies quite generally to both compressible and incompressible flow.

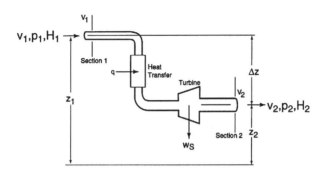

FIGURE 3.8 Diagram depicting the various terms of the energy balance, Equation 3.3.85.

We note that in most heat transfer processes, kinetic and potential energy changes are negligible. If, in addition, no shaft work is involved, we obtain:

$$\Delta H = q \qquad (3.3.86)$$

This expression is immediately recognized as the equation which, in differential or integral form, is used in the analysis of heat exchange processes.

Illustration 3.3.12   A Moving Boundary Problem: Freeze-Drying of Food

In a great many physical processes involving two phases, the phase boundary undergoes a continuous movement caused by energy and mass transport with or without chemical reaction. Examples of this type of behavior are numerous and important: evaporation, condensation, freezing and melting phenomena, crystal growth and dissolution, metal or polymer casting, combustion of solid or liquid fuels, freeze-drying of foods, and others.

The state variables in these processes, such as temperature or concentration, are in principle functions of both distance and time, leading to PDEs that are usually coupled and nonlinear. To reduce the model to a manageable set of ordinary differential and algebraic equations, the following assumptions are often made.

1. The "core" contained by the moving front, such as a liquid fuel droplet, has uniform properties and can be treated as an unsteady stirred tank.
2. The movement of the front itself is sufficiently slow so that the transport gradients outside the core attain a *quasi-steady-state*. It will be recalled that this concept was also encountered in Illustration 3.2.2.
3. The processes involved — transport and reaction — are dominated by a rate-controlling slow step.

Thus, although both time and distance are retained as variables, distance (expressed through the changing size or mass of the core) becomes a *dependent* variable for the core unsteady balance but is retained as an *independent* variable for

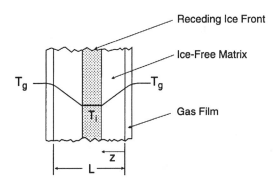

FIGURE 3.9   Temperature profiles in the freeze-drying of a slab of meat.

the external, quasi steady-state balance. Time is an independent variable as well, but appears only in the core balance.

A systematic way of modeling these systems is to start with unsteady mass and energy balances about the core, followed by a consideration of the quasi steady-state process outside the moving boundary. It is good practice to keep track of the number of dependent variables that ultimately must be matched by the number of equations.

In the process to be considered here, we wish to derive a model which would allow us to obtain relevant heat and mass transport coefficients from freeze-drying rate data. The food to be dried, e.g., a slab of frozen poultry meat, has an initial (frozen) water content of m_0 kg. It is heated with an electric heater and, in the experiment in question, provided with thermocouples to measure surface temperature T_g. Sublimation of the ice takes place in a vacuum chamber and water loss is monitored by means of a spring balance. A sketch of the configuration appears in Figure 3.9. As sublimation progresses, the core ice front, assumed to be at the wet-bulb temperature T_{wb}, recedes into the interior, exposing an ice-free matrix which increases in thickness with time. Heat conduction through this matrix is assumed to be at a quasi steady-state so that a linear temperature gradient prevails at any given instant.

We start with a mass balance around the core and add equations as the need arises.

Core mass balance:

$$\text{Rate of moisture in} - \text{Rate of moisture out} = \frac{\text{Rate of change of}}{\text{moisture content}}$$

(3.3.87)

$$0 - F = \frac{d}{dt}m$$

where F equals the rate of sublimation of ice.

Core energy balance:

$$\text{Rate of energy in} - \text{Rate of energy out} = \begin{array}{c}\text{Rate of change of}\\\text{energy content}\end{array}$$

$$q - F\Delta H_s = \frac{d}{dt}(H_{ice} + H_{matrix})$$

(3.3.88)

We choose the reference temperature as that of the ice and its matrix, so that $H_{ice} = H_{matrix} = 0$ and the right side of Equation 3.3.88 becomes zero. We then obtain, after introduction of the pertinent auxiliary relation for q,

$$U2A\ (T_g - T_i) - \Delta H_s F = 0$$

(3.3.89)

where ΔH_s = enthalpy of sublimation of ice. We note that the heat transfer coefficient U depends on the distance of conduction z and is given by the relation:

$$\frac{1}{U} = \frac{1}{h} + \frac{z}{k}$$

(3.3.90)

with h and k denoting the external film coefficient and the matrix thermal conductivity, respectively. Combination of these three equations yields:

$$\frac{2A(T_g - T_i)}{\dfrac{1}{h} + \dfrac{z}{k}} = -\Delta H_s \frac{d}{dt}m$$

(3.3.91)

We note that we still have, at this stage, two dependent variables z and m. An additional equation, therefore, will be required which relates z to m. Some reflection will show that this relation can be obtained from a cumulative mass balance on the core ice. We have

$$\text{Initial ice} = \text{Ice sublimated} + \text{Ice left over}$$

$$m_0 = m_0 \frac{L - 2z}{L} + m$$

(3.3.92)

from which there results:

$$z = \frac{m_0 - m}{m_0} \frac{L}{2} = f \frac{L}{2}$$

(3.3.93)

where f = fraction of ice removed.

The ODE (Equation 3.3.91) now becomes:

$$\frac{2A(T_g - T_i)}{\dfrac{1}{h} + \dfrac{L}{2k}f} = -\frac{\Delta H_s}{m_0} \frac{df}{dt}$$

(3.3.94)

which upon integration by separation of variables leads to the expression:

$$\frac{2A(T_g - T_i)}{\Delta H_s} t = \frac{1}{h} f + \frac{L}{4k} f^2 \qquad (3.3.95)$$

Symbolically we can write:

$$t/f = af + b \qquad (3.3.96)$$

Plots of experimental t/f values vs. f can then be used to evaluate matrix conductivity k from the slope a and the film coefficient h from the intercept b.

Experimental data have shown good agreement with this model up to values of $f \approx 0.85$. Beyond that point deviations from the straight-line relation (see Equation 3.3.93 in Practice Problem 3.3.5) occur which have been attributed to moisture adsorption on the matrix. This causes an increase in ΔH_s which is now the enthalpy of desorption and a resultant change in slope and intercept.

The reader is referred to Chapter 4, Illustration 4.3.2 and Practice Problems 3.3.5 and 4.4 for additional moving boundary problems. A PDE model for a moving boundary problem appears in Illustration 8.3.2.

Comment:

We note that this problem was not placed in the category of simultaneous mass and energy balances, dealt with in Section 3.5. The reason for this is that the balances here are uncoupled and can be solved independently. Section 3.5 treats the more general case of coupled equations.

Practice Problems

3.3.1 Design of a Hot-Wire Anemometer — A hot-wire anemometer consists of a thin wire, usually made of platinum, whose electrical resistance varies with temperature. By passing an electrical current through it, its temperature is raised, and heat transfer occurs to the surrounding medium, thus reducing the temperature of the wire and bringing about a change in its electrical resistance. The anemometer is incorporated in an electrical circuit called a Wheatstone Bridge which allows this change in resistance to be monitored.

The heat loss will depend on the temperature of the surrounding medium as well as the associated heat transfer coefficient which, in turn, depends on the velocity of the medium and its physical properties. The higher the velocity, the larger the rate of heat loss and, hence, the change in the electrical resistance of the wire. Thus, the anemometer can be used, after appropriate calibration, to measure either the temperature or the velocity of the surrounding medium. We note that a similar device, known as a thermal conductivity cell or catharometer, is used to monitor *compositional* changes in a gas which affect the thermal conductivity of the medium and, hence, the rate of heat loss. Such devices are routinely used in gas chromatographs where advantage is taken of the large difference in the thermal conductivity of the carrier gas helium and the partitioned solutes. The chromatogram of solute peaks one obtains is directly driven by signals from the Wheatstone Bridge caused by changes in the wire resistance.

The case we wish to consider is the use of the anemometer in the measurement of air velocities in the range v = 1 to 10 m/s. We choose a surface temperature T_s = 125°C — this is arbitrary, other values could be chosen without invalidating the procedures — and proceed to calculate the electrical current i required to maintain the wire at this temperature over the velocity range in question. This value of i is needed for a proper design of the Wheatstone Bridge, i.e., for determining the magnitude of the resistances to be used in the circuit, given a constant voltage supply V. A range of required i values corresponding to v = 1 to 10 m/s is established that provides us, as well, with an indication as to whether the measuring devices used in the bridge — typically an ammeter or rheostat — have sufficient sensitivity to meet the desired precision in the measured velocity.

The following data are provided:

Wire diameter d = 10^{-4} m
Wire surface area A = 10^{-6} m^2
Wire resistance R = 0.1 Ω
Air temperature T_a = 25°C

Values for the heat transfer coefficient h are obtained from the appropriate correlation listed in Table 3.10. The required physical properties can be read from Table 3.8.

(Hint: Calculate the convective heat transfer rate q and set it equal to the power output of the wire P = i^2R. Check for additional radiation heat transfer using an emissivity for the platinum wire of ε = 0.1.)

Answer: i = 0.63 – 1.05 A

Comment:

The current range is such that a milliammeter accurate to 1 mA would yield the velocity to three significant figures, one with an accuracy of 0.1 mA to four significant figures. Frequently one wishes to monitor velocity *fluctuations*, such as those that occur in turbulent flow and those results serve as a guide as to whether the required precision in v can be met.

3.3.2 Conduction in Systems with Heat Sources —
(a) Derive the equations which apply to conduction in (1) a slab, (2) a sphere with uniformly distributed heat sources generating heat at the constant rate of S_s (J/m^{3}s).
(b) For a slab, consider the faces at x = 0 and x = L to be held at the temperature T_0 by appropriate cooling. Integrate the model equations to obtain the temperature distribution.
(c) Solve the same problem for a long cylinder of radius R.
(d) Show that if the slab is immersed in a bath of temperature T_b, the difference between the surface and bath temperatures is given by $T_s - T_b = S_sL/h$, where h = heat transfer coefficient to the bath.

Answers: (b) $T - T_s = \dfrac{S_s L^2}{2k}\left[\left(\dfrac{x}{L}\right) - \left(\dfrac{x}{L}\right)^2\right]$

$\qquad$ (c) $T - T_c = \dfrac{S_s R^2}{4k}\left[1 - \left(\dfrac{r}{R}\right)^2\right]$

3.3.3 Maximum Temperature in a Nuclear Reactor Fuel Element — In a typical nuclear reactor, heat generated by the fission process in the fuel element is removed by pressurized water flowing in an annulus surrounding the fuel rod. The maximum temperature occurs at the center of the rod and can in principle be calculated from energy balances and temperature distributions in the fuel element and the coolant. Here we shall assume that the water flow rate and exit temperature are known from measurements. This provides a value for the enthalpy change in the fluid that can be equated to the total amount of heat transferred, and the rod average surface temperature calculated from that expression. T_{Max} is then obtained from the expression given in Practice Problem 3.3.2(3). Use arithmetric temperature average in place of LMTD.

Data:
$\qquad$ Water flow rate $F = 2.28$ kg/s
$\qquad$ Water inlet temperature $T_1 = 25°C$
$\qquad$ Water outlet temperature $T_2 = 150°C$
$\qquad$ Convective heat transfer coefficient $h = 10{,}000$ J/m²sK
$\qquad$ Rod diameter $d = 5.0 \times 10^{-2}$ m
$\qquad$ Rod length $L = 10$ m
$\qquad$ Rod thermal conductivity $k = 28.8$ J/msK
$\qquad$ Rod heat generation $S = 2 \times 10^7$ J/m³s

Answer: $T_{Max} = 598°C$

3.3.4 Hairpin Heat Exchanger — Derive the equations which apply to a hairpin heat exchanger. In this device, cold fluid enters a tube in the shape of a hairpin, i.e., the tube has a 180° turn at the end of the shell and the tubular fluid exits the exchanger at the same end as it enters.

3.3.5 Freezing of a Liquid — A liquid is exposed to a fluid medium at $T_\infty < T_f$, where T_f is the freezing point of the liquid. We consider two cases:

1. The liquid is assumed to be at its freezing point and heat transfer takes place from the freezing liquid to the colder medium with a film coefficient h_1. Show that the thickness z of the liquid at any given time t is given by the relation:

$$z^* = \sqrt{1 + 2\tau} - 1 \qquad (3.3.97)$$

where z^* = dimensionless solid thickness = $\dfrac{h_1}{k} z$

τ = dimensionless time = $th_1^2 \dfrac{T_f - T_\infty}{\rho(-\Delta H_f)k}$

ΔH_f = latent heat of freezing (negative)

k = thermal conductivity of solid

(Hint: Use the procedure which was applied in Illustration 3.3.10.)

2. The liquid, here assumed to be water, is initially at the temperature $T_i > T_f$. It has been shown that in this case the relation between ice thickness z and time t is given by:

$$\tau = \frac{z}{H\theta} - \frac{1}{(H\theta)^2} \ln\left(1 + \frac{H\theta z^*}{1 + H\theta}\right) \qquad (3.3.98)$$

where H = ratio of film coefficients = $\dfrac{h_2}{h_1}$

h_2 = film coefficient ice-to-underlying water

θ = dimensionless temperature = $(T_i - T_f)/(T_f - T_\infty)$

3.3.6 Production of Flakice — An old and popular method of making ice flakes is to use a horizontal rotating cylinder partially submerged in water, with the drum internally chilled with a cold brine spray. The thin ice layer formed on the exterior surface is scraped off as the revolving drum surface emerges from the water.

Using the following data, calculate the time required to form an ice layer 1 mm thick:

Temperature of water T_i = 4°C
Temperature of brine T_∞ = −15
Density of ice ρ = 920 kg/m^3
Thermal conductivity of ice k = 2.2 J/smK
Latent heat of freezing ΔH_f = −3.34 × 10^5 J/kg
Film coefficient spray-to-ice h_1 = 500 J/m^{2}sK
Film coefficient ice-to-water h_2 = 50 J/m^{2}sK

(Hint: Use Equation 3.3.98.)
Answer: 46 s

3.3.7 Heat Losses from Furnace Walls — The heat losses from a rectangular furnace at 3000 K with a total surface area A = 200 m^2 and an estimated average surface temperature of 250°C are to be estimated. The internal insulation consists of 10 cm of fire brick which is covered by a retaining wall of dull sheet metal with an estimated emissivity ε = 0.8. Consider both radiation and convection to still air at 25° (h = 5 J/m^{2}sK).

(a) Calculate the heat losses.
(b) Recalculate the losses if the insulation thickness is doubled.

Answer: (a) 822 kJ/s

3.3.8 Pumping Up a Bicycle Tire — A racing bicycle is to be pumped up to a pressure of $p_2 = 5$ atm. Calculate the adiabatic temperature attained.
Answer: 199°C

Note that in practice this temperature is not reached because of heat loss to the tire and surroundings.

3.3.9 Temperature Rise Due to a Kinetic Energy Change —

(a) Air flowing at 10 m/s in a pipe is brought to a sudden stop by closure of a valve. What is the associated temperature rise?
(b) Water flowing at 1 m/s is similarly brought to a stop. Calculate its temperature rise.

(Hint: Use Equation 3.3.85.)
Answers: (a) 50°C; (b) 0.12°C

Comment:
The high value obtained for air is due to its higher permissible velocity as well as its low heat capacity. The results indicate that kinetic energy changes may have to be taken into account in heat transfer operations involving gases with relatively low heat flux.

3.3.10 Temperature Rise Due to Pumping — The power input into a fluid by a pump has, as can be seen from Equation 3.3.85, an associated temperature rise which, if adiabatic, can be directly calculated from ΔH. Pumps are generally characterized by volumetric flow rate Q and the pressure increase they produce, usually expressed as "head" in meters of water height. Consider a pump taking a water inflow of $Q = 1$ m³/s at atmospheric pressure and producing a head of 50 m of water. Calculate the attendant temperature rise, assuming that there are no heat losses.
(Hint: Work done by the pump per unit time equals the product of volumetric flow rate times pressure difference generated by the pump.)
Answer: 0.12°C

Comment:
The temperature rise is seen to be trivial in the case of a single pass through the pump. It does become significant, however, in the case of a *recirculating* pump. The temperature rise, again assuming adiabatic operation, would then be 1.2°C after 10 passes, 12°C after 100 passes, etc. These temperature rises are no longer insignificant and can in some instances be a hindrance unless appropriate cooling is provided.

3.4   FORCE AND MOMENTUM BALANCES

We turn here to the consideration of models that call for the use of force or momentum balances. We recall from Newton's law that force is equivalent to rate of momentum change, since $\mathbf{F} = m\ dv/dt = d(mv)dt$, where mv = momentum $\mathbf{M}$. Depending on circumstances, one can express the terms in these balances either as a force or as momentum change. For example, the momentum imparted in the transverse direction by a moving fluid to a pipe wall or to the surface of an immersed body is most conveniently expressed in terms of a shear stress τ (Pa), a pressure drop ΔP, or a drag force F_D. On the other hand, the momentum carried by a moving fluid to a turbine blade is best expressed in terms of the momentum flow $d\ mv/dt = \rho Qv$. Note that $\mathbf{v}$, $\mathbf{F}$ and $\mathbf{M}$ are all vectors.

3.4.1   MOMENTUM FLUX AND EQUIVALENT FORCES

Here again as in the case of energy flux, the complications due to different driving forces and distinction between stagnant film and equimolar diffusion seen in the mass balances do not arise. We make, however, the usual distinction between diffusive transport, associated with viscous or laminar flow, and convective transport which is associated with turbulent flow. These modes are best expressed in terms of shear stress τ and take the form:

Laminar flow:

(Newton's viscosity law)

$$\tau = -\mu \frac{dv}{dx} \tag{3.4.1}$$

Turbulent flow:

Pipes

$$\tau = f \frac{\rho v^2}{2} \frac{A_c}{A_s} \tag{3.4.2}$$

Submerged objects

$$\tau = C_D \frac{\rho v^2}{2} \frac{A_c}{A_s} \tag{3.4.3}$$

where f and C_D are the friction factor and drag coefficient, respectively, to be discussed below, and A_c/A_s is the ratio of cross-sectional to surface area of the object. Equation 3.4.1 is an empirical law proposed by Newton, while Equations 3.4.2 and 3.4.3 are obtained by equating the shear stress force with frictional or drag forces. These forces are further discussed below.

3.4.2   TRANSPORT COEFFICIENTS

We start this section in the usual way by considering molecular or diffusive transport. The relevant parameter here is the viscosity μ, values of which are listed for various substances in Table 3.13.

TABLE 3.13
Viscosities of Gases and Liquids at 20°C

	Substance	Viscosity (cP = 1 mPas)
Gases	Air	1.8×10^{-2}
	Nitrogen	1.8×10^{-2}
	Oxygen	2.0×10^{-2}
	Carbon dioxide	1.5×10^{-2}
	Steam (100°)	1.3×10^{-2}
	Methane	1.1×10^{-2}
	i–Butane	0.76×10^{-2}
Liquids	Water	1.0
	Ethyl alcohol	1.2
	Diethyl ether	0.25
	Benzene	0.65
	Bromine	0.95
	Mercury	1.6
	Sulfuric acid	19
	Sodium (250°C)	0.38
	Potassium (250°C)	0.26
	Lead (550°C)	1.7
	Glycerol	1070

For gases, viscosity is seen to be of the order 10^{-2} cP = 10^{-5} Pas. For liquids of normal fluidity, μ is in the range 10^{-1} to 1 cP. Exceptions occur in such cases as sulfuric acid and glycerol, the latter having a viscosity three to four orders of magnitude higher than "normal."

Temperature dependence of μ is strong in the case of liquids, decreasing exponentially with absolute temperature. For water, for example, the decrease is by a factor of 6.4 between 0°C and 100°C. Gas viscosities at low densities, on the other hand, vary only weakly with the square root of absolute temperature and not at all with pressure.

Turning next to turbulent transport, we consider associated friction factors f and drag coefficients C_D. The concept of these factors arises from the assumption that the friction force F_f is proportional to some form of the exposed area A (pipe or submerged object) and the kinetic energy E_K of the fluid. f and C_D act as proportionality constants. Thus,

$$F_f = fAE_K \text{ or } C_DAE_K \tag{3.4.4}$$

Evaluating these expressions for pipes and submerged objects ultimately leads to the following expressions:

Pipes:

(Fanning equation)
$$\frac{\Delta p}{\rho} = h_f = 4f\frac{v^2}{2}\frac{L}{D} \tag{3.4.5}$$

Submerged objects:

$$F_D = C_D A_c \frac{\rho v^2}{2} \tag{3.4.6}$$

where L and D are the length and diameter of the pipe, Δp the pressure drop over the length L, and h_f the so-called friction head. For flow around submerged objects, F_D is the drag force, and A_c the exposed cross-sectional area.

Tabulations of C_D and f appear in the accompanying Table 3.14. Both coefficients depend on Reynolds number and, in the case of packed beds, on the void fraction ϵ as well. Surface roughness plays an additional role that is not considered in the Table 3.14, i.e., the tabulations apply to smooth surfaces.

The tabulations include correlations for both laminar and turbulent flow. The transition from one to the other occurs at fairly precise values of the Reynolds number. Thus, for spheres, turbulent flow sets in at Re ≈ 0.1, for pipes at Re ≈ 2100. In the laminar regime, a relatively simple dependence on Re^{-1} is obtained in most cases. If the pertinent correlations are substituted in Equations 3.4.5 and 3.4.6, two celebrated relations result, the Hagen-Poiseuille law for circular pipes, and Stokes' law for the drag force on a sphere. Thus,

Pipe (Hagen-Poiseuille):

$$\Delta p = 128 \frac{\mu Q L}{\pi d^4} \quad \text{or} \quad Q = \frac{\pi}{128} d^4 \frac{\Delta P}{\mu L} \tag{3.4.7}$$

Sphere (Stokes):

$$F = 3\pi d \mu v \tag{3.4.8}$$

Of note in particular is the strong dependence of the pressure drop in pipes on pipe diameter. Thus, halving it increases Δp by a factor of 16. The drag force on spheres on the other hand shows a simple linear dependence on both d and v.

We note that both expressions (Equations 3.4.7 and 3.4.8) were originally derived by differential force or momentum balances to arrive at velocity distributions as primary information. These are then integrated over the cross-sectional area of the pipe to obtain volumetric flow rate Q or, in the case of the sphere, substituted into Newton's viscosity law and the result integrated over the surface to obtain the drag force F_D. The latter derivation, first given by Stokes, was based on the well-known Navier-Stokes equations consisting of three nonlinear PDEs and the continuity equations as a starting model.

We now present a number of illustrative examples, many of which have by now become classical problems. We start with static systems that involve no flow, hence, require force balances. The forces acting on submerged surfaces in the atmosphere and in pressurized containers are considered. Particle fall, rise, or suspension in a flowing fluid is taken up next, again requiring a force balance. We then turn our full attention to flowing fluids and examine the forces due to momentum changes in the

TABLE 3.14
Drag Coefficients and Friction Factors

A. Flat Plate

Range	C_D
Re $< 5 \times 10^5$	$\dfrac{1.33}{\text{Re}^{1/2}}$
$5 \times 10^5 <$ Re $< 10^7$	$\dfrac{0.074}{\text{Re}^{1/2}} - \dfrac{1700}{\text{Re}}$
Re $> 10^7$	$\dfrac{0.072}{\text{Re}^{1/5}}$

B. Sphere

Range	C_D
Re < 0.1	$\dfrac{24}{\text{Re}}$
$2 <$ Re < 500	$\dfrac{18.5}{\text{Re}^{3/5}}$
$500 <$ Re $< 2 \times 10^5$	0.44

C. Cyclinder

Range	C_D
Re < 10	$\dfrac{0.33}{\text{Re}}$
$3 \times 10^4 <$ Re $< 2 \times 10^5$	1.2
Re $> 10^5$	0.36

D. Inside Smooth Tubes

Range	f
Re < 2100	$\dfrac{16}{\text{Re}}$
$2100 <$ Re $< 10^5$	$\dfrac{0.079}{\text{Re}^{1/4}}$

E. Packed Beds

Range	f
Re < 10	$\dfrac{(1-\varepsilon)^2}{\varepsilon^3} \dfrac{75}{\text{Re}}$
Re > 1000	$0.88 \dfrac{1-\varepsilon}{\varepsilon^3}$

fluid as well as the full panoply of forces which arise in steady flows and lead to the Bernoulli equation and the mechanical energy balance. A number of additional examples are provided that complete the survey. We note that many, if not most, problems in fluid mechanics require, in addition to a force/momentum balance, the use of the continuity equation, i.e., a mass balance. In a good many cases an energy balance must be invoked as well. These problems are not considered here, but come under scrutiny in Section 3.6 devoted to simultaneous mass, energy, and momentum balances.

Illustration 3.4.1   Forces on Submerged Surfaces: Archimides' Law

We start by presenting the general formula for the force F acting on submerged surfaces of arbitrary shape and area A due to the so-called hydrostatic head h of the fluid. It takes the form:

$$dF = pdA \tag{3.4.9}$$

where p = hydrostatic pressure. By means of a force balance it can be established that p is related to h by the expression:

$$p = \rho gh \tag{3.4.10}$$

where ρ = density of the fluid. This expression is known as the *fundamental equation of fluid statics.* We proceed to apply it to a number of cases of interest.

(1) *Flat horizontal surface:*
Substitution of Equation 3.4.10 into 3.4.9 yields:

$$dF = \rho ghdA \tag{3.4.11}$$

which upon integration for h = constant leads to the relation:

$$F = \rho ghA \tag{3.4.12}$$

(2) *Flat vertical surface:*
Equation 3.4.11 is applied again, yielding:

$$dF = \rho ghdA \tag{3.4.13}$$

or

$$F = \rho g \int_{h_1}^{h_2} hdA \tag{3.4.14}$$

where the hydrostatic head h now varies over the surface area and it is recognized that for a plate of width W, dA = Wdh. We also recognize that $\int hdA = h_{cg}A$, where

h_{cg} is the centroidal distance, or the distance of the center of gravity of the plate from the fluid surface. We then obtain for the total force F the abbreviated expression:

$$F = \rho g h_{cg} A \tag{3.4.15}$$

Suppose, for example, that the vertical surface is a rectangular wall of height H = 10 m and width W = 1 m, with the upper edge 10 m below the water surface. The centroid of the rectangle will be at mid-height and its distance from the water surface $h_{cg} = 10 + 5 = 15$ m. Hence the total (horizontal) force acting on the submerged wall is

$$F = \rho g h_{cg} HW = (1000)(9.81)(15)(10)(1) = 1.47 \text{ MN}$$

(3) Arbitrary surfaces:
Integration of the Expression 3.4.11 over curved and other surfaces of arbitrary shape can be cumbersome, even after decomposing the total force F into horizontal and vertical components F_h and f_v. The difficulty can be circumvented by applying the following two simple rules:

1. The horizontal force component F_h equals the force on the area A_p formed by projecting the surface onto a vertical plane. Thus,

$$F_h = \rho g (h_{cg})_p A_p \tag{3.4.16}$$

where $(h_{cg})_p$ = distance of the centroid of the projected area to the surface.
2. The vertical force component F_v equals the weight of the entire column of fluid W_f, both liquid and atmosphere, resting on the submerged surface. Thus,

$$F_v = W_f \tag{3.4.17}$$

The total force is then obtained as the square root of the sum of squares:

$$F = (F_h^2 + F_v^2) \tag{3.4.18}$$

Suppose, for example, that the vertical plate considered previously is now inclined with an angle $\alpha = 30°$ to the water surface. The projected area A_p is then HW sin $\alpha = (10)(1) \sin 30° = 5$ m². The centroidal distance $(h_{cg})_p$ is the same as before and we obtain:

$$F_h = \rho p (h_{cg})_p A_p = (1000)(9.81)(15)(5) = 0.74 \text{ MN}$$

i.e., one-half the value for the vertical plane.

(4) Archimides' law:
It is now possible to give a simple explanation of Archimides' law. For a submerged body of arbitrary shape, the horizontal component $F_h = 0$, since the

projections to the left and right side vertical planes will have the same area A_p and centroidal distance h_{cg} but with associated forces of opposite sign. We are left with the vertical component F_v which will be the difference between the fluid weights resting on the upper and lower surfaces of the body, W_1 and W_2. We, therefore, obtain:

$$F = F_v = W_2 - W_1 =$$
Weight of fluid contained in the volume of the body   (3.4.19)

This in effect confirms Archimides' law which states that the vertical force, or buoyancy, equals the weight of the displaced fluid.

Illustration 3.4.2   Forces Acting on a Pressurized Container: The Hoop-Stress Formula

In the design of pressure vessels, such as gas cylinders, one wishes to know the minimum wall thickness required to withstand a given internal pressure. That internal pressure would have to overcome the tensile strength or stress τ_t of the material to rupture the vessel. To prevent rupture, the forces due to the tensile strength and the pressure must, at a minimum, be in balance. Integration of the forces over the surface can be avoided by making use of the fact that the net force due to the pressure equals the force acting on the *projected* area of the vessel surface. This can be shown, i.e., for a cylinder, by integration of the component force $pLR \sin \alpha$ so that:

$$F_{net} = pLR \int_{2\pi}^{0} \sin \alpha \, d\alpha = 2pRL \qquad (3.4.20)$$

where $2RL = dL$ is seen to be the projection of the cylinder surface onto a plane. Equating this force to the tensile force holding the vessel together we obtain, for a cylinder and sphere respectively,

Cylinder $p = \tau_t \dfrac{\Delta d}{d}$ (3.4.21)

Sphere $p = 4\tau_t \dfrac{\Delta d}{d}$ (3.4.22)

where Δd is taken to be the wall thickness. These are the so-called *hoop stress formulae* for the cylinder and sphere that are the most commonly encountered geometries. One notes that the sphere can accommodate a permissible pressure four times that of the cylinder. This fact is often taken advantage of in the design of pressure vessels. Note also that the allowable pressure for a particular vessel varies inversely with diameter. For high pressure applications, therefore, it is preferable to use small diameter containers in order to avoid excessively thick walls (Δd) with an attendant increase in weight. Table 3.15 lists some representative values of tensile

TABLE 3.15
Tensile Strength of Metals and Alloys

Metal/Alloy	Tensile Strength τ_t (MPa)
Aluminum alloys	100–325
Aluminum alloy 360	325
Beryllium copper 25	500–1400
Inconel	800
Lead	17
Nickel	460
Steel (carbon)	450
Steel (stainless 304)	550

strength for various metals. They range from 17 MPa for the softest metal, lead, to over 1000 Mpa for beryllium copper.

To obtain an idea of the required wall thickness in pressure vessels, we consider a standard commercial nitrogen cylinder. Such cylinders and those of other permanent gases (hydrogen, oxygen, argon, helium) are usually made of carbon steel, have diameters of approximately 0.15 m, and are typically filled to a pressure of 15 Mpa. Equation 3.4.21 then yields $\Delta d = pd/\tau_t = (15)(0.15/450) = 0.5$ cm. This is the minimum required thickness. In practice it will be augmented by a safety factor of at least 2. Aluminum alloys that would meet the tensile strength requirements and make for much lighter cylinders, have not come into general use for pressure vessels, in part because of their higher cost.

Illustration 3.4.3   The Effects of Surface Tension:
Laplace's Equation; Capillary Rise

A liquid being unable to expand freely like a gas will form an interface with a second liquid or a gas. This arises essentially because within the liquid interior, molecules are densely packed and repel each other while at the surface; with half the neighbors missing, the packing is looser and the molecules attract one another. The net effect is that the surface is under tension, the tensile attractive forces counterbalancing the repulsive forces which prevail in the interior (Figure 3.10). The quantity which characterizes this effect is the surface tension γ, with units of N/m or Nm/m^2. The latter unit reveals that surface tension is equivalent to the energy to form or eliminate a unit area of surface. Values of γ for various liquids are summarized in Table 3.16 and generally range from 2×10^{-2} to 8×10^{-2} N/m, the higher values corresponding to polar liquids with stronger attractive forces due to hydrogen bonding. For liquid metals, e.g, mercury, those forces are even larger, leading to surface tensions that are an order of magnitude higher than normal.

As a consequence of surface tension, a liquid in contact with a solid surface will have a contact angle θ with that solid, as shown in Figure 3.10C. If $\theta < 90°$, the internal attractive forces are small and the liquid is said to wet the solid; if θ is in the range 90 to 180°, the liquid is termed nonwetting. Water and organic solvents

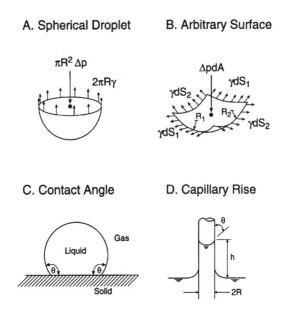

FIGURE 3.10 Aspects of surface tension: (A) balance of forces in a spherical droplet, (B) balance of forces in an arbitrary surface, (C) contact angle for a nonwetting liquid, (D) capillary rise of a wetting liquid.

are extremely wetting in contact with clean glass, with $\theta \approx 0$. Mercury, on the other hand, has a high contact angle of $\theta = 130°$ due to its abnormally large surface tension, i.e., high internal attractive forces. Surface tension and contact angle depend on the nature of the surface. Thus, water will wet clean glass, but not wax, which is hydrophobic. In the former case, the strong hydrophilic nature of the glass will overcome the internal attractive forces of the water and cause spreading. On hydrophobic surfaces, water droplets maintain their integrity.

Laplace's Equation — A second consequence of surface tension is that the interior pressure caused by the repulsive forces is higher than the exterior (usually

TABLE 3.16
Surface Tension of Various Liquids at 20°C and in Contact with Air

Liquid	Surface Tension γ (N/m)
Benzene	2.9×10^{-2}
Carbon tetrachloride	2.7×10^{-2}
Ethanol	2.3×10^{-2}
Gasoline	2.2×10^{-2}
Glycerine	6.3×10^{-2}
Mercury	4.8×10^{-1}
SAE 10 oil	3.6×10^{-2}
Water	7.3×10^{-2}

atmospheric) force and is precisely balanced by the surface tensile force. Thus, for a spherical droplet (see Figure 3.10A):

$$\frac{\pi d^2}{4}\Delta p \quad = \quad \pi d\gamma$$

$$\text{Pressure Force} \qquad \text{Tensile Force}$$

(3.4.23)

so that

$$p_{int} - p_{ext} = \Delta p = 4\gamma/d \tag{3.4.24}$$

This equation can be generalized to an arbitrary curved surface and terms of its principal (and orthogonal) radii of curvature, and is then known as Laplace's equation (see Figure 3.10B):

$$\Delta p = \gamma\left[\frac{1}{R_1}+\frac{1}{R_2}\right] = 2\gamma\left[\frac{1}{d_1}+\frac{1}{d_2}\right] \tag{3.4.25}$$

Capillary Rise — Yet another consequence of surface tension is that the tendency to spread in contact with a solid causes liquids with $\theta < 90°$ to rise in capillary tubes. The physical situation is depicted in Figure 3.10D. A vertical force balance for this configuration leads to the equation:

$$\pi d\gamma\cos\theta \quad = \quad \rho g h\frac{\pi d^2}{4}$$

$$\text{Tensile Force} \qquad \text{Gravitational Force}$$

(3.4.26)

or

$$h = \frac{4\gamma\cos\theta}{\rho g d} \tag{3.4.27}$$

For $\theta > 90$, $\cos\theta < 0$, hence h is negative and a depression results.

Capillary rise is the means by which nutrients dissolved in water are conveyed to the upper reaches of a plant or tree. Let us calculate the diameter of capillary required to convey water to the top of a full-grown tree, h = 10 m. The water will be in contact with hydrophilic cell material so that we can assume, as a first approximation, $\theta \approx 0$. We obtain from Equation 3.4.27:

$$d = \frac{4\gamma}{\rho g h} = \frac{(4)(7.3\times10^{-2})}{(1000)(9.81)(10)} = 2.98\times10^{-6}\ m$$

Thus, a cellular capillary of the order 3 microns in diameter will convey the water to the required height.

Illustration 3.4.4   The Hypsometric Formulae

The hypsometric formulae are expressions that relate pressure and temperature to atmospheric altitude. Before precise measurements of T and p became available, this relation was established by combining the differential form of the fundamental equation of fluid statics, Equation 3.4.10, with the adiabatic equation of state, Equation 3.3.77 (see also Practice Problem 3.4.4). Actual measurements of atmospheric temperatures revealed a more complex relation to exist than that obtained by assuming adiabatic expansion of the air. While pressure declines smoothly and exponentially with altitude, temperature is less predictable, one might even say erratic. Its variation can be broken up into the following regions.

In the so-called troposphere, i.e., up to an altitude of 11 km, a simple linear relation applies:

$$T(K) = T_0 - Bz \qquad (3.4.28)$$

where $T_0 = 288.16$ K (15°C) and $B = 6.5 \times 10^{-3}$ K/m.

Between 11 and 20.1 km, the temperature remains constant at -56.5°C, whereupon a reversal occurs which causes it to rise to ~ –3°C at an altitude of approximately 48 km. It remains at that level up to 52 km, after which it resumes a rapid linear decline.

To obtain a relation between pressure and altitude in the troposphere, we introduce the temperature–altitude relation (Equation 3.4.28) into the differential form of Equation 3.4.10 and obtain:

$$dp = -\rho g dz = -\frac{p}{RT} g\, dz \qquad (3.4.29)$$

or

$$dp = -\frac{pg}{R(T_0 - Bz)}\, dz$$

which yields, after integrating by separation of variables:

$$p = p_0\left(1 - \frac{Bz}{T_0}\right)^{g/RB} \qquad (3.4.30)$$

where $g/RB = 5.26$ for air. This is the hypsometric formula for pressure, applicable up to altitudes of 11 km.

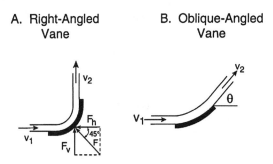

FIGURE 3.11   Fluid forces on stationary vanes of different inclinations.

Let us as an example calculate the conditions which prevail at an altitude of 3000 m. From Equation 3.4.28, we obtain:

$$T = 288.16 - (6.5 \times 10^{-3})(3000) = 268.66 \text{ K}$$

i.e., approximately –5°C, and from Equation 3.4.30:

$$p = 101.3\left[1 - \frac{(6.5 \times 10^{-3})(3000)}{288.16}\right]^{5.26} = 70.1 \text{ kPa}$$

Similar calculations for the upper end of the troposphere, z = 11 km, yield a value of p = 22.6 kPa, i.e., the pressure will at this point have dropped to approximately one-fifth of an atmosphere. Action movies depicting decompression of airliners give a graphical description of the effect of this drop.

Illustration 3.4.5   Momentum Changes in a Flowing Fluid: Forces on a Stationary Vane

We start by considering the rate at which momentum M is carried by a fluid in steady flow. That quantity is given by:

$$\overset{r}{F} = \frac{dM}{dt} = Fv = \rho Qv \tag{3.4.31}$$

where F and Q are the usual mass and volumetric flow rate, and **F** the vectorial force associated with the momentum flow dM/dt.

Consider a fluid jet of cross-sectional area A = 10^{-2} m² flowing at a volumetric flow rate Q = 10^{-2} m³/s, impinging on a 90° vane as shown in Figure 3.11. We decompose **F** into horizontal and vertical components F_h and F_v and perform an integral momentum balance on each. Thus,

Horizontal component F_h:

$$\text{Rate of momentum in} - \text{Rate of momentum out} = \text{Force}$$

$$\rho Q v_h - 0 = F_h \tag{3.4.32}$$

and we obtain:

$$F_h = \rho Q \, Q/A = (1000)(10^{-4})/10^{-2} = 10 \text{ N}$$

Vertical component F_v:

$$\text{Rate of momentum in} - \text{Rate of momentum out} = \text{Force}$$

$$0 - \rho Q v_v = F_v \tag{3.4.33}$$

so that:

$$F_v = -\rho Q \, Q/A = (1000) \, 10^{-4}/10^{-2} = -10 \text{ N}$$

The total force F_t equals the square root of the sum of squares of the components, which yields:

$$F_t = \sqrt{F_h^2 + F_v^2} = \sqrt{10^2 + (-10)^2} = 14.1 \text{N}$$

Consider next a similar vane whose upper part is inclined with an angle $\theta = 30°$. The associated component forces are

Horizontal component F_h:

$$\text{Rate of momentum in} - \text{Rate of momentum out} = \text{Force}$$

$$\rho Q v_h - \rho Q v_h \cos\theta = F_h$$

so that:

$$F_h = \rho Q \, (Q/A)(1 - \cos\theta) = 1000 \, (10^{-4}/10^{-2}) \, (1 - 0.866) = 1.34 \text{ N}$$

Vertical component F_v:

$$\text{Rate of momentum in} - \text{Rate of momentum out} = \text{Force}$$

$$0 - \rho Q v_v \sin\theta = F_v$$

and

$$F_v = -\rho Q (Q/A) \sin\theta = -1000 (10^{-4}/10^{-2}) \frac{1}{2} = -5 \text{N}$$

We have:

$$F_t = \sqrt{F_h{}^2 + F_v{}^2} = \sqrt{1.34^2 + (-5)^2} = 5.18\,\text{N}$$

As expected, this force is considerably less than that experienced by a 90° vane.

Illustration 3.4.6   Particle Movement in a Fluid

The behavior of particles rising or falling through a fluid, or in suspension in a flowing medium, represents yet another classical example of the application of a force balance. A distinction is made between the steady-state in which the sum of forces is zero and the unsteady state which requires inclusion of an acceleration term. A particle released in a medium of higher density will commence to rise with a steadily increasing velocity and attendant increase in the drag force. A state is ultimately reached when that force is exactly in balance with the gravity and buoyancy forces. The particle is then said to have attained its terminal velocity. A body falling in a medium of higher density undergoes a similar period of acceleration and ultimate attainment of a steady velocity. In the third case considered, that of a particle in suspension, the steady-state is assumed to have already been attained and the sum of forces is equal to zero.

Steady-State — The forces in balance to be considered here are three-fold: gravity force F_g, buoyancy force F_b, and drag force F_d. We first examine the case of a falling particle in which the gravity force F_g acts downward, and F_b and F_d act upward. We obtain:

$$\Sigma \text{ Forces} = 0 \tag{3.4.34}$$

or

$$F_g - F_d - F_b = 0$$

and expanding these terms by appropriate auxiliary relation,

$$\underset{\text{Gravity}}{V_p \rho_p g} - \underset{\text{Drag}}{C_D \rho_f A_c \frac{v_t^2}{2}} - \underset{\text{Buoyancy}}{V_p \rho_f g} = 0 \tag{3.4.35}$$

Here the subscripts $_p$ and $_f$ denote properties of the particle and fluid, respectively, and A_c is the cross-sectional area of the particle at right angles to the direction of motion. This equation applies to a particle suspended in a flowing fluid as well. For a rising particle $\rho_f > \rho_s$, and the sign of the drag force is reversed. Grouping together the terms dependent on terminal velocity v_t, Equation 3.4.35 yields the following expressions for the various cases considered:

Falling particle and particle in suspension:

$$C_D v_t^2 = \frac{2 V_p g}{A_c} \left(\frac{\rho_p - \rho_f}{\rho_f} \right) \tag{3.4.36}$$

Rising particle:

$$C_D v_t^2 = \frac{2 V_p g}{A_c} \left(\frac{\rho_f - \rho_p}{\rho_f} \right) \tag{3.4.37}$$

Equations 3.4.34 to 3.4.37 have general validity irrespective of the flow regime or the geometry of the particle.

Let us now consider a specific case, that of a falling or suspended sphere, and introduce the drag coefficients listed in Table 3.14 for the laminar regime, $C_D = 24/Re$ and that for the turbulent regime, $C_D = 0.44$. We obtain, taking $g = 9.81$ m²/s into account,

Laminar region, Re < 0.1:

$$v_t = 0.545 \frac{\rho_f}{\mu} d^2 \left(\frac{\rho_p - \rho_f}{\rho_f} \right) \tag{3.4.38}$$

Turbulent region, 500 < Re < 2 × 10⁵:

$$v_t = 5.45 \left[d \left(\frac{\rho_p - \rho_f}{\rho_f} \right) \right]^{1/2} \tag{3.4.39}$$

We first note that in both the laminar and turbulent cases the terminal velocity or fluid velocity required to keep a particle in suspension is proportional to the diameter of the sphere, although only weakly so in the turbulent regime. This is in agreement with the conventional wisdom that "larger bodies fall faster." Viscosity plays a role in the laminar region as expected, and the quotient $(\rho_p - \rho_f)/\rho_f$ may be regarded as a dimensionless "driving force" for the falling particle in both laminar and turbulent reactions.

A second point to note is that the two variables of greatest interest, D and v_t, appear in combination in the Reynolds number. Thus, with only one of them specified (which is the usual case), one cannot determine the Reynolds number and, hence, the flow regime and pertinent drag coefficient C_D. In most practical cases it is, therefore, difficult to decide which of the two equations (3.4.38 or 3.4.39) is applicable, or whether one is located in the transition regime between the two cases.

One can circumvent this difficulty by introducing the lower limits of validity of the drag coefficients (see Table 3.14) into rearranged forms of Equations 3.4.38 and

3.4.39, and using the result to establish upper and lower bounds on the terminal velocities or diameters in each regime. For example, to establish the upper bound for the diameter of a sphere falling in water in the laminar region, we obtain, in the first instance:

$$v_t d = 0.545 \frac{\rho_f}{\mu} d^3 \left(\frac{\rho_p - \rho_f}{\rho_f} \right) \qquad (3.4.40)$$

where $v_t d$ has to satisfy the relation $Re < 0.1$ and, hence, using a kinematic viscosity for water $v = \mu/\rho_f = 10^{-6}$ m²/s, the inequality:

$$v_t d < 10^{-7} \text{ m}^2/\text{s} \qquad (3.4.41)$$

Combining Equations 3.4.40 and 3.4.41, it follows that the diameter has to fulfill the condition:

$$d^3 < \frac{1}{0.545} \times 10^{-13} \left(\frac{\rho_f}{\rho_p - \rho_f} \right) \qquad (3.4.42)$$

whence there results:

$$d < 6.04 \times 10^{-5} \left(\frac{\rho_f}{\rho_p - \rho_f} \right)^{1/3} \text{ m} \qquad (3.4.43)$$

We have done similar calculations for d in the turbulent region and for v in both the laminar and turbulent regions, and summarize the results in Table 3.17.

For water, one can assume the density ratio $\left(\frac{\rho_f}{\rho_p - \rho_f} \right)^{1/3}$ to be of the order of one. It follows that for the laminar region Equation 3.4.38 to apply, the particle diameter has to be less than about 0.06 mm; for the turbulent Equation 3.4.39 to apply, greater than about 2 mm. Similar statements can be made for particles falling in air and for the bounds on velocity. One notes that the regions inbetween the two regimes, which is the transition region, encompasses some two orders of magnitude in both velocity and diameter. Table 3.17 serves the useful purpose of providing a range of diameters and velocities that span the transition region. If, for example, the given diameter of a sphere is 10^{-4} m = 0.1 mm, the table signals that the transition region applies. One can then substitute the transition relation $C_D = 18.5/Re^{3/5}$ (see Table 3.14) into Equation 3.4.36 and solve for the desired velocity.

The Unsteady-State and Approach to Steady-State — It is frequently necessary in problems involving rising or falling particles to calculate distance traveled in a given time, or conversely, the time necessary to travel a given distance. In problems involving settling tanks, for example, one may wish to know the time necessary for

TABLE 3.17
Bounds on Diameter and Terminal Velocity for a Sphere Falling in Water and Air

Regime	Velocity (m/s)	Diameter (m)
Water		
Laminar	$v_t < 1.8 \times 10^{-3} \left(\dfrac{\rho_p - \rho_f}{\rho_f} \right)^{1/3}$	$d < 5.7 \times 10^{-5} \left(\dfrac{\rho_f}{\rho_p - \rho_f} \right)^{1/3}$
Turbulent	$v_t > 0.25 \left(\dfrac{\rho_p - \rho_f}{\rho_f} \right)^{1/3}$	$d > 2.0 \times 10^{-3} \left(\dfrac{\rho_f}{\rho_p - \rho_f} \right)^{1/3}$
Air		
Laminar	$v_t < 4.4 \times 10^{-3} \left(\dfrac{\rho_p - \rho_f}{\rho_f} \right)^{1/3}$	$d < 3.6 \times 10^{-4} \left(\dfrac{\rho_f}{\rho_p - \rho_f} \right)^{1/3}$
Turbulent	$v_t > 0.02 \left(\dfrac{\rho_p - \rho_f}{\rho_f} \right)^{1/3}$	$d > 1.3 \times 10^{-2} \left(\dfrac{\rho_f}{\rho_p - \rho_f} \right)^{1/3}$

a particle of given size to settle to the bottom, i.e., to fall a given distance (see Practice Problem 3.4.7). In Practice Problem 1.2, a marker particle to be used by divers was to be designed which would rise with a given steady velocity. Here again it would be desirable to know the length of time the particle spends in the unsteady state, so that deviations from the desired design velocity can be assessed.

To model the unsteady-state, full use must be made of Newton's law, i.e., an acceleration term has to be added to the previous steady-state balance. Thus, for falling particles,

$$F_g - F_d - F_b = m \frac{dv}{dt} \tag{3.4.44}$$

Expansion in terms of the usual auxiliary relation then yields:

$$V_p \rho_p g - C_D \rho_f A_c \frac{v^2}{2} - V_p \rho_f g = \rho_p V_p \frac{dv}{dt} \tag{3.4.45}$$

which can be formally integrated to yield the time dependence of the velocity. If the particle ultimately reaches its terminal velocity in the turbulent region, integration of C_D would have to take account of the full spectrum of C_D variations with Reynolds number, i.e., velocity. We circumvent this difficulty by considering the limiting case of laminar flow. This not only describes the behavior of particles that fall entirely in the laminar region but also provides an upper bound to the time involved and a lower bound to the distance traveled.

Integration by separation of variables of Equation 3.4.45 then yields:

$$t = -\frac{1}{B}\ln\left(1 - \frac{B}{A}v\right) \qquad (3.4.46)$$

where

$$A = \frac{\rho_p - \rho_f}{\rho_p}g, \quad B = 18\frac{\mu}{\rho_p d^2}$$

Comparison with the laminar flow Equation 3.4.36 shows that $B/A = 1/v_t$, i.e., the inverse of the steady-state terminal velocity. Hence, Equation 3.4.46 becomes:

$$t = -\frac{\rho_f d^2}{18\mu}\ln\left(1 - \frac{v}{v_t}\right) \qquad (3.4.47)$$

To obtain a sense of the order of magnitude of the times involved, consider a sphere of density $\rho_p = 2000$ kg/w^3 and diameter just below the upper bound given in Table 3.18, $d = 10^{-5}$ m, falling through water. For a 95% approach to the steady-state terminal velocity, we obtain:

$$t = -\frac{(2000)(10^{-5})^2}{(18)(10^{-3})}\ln(1 - 0.95) = 3.3 \times 10^{-5}\text{ s}$$

In general calculations for other cases, such as falling through air or when all three flow regimes are involved, show that the times required to attain the steady-state terminal velocity are quite short and can often be neglected in calculations involving falling or rising particles.

TABLE 3.18
Representative Ranges of Velocities in Steel Pipes

Type of Fluid	Type of Flow	v, m/s
Nonviscous liquid	Inlet to pump	0.6–0.9
	Process line or pump discharge	1.5–2.5
Viscous liquid	Inlet to pump	0.06–0.25
	Process line or pump discharge	0.15–0.6
Gas		9–36
Steam		9–23

Source: From C.J. Geankoplis. *Transport Processes and Unit Operations,* Allyn and Bacon, Boston, 1978. With permission.

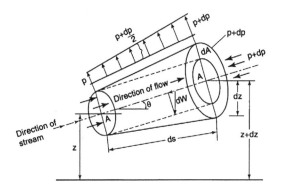

FIGURE 3.12   Derivation of Bernoulli's equation.

Illustration 3.4.7   The Bernoulli Equation:
Some Simple Applications
It is not often realized that the celebrated Bernoulli equation and its extension, the
mechanical energy balance (see Illustration 3.4.8), in fact, are force balances. The
reason they are often viewed as energy balances is due to the fact that the terms
appearing in them have units of energy/mass. Those units arise in the final manipulations of the equation and lead to a form of greater convenience.

The Bernoulli equation can be derived in different ways. One can proceed "from
the top down," i.e., one can start with the general three-dimensional viscous flow
force balance, the Navier-Stokes equations, and after various simplifications, including the imposition of the so-called irrotational flow condition (essentially equivalent
to frictionless flow) arrive at the Bernoulli equation. This approach has the advantage
of resulting in a more general form of the equation which can be applied to any two
points of the flow field and is taken up in Chapter 8. Here we approach the problem
"from the bottom up" by starting with a one-dimensional force balance along a
stream tube, shown in Figure 3.12. The following assumptions are made:

1. Flow is steady, i.e., the variables involved change with distance only.
2. The fluid is inviscid, i.e., friction forces are neglected.
3. No work is done by or on the fluid.

With these assumptions in place the only forces to be considered are those due
to pressure, gravity, and momentum. We take these up in turn.

Gravity — Here the component of the gravity component or weight in the vertical

direction is taken, using an average cross-sectional area of $\left(A + \dfrac{dA}{2} \right)$. Thus,

$$dF_g = -\left(A + \frac{dA}{2} \right) ds \, \rho \, g \sin \theta \qquad (3.4.48)$$

or, neglecting the second order differential,

$$dF_g = -A \, \rho \, g \, dz \qquad (3.4.49)$$

Momentum — Since the flow is steady and there is no change in direction, no velocity components need to be considered and one obtains directly, using Equation 3.4.31:

$$dF_m = -\rho Q \, dv = -\rho A \, v \, dv \qquad (3.4.50)$$

Pressure — A subtlety enters the picture here. In addition to the pressure forces acting on each cross-sectional area, there is a pressure force along the slanted tube walls that has a streamwise component $\left(p + \dfrac{dp}{2}\right) dA$ (see Figure 3.12). The net pressure force is then given by:

$$dF_p = Ap + \left(p + \frac{dp}{2}\right) dA - (p + dp)(A + dA) \qquad (3.4.51)$$

which, upon neglecting second order differentials becomes:

$$dF_p = -A \, dp \qquad (3.4.52)$$

Collecting terms and dividing by $A\rho$, we obtain the following differential form of the Bernoulli equation:

$$\frac{dp}{\rho} + v \, dv + g \, dz = 0 \qquad (3.4.53)$$

We note that the equation applies to both incompressible and compressible flow. For the former, $\rho = $ constant, and one obtains by direct integration:

$$\frac{p_2 - p_1}{\rho} + \frac{v_2^{\,2} - v_1^{\,2}}{2} + g(z_2 - z_1) = 0 \qquad (3.4.54)$$

For compressible flow, the variation of density with pressure has to be taken into account using an appropriate equation of state. This is taken up in the Section 3.6 on simultaneous mass, energy, and momentum balances.

Equation 3.4.54 is sometimes cast in the form:

$$\frac{p}{\rho g z} + \frac{v^2}{2 g z} + z = \text{constant} \qquad (3.4.55)$$

which states that the sum of pressure, kinetic and potential energy per unit mass is constant along a specified stream tube. This has led to the erroneous conclusion that Bernoulli's equation is derived from an energy balance.

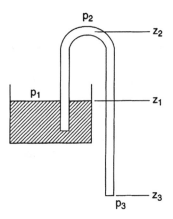

FIGURE 3.13   Pressures and elevations in a siphon.

An important result of Equation 3.4.55 is that an increase in elevation z (at constant v) or an increase in velocity v (at constant z) causes a *decrease* in pressure. This qualitative relation, sometimes referred to as the Bernoulli effect, has many important practical consequences. Flow around an airfoil or airplane wing increases in velocity along the upper surface because of its bulging curvature, while velocity along the lower surface remains essentially constant. As a consequence, pressure along the top is less than along the bottom surface and it is this difference in pressure forces that provides the necessary lift for the aircraft. Another example is the velocity increase that results from a constriction in a conduit. The associated drop in pressure is used among other things to measure flow rate (Venturi and orifice meter) or to create a vacuum (jet pump or aspirator, see example below). We now consider some elementary applications of the Bernoulli equation.

The Syphon — This simple device, known from everyday life, is used to empty containers which cannot be conveniently moved. The sketch in Figure 3.13 shows the pertinent elevations and pressures. We apply Bernoulli's equation to locations 1 and 3, noting that $p_1 = p_3 = 1$ atm, hence, $\Delta p = 0$, and that $v_1^2/2g \approx 0$, i.e., negligible compared to $v_2^2/2g$. One obtains:

$$z_1 - z_3 = \frac{v_3^{\,2}}{2g} = \frac{(Q/A)^2}{2g} \qquad (3.4.56)$$

This result shows that in order to have a positive flow rate $Q > 0$, the difference in elevation must be positive, i.e., $z_1 > z_3$. This is, of course, well known to anyone who has successfully used a syphon. The above provides the scientific explanation for the phenomenon.

A comment is appropriate regarding conditions at location 2. The pressure here will be less than 1 atm, but usually not by much since z_2 is only marginally above z_1 in most applications. If circumstances force the use of higher values of z_2, a point may be reached where p_2 equals the vapor pressure of the liquid. When this occurs, partial vaporization takes place, resulting in a so-called vapor lock, and flow ceases.

For water, which has a vapor pressure of 3.2 kPa at 25°C, this occurs at an elevation difference of $z_1 - z_3 \sim 9.7$ m. For more volatile liquids with higher vapor pressures, the height required is much less, and it is here that some caution must be exercised. We note that a similar phenomenon occurs when a pump inlet is located much higher than the system inlet. To prevent this from happening, pumps are usually positioned close to the system inlet.

Jet Pumps: Aspirators — In these devices, a drop in pressure is artificially induced by constricting the conduit carrying the flowing liquid. We consider the case where the upstream diameter is 3 cm, and the constriction diameter 0.3 cm, i.e., a reduction by a factor of 10. Water flow at $Q = 5 \times 10^{-4}$ m³/s is used, with an upstream pressure p_1 of 110 kPa. We wish to calculate the resulting pressure at the constriction, p_2. Applying Bernoulli's equation to the two points we obtain:

$$\frac{v_2^2 - v_1^2}{2} = \frac{p_1 - p_2}{\rho} \tag{3.4.57}$$

or, using $Q = Av$, and solving for p_2:

$$p_2 = p_1 - \frac{\rho Q^2}{2gA_1^2}\left(\frac{d_1^4}{d_2^4} - 1\right) = 1.1 \times 10^{-5} - \frac{10^3 \times 10^{-8}(10^{-4} - 1)}{2\pi^2 0.03^4 / 16} \tag{3.4.58}$$

$$p_2 = 1.1 \times 10^{-5} - 10^{-5} = 10^4 \text{ Pa}$$

i.e., the pressure has been reduced to one-eleventh its original value.

One can, in principle, by increasing flow rate or the diameter ratio d_1/d_2 reduce the pressure to zero. A limiting factor intervenes, however, which is the vapor pressure of the liquid. A water aspirator running with cold water at 6°C could at best produce a vacuum equal to the water vapor pressure at that temperature, i.e., 0.94 kPa. This still represents a hundred-fold decrease in ambient pressure. To circumvent this limitation, devices called diffusion pumps are available which utilize liquids of low vapor pressure, such as mercury or specialty oils, as the driving fluid. The liquid is recirculated by first vaporizing it, then condensing the vapor in a vertical water cooled condenser and allowing the condensate to pass through the constriction by gravity. A vacuum as low as 10^{-8} atm can be achieved by this method.

Discharge from a Tank — We consider here the discharge of a liquid through a nozzle attached to the side of a tank, as shown in Figure 3.14. If the ratio of nozzle and tank diameters is small, which is usually the case, one can neglect the velocity term at location 1, as was done in the case of the syphon. Similarly, one can again set $p_1 = p_2 = p_{atm}$, so that the only terms remaining in the Bernoulli equation are those due to the exit velocity v_2 and the change in elevation Δz. The liquid level is assumed to be constant. One then obtains:

$$v_2 = (2g\, \Delta z)^{1/2} \tag{3.4.59}$$

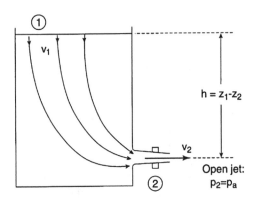

FIGURE 3.14   Operating variables in the gravitational discharge of a liquid from a tank.

This formula, discovered by Torricelli in 1644 and expressed by him in a theorem, states that the discharge velocity equals the speed which a frictionless particle in free fall would attain. In other words the potential energy of the surface fluid is entirely converted into kinetic energy at the exit which is consistent with the absence of friction and pressure work.

Illustration 3.4.8   The Mechanical Energy Balance

Bernoulli's equation provides a good deal of important qualitative information, as well as near quantitative results if the locations in the flow field considered are close enough, and the fluid has a low viscosity. When this no longer applies, the effect of friction has to be taken into account by formally incorporating the Fanning equation (Equation 3.4.5) into the Bernoulli equation and at the same time including so-called shaft work w_s done by a pump or on a turbine. This leads to the so-called mechanical energy balance, which from incompressible flow takes the form:

$$\frac{\Delta p}{\rho} + \Delta \frac{v^2}{2} + g\Delta z - \frac{4fv^2}{2}\frac{L}{d} \pm w_s = 0 \qquad (3.4.60)$$

where Δp now includes the effect of friction.

A number of points relevant to the use of Equation 3.4.60 are noted.

First, we encounter again the dilemma we had seen in connection with the drag coefficient C_D. With either one of v or d unknown, the Reynolds number and the associated friction factor cannot be calculated. Hence, Equation 3.4.60 cannot be applied to calculate required pressure drop or shaft work. The convenient upper and lower bounds on d and v we had provided for falling particles (see Table 3.18) cannot be duplicated easily here, and one must be resorted to a trial and error procedure. For example, given the velocity v, one starts by assuming a diameter, calculates the associated friction head h_f, and compares the result with the diameter obtained from the Fanning equation for a known flow rate Q. Thus,

$$h_f = 4f \frac{v^2}{2} \frac{L}{d} = \frac{64}{\pi^2} f \frac{Q^2}{2} \frac{L}{d^5} \tag{3.4.61}$$

and

$$d = \left(3.2f \frac{Q^2}{\pi^2 h_f} L \right)^{1/2} \tag{3.4.62}$$

As a guideline for these calculations, we have provided in Table 3.19, a listing of typical velocity ranges for flow in steel pipes which eases the work considerably.

A second point that needs to be addressed is the friction loss due to fittings and valves. These are expressed either as equivalent kinetic energy terms $h_f = K \cdot v^2/2$ or equivalent dimensionless pipe lengths L_f/d. The two quantities are then added to the kinetic energy or friction terms in the mechanical energy balance.

Representative values for K and L_f/d are given in Table 3.19. It is evident that the effects are not negligible, ranging from 0.1 m to 100 m and more in the case of a ball valve. In intricate networks with many valves and fittings they can quickly become the overriding factor in determining friction losses.

The final point to be considered concerns the friction losses in noncircular ducts or conduits which are not running full. It is customary in these cases to introduce an effective or hydraulic diameter d_h and use it in the calculation of Reynolds number and friction losses. d_h is defined as follows:

$$d_h = \frac{4 \text{ cross-sectional area of flow}}{\text{wetted perimeter of channel}} \tag{3.4.63}$$

TABLE 3.19
Friction Losses for Turbulent Flow Through Valves and Fittings

Type of Fittings/Valves	Equivalent K	Equivalent L_f
Elbow 90°	0.75	35
Tee	1.0	50
Gate valve		
Wide open	0.17	9
Half open	4.5	225
Globe valve		
Wide open	6.0	300
Half open	9.5	475
Ball valve	70	3500
Entrance	0.5	25
Exit	1.0	50

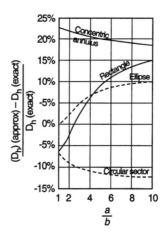

FIGURE 3.15   Correction factors to be applied to hydraulic diameter d_h for calculation of pressure drop in laminar duct flow. (F.M. White. *Viscous Fluid Flow,* McGraw-Hill, New York, 1974. With permission.)

The procedure works well for turbulent flow and for laminar flow in circular pipes. For other geometries carrying laminar flow, deviations from the results obtained using Equation 3.4.63 occur. The degree of deviation and the correction to be applied can be deduced from Figure 3.15.

We conclude this section with a simple example demonstrating the use of the mechanical energy — oil is to be pumped through a 10 cm diameter horizontal steel pipe over a distance of 15 km and at a rate of 10^{-3} m³/s. The kinematic viscosity of the oil is $v = \mu/\rho = 10^{-2}$ m²/s, and its density 750 kg/m³. It is desired to calculate the pressure drop and the required horsepower of the pump (1 hp = 0.746 kW).

We start by computing the Reynolds number to establish the flow regime. This yields:

$$Re = \frac{dv\rho}{\mu} = \frac{4Q}{\pi d^2 v} = \frac{4 \times 10^{-3}}{(\pi)(10^{-2})(10^{-2})} = 12.7$$

i.e., the flow is in the laminar regime.

Since both kinetic and potential energy changes are zero and there is no shaft work in the control volume considered, the mechanical energy equation reduces to the Fanning equation, so that:

$$\Delta p = 4 \frac{16}{Re} \rho \frac{v^2}{2} \frac{L}{d}$$

where $v = Q/A = 4 \times 10^{-3}/\pi \, 0.1^2 = 0.127$ m/s. We obtain:

$$\Delta p = \frac{(4)(16)}{12.7} \, 750 \, \frac{0.127^2}{2} \, \frac{15 \times 10^3}{0.1}$$

$$\Delta p = 4.57 \, \text{MPa}$$

The power required is obtained by multiplying the pressure drop by the volumetric flow rate so that:

$$P = 4.57 \times 10^3 \, \text{kPa} \times 10^{-3} \, \text{m}^3/\text{s} = 4.57 \, \text{kW} = 6.13 \, \text{hp}$$

Hence, a 6.5 horsepower motor is required as a minimum to drive the pump, not taking into account motor and pump efficiencies.

Illustration 3.4.9 Viscous Flow in a Parallel Plate Channel: Velocity Distribution and Flow Rate — Pressure Drop Relation

The forces operative in viscous or laminar flow can be defined with precision without recourse to empirical friction factors. They are the forces due to the pressure drop and that caused by the Newtonian shear stress (Equation 3.4.1).

We consider flow between two parallel plates held apart by two narrow vertical walls of height T. Because of their small dimension compared to that of the plates, frictional forces due to these walls are neglected. A force balance over a finite length L of a slit of height 2x then leads to the expression:

$$(p_1 - p_2)2xW = \tau 2LW = -\mu \frac{dv}{dx} 2LW \tag{3.4.64}$$

where W = width of the channel and x = distance from the center plane.

Integration by separation of variables yields in the first instance:

$$\frac{\Delta p}{\mu L} \frac{x^2}{2} = -v + C \tag{3.4.65}$$

where the integration constant $C = \dfrac{\Delta P}{\mu L} \dfrac{T^2}{8}$, is obtained from the so-called no-slip condition which states that the velocity at the wall, i.e., at x = T/2, is zero. The final result is then given by:

$$v(x) = \frac{\Delta P}{8\mu L} T^2 \left[1 - \left(\frac{2x}{T} \right)^2 \right] \tag{3.4.66}$$

This is a parabolic velocity distribution, symmetric about the center line, much like the profile obtained in viscous flow through a circular pipe, with x replacing radial distance r. The maximum velocity occurs at the centerline and is given by:

$$v_{Max} = \frac{\Delta p}{8\mu L} T^2 \qquad (3.4.67)$$

To obtain a flow rate-pressure drop relation which is the quantity of greatest interest in engineering calculations, the profile (Equation 3.4.66) is integrated over the cross-sectional area of flow to yield:

$$Q = \frac{\Delta p}{12\mu L} T^3 W \qquad (3.4.68)$$

It follows from this expression that the *average* velocity, equal to Q/TW, is given by:

$$v_{avg} = \frac{\Delta p}{12\mu L} T^2 = \frac{2}{3} v_{Max} \qquad (3.4.69)$$

Similar force balances can be performed for viscous flow in circular and annular conduits. The results are, for convenience, summarized in Table 3.20. One notes from these that in all cases pressure drop varies directly with flow rate Q, length of conduit L, and viscosity μ, but is inversely proportional to the fourth power of a linear dimension of the conduit or a combination thereof. For the circular pipe that dimension is the diameter, D_1; for the annulus, the outer diameter D_o; and for the parallel plate channel, a combination of channel height T and its width W.

We note that the force balances leading to these expressions are all of the one-dimensional type and yield simple ODEs which can be integrated by separation of variables. For flow in more complex geometries, such as rectangular, triangular, and elliptical channels, force balances in more than one dimension have to be performed, leading to PDEs. A discussion of these cases is taken up in Chapter 8.

Illustration 3.4.10   Non-Newtonian Fluids

Deviations from Newtonian behavior occur when the simple linear relation between shear stress τ and shear rate dv/dx expressed by Equation 3.4.1 no longer holds. Such non-Newtonian fluids are encountered with considerable frequency and include polymer solutions, molten polymers, suspensions of solids in liquids, and such food products as tomato paste, apple sauce, and honey. To accommodate such fluids, Newton's viscosity law has to be modified, usually to a nonlinear form, and this has led to the formulation of a number of new shear stress-shear rate relation which we summarize below:

Bingham Plastic Fluids — These are the simplest non-Newtonian fluids and differ from linear Newtonian behavior only by the inclusion of a constant yield stress term τ_o which is required to initiate flow.

Bingham Model:

$$\tau = -\mu \frac{dv}{dx} + \tau_o \qquad (3.4.70)$$

TABLE 3.20
Velocities and Flow Rates in Viscous Flow Through Various Conduits

1. Circular Pipe

Velocities

$$v(r) = \frac{\Delta p}{16 \mu L} d^2 \left[1 - \left(\frac{2r}{d} \right)^2 \right]$$

$$v_{Max} = \frac{\Delta p}{16 \mu L} d^4; \quad v_{avg} = v_{Max} / 2$$

Flow rate

$$Q = \frac{\pi \Delta p}{128 \mu L} d^4$$

(Hagen-Poiseuille equation)

2. Annulus

Velocity

$$v(r) = \frac{\Delta p}{16 \mu L} d_o^2 \left[1 - \left(\frac{2r}{d_o} \right)^2 - \frac{1 - (d_i / d_o)^2}{\ln(d_o / d_i)} \ln \frac{d_o}{r} \right]$$

Flow rate

$$Q = \frac{\pi \Delta p}{128 \mu L} d_o^4 \left[1 - \left(\frac{d_i}{d_o} \right)^4 - \frac{[1 - (d_i / d_o)^2}{\ln(d_o / d_i)} \right]$$

3. Parallel plates

Velocities

$$v(x) = \frac{\Delta p}{8 \mu L} T^2 \left[1 - \left(\frac{2x}{T} \right)^2 \right]$$

$$v_{Max} = \frac{\Delta p}{8 \mu L} T^2; \quad v_{avg} = \frac{2}{3} v_{Max}$$

Flow rate

$$Q = \frac{\Delta p}{12 \mu L} T^3 W$$

Examples of Bingham fluids are drilling muds, paper pulp, sewage sludge, greases, toothpaste, and a variety of food products such as chocolate and margarine.

Power Law Fluids — These are fluids for which the shear rate dv/dx carries an exponent n ≠ 1. We distinguish two cases:

(a) Pseudoplastic fluids: Here n < 1 and we obtain the following expression, known as the Ostwald-de Wael equation (Pseudoplastic or Ostwald-de Wael Model):

$$\tau = K \left(-\frac{dv}{dx} \right)^n \quad n < 1 \tag{3.4.71}$$

where K is the so-called consistency index in Ns^n/m^2 and n the flow behavior index which is dimensionless.

(b) Dilatant fluids: These are less common than pseudoplastic fluids and include wet sand and other suspensions containing a high concentration of suspended particles. The power law takes the form (Dilatant Model):

$$\tau = K\left(-\frac{dv}{dx}\right)^n \quad n > 1 \qquad (3.4.72)$$

A number of fluids show more complex behavior, they are briefly summarized below.

Time-Dependent Fluids — These are fluids which exhibit a reversible change with time of the shear stress at constant rate of shear. One again distinguishes two cases:

(a) Thixotropic fluids: Here the shear stress undergoes a reversible *decrease* with time. Examples include some polymer solution, paints, and some food products.
(b) Rheopectic fluids: The reverse occurs here, i.e., shear stress increases with time under conditions of constant shear rate. Examples include certain suspensions and solutions.

Viscoelastic Fluids — These fluids experience elastic recovery from deformation during flow, i.e., they show both viscous and elastic properties. Examples are bitumens and certain polymer melts.

The coefficients K and n in power law fluids given under Power Law Fluids are determined by viscometry and are reported in the following modified form:

$$K' = K\left(\frac{3n+1}{4n}\right)^n \qquad (3.4.73)$$

or

$$\gamma = 8^{n-1} K' \qquad (3.4.74)$$

where γ is often referred to as a generalized viscosity coefficient. Some typical values of these coefficients are listed in Table 3.21.

To calculate friction factors f, one uses a modified Reynolds number defined as follows:

$$Re_{mod} = \frac{d^n V^{2-n} \rho}{\gamma} = \frac{d^n v^{2-n} \rho}{K 8^{n-1}\left(\dfrac{3n+1}{4n}\right)^n} \qquad (3.4.75)$$

That Reynolds number is then used to calculate f_{mod} by the standard Newtonian relations, e.g., $f_{mod} = 16/Re_{mod}$ for laminar flow, and the value thus found substituted into the Fanning Equation 3.4.5 to obtain the pressure drop.

TABLE 3.21
Flow Parameters of Power Law Fluids

Fluid	n	$K' \left(\dfrac{Ns^n}{m^2} \right)$	$\gamma \left(\dfrac{Ns^n}{m^2} \right)$
Paper pulp in water (40%)	0.58		9.1
Clay in water (25%)	0.19		0.30
Napalm in kerosene (10%)	0.52		1.8
Applesauce	0.65	0.5	
Honey	1.0	5.6	
Cream	1.0	0.014	

Consider the case of a 25% clay suspension in water being pumped through a pipe of inside diameter $d = 0.1$ m and length $L = 1500$ m with a velocity $v = 0.1$ m/s. It is desired to calculate the associated pressure drop. Flow parameters are taken from Table 3.21 and density $\rho = 1500$ kg/m³. We obtain:

$$\text{Re}_{\text{mod}} = \frac{d^n v^{2-n} \rho}{\gamma} = \frac{(0.1^{0.19})(0.1^{1.81})(1500)}{0.3} = 50$$

i.e., the flow is laminar. Substitution into the Fanning Equation 3.4.5 then yields:

$$\Delta p = \frac{16}{\text{Re}_{\text{mod}}} \rho \frac{v^2}{2} \frac{L}{d} = \frac{16}{50} 1500 \frac{0.1^2}{2} \frac{1500}{0.1}$$

$$\Delta p = 36 \, \text{kPa}$$

Practice Problems

3.4.1 Force on a Submerged Hinged Gate — A hinged submerged rectangular steel gate 1 m long × 0.5 m wide separates a water reservoir from an underground cavern connected to the atmosphere. The gate is inclined by 30° to the horizontal water surface, located 10 m above the upper edge of the gate. Calculate the total force required to lift the gate.
   Answer: 5.03×10^4 N

3.4.2 The Barbecue Propane Cylinder — Propane cylinders contain the gas in liquified form, hence are subject to a much lower internal pressure which is the vapor pressure of liquid propane (approximately 0.96 MPa at 25°C). As a consequence, propane cylinders have a characteristically wider diameter, 0.3 to 0.4 m than those of compressed permanent gases. For a propane cylinder with a diameter $d = 0.3$ m, calculate the minimum wall thickness Δd.
   Answer: 0.64 mm

Comment:
   In actual practice, a wall thickness of about 3.6 mm is used, i.e., larger by a factor of more than 6. This is done to impart greater structural strength to the vessel as well as to guard against vapor pressure increases caused by a rise in temperature.

3.4.3 Power Required to Form a Water Spray — 0.1 kg/s of water is to be passed through a perforated nozzle to produce a spray with drop diameter d = 1 mm. Calculate the power requirement and the upstream water pressure needed.
   (Hint: Recall that the energy needed to form or destroy a surface is given by the product of surface tension and area.)
   Answer: 4.4×10^{-2} J/s, 440 Pa above atmosphere

3.4.4 Hypsometric Formula Revisited — (a) Derive a hypsometric formula based on the assumption that the adiabatic relation (Equation 3.3.73) applies. (b) Compare the result with that obtained by Equation 3.4.30 for an altitude of 3000 m. Use the value $\gamma = 1.4$ for air.

$$\text{Answer: (a)} \quad z = \frac{\gamma}{\gamma - 1} \frac{P_1}{pg} \left[1 - \left(\frac{P_2}{P_1} \right)^{\frac{\gamma - 1}{\gamma}} \right]$$

3.4.5 Forces Acting on a Moving Turbine Blade — Consider the case of a jet, velocity v_j, impinging on a blade moving with the velocity v_r. Assume that the entire flow rate Q is deflected by the vane.

   (a) Derive expressions for the horizontal and vertical force components.
   (b) Show that the optimum blade velocity leading to maximum power output of the turbine equals one half the jet velocity.

3.4.6 Jet Velocity of a Rocket Motor — Consider a rocket motor with an exit cross-sectional area of 1 m² and a discharge temperature of 2000°K. Assume an average molar mass of the exiting gas of 25.

   (a) What must the jet velocity be if the pay load per rocket motor is 10,000 kg?
   (b) What information is needed to calculate the rate at which a liquid fuel using liquid O_2 as oxidant is consumed to produce the desired velocity?

   Answer: (a) 810 m/s

3.4.7 Solids Removal in a Settling Tank — An aqueous suspension of spherical particles of density $\rho = 2000$ kg/m³ and ranging in size from 0.05 to 5 mm is fed into a settling tank which is filled to a height of 10 m. Calculate the *minimum* time required for all particles to settle.
   (Hint: Consult Tables 3.14 and 3.17.)
   Answer: 7350 s

Comment:
   We speak of minimum time since the later stages of the process involve so-called hindered settling during which the particle velocity will be considerably less

than the free-fall terminal velocity. In the laminar region, for example, the terminal velocity becomes, after empirical correction to account for hindered settling:

$$v_t \frac{d^2 g \varepsilon^2 (\rho_p - \rho_f)}{18 \mu 10^{1.82(1-\varepsilon)}} \qquad (3.4.76)$$

where ε = void fraction of the slurry. Since ε varies with time, a steady terminal velocity is never attained and the calculations become correspondingly more complex.

3.4.8 Fluidization of a Catalyst Particle — Catalyst particles of density $\rho_p = 2000$ kg/m³ and diameter d = 0.03 mm are to be fluidized, i.e., suspended in a gas stream of viscosity $\mu = 2 \times 10^{-5}$ Pas and density 1.3 kg/m³. Calculate the minimum gas velocity required to achieve this.
    Answer: 0.049 m/s

3.4.9 Pumping of a Solvent: Vapor Lock — Calculate the maximum height to which a liquid solvent can be pumped without forming a vapor lock. Data: vapor pressure at 25°C, 400 mmHg, density $\rho = 730$ kg/m³.
    Answer: 6.7 m

Comment:
    We speak of *maximum* height since frictional pressure losses will further reduce the allowable height. Refine your calculations by taking this into account using the following data: diameter d = 5 cm, flow rate Q = 10^{-3} m³/s, viscosity $\mu = 0.5$ mPas.

3.4.10 Design of a Venturi Meter — Air fed to a small packed gas scrubber at 25°C and 1 atm is to be metered through a Venturi meter. In such meters, the upstream pipe diameter is gradually and linearly tapered down to a constriction diameter of d_c, and just as gradually and smoothly enlarged again to its original value. The pressure difference between an upstream location and the constriction serves as a measure for the flow rate (Equation 3.4.58).
    Flow rates are expected to be in the range $10^{-3} - 10^{-1}$ kg/s. The supply line is made of 5.3 cm I.D. PVC pipe (nominal 2 in.). Pressure drop is to be measured by means of a U-tube water manometer which should yield "acceptable" readings of 5 and 50 cm water for the extreme values of flow rates.

(a) Show that this expression yields constriction diameters d_c of 1.9 cm for the lowest flow rate and 3.3 cm for the high end of the range.
(b) Choose a compromise diameter of 2.5 cm and show that the use of two manometers, one inclined and one vertical, would give acceptable readings over the stipulated flow rate range.

3.4.11 Pumping Costs — Water is to be pumped from one reservoir to another, the vertical distance between their surfaces, open to the atmosphere, being 100 m. A pipe 400 m long and with inside diameter of 0.3 m is to carry the flow at the rate of 0.1 m³/s. Friction losses include those due to four elbows, a half-open gate valve, and entrance as well as exit losses. The friction factor for the pipe in question is f = 0.02. Calculate the pumping cost per 1000 m³ water, if the cost of 1 kW hr is $0.03.
    Answer: 8.9 cents

3.4.12 Viscous Flow in an Annulus — Derive the velocity profile and the flow rate–pressure drop relation for Newtonian flow in an annulus given in Table 3.20.

3.4.13 Flow Rate–Pressure Drop Relation for a Bingham Fluid — Derive the Q – Δp relation for the flow of a Bingham fluid through a circular pipe.

Answer: $Q = \dfrac{\pi \Delta p d^4}{128 \mu L} - \dfrac{\pi \tau_o}{24 \mu} d^3$

3.5   COMBINED MASS AND ENERGY BALANCES

Whenever an operation involving a change in mass takes place under nonisothermal conditions, an energy balance will in general have to be invoked as well. Simultaneous mass and energy balances, thus, will be required in cases where the heat of reaction is significant, or heats of solution play a role in operations involving phase changes, principally vaporization, condensation, freezing, and melting and, in general, in any process in which the temperature variable is linked to a mass balance. When the mass and energy balances are not coupled, they can be solved independently by the methods described in the preceding two sections.

The pertinent flux equations and transport coefficients having been discussed in Section 3.3 and 3.4, we can in principle proceed with our illustrations. It must be kept in mind, however, that temperature may affect transport coefficients and on rare occasions may affect the flux equations as well. The latter is the case for example in thermal diffusion, in which mass transport affects the energy flux equations. This will be dealt with when required, but in general we will confine ourselves to cases where the relations given in the preceding two sections apply directly.

We start by revisiting the three classical cases considered in Section 3.3 on mass balances, i.e., the CSTR, the tubular reactor, and the catalyst pellet, and extend the models to nonisothermal processes. We examine humidification, dehumidification, and water cooling as well as the important concept of the wet-bulb temperature that is based on simultaneous mass and energy balances. Several additional topics are also addressed. As usual, the practice problems provide further examples of interest.

Illustration 3.5.1   Nonisothermal CSTR with Second Order Homogeneous Reaction A + B → P

This is the same reactor that was considered under isothermal conditions in Illustration 3.2.3 We repeat the relevant mass balance in terms of conversion X for completeness, noting that k_r is now a function of temperature.

$$-k_r(T)C_{Af}C_{Bf}\tau(1-X)^2 + C_{Af}X = \tau \frac{dX}{dt} \qquad (3.2.33)$$

To this is now added an energy balance which is derived in the usual fashion:

$$\text{Rate of energy in} - \text{Rate of energy out} = \frac{\text{Rate of change of}}{\text{energy contents}}$$

$$H_f - (H \pm q) = \frac{d}{dt}(H) \tag{3.5.1}$$

where q is the rate of heat transfer due to heating or cooling and $H_f - H$ comprises the sensible heat change as well as the heat of reaction ΔH_r. Introducing the relevant auxiliary relation we obtain the following relation:

$$Q\rho C_p(T_f - T) - [k_r(T)C_A C_B](V)(\Delta H_r)$$

$$\text{Sensible heat} \qquad \text{Heat of reaction}$$

$$\pm UA(T_e - T) = V\rho C_p \frac{dT}{dt} \tag{3.5.2}$$

$$\text{Heat transfer} \quad \text{Sensible heat change}$$

We note that ΔH_r takes a negative sign for exothermic reactions so that the reaction term represents energy input to the tank contents. The heat transfer term will be negative for cooling (i.e., for exothermic reactions) and positive for heating (endothermic reaction).

In terms of conversion X, we obtain:

$$Q\rho C_p(T_f - T) - k_r(T)C_{Af}C_{Bf}(1 - X)^2 V\Delta H_r \pm UA(T_{ext} - T) = V\rho C_p \frac{dT}{dt} \tag{3.5.3}$$

Equations 3.2.32 and 3.5.3 are two coupled ODEs in temperature T and conversion X which are not easily uncoupled and must in general be solved numerically. Temperature dependence of k_r is given by the usual Arrhenius expression:

$$k_r(T) = A_r \exp(-E_a/RT) \tag{3.5.4}$$

where E_a = activation energy and A_r is the so-called pre-exponential factor.

Illustration 3.5.2   Nonisothermal Tubular Reactors: The Adiabatic Case

We revisit here the tubular plug or piston flow reactor which was considered under isothermal conditions and for a first order reaction in Illustration 3.2.4. We shall assume constant physical properties, i.e, a constant or average density and heat capacity and, hence, constant flow velocity.

We start by generalizing the mass balance by applying it to an arbitrary reaction rate r. The previous mass balance (Equation 3.2.34) then becomes:

Mass balance:

$$v\frac{dC_i}{dz} \pm r_i = 0 \tag{3.5.5}$$

where i denotes the species reacted or produced.

The energy balance, which complements Equation 3.5.5 is derived as follows:

$$\text{Rate of energy in} - \text{Rate of energy out} = 0$$

$$(H|_z \pm q_{avg}) - H|_{z+\Delta z} = 0 \tag{3.5.6}$$

where the difference in enthalpies is composed of a sensible heat term $v\rho\frac{\pi d^2}{4}Cp(T|_z - T|_{z+\Delta z})$ and a heat of reaction term $\pm(r_i)_{avg}\Delta H_r\frac{\pi d^2}{4}\Delta z$. The heat transfer term is expressed as usual in the form $\pm U\pi D\Delta z\,(T_{ext} - T)_{avg}$. Upon dividing by Δz and going to the limit one obtains:

$$v\rho\frac{\pi d^2}{4}Cp\frac{dT}{dz} \pm r_i\Delta H_r\frac{\pi d^2}{4} \pm U\pi d(T_{ext} - T) = 0 \tag{3.5.7}$$

where the negative signs refer to an endothermic reaction and the positive signs to an exothermic one.

Equations 3.5.5 and 3.5.7 represent the working model equations for nonisothermal tubular reactors. More refined models that account for variations in density and velocity as well as temperature and pressure are taken up in the next section (Illustration 3.6.8). These equations in temperature and concentrations are coupled and nonlinear, and are generally solved by means of standard ODE packages. For q = 0 (adiabatic operation), certain simplifications arise which are taken up below.

The Adiabatic Case — We aim here, in the first instance, to establish a relation between the dependent variables T and C_i. To do this, we resort to our old trick of eliminating the independent variable by dividing the two ODEs, (Equations 3.5.5 and 3.5.7), and obtain, after omission of the heat transfer term,

$$\frac{dT}{dC_i} = \pm\frac{\Delta H_r}{\rho Cp} \tag{3.5.8}$$

or upon integration,

$$T - T_f = \pm\frac{\Delta H_r}{\rho Cp}(C_A - C_{Af}) \tag{3.5.9}$$

where the subscript $_f$ denotes inlet or feed conditions. This relation reveals that in an adiabatic reactor, concentrations, and conversions vary linearly with temperature. It carries the added advantage that upon substitution into Equation 3.5.5 a set of i *independent* ODEs is obtained. For example for a reaction which is first order in C_A, and endothermic, Equation 3.5.5 becomes:

$$v\frac{dX}{dz} + A_r \exp\left\{-E_a / R\left[\frac{\Delta H_r C_{Af}}{\rho Cp} X_i - T_f\right]\right\}(1-X) = 0 \qquad (3.5.10)$$

where A_r is the usual Arrhenius pre-exponential factor, E_a the activation energy, and X the conversion. The equation can be formally integrated by separation of variables. Thus, the solution of this particularly simple case consists of the evaluation of a single integral in place of the integration of a set of i coupled and generally nonlinear ODEs.

Illustration 3.5.3   Heat Effects in a Catalyst Pellet: Maximum Pellet Temperature

In our previous Illustration 3.2.5, dealing with isothermal diffusion and reaction in a spherical pellet, we had considered the model that yields the concentration profile of a reactant within the catalyst particle. This primary information was then converted by integration over the pellet into the so-called catalyst effectiveness factor E_i, which is a measure of the diffusional resistance within the pellet. Such isothermal effectiveness factors apply to small particles of high thermal conductivity and a relatively low rate of conversion.

In general, the heat of reaction which is of the order of ± 100 kJ/mol or more, cannot be ignored and the mass balance must then be complemented by an appropriate shell energy balance. That balance has to consider heat conducted into and out of the shell in the radial direction, as well as heat generated or consumed within the shell itself.

We assume the same spherical geometry and first order reaction as before and consider the reaction to be exothermic which is the more common case. The following formulation is then obtained:

$$\text{Rate of energy in} - \text{Rate of energy out} = 0$$

$$\left[-k_{eff} 4\pi r^2 \frac{dT}{dr}\bigg|_r\right] - \left[\begin{array}{c} -k_{eff} 4\pi r^2 \frac{dT}{dr}\bigg|_{r+\Delta r} \\ +k_r(T)C_A 4\pi r^2 \Delta r \Delta H_r \end{array}\right] = 0 \qquad (3.5.11)$$

Dividing by $4\pi\Delta r$ and letting $\Delta r \to 0$, noting as we do so that both the area term $4\pi r^2$ and the temperature derivative have to be differentiated, we obtain, after cancellation of terms and rearrangement,

$$\frac{d^2T}{dr^2} + \frac{2}{r}\frac{dT}{dr} - k_r(T)C_A \Delta H_r / k_{eff} = 0 \qquad (3.5.12)$$

where k_r = rate constant, k_{eff} = effective thermal conductivity.

This expression is supplemented by the mass balance given previously in Section 3.2 in which the rate constant k_r is now a function of temperature.

$$\frac{d^2C}{dr^2} + \frac{2}{r}\frac{dC}{dr} - k_r(T)C_A / D_{eff} = 0 \qquad (3.2.41)$$

The two equations which are coupled by the two state variables, C_A and T, generally have to be solved numerically. The resulting concentration profile $C_A = f(r)$ can then be integrated over the pellet volume as was done in the isothermal case to obtain the nonisothermal effectiveness factor E_{ni}.

$$E_{ni} = \frac{\int_0^R k_r(T)C_A(r)dV_p}{k_r(T_s)C_{As}V_p} \qquad (3.5.13)$$

Here the reference state is taken to be the surface concentration C_{As} and surface temperature T_s, i.e., the conditions which would prevail in the absence of transport resistances.

A plot of E_{ni} vs. the Thiele modulus $[k_r(T_s)R^2/D_{eff}]^{1/2}$ is shown in Figure 3.16 where the rate constant k_r is evaluated at the surface temperature T_s. Two thermal

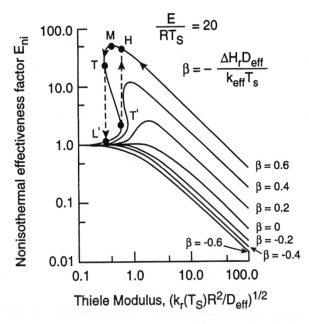

FIGURE 3.16   Plot of the nonisothermal effectiveness factor E_{ni} as a function of the Thiele modulus. Jump changes in E_{ni} occur at T and T¹ and hysteresis effect results. (P.B. Weisz and J.S. Hicks. *Chem. Eng. Sci.*, 17:265, 1962. With permission.)

parameters make their appearance, the Arrhenius number E_a/RT_s and the dimension-less heat of reaction parameter $\beta = \dfrac{-\Delta H_r D_{eff}}{k_{eff} T_s}$. For $\beta = 0$, i.e., infinite thermal conductivity, $k_{eff} \rightarrow \infty$, the effectiveness factor reduces to that of the isothermal case. $\beta > 0$ denotes exothermic reactions and here the rise in temperature in the interior of the pellet is seen to have a significant impact on E_{ni} which may rise above unity and reach values as high as 100 or more. This is evidently due to the strong exponential dependence of reaction rate on temperature occasioned by the Arrhenius relation. As expected, the effect varies directly with the heat generated (ΔH_r) and inversely with the rate of heat removal (k_{eff}). Thus, exothermicity, far from being undesirable, has a beneficial effect on catalytic conversion. One has to guard, how-ever, against an excessive rise in temperature which might adversely affect catalyst structure, causing a decrease or even cessation of catalytic activity. Sintering of a metallic catalyst is an example of what should be avoided.

For endothermic reactions, $\beta < 0$ applies, ΔH_r now being positive, and a drop in E_{ni} occurs to values below those seen in the isothermal case.

So far in our model, no consideration was given to the external film resistance which may become a significant factor in controlling the rate of heat removal of exothermic reactions. In fact, it has been found that in gas–solid systems, and if the reaction is fast enough, temperature gradients will occur primarily in the gas film. As heat effects become progressively more dominant, the following changes in mechanism occur.

1. When the reaction is very slow, the pellet acts as a stirred tank, i.e., both temperature and concentrations are uniform within the particle.
2. For moderate reaction rates, temperature gradients make their first appear-ance but are still small enough to justify the use of the isothermal E_i.
3. For higher reaction rates, transport resistance within the particle becomes more important and a good deal of the reaction takes place in a thin shell near the surface of the particle. The nonisothermal effectiveness factor E_{ni} now applies.
4. Finally, when the reaction is very fast, reactants are practically consumed at the hot pellet surface and mass transfer through the gas film becomes the controlling factor.

An additional important point needs to be noted in nonisothermal systems. As can be seen from the effectiveness plots, Figures 3.9 and 3.16, the isothermal factor E_i yields a single-valued function which rises smoothly to $E_i = 1$ as the Thiele modulus is decreased. E_{ni} is single-valued at high values of the modulus, but as the latter is reduced and E_{ni} rises above unity, a point is reached where E_{ni} becomes multivalued. Three steady-states are obtained of which only the upper and lower ones are stable. This results in a hysteresis effect which is sketched in Figure 3.16. As the modulus is decreased, E_{ni} first rises to a maximum value M, then begins to decline until the tangent point T is reached. Here the effectiveness factor undergoes a sudden jump decrease to the lower value L. Beyond that point, E_{ni} continues a smooth decline with decreasing modulus values toward the limiting value of unit. A similar jump *increase* in E_{ni} to a value H occurs at the tangent point T′ as one moves in the opposite direction of increasing modulus values. The temperature associated with T′ is sometimes referred to as the ignition temperature. Similar multiplicities and jump discontinuities have been observed in other nonisothermal systems, including exothermic reactions in CSTRs (see Practice Problem 3.5.3). A more detailed discussion of this type of behavior is in Chapter 4, Section 4.5.

Maximum Temperature — The possible effect of temperature on catalyst activity and structure make it desirable to have an estimate of its maximum possible value. That temperature will, for symmetry reasons, be located at the center of the sphere and can in principle be deduced from Equations 3.2.41 and 3.5.12. A more convenient way is to proceed as follows. One performs integral mass and energy balances over the entire pellet, taking account of the fact that whatever mass and energy enters or leaves through a spherical surface must be balanced by consumption of reactant or the total production of heat in the interior. We obtain the following two formulations:

$$\text{Rate of mass in} - \text{Rate of mass out} = 0$$

$$-D_{eff} 4\pi r^2 \frac{dC_A}{dr} - \int_0^r r_A 4\pi r^2 dr = 0 \tag{3.5.14}$$

and

$$\text{Rate of energy in} - \text{Rate of energy out} = 0$$

$$\left(\Delta H_r \int_0^r r_A 4\pi r^2 dr \right) - \left(-k_{eff} 4\pi r^2 \frac{dT}{dr} \right) = 0 \tag{3.5.15}$$

Division of the two equations eliminates the (unknown) integral and the independent variable dr yielding:

$$\frac{dT}{dC_A} = \frac{D_{eff} \Delta H_r}{k_{eff}} \tag{3.5.16}$$

Note that the expression holds for arbitrary reaction rates r_A.

Integrating from pellet center (c) to its surface (s), one obtains:

$$T_s - T_c = \frac{D_{eff} \Delta H_r}{k_{eff}} (C_{As} - C_{Ac}) \tag{3.5.17}$$

where $T_c = T_{max}$ and corresponds to a concentration at the center of $C_{Ac} = C_{min}$. That minimum concentration is not known *a priori* but would at worst be zero. The highest possible temperature in the pellet would then be ($\Delta H_r < 0$):

$$T_{max} = T_s - \frac{D_{eff}\Delta H_r}{k} C_{As} \qquad (3.5.18)$$

Comments:

One notes that use was again made of one of our favorite "tricks" (a perfectly legitimate one) of eliminating unwanted or unknown quantities by division of the model equations. The procedure was previously seen in modeling the countercurrent shell-and-tube heat exchanger and was suggested as a solution method in Practice Problem 2.3 dealing with Rayleigh distillation.

The question arises as to what countermeasures could be taken if T_{max} turns out to exceed permissible limits. ΔH_r itself is a given which cannot be altered, but both D_{eff} and k_{eff} can be modified in the right direction by decreasing porosity; in other words, compacting the pellet. Diffusivity would then decrease and thermal conductivity k_{eff} increase, while concentration C_{Ac} would likely become a non-zero quantity. Alternatively, k_{eff} could be increased and T_{max} decreased by choosing a catalyst support of higher conductivity. Considerable latitude is available to counter undesirable temperature effects.

Illustration 3.5.4   The Wet-Bulb Temperature

When a flowing gas comes in contact with a liquid surface, evaporation takes place from the liquid to the gas stream. Let us assume that both are at the same temperature at the start. Initially the energy required for the evaporation process, i.e., the latent heat ΔH_v, comes from the liquid itself which consequently experiences a drop in temperature. That drop, once triggered, causes a corresponding amount of heat transfer to take place from the gas to the liquid. At this intermediate stage, the latent heat of vaporization is provided both by the liquid itself, as well as by heat transfer from the warmer gas. As the liquid temperature continues to drop, the rate of heat transfer increases until a stage is reached where the entire energy load is supplied by the gas itself. A steady-state is attained in which the rate of evaporation is exactly balanced by the rate at which heat is transferred from the gas to the liquid. The liquid is then said to be at its wet-bulb temperature, T_{wb}, as shown in Figure 3.17. The corresponding air temperature is referred to as the dry-bulb temperature, T_{db}. The wet-bulb temperature and it associated saturation humidity $Y_{wb} = Y^*$ plays an important role in humidification and dehumidification operations, to be taken up below, in air conditioning, water cooling operations, and in drying processes (see Illustration 2.5). The relation between T_{wb}, Y_{wb}, and the system parameters is established by equating the rate of heat transfer from air (T_{db}, Y_{db}) to water, to the rate of evaporation, i.e., the rate at which moisture is transferred from the water surface to the air. Thus,

$$\text{Rate of evaporation} = \text{Rate of heat transfer}$$
$$k_Y A(Y_{wb} - Y_{db})\Delta H_v = hA(T_{db} - T_{wb}) \qquad (3.5.19)$$

where Y = absolute humidity (kg moisture/kg dry air) and k_Y is the associated mass transfer coefficient in units of (kg/m^{2}sΔY). (See, in this connection, Table 3.6.)

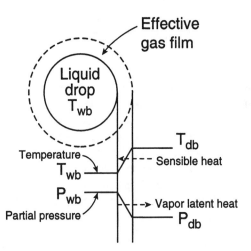

FIGURE 3.17 Temperature and partial pressure distributions around a liquid droplet exposed to a flowing gas stream.

Cancelling terms and rearranging we obtain:

$$\frac{Y_{wb} - Y_{db}}{T_{wb} - T_{db}} = -\frac{h}{k_Y \Delta H_v} \qquad (3.5.20)$$

where the term $(T_{db} - T_{wb})$ is referred as the wet-bulb depression.

Comments:

One notes from Equation 3.5.20 that the humidity of the air Y_{db} can, in principle, be established from measured values of T_{db}, T_{wb}, and Y_{wb}, the latter being obtained from the relation:

$$Y_{wb} = \frac{P_{H_wO}}{P_{Tot} - P_{H_wO}} \frac{M_{H_2O}}{M_{air}} \qquad (3.5.21)$$

where $P^o_{H_2O}$ = partial pressure of water, and M = molar mass. T_{db} is measured by exposing a dry thermometer to the flowing air, while T_{wb} is obtained in similar fashion using a thermometer covered with a moist wick or cloth.

The temperature and concentration changes which arise in air–water contact, and indeed the air–water system itself, are of such importance in the physical sciences that they have led to the construction of so-called Psychrometric or Humidity Charts. These charts summarize in convenient fashion the thermal and concentration variables relevant to operations involving the air–water system. Among other things, they allow the calculation of air humidity Y from measured values of the wet and dry-bulb temepratures T_{wb} and T_{db}.

Illustration 3.5.5 Humidity Charts: The Psychrometric Ratio

We start by defining and deriving a set of variables which appear implicitly or in explicit form in the Humidity Charts, shown in Figures 3.18 and 3.19.

Absolute Humidity Y — This quantity was already referred to in connection with the wet-bulb temperature and is redefined here for convenience:

$$Y\left(\frac{kg\,H_2O}{kg\,dry\,air}\right) = \frac{18}{29}\frac{P_{H_2O}}{P_{Tot} - P_{H_2O}} \tag{3.5.22}$$

Y appears as the right-hand side ordinate in the humidity charts.

Relative Humidity RH — To obtain a sense of the relative degree of saturation of the air, one defines:

$$RH = \frac{P_{H_2O}}{(p^o_{H_2O})_{sat}}100 \tag{3.5.23}$$

where the pressure ratio in effect expresses the fractional water content of the air, ranging from 0% (dry air) to 100% (fully saturated air). RH appears in the humidity charts as a set of parametric curves which rise smoothly from left to right.

Percentage Humidity PH — The relative degree of saturation also can be expressed in terms of a ratio of absolute humidities rather than partial pressures. Thus,

$$PH = \frac{Y}{Y_{sat}}100 \tag{3.5.24}$$

Some humidity charts use this quantity rather than the relative humidity RH to express the relative saturation of the air.

Dew Point T_{dp} — This is the temperature at which an air–water mixture, cooled at constant total pressure P_{Tot} and absolute humidity Y, becomes saturated, i.e., attains a relative humidity of 100%. Its value is established by moving from the initial defining point of a given air–water mixture on the humidity chart along a *horizontal* line to the eventual intersection with the curve of 100% relative humidity.

Humid Volume V_H — The humid volume of an air–water mixture is the volume in cubic meters per kilogram of dry air measured at $P_{Tot} = 101.3$ kPa (1 atm) and the temperature T of the mixture. Its value is established via the ideal gas laws which yield the following expressions:

$$V_H(m^3 / kg\,dry\,air) = \frac{22.41}{273}T(K)\left[\frac{1}{29} + \frac{Y}{18}\right]$$

or

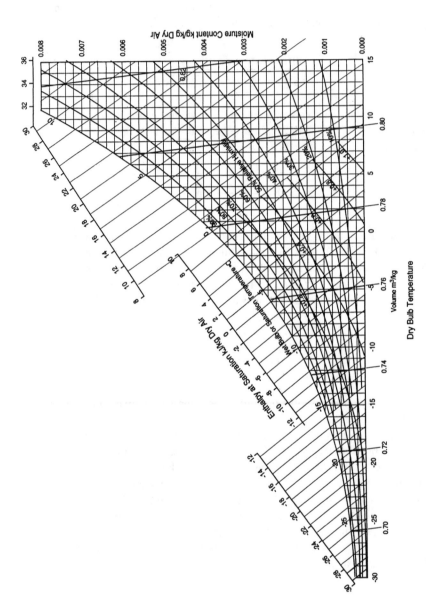

FIGURE 3.18 Psychrometric or humidity chart for air–water. Total pressure = 1 atm, reference temperature 0°C, low temperature range. (Courtesy of the Carrier Corporation. With permission.)

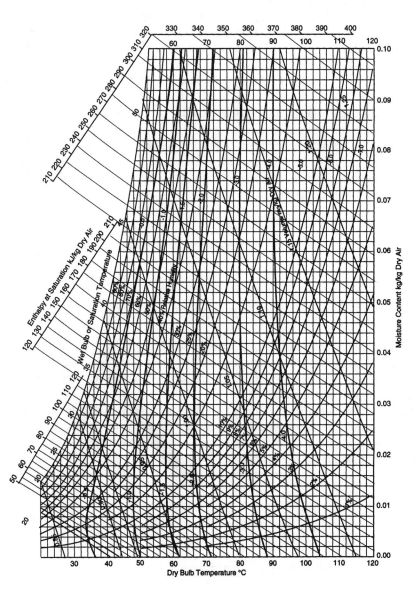

FIGURE 3.19 Psychrometric or humidity chart for air–water. Total pressure 1 atm, reference temperature 0°C, high temperature range. (Courtesy of the Carrier Corporation. With permission.)

$$V_H = (2.83 \times 10^{-3} + 4.56 \times 10^{-3} \, Y) \, T(K) \qquad (3.5.25)$$

Values of V_H appear in the humidity charts as a set of lines of negative slope. Alternatively they can be calculated from Equation 3.5.25.

Humid Heat C_s — This quantity represents the heat required to raise the temperature of 1 kg of dry air and the associated water vapor it contains by 1°. The heat capacities of water and air can be assumed constant and are set at 1.88 kJ/kg water vapor and 1.0005 kJ/kg dry air. One obtains:

$$C_s \, (kJ/kg \text{ dry air}) = 1.0005 + 1.88 \, Y \qquad (3.5.26)$$

Humid heat does not usually appear explicitly in the humidity charts but is contained in the enthalpies shown there.

Enthalpy H — With the humid heat C_s in hand, we are in a position to formulate the enthalpy of an air–water system. With T^0 chosen as the datum temperature for both components and adding sensible heat of the air–water mixture to the latent heat of evaporation of water ΔH_v^0 at T^0, we obtain:

$$H \, (kJ/kg \text{ dry air}) = \underset{\text{Sensible Heat}}{\underbrace{C_s \, (T - T^0)}} + \underset{\text{Latent Heat}}{\underbrace{Y \, \Delta H_v^0}}$$

or

$$H = (1.0005 + 1.88 \, Y)(T - T^0) + Y \, \Delta H_v^0 \qquad (3.5.27)$$

where the datum temperature T^0 is usually set equal to 0°C for both liquid water and dry air. Values of the enthalpies of various air–water mixtures are read from the left hand oblique ordinates. Note that H increases with increasing temperature as well as with increasing humidity.

Adiabatic Saturation Temperature T_{as} — This special temperature arises when a flowing stream of air is humidified in contact with constantly recirculated water (see Figure 3.20). Both the recirculated water and the exiting gas stream attain the so-called adiabatic saturation temperature T_{as} which is lower than the "dry-bulb" temperature of the entering air stream because of the evaporative cooling. If care is

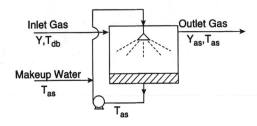

FIGURE 3.20 Flowsheet describing the attainment of the adiabatic saturation temperature T_{as}.

taken to introduce the make-up water at the same adiabatic saturation temperature and the datum temperature is set at T_{as}, a simple energy balance will yield:

$$\text{Rate of energy in} - \text{Rate of energy out} = 0$$

$$[C_s(T_{db} - T_{as}) + Y_{db}\Delta H_v^0] - [C_s(T_{as} - T_{as}) + Y_{as}\Delta H_v^0] = 0 \tag{3.5.28}$$

which upon rearrangement leads to the expression:

$$\frac{Y_{as} - Y_{db}}{T_{as} - T_{db}} = -\frac{C_s}{\Delta H_v^0} \tag{3.5.29}$$

Plots of this equation appear in the humidity charts as lines of negative slope extending from the abscissa to the 100% relative humidity curve. The lines are slightly curved due to the dependence of C_s on Y_{db}.

The Psychrometric Ratio and the Lewis Relation — The striking similarity between the adiabatic saturation and wet-bulb relations, Equations 3.5.29 and 3.5.20, led to a detailed examination of the ratio of the slopes of the two relations, $h/k_Y C_s$, also known as the Psychrometric Ratio. These studies culminated in the finding that for the water–air system, and *only for that system*, its value is approximately unity. Thus,

$$\text{Psychrometric Ratio } h/k_Y C_s \approx 1 \tag{3.5.30}$$

This expression, now known as the *Lewis relation* leads to the conclusion that the adiabatic saturation and wet-bulb temperatures are essentially identical. It has other important implications as well, as will be shown in Illustration 3.5.6. The values read at the intersection of adiabatic saturation and 100% relative humidity curves are thus both wet-bulb and adiabatic saturation temperatures. These can in turn be used as model variables in such diverse processes as wet-bulb thermometry, adiabatic humidification and cooling, as well as in the drying of solids (see Illustration 2.7).

Let us illustrate the various uses to which the humidity charts may be put with a concrete example. We choose a water–air mixture of 25% relative humidity, 1 atm total pressure, and a temperature of 50°C (dry bulb), and proceed to calculate various properties of interest using the chart shown in Figure 3.19.

(a) Absolute humidity: This value is read from the right-side rectangular ordinate and yields:

$$Y = 0.0195 \text{ kg } H_2O/\text{kg dry air}$$

(b) Dew point: One follows the horizontal line through the point $Y = 0.0195$ and $T_{db} = 50°C$ to its intersection with the 100% relative humidity curve and obtains:

$$T_{dp} = 24.5°C$$

This corresponds to the temperature at which, upon isobaric cooling of the mixture, the first condensation of water occurs.

(c) Wet-bulb temperature: Here the procedure is to follow the adiabatic saturation line to its intersection with the 100% relative humidity curve. One obtains:

$$T_{wb} = 30.4°C$$

Note that the wet-bulb temperature is not identical to the dew point.

(d) Water partial pressure: This quantity can be obtained directly from the absolute humidity and the Relation 3.5.20. Solving it for $P_{H_2O}^o$ yields:

$$P_{H_2O} = \frac{(29)Y P_{Tot}}{18 + 29Y} = \frac{(29)(0.0195)(101.3)}{18 + (29)0.0195} = 3.09 \text{ kPa}$$

(e) Water vapor pressures: Here the relative humidity RH is used in conjunction with the value of $P_{H_2O}^o$ just calculated to obtain:

$$P^o_{H_2O} = \frac{P_{H_2O}}{RH} 100 = \frac{3.09}{25} 100 = 12.4 \text{ kPa}$$

The humidity chart allows us to dispense with the usual tabulations of water vapor pressures.

(f) Humid volume: The plots for V_H are shown as steep lines of negative slope. The point $Y = 0.0195$ and $T_{db} = 50°C$ is located between the lines for $V_H = 0.90$ and 0.95. Linear interpolation of the two values yields:

$$V_H = 0.945 \text{ m}^3/\text{kg dry gas}$$

(g) Enthalpy: This value is read from the oblique left-hand ordinate of the humidity chart and comes to

$$H = 103 \text{ kJ/kg dry air}$$

(h) Water removal load: Suppose the air mixture considered here is to be cooled and dehumidified to $T_{db} = 15°C$ and relative humidity RH = 20%. The water to be removed can then be calculated as follows.

Initial absolute humidity $Y_i = 0.0195$ kg H_2O/kg dry air
Final absolute humidity $Y_f = 0.0021$
(Figure 3.18)
Water to be removed $Y_i - Y_f = 0.0195 - 0.0021 = 0.0174$ kg H_2O/kg dry air

Alternatively, the result may be expressed in terms of volumetric units by dividing it by the humid volume of the original mixture: water to be removed = $(Y_i - Y_f)/V_H = 0.0174/0.945 = 0.0184$ kg/m³ initial mixture.

(i) Water removal heat load: In addition to the amount of water to be removed, an important parameter in the design of a dehumidification unit is the associated heat load. That quantity is computed from the relevant enthalpies read from the humidity charts.

Initial enthalpy	H_i = 103 kJ/kg dry air
Final enthalpy (Figure 3.19)	H_f = 20.3 kJ/kg dry air
Heat load	$H_i - H_f$ = 103 – 20.3 = 82.7 kJ/kg dry air
(Alternatively, using volumetric units)	
Heat load	$(H_i - H_f)/V_H$ = 82.7/0.945 = 87.5 kJ/m³ initial mixture

Illustration 3.5.6 Operation of a Water Cooling Tower

Process water that has been used in a plant for cooling purposes is generally cycled through a cooling tower where it is contacted in countercurrent flow with air and undergoes evaporative cooling. After the addition of make-up water it is returned to the plant for reuse. Such cooling towers usually contain stacked packings of large size and voidage to minimize pressure drop. They are employed, among other installations, in nuclear power generating plants where they are conspicuous by virtue of their large size and parabolic shape.

As in all packed column operations, the fundamental model equations consist of differential balances over each phase; the principal difference here being the use of both mass and energy balances. The pertinent variables and the differential elements around which the balances are taken are displayed in Figure 3.21A.

Water Balance Over Gas Phase (kgH_2O/m^2s) — This balance is no different from similar mass balances used for packed absorption and distillation columns (see Illustrations 2.3 and 3.2.8) and takes the form:

$$\text{Rate of water vapor in} - \text{Rate of water vapor out} = 0$$

$$G_s Y \mid_z - [G_s Y \mid_{z+\Delta z} + N_{avg}] = 0 \qquad (3.5.31)$$

which upon introduction of the auxiliary mass transfer rate equations, division by Δz and letting $\Delta z \to 0$ yields the usual form of ODE applicable to these cases:

$$G_s \frac{dY}{dz} + K_y a(Y^* - Y) = 0 \qquad (3.5.32)$$

where $Y^* - Y$ is the absolute humidity driving force.

Water Balance over Water Phase — This balance is omitted since the water losses are usually less than 1% so that $L = L_s \approx$ constant.

Gas Phase Energy Balance (kJ/m^2s) — Here we must be careful to include both sensible heat transfer as well as the latent heat brought into the air by the water vapor. We obtain:

A. Column Variables

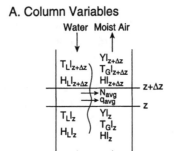

B. Operating Diagram

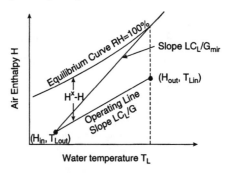

FIGURE 3.21   Variables and operating diagram for a packed water cooling tower.

Rate of energy in − Rate of energy out = 0

$$\left[\begin{array}{l} G_s H\mid_z + q_{avg} \\ + \Delta H_v{}^0 N_{avg} \end{array}\right] - G_s H\mid_{z+\Delta z} = 0 \tag{3.5.33}$$

which after applying the same procedure used in "Water Balance Over Gas Phase" yields:

$$G_s \frac{dH}{dz} - Ua(T_L - T_G) - \Delta H_v{}^0 K_y a(Y * -Y) = 0 \tag{3.5.34}$$

Here T_L and T_G are the water and air temperatures respectively and H = enthalpy of the water–air mixture. We note that the sensible heat transfer $Ua(T_L - T_G)$ equals the corresponding sensible heat term in Equation 3.5.27.

Liquid Phase Energy Balance (kJ/m²s) — A completely analogous derivation to the gas phase balance yields:

$$LC_{pL} \frac{dT_L}{dz} - Ua(T_L - T_G) - \Delta H_v{}^0 K_y a(Y^* - Y) = 0 \qquad (3.5.35)$$

The model is completed by adding the relevant equilibrium expression which can be read from the 100% relative humidity curves of the Psychrometric Charts and also is available in analytical form.

Equilibrium Relation —

$$Y^* = f(T_L) \qquad (3.5.36)$$

Equations 3.5.32 and 3.5.34 to 36, together with the previously given expression for H, Equation 3.5.27, constitute a set of five equations in the five state variables Y, Y*, T_G, T_L, and H.

Although a numerical solution of these equations is nowadays easily implemented, early workers in the field were constrained to cast about for alternative ways of solving the model. To do this, they used the ingenious device of introducing the Lewis relation into the gas phase balance, Equation 3.5.34, which has the effect of combining T_G and Y into a single variable, the gas phase enthalpy H. We sketch the procedure below, using *interfacial* values in place of Y* and T_L to accommodate the film coefficients h and k_Y used in the Lewis relation. We obtain, in the first instance,

$$G_s \frac{dH}{dz} - k_Y a[(C_s T_i + \Delta H_v{}^0 Y_i^*) - (C_s T_G + \Delta H_v{}^0 Y)] \qquad (3.5.37)$$

where it is seen from Equation 3.5.27 that the bracketed terms ( ) represent enthalpies of water–air mixtures. We, therefore, can write:

$$G_s \frac{dH}{dz} - k_Y a(H_i - H) = 0 \qquad (3.5.38)$$

where $H_i - H$ can be considered an enthalpy driving force which replaces the previous temperature and humidity driving forces.

We can now argue that the Two-Film Theory applies to this system as well and that Equation 3.5.38 can be cast in the form:

$$G_s \frac{dH}{dz} - K_Y a(H^* - H) = 0 \qquad (3.5.39)$$

where K_Y is now the overall mass transfer coefficient and H* the gas enthalpy in equilibrium with the bulk water temperature T_L.

This equation is of the same form as the gas phase differential balances encountered in absorption and distillation (Equations 2.20 and 3.2.53) so that the graphical design procedures used there can be replicated (Figure 2.3), provided an appropriate operating line can be constructed. That line is obtained from an overall two-phase integral heat balance and takes the form:

$$G_s (H_1 - H) = L_s C_L (T_{L1} - T_L) \tag{3.5.40}$$

and in its overall version

$$G_s (H_1 - H_2) = L_s C_L (T_{L1} - T_{L2}) \tag{3.5.41}$$

The gas phase balance (Equation 3.5.39) can in turn be formally integrated to yield the familiar HTU-NTU relation:

$$Z = \frac{G_s}{K_y a} \int_{H_{in}}^{H_{out}} \frac{dH}{H*-H} = (HTU)(NTU) \tag{3.5.42}$$

The model is then completed with the addition of the equilibrium relation:

$$H* = f(T_L) \tag{3.5.43}$$

The original set of five equations, three of which were ODEs, have thus been reduced to the three relations (Equations 3.5.40, 3.5.42, and 3.5.43). What is more, it has been cast into the familiar form of an HTU-NTU relation, joined to an operating line and equilibrium relation. The graphical procedure used to solve this set is outlined in Figure 3.21 and follows the usual route of drawing an operating line of slope LC_L/G_s through the point (H_1, T_{L1}) and evaluating the NTU integral using the enthalpy driving force $H* - H$ read from the graph. Note that it is now G_{Min}, not L_{Min} which corresponds to an infinitely high tower.

The equilibrium relation $H* = f(T_L)$ is constructed from the 100% relative humidity curve of the Psychrometric Charts, where $H*$ values are established on the oblique left-hand side ordinate and T_L takes the place of the dry-bulb temperature of the abscissa.

We note that the procedure is primarily used for design purposes or for the estimation of the parameter $K_y a$ from experimental (H, T_L) data given by the operating line. For other calculations, involving, for example, process calculations for a column of given length Z, the full set of the original five model equations has to be solved or else a trial-and-error graphical procedure resorted to.

Illustration 3.5.7   Design of a Gas Scrubber Revisited: The Adiabatic Case

In Illustration 2.3 we had presented the model equations required to calculate the design height of a gas scrubber. The tacit assumption was made that the operation is isothermal so that the equilibrium curve could be taken to apply to a single temperature, that of the incoming feed and solvent. Above solute concentrations of 1 to 5%, heat effects can no longer be ignored and a corresponding shift in the

A. Operating Diagram

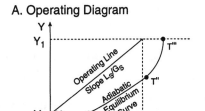

B. Enthalpy Balance

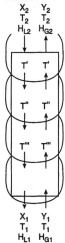

FIGURE 3.22 Operating diagram (A) and column variables (B) for an adiabatic gas scrubber.

equilibrium curve to lower solubilities takes place due to the heat of the solution. In principle a temperature rise occurs in both phases, but due to the low volumetric heat capacities of the gas phase the enthalpy changes are almost entirely confined to the liquid, with both phases attaining the same temperature. This has led to the concept of an adiabatic equilibrium curve which is constructed by using the predicted temperature rise to calculate local equilibrium gas solubilities as a function of solute concentrations in the gas phase. The relevant equations for the construction of the adiabatic operating diagram, Figure 3.22A, are as follows:

- The mass balances and the resulting operating line are unaffected by the heat effects and remain unchanged (see Equation 2.23). Hence,

$$(Y - Y_2)G_s = (X - X_2)L_s \qquad (3.5.42)$$

- To calculate the temperature rise, we draw on an integral enthalpy balance over both phases (Figure 3.22B). Choosing as a reference state the solute at the temperature of the incoming solvent and setting $H_{ref} = H_{L2} = 0$, we obtain:

$$H_L \text{ (kJ/kg solution) } L\text{(kg solution/s)} =$$
$$G_s \text{ (kg carrier/s) } \Delta H_{soln} \text{ (kJ/kg solute) } [Y - Y_2] \qquad (3.5.45)$$

where the enthalpy of the liquid is given by the auxiliary relation:

$$H_L = C_L \text{ (kJ/kg K) } [T_L - T_{L2}] - \Delta H_{soln} \text{ (kJ/kg solution)} \qquad (3.5.46)$$

We obtain for the local temperature rise:

$$T_L - T_{L2} = \frac{G_s}{L_s} \frac{X}{1+X} \frac{\Delta H_{soln}}{C_L}(Y - Y_2) + \frac{\Delta H_{soln}}{C_L} \qquad (3.5.47)$$

where the factor $X/1+X$ was used to convert total liquid flow rate L to solvent flow rate L_s.

To construct the adiabatic equilibrium curve, one chooses a pair of values (X,Y) on the operating line, calculates T_L from Equation 3.5.47, and with the values Y, T_L in hand, establishes X from available equilibrium isotherms. X, Y values obtained determine a point on the adiabatic equilibrium curve.

The remainder of the calculations proceed as outlined in Chapter 2, Illustration 2.1, i.e., the adiabatic operating diagram, Figure 3.22A, is used to compute NTU, which is multiplied by HTU to obtain the design height H = (HTU)(NTU) (Equation 2.26).

Comments:
One notes the simplifications which result from confining the heat effects to the liquid phase. Had this not been done, an additional enthalpy balance for the gas phase would have been required and the concept of an adiabatic equilibrium curve would be jeopardized due to the temperature difference in the two phases. Once the temperature rise has been accounted for, the entire procedure reverts to the familiar territory of the isothermal case. The comfort of familiarity is not to be underestimated, even when dealing with engineering problems.

Heat effects due to the evaporation of solvent have not been accounted for but are often minor due to the relatively low vapor pressure of commonly used solvents. When they can no longer be ignored, both mass and enthalpy balances for the solvent have to be introduced. The simple HTU-NTU concept is then lost and one usually has to resort to numerical solutions of the model equations.

Illustration 3.5.8   Flash Vaporization

In flash vaporization, a liquid mixture is partially vaporized, allowed to come to equilibrium with the residual liquid, and the resulting vapor and liquid phases separated and withdrawn (Figure 3.23A). Of interest here are the resulting liquid

A. Process Flow Sheet

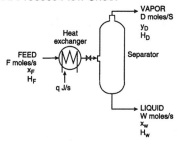

B. Phase Equilibrium

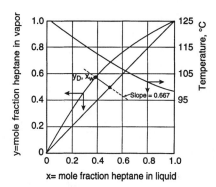

FIGURE 3.23 Flash vaporization of a binary liquid mixture: (A) flow diagram showing heat exchanger, expansion valve, and separator; (B) equilibrium compositions and boiling points at 1 atm of n-heptane n-octane mixtures. (R.E. Treybal. *Mass Transfer Operations,* McGraw-Hill, New York, 1968. With permission.)

and vapor compositions x_w and y_D and the heat requirement q. Note that this is now a steady-state operation. We have

Total mole balance:

$$\text{Rate of moles in} - \text{Rate of moles out} = 0$$

$$F - (D + W) = 0 \tag{3.5.48}$$

Component mole balance (binary system):

$$\text{Rate of moles in} - \text{Rate of moles out} = 0$$

$$x_F F - (y_D D + x_w W) = 0 \tag{3.5.49}$$

Energy balance:

$$\text{Rate of energy in} - \text{Rate of energy out} = 0$$

$$(FH_F + q) - (DH_D + WH_w) = 0 \tag{3.5.50}$$

Equilibrium relation:

$$y_D = f(x_w) \tag{3.5.51}$$

In problems of this type, x_F, T_F, and therefore H_F are known, and either D or W are usually prescribed. Since the equilibrium relation is generally nonlinear, three of the four model equations will be nonlinear. To avoid a numerical solution which can be implemented with standard packages, the following graphical procedure recommends itself:

Upon elimination of F from Equations 3.5.48 and 3.5.49 we obtain:

$$\frac{W}{D} = -\frac{y_D - x_F}{x_w - x_F} \tag{3.5.52}$$

This is the equation of a line of slope W/D passing through the points (y_D, x_w) and (x_F, x_F). The situation is depicted in Figure 3.23B for the system n-heptane/n-octane. Let us consider a concrete example for this system.

Given F = 100 moles, $x_F = 0.5$, $T_F = 25°C$, and D prescribed at 60 moles, we wish to calculate x_w, y_D, and the heat load q. Additional data are:

	n-heptane	n-octane
Liquid heat capacity Cp kJ/mol	0.213	0.242
Latent heat ΔH_c kJ/mol	31.0	35.6

From Equation 3.5.48 we obtain W = 40 moles and, hence, $-W/D = 40/60 = -0.667$. A line with this slope is drawn through the point (x_F, x_F) and intersects the equilibrium curve at $y_D = 0.575$, $x_w = 0.387$, and T = 103°C.

Using the feed temperature $T_F = 25°C$ as datum, the enthalpies needed for the calculation of the heat load q are established as follows:

$$H_F = 0$$

$$H_w = [(x_w Cp)_{C_7} + (x_w Cp)_{C_8}](T - T^0) = [(0.387)(0.213) + (0.613)(0.242)](103 - 25)$$

$$H_w = 18.0 \text{ kJ / mol liquid}$$

$$H_D = y_D[(Cp)_C(T - T^0) + \Delta H_v]_{C_7} + (1 - y_D)[Cp(T - T^0) + \Delta H_v]_{C_8}$$

$$= 0.575[0.213(103 - 25) + 31.0] + (1 - 0.575)[0.242(103 - 25) + 35.6]$$

$$H_D = 50.6 \text{ kJ / mol vapor}$$

Hence, the required total heat load is given by:

$$q = DH_D + WH_w = (60)(50.6) + (40)(18)$$
$$q = 3,760 \text{ kJ/100 moles feed}$$

Illustration 3.5.9   Steam Distillation

It frequently occurs, particularly in the food and pharmaceutical industries, that a heat sensitive and nonvolatile solute has to be separated from a high-boiling organic solvent in which it is dissolved. Conventional distillation does not recommend itself since the required high temperatures would decompose or otherwise adversely affect the solute. Steam distillation is an ingenious procedure designed to avoid this difficulty. In it, live steam is passed into the solution, which initially condenses in contact with the colder solution, but thereafter merely acts as carrier vapor, the latent heat of the solvent being provided by external heating. The crux and the advantage of the procedure is that each of the two immiscible phases, organic and condensed steam, exerts its own vapor pressure so that $P_{Tot} = P^o_{H_2O} + p_L$ where p_L = solvent partial pressure in the exiting vapor. This is in contrast to conventional distillation, where perforce we must have $P_{Tot} = p_L$. Thus, in steam distillation the solvent partial pressure and, hence, the boiling temperature will be considerably *lower* than that prevailing in conventional distillation.

Suppose it is desired to calculate the steam consumption in such a process. It would appear that this would call for simultaneous mass and energy balances, but as it turns out, mass balances alone are sufficient. This can be shown by making solvent and steam balances about the still, as follows.

Unsteady, integral solvent balance (mol/s):

$$\text{Rate of solvent in} - \text{Rate of solvent out} = \frac{\text{Rate of change of}}{\text{solvent content}}$$

$$0 - y_L D = \frac{d}{dt} n_L \tag{3.5.53}$$

or in terms of partial pressure:

$$-\frac{p_L}{P^o_{H_2O} + p_L} D = \frac{d}{dt} n_L$$

where n_L = moles solvent in still, D = total mol/s leaving the still.

Steady-state steam balance (mol/s):

$$\text{Rate of steam in} - \text{Rate of steam out} = 0$$

$$S - \frac{P^o_{H_2O}}{P^o_{H_2O} + p_L} D = 0 \tag{3.5.54}$$

where S = mol/s incoming steam and is assumed known.

Since we have three dependent variables at this stage, n_L, p_L, and D, a third equation is required which is given by an appropriate equilibrium relation. We assume that Raoult's law applies over the range of distillation and obtain:

Raoult's law:

$$p_L = P_L^o \frac{n_L}{n_L + n_s} \tag{3.5.55}$$

where N_s = moles solute in still = constant.

Eliminating D between Equations 3.5.51 and 3.5.52 and integrating we obtain:

$$\int_0^t S\,dt = -\int_{N_L^i}^{N_L^f} \frac{P_{H_2O}^o}{P_L^o} \frac{n_L + n_s}{n_L} \, d\, n_L \tag{3.5.56}$$

where $\int_0^t S\,dt$ represents the desired steam consumption. If the reasonable assumption is made that the pure component vapor pressure ratio $p_{H_2O}^o / p_L^o$ does not vary significantly over the range of distillation, we obtain:

$$\text{Steam consumption} \int_0^t S\,dt \cong \frac{P_{H_2O}^o}{P_L^o} \left[n_L^i - n_L^f - n_s \ln \frac{n_L^f}{n_L^i} \right] \tag{3.5.57}$$

where the superscripts $_i$ and $_f$ denote the initial and final states, respectively, and the pure component vapor pressures are evaluated at an average temperature between the two states.

Comments:

It is evident in this illustration that a good physical understanding of the process is a prerequisite for establishing a correct model. A good grasp of phase equilibria is needed to arrive at the relation $p_{Tot} = P_{H_2O}^o + p_L$ and to appreciate its consequence, i.e., a lowering of the boiling point.

It comes as somewhat of a surprise that no energy balance is required. This is due to the fact that the steam merely acts as a carrier and not as a source of latent heat of vaporization which is instead supplied by external heating. The heat load of the heater is easily calculated from the total latent heat of vaporization: $q_{ext} = (n_L^i - n_L^f)\Delta H_v$.

The illustration again highlights the necessity to proceed step-by-step in setting up a model, starting with the simplest balances that are usually the mass balances and equilibrium relations. The procedure is terminated when the number of equations equals the number of unknowns. In this way the introduction of unnecessary equations, i.e., an energy balance, is avoided.

Practice Problems

3.5.1 Optimum Temperature for a Reversible Reaction — Consider the reversible

first order reaction $A \underset{k_r}{\overset{k_f}{\rightleftarrows}} B$ taking place in a continuous flow stirred tank reactor.

It is desired to maximize the yield of the product B.

Two cases present themselves. If the activation energy of the forward reaction E_f is greater than that of the reverse reaction, which is the usual case for endothermic reactions, the forward reaction will be favored both kinetically and thermodynamically (equilibrium) by increasing the temperature and the best temperature will be the highest possible one. For exothermic reactions, $E_f < E_r$, a low temperature is favored from the thermodynamic point of view, but a high one from that of the kinetics of the reactions. An optimum intermediate temperature T_{opt} will then exist which maximizes conversion.

Show that a material balance for the system yields:

$$C_B = \frac{k_f C_{AF} \tau}{1 + k_f \tau + k_r \tau}$$

where τ is the usual residence time V/Q, and C_{AF} = concentration of reactant in the feed.

From this expression derive the optimum temperature which is given by:

$$T_{opt} = -\frac{E_r}{R \ln\left[\frac{E_f}{(E_r - E_f)} (A)_r \tau \right]} \tag{3.5.58}$$

where A_r is the pre-exponential factor of the Arrhenius equation for the reverse reaction. Note that in this case no energy balance needs to be invoked even though temperature effects are being considered.

3.5.2 Optimum Temperature for Parallel Reactions — Here we consider three parallel irreversible first order reactions that lead to three different products of which only one is the desired one:

$$A \begin{cases} \overset{k_1}{\longrightarrow} R \,(\text{desired}) \\ \overset{k_2}{\longrightarrow} S \,(\text{byproduct}) \\ \overset{k_3}{\longrightarrow} T \,(\text{byproduct}) \end{cases}$$

For the case $E_1 > E_2$, $E_1 < E_3$, the first condition requires a high temperature, for a good yield of R, while the second condition requires a low temperature. Why? An intermediate optimum temperature then exists which results in the highest yield of R. Show by a procedure similar to that called for in Problem 3.5.1, that this temperature is given by:

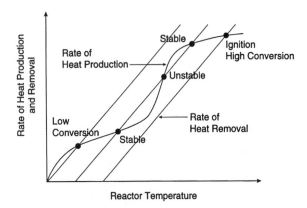

FIGURE 3.24   The van Heerden diagram for an exothermic reaction with cooling in a CSTR. The diagram shows the various possible steady-states at different cooling water temperatures.

$$T_{opt} = \left[\frac{R}{E_3 - E_2} \ln \frac{E_3 - E_1}{E_1 - E_2} \frac{A_3}{A_2} \right]^{-1} \qquad (3.5.59)$$

Note that here again, as in the previous problem, no energy balance arises.

3.5.3 The van Heerden Diagram: Multiple Steady States — The van Heerden Diagram, shown in Figure 3.24, is a plot of the steady-state heat production and removal in a nonisothermal CSTR vs. the tank or effluent temperature. The rate of heat production due to the exothermicity of the reaction shows an inflection, while the rate of heat removal brought about by a cooling coil or water jacket is a straight line. An average cooling water temperature is assumed for simplicity. Steady-state conditions apply at the intersections of heat production and heat removal curves.

The situation which arises here is similar to that seen with a nonisothermal catalyst pellet (Illustration 3.5.3). At low reactor temperatures a single steady-state is obtained, with a low conversion to product. As the temperature is increased, i.e., the cooling line moves to the right, a region is reached where three steady-states exist. Of these, only the upper and lower ones are stable, while the intermediate state is metastable or unstable. With a further increase in reactor temperature, the region of multiplicities is left behind and we return to a single steady-state. This state, however, now produces a high reactant conversion and the temperature at which this occurs is, therefore, termed the *ignition temperature*.

(a) Give qualitative reasons for the shape of the exotherm.
(b) Derive and analyze the equation for heat removal, assuming a constant average cooling water temperature.
(c) Sketch the case where the area of the cooling coil is progressively increased. Is there a jump in temperature similar to that seen in the catalyst pellet and, if so, at which point does it occur?

(d) By considering small disturbances about the three steady-states, arrive at a logical argument as to why the upper and lower states should be stable, while the intermediate state is unstable.

3.5.4 Meteorology —
(a) Using the Humidity Charts and given a daytime temperature and relative humidity as well as a forecast night-time temperature, predict whether dew would form.
(b) Again using the Psychrometric Charts and assuming a strong wind is blowing, indicate under what conditions frost may form even though the temperature remains above $0°C$. What is the maximum temperature which will allow this to happen?

3.5.5 Adiabatic Saturation of Air — Air at $60°C$ and relative humidity of 20% is to be cooled and humidified to a relative humidity of 80% in a spray chamber with recirculation of water.

Calculate the final absolute humidity H_f and temperature T_f. How much heat is removed from the air in the process and what is the percentage change in volume? What is the lowest temperature to which air can be cooled in such a process?

3.5.6 Air Supply to a Drier — An air drier requires 1 kg/min. (dry base) m^3/min. of air at $80°C$ and RH = 20%. The available air is at $25°C$ and RH = 50% and is to be brought to the desired conditions by direct injection of steam. What is the minimum rate at which steam must be supplied, given that its latent heat is 2450 kJ/kg?
Answer: 0.08 kg/min.

3.5.7 Design of a Cooling Tower — Water is to be cooled from $43.3°C$ to $29.7°C$ in a packed column using air entering countercurrently at $29.5°C$ and a wet-bulb temperature of $23.3°C$. The water flow rate is 2.71 kg/m²s and air flow is to be set at 1.5 times the minimum value. The overall mass transfer coefficient for the packing used is estimated at $K_Ga = 3.1 \times 10^{-4}$ mol/m³s Pa. Calculate the height of the tower. (Hint: Use Table 3.6 to express K_Ga in appropriate units.)
Answer: 6.6 m

3.5.8 Breathing Losses in a Solvent Storage Tank — During a rise in ambient temperature the solvent-laden air in the head space of storage tanks expands and is partially expelled into the atmosphere through a vent pipe. When the temperature drops, the process reverses itself and fresh solvent-free air enters the head space. Subsequent cycles of rising and falling temperature cause a cumulative loss in solvent. An accurate calculation of this loss would require a knowledge of the time and space dependent concentrations and temperatures in the tank and would, thus, call for the solution of a set of PDEs along with the appropriate equilibrium relation.

The somewhat irregular geometry (tank + vent-pipe) and the possibility of both conductive and free convective transport, plus uncertainties in the external heat transfer resistance make this a formidable problem to solve. Fortunately, for environmental assessments and other purposes it is often sufficient to estimate the *maximum possible* emissions rather than the detailed daily and hourly variations. This can be achieved by assuming that the tank contents are well mixed and in thermal and phase equilibrium at any instant. In other words, the air-solvent mixture expanding into the atmosphere is taken to be saturated at the ambient temperature of the moment. Since the temperature variations involved are rarely more than 20 to 25°C, a linearized version of the vapor pressure p_s° of the solvent may be used: $p_s^\circ = aT + b$.

Use this expression, together with integral unsteady balances for the solvent vapor and air to show that the maximum moles solvent lost, n_s, during a temperature rise from T_1 to T_2 is given by:

$$n_s = \frac{V}{R}\left[\left(a + \frac{ab}{p_T - b}\right)\ln\frac{P_T - b - aT_1}{P_T - b - aT_2}\frac{T_2}{T_1} + b\left(\frac{1}{T_2} - \frac{1}{T_1}\right)\right]$$

where V = volume of head space, R = gas constant, and P_T = total pressure.

3.5.9 Design of a Partial Condenser — Partial condensers are used extensively in distillation processes whenever it is desired or convenient to withdraw part of the product as vapor while the liquid portion is recycled for further processing or to provide reflux for distillation columns. The design of such condensers requires a knowledge of the relevant compositions as well as the cooling requirements.

For the system described in Illustration 3.5.8, calculate (a) the equilibrium vapor and liquid compositions and (b) the cooling requirements q(J/s) for a vapor feed composition $x_F = 0.8$ mol fraction n-heptane and a vapor to liquid split V/L (mol/mol) = 0.5.

Answer: (a) $x_L = 0.75$, $y_V = 0.86$

3.5.10 Cryogenic Liquefaction: Simultaneous Steady-State Algebraic Mass and Energy Balances — The field of cryogenics is generally associated with temperatures below −150°C and includes as an important application the liquefaction of the so-called permanent gases, among them He (b.p. 4.2 K), H_2 (b.p. 20.3 K), N_2 (b.p. 77.4 K), O_2 (b.p. 90.1 K), and CH_4 (b.p. 111.7 K).

Contemporary industrial liquefaction processes are based on two classical cycles developed at the turn of the century by C. von Linde and G. Claude. In the Linde process, cooling and ultimate condensation is achieved by expansion through a valve utilizing the Joule-Thomson (J-T) effect (Figure 3.25A). The Claude process removes energy from part of the gas stream by allowing it to do work in an expansion engine, as well as by utilizing a J-T valve. J-T expansion is irreversible and taken to be *isenthalpic*. (Recall that for steady flow systems, $\Delta H + \Delta(K \cdot E) + \Delta(P \cdot E) \pm W_s \pm q = 0$ so that for negligible potential and kinetic energy changes, and heat transfer, $\Delta H = 0$.) Expansion in an engine, on the other hand, can be considered *isentropic* in the limit of reversible (100% efficiency) and adiabatic operation. The important calculations can then be performed by combining simple mass and energy balances with the use of so-called Mollier diagrams. These diagrams are plots of temperature T vs. entropy S, and contain the isobaric and isenthalpic pathways as

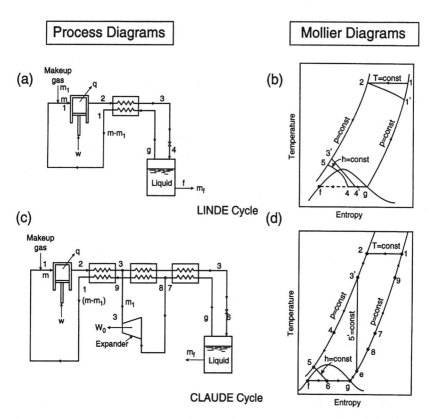

FIGURE 3.25   Flow diagrams (a and c) and T-S Mollier diagrams (b and d) for the Linde and Claude processes used in the cryogenic liquefaction of gases. (R. Barron. *Cryogenic Systems,* McGraw-Hill, New York, 1966. With permission.)

parametric curves. In these calculations it is customary initially to neglect all irreversibilities except those at the J-T valve, bringing them in at a later stage using expander and heat exchanger efficiencies. The path for nonideal operations is indicated by primed numbers.

In a typical Linde process, the gas is first compressed isothermally (path 1 → 2), followed by isobaric cooling by cold return vapor from the liquefier (path 2 → 3), Figure 3.25B. It is then allowed to expand through a J-T valve, which leads into the two phase region (path 3 → 4). Uncondensed vapor is returned to the compressor after passage through the isobaric heat exchanger. Note that the latter carries a high-pressure gas stream to the liquefier and a low pressure return to the compressor. The pathways of the Claude process can be established in similar fashion (see Figure 3.25D), the main difference here being the isentropic expansion step of a part of the feed stream which is added to the cold return vapor (Figure 3.25C).

(a) What is the significance of the horizontal "tie-line" f-g in the two-phase region? How would you estimate liquid yield by visual location of points 4 or 6?

(b) Show that for the Claude cycle, the liquid yield y is given by:

$$y = m_f / m = \frac{H_1 - H_2}{H_1 - H_f} + x \frac{H_3 - H_e}{H_1 - H_f}$$

where x = fraction of gas diverted to the expander (subscripts refer to the streams shown in the diagrams of Figure 3.25). Use this expression to derive the liquid yield for the Linde process. Which process provides the higher yield and what are the penalties to achieve this?

(c) Heat exchanger effectiveness ε (see Illustration 3.3.2) can be defined in terms of the stream enthalpies as follows:

$$\varepsilon = \frac{H_1^{\,1} - H_g}{H_1 - H_g}$$

Show that for the Linde process this results in the revised liquid yield:

$$y = \frac{H_1 - H_2 - (1 - \varepsilon)(H_1 - H_g)}{H_1 - H_f - (1 - \varepsilon)(H_1 - H_g)}$$

(d) When confronted with a fraction, one should instinctively look for parameter values which reduce the numerator or denominator to zero. Do this for part (c) and indicate why proper heat exchanger design is particularly crucial in cryogenic liquefaction processes.

3.6 COMBINED MASS, ENERGY, AND MOMENTUM BALANCES

When pressure or viscous forces, or those due to a change in the rate of momentum, begin to have a significant influence on a process, a momentum or force balance has to be invoked in addition to the mass and energy balances. This requirement arises in the important field of compressible flow, tubular reactions involving gas flow, vaporizers and condensers, as well as a host of other applications. Use of an additional balance brings about an increase in the number of equations and the complexity of the model. Numerical methods are used with greater frequency although many problems can still be solved analytically and the result used for a more meaningful analysis of the process.

We start our illustrations by considering both isothermal and adiabatic compressible flow in a pipe. We encounter here the concept of the velocity of sound and an illustration is devoted to the derivation and analysis of this topic. Additional problems involving compressible flow are addressed after which we examine the simultaneous conservation laws which apply to vaporization and condensation processes, as well as chemical reactions. Some additional important aspects are left to the Practice Problems.

The reader should be prepared to face a considerable escalation in the complexity of the models and in the variety of equations that arise. We shall try to be helpful in this endeavor.

Illustration 3.6.1　Isothermal Compressible Flow in a Pipe

In deriving the integrated forms of the Bernoulli and Mechanical Energy Equations 3.4.54 and 3.4.60 the assumption had been made that flow was incompressible, i.e., that both velocity v and density ρ were constant along the pipe. These conditions apply to the flow of liquids or in gas flow where the pressure drop does not amount to more than 5 to 10% of the total pressure. Air flow in large ventilation ducts falls in this category.

When pressure drop exceeds these limits, compressibility effects can no longer be disregarded. Not only does pressure decrease significantly, but so does the density, while velocity experiences a corresponding increase in order to maintain constant mass flow rate. One must then return to the differential form of the mechanical energy balance that is obtained by extending the differential Bernoulli Equation 3.5.53. We obtain, for a horizontal pipe,

$$\frac{dp}{\rho} + vdv + 2\frac{fv^2}{d}dz = 0 \qquad (3.6.1)$$

where z is the distance along the pipe. Friction factor f is constant since ρv and, hence, the Reynolds number are constant by virtue of the steady-state mass balance or continuity equation:

$$F \text{ (kg/s)} = \rho_1 v_1 A_1 = \rho_2 v_2 A_2 = \rho v A = \text{constant} \qquad (3.6.2)$$

or

$$G \text{ (kg/sm}^2\text{)} = \rho_1 v_1 = \rho_2 v_2 = \rho v = \text{constant} \qquad (3.6.3)$$

Dividing Equation 3.6.1 by v^2 and assuming ideal gas behavior, we obtain from Equation 3.6.3 $v^2 = G^2/(pM/RT)^2$ and Equation 3.6.1 becomes:

$$\frac{Mpdp}{G^2RT} + \frac{dv}{v} + 2f\frac{dz}{d} = 0 \qquad (3.6.4)$$

Integrating each term in turn yields the relation:

$$\frac{1}{2}\frac{M}{G^2RT}(p_2^2 - p_1^2) + \ln\frac{v_2}{v_1} + 2f\frac{L}{d} = 0 \qquad (3.6.5)$$

The logarithmic term is usually small and can be neglected, so that Equation 3.6.5 can be solved for p_2, and the pressure drop $\Delta p = p_2 - p_1$ for a given system calculated.

Alternatively, an explicit equation in the mass velocity G may be obtained as follows. We differentiate the continuity equation for a duct of constant cross-section and obtain $dv/v = -d\rho/\rho = dp/p$. Introducing this relation into Equation 3.6.4, integrating as before, and solving for G yields:

$$G = \frac{M(p_1^{\,2} - p_2^{\,2})}{RT[2fL/d - \ln p_1/p_2]} \tag{3.6.6}$$

Illustration 3.6.2   Propagation of a Pressure Wave, Velocity of Sound, Mach Number

Pressure waves, such as those due to sound, explosions, or other disturbances, travel with a finite speed through a particular medium which may be a gas, liquid, or solid. Our primary interest here will be in the propagation velocity of such waves through a gas, although the general case of an arbitrary medium also will be addressed briefly. These velocities can be explicitly derived by a judicious application of mass (continuity), energy, and momentum balances. To do this, we consider the pressure disturbance caused by a piston moving with a velocity v_2 in a gas initially at rest, $v_1 = 0$, and at a pressure p_1. Figure 3.26A shows the pressure wave at a particular time and position moving with the propagation velocity a. In Figure 3.26B we have brought the wave to a standstill in a fixed control volume by superimposing a velocity (a) on the disturbance. Experiments have shown that the process of pressure prop-

A. Moving Wave

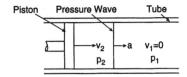

B. Fixed Control Volume

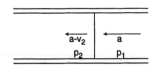

FIGURE 3.26   Pressure wave generated by a moving piston: (A) shows the variables for a moving wave at a particular time and position; in (B) the wave is fixed in space by imposing a negative velocity, $-v_2$.

agation is both adiabatic and frictionless. Balances taken about the stationary wave are then as follows:

Continuity equation:

$$\rho_1 aA = \rho_2(a - v_2)A \tag{3.6.7}$$

Momentum balance:

$$(p_1 - p_2)A = \rho_1 aA[(a - v_2) - a] \tag{3.6.8}$$

Energy balance:

$$\frac{(a - v_2)^2 - a^2}{2} = \frac{\gamma}{\gamma - 1}\left(\frac{p_1}{\rho_1} - \frac{p_2}{\rho_2}\right) \tag{3.6.9}$$

This is but one of many versions of the energy equation one encounters in the literature. It is seen to be a reduced form of the general balance (Equation 3.3.85) with the right side representing the enthalpy change ΔH. Derivation of Equation 3.6.9 is left to the exercises, see Practice Problem 3.6.4.

Eliminating ρ_2 and v_2 from these three equations and solving for the propagation velocity we obtain the expression:

$$a = \left(\frac{\gamma p_1}{\rho_1}\right)^{1/2}\left[\frac{\gamma - 1}{2} + \frac{p_2}{p_1}\frac{\gamma + 1}{2}\right]^{1/2}\frac{1}{\gamma^{1/2}} \tag{3.6.10}$$

This relation is quite general and applies to the propagation of an arbitrary pressure disturbance in a gas with a heat capacity ratio of $\gamma = C_p/C_v$. For explosions, the pressure ratio $p_2/p_1 > 1$, so that pressure propagation velocities of considerable magnitude may be attained.

Velocity of sound — Consider now the case $p_2/p_1 = 1$. This situation arises in the propagation of sound where upstream and downstream pressures are equal. We obtain from Equation 3.6.10:

$$a = c = (\gamma p/\rho)^{1/2} \tag{3.6.11}$$

and for an ideal gas

$$c = (\gamma RT/M)^{1/2} \tag{3.6.12}$$

Thus, the velocity of sound c is seen to vary directly with temperature and inversely with the molar mass of an ideal gas.

For the propagation through both gases as well as liquids and solids, a slightly modified approach leads to the general relation:

TABLE 3.22
Velocity of Sound of Various Materials
at 15.5°C and 1 atm

Material	Velocity c, m/s
(1) Gases	
Hydrogen	1294
Helium	1000
Air	340
Carbon dioxide	266
(2) Liquids	
Water	1490
Ethyl alcohol	1200
Glycerin	1860
Mercury	1450
(3) Solids	
Ice	3200
Aluminum	5150
Steel	5060

$$c = \left(\gamma \frac{\partial p}{\partial \rho} \Big|_T \right)^{1/2} \qquad (3.6.13)$$

where $\partial p / \partial \rho$ is the inverse of the compressibility of the medium.

Note that c varies in the progression $c_{solid} > c_{liquid} > c_{gas}$ which is in the same sequence as $\partial p / \partial \rho$. A listing of the speed of sound in various media is given in the accompanying Table 3.22.

Mach Number — This is a conveniently defined velocity ratio which is a measure of the departure of velocity v of a gas from its speed of sound:

$$Ma = v/c \qquad (3.6.14)$$

For sonic flow, the Mach number $Ma = 1$.

A distinction is made, particularly by aerodynamicists, among the following flow regimes:

$Ma < 0.3$ Incompressible Flow — Density effects are small.

$0.3 < Ma < 0.8$ Subsonic Flow — Density effects are important.

$0.8 < Ma < 1.2$ Transonic Flow — This regime straddles sonic gas flow and is characterized by the appearance of so-called shock waves. These are comprised of narrow regions across which a sudden transition from subsonic flow ($Ma < 1$) to supersonic flow ($Ma > 1$) occurs, with an attendant jump change in pressure.

$1.2 < Ma < 3.0$ Supersonic Flow — Existence of shock waves; no subsonic flow, i.e., shock transitions are from a low to a higher *supersonic* Mach number.

3.0 > Ma Hypersonic Flow — Strong effect of shock waves and other flow changes.

Illustration 3.6.3 Adiabatic Compressible Flow in a Pipe

In the case of isothermal pipe flow (Illustration 3.6.1) we were able to arrive at an expression for flow rate as a function of pressure drop by a simple integration of the mechanical energy balance, using as adjuncts the ideal gas law and the continuity equation. In the adiabatic case, temperature is no longer constant and the full complement of balances, together with auxiliary relations, has to be used.

Mass balance:

$$F = \rho \, v \, A = \text{constant} \qquad (3.6.2)$$

or

$$G = \rho \, v = \text{constant} \qquad (3.6.3)$$

or

$$\frac{d\rho}{\rho} = -\frac{dv}{v}$$

Energy balance (q = 0):

$$\frac{v_2^{\,2} - v_1^{\,2}}{2} = \frac{\gamma}{\gamma - 1}\left(\frac{p_1}{\rho_1} - \frac{p_2}{\rho_2}\right) \qquad (3.6.9)$$

or

$$\frac{p}{\rho}\left(1 + \frac{\gamma - 1}{2\gamma}\frac{v^2 \rho}{p}\right) = \text{constant} \qquad (3.6.15)$$

Mechanical energy balance (force balance):

$$\frac{dp}{\rho} + vdv + 2f\frac{v^2}{d^1}dz = 0 \qquad (3.6.1)$$

Ideal gas law:

$$\rho = \frac{pM}{RT} \qquad (3.6.16)$$

The model is then comprised of four equations in the four state variables p, ρ, v, and T. Frequently the Mach number is introduced as an additional variable, requiring a fifth relation:

$$Ma = v\,/\,c = \left[= \left(\gamma \frac{RT}{M} \right)^{1/2} \right] \text{for ideal gas} \qquad (3.6.17)$$

Full solutions of various forms of this formidable set exist, of which a particularly useful one has been cast into graphical form, to be discussed below. One relation, that of the pressure drop as a function of Mach number, is of special interest and can be obtained by differentiating Equation 3.6.15 and using the other two balances to eliminate dv and dρ. We obtain:

$$\frac{dp}{dz} = \frac{-2f\rho v^2}{d} \left[\frac{1 + (\gamma - 1)Ma^2}{1 - Ma^2} \right] \qquad (3.6.18)$$

Several features of pipe flow are revealed by this relation. For small Mach numbers, Ma $\rightarrow$ 0, or $\partial p / \partial \rho \rightarrow 0$, it reduces to the equation for incompressible flow in a horizontal pipe. For more substantial Mach numbers, 0.3 < Ma < 1, the pressure drop is negative in the direction of flow and compressible flow can proceed. As Ma is increased toward unity, pressure drop and, hence, flow rate increase rapidly until, at a value of Ma = 1, the pressure gradient becomes infinite, pressure itself is at a minimum, and the fluid velocity equals the velocity of sound. Beyond that point, at Ma > 1, the pressure drop becomes positive and flow ceases. We conclude from this that the maximum velocity attainable in a duct of constant cross-section is the velocity of sound. Since velocity increases with distance along the pipe, this maximum will be reached at the pipe outlet. To obtain supersonic flows in a duct, the cross-sectional area must increase in the direction of flow. This will be demonstrated in Illustration 3.6.6.

To provide a physical underpinning to this phenomenon of limiting sonic flow, we display in Figure 3.27 the pressure profiles that result from a progressive increase in inlet pressure. Figure 3.27A shows a modest pressure drop obtained at low flow rates. An increase in inlet pressure propagates downstream, adjusting pressure to a steeper gradient and, hence, higher flow rates (Figure 3.27B). As pressure is increased further, a point is ultimately reached where the flow at the outlet reaches sonic velocity. An additional increase in inlet pressure at this point will no longer be able to propagate downstream to adjust the pressure gradient since to do so it would have to exceed the speed of sound. The pressure increase beyond the sonic level will be held back as a standing discontinuity or pressure shock wave at or near the pipe inlet (Figure 3.27C).

A consequence of this phenomenon is that a pipe of given length and diameter cannot accommodate arbitrarily high gas flow rates. Beyond a certain value G* = G_{Max}, an increase in inlet pressure will not result in increased flow. To accommodate flow rates higher than G_{Max}, one has to either increase the diameter or reduce the

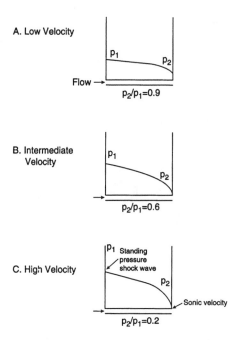

FIGURE 3.27 Pressure profiles in compressible duct flow with increasing inlet pressure: (A) low flow rates, (B) intermediate flow rates, (C) sonic velocity at the exit-standing shock at inlet.

effective length of the pipe by recompressing the gas at intervals. The latter method is standard practice in the operation of long-distance gas transmission lines.

If instead of increasing inlet pressure we progressively *reduce outlet pressure*, a similar sequence of events will take place. Flow will increase until we attain sonic velocity at the outlet. Further reductions in pressure will result in a standing shock wave that is now at or near the *outlet*, and flow will remain constant at G_{Max}. Another way of putting this is to say that the flow rate anticipated from an increase in pressure is "choked" down to the value G_{Max}.

The question arises as to whether such limiting velocities materialize in liquid flows. In Table 3.17, we indicated that liquid velocities in pipe flow, i.e., those used in conventional operations with standard pumps and construction materials are of the order 1 m/s. Sonic velocities in liquids, on the other hand, are three orders of magnitude higher (Table 3.22). The pressures required to generate sonic flow, therefore, would be enormous and beyond the ordinary strength of the containing pipes. Hence, limiting flow considerations do not in general arise in the case of liquids.

Illustration 3.6.4 Compressible Flow Charts

The complexity of the full model for compressible flow, Equations 3.6.2 to 3.6.17 have led to their solution by numerical methods and the compilation of the results in the form of convenient flow charts. A typical result is shown in Figure 3.28 which represents a plot of the downstream to upstream pressure ratio p_2/p_1 against the

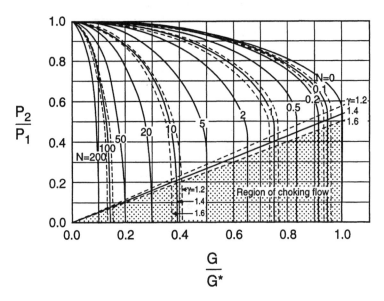

FIGURE 3.28   Chart for the computation of compressible flow in ducts. p_2/p_1 = downstream to upstream, pressure ratio, G/G^* = dimensionless mass velocity, N = dimensionless pipe number fL/d. (O. Levenspiel, *AIChE J.*, 23:402, 1977. With permission.)

dimensionless mass velocity $G/G^* = G/G_{Max}$, where G_{Max} is the flow corresponding to the sonic velocity in frictionless flow, given by:

$$G^* = G_{Max} = p_1 \left[\frac{M\gamma}{RT_1} \left(\frac{2}{\gamma+1} \right)^{(\gamma+1)/(\gamma-1)} \right]^{1/2} \qquad (3.6.19)$$

The parameter $N = f\dfrac{L}{d_h}$, also called the pipe number, represents the piping configuration with d_h = hydraulic diameter, equal d for a cylindrical pipe, L its length, and f the friction factor. As noted before, the Reynolds number, of which f is a function, can be written in the form Re = Gd/μ. Since G is constant for ducts of constant cross-section, Re and f will likewise be constant along the entire length of the pipe.

The plots show that for a given pipe configuration N, the mass velocity G through a pipe of length L and diameter d initially increases as inlet pressure p_1 is increased or p_2 is dropped. Flow is subsonic throughout the pipe under these conditions. Further reductions in the pressure ratio lead to an additional increase in G until a critical ratio $(p_2/p_1)_c$ is reached. At this point G has reached a maximum and remains constant at that value with further decreases in the pressure ratio. We are now in the domain denoted as "region of choking flow." Note that the sonic velocity at which this occurs decreases with increasing friction. For frictionless flow, N = 0, the critical pressure ratio reaches a maximum and is given by:

$$(p_2 / p_1)_c = \left(\frac{2}{\gamma+1}\right)^{\gamma/\gamma-1} \tag{3.6.20}$$

with

$$(T_2/T_1)_c = 2/(\gamma + 1) \tag{3.6.21}$$

For air, $\gamma = 1.4$, so that for frictionless flow of air the critical ratios are given by $(p_2/p_1)_c = 0.53$ and $(T_2/T_1)_c = 0.83$. These are useful limiting numbers to remember for *all* gas flows, since γ has only a marginal effect on their values.

Suppose now that we wish to establish whether a pipe of given length L and diameter d will accommodate a prescribed air flow. Let us set $L = 10$ m, $d = 0.0525$ m, $G = 7500$ kg/m²s, $T_0 = 20°C$, $P_1 = 1.0$ MPA. f is found to be 0.003 for the flow rate and pipe in question. We obtain from Equation 3.6.19:

$$G^* = G_{Max} = P_1 \left[\frac{M\gamma}{RT_0}\left(\frac{2}{\gamma+1}\right)^{(\gamma+1)/(\gamma-1)}\right]^{1/2}$$

$$= 1\times10^6 \left[\frac{(29)(1.4)}{(8314)(293)}\left(\frac{2}{1.4+1}\right)^{(1.4+1)/(1.4-1)}\right]^{1/2}$$

$$G^* = 1970 \, kg \, / \, m^2 s$$

where 8314 is the value for R in units of kg m²/kmol s²K.

Thus $G/G^* > 1$, and the prescribed flow does not materialize. Instead it is reduced or "choked" to a value set by the pipe number N. We have:

$$N = fL/d = (0.003)(10/0.0525) = 0.57$$

The corresponding value of G/G^* read from the chart is 0.825, so that the actual flow rate which materializes is

$$G = 0.825 \, G^* = (0.825)(1970) = 1625 \, kg/m^2 s$$

i.e., 26% of the prescribed value.

Illustration 3.6.5   Compressible Flow in Variable Area Ducts with Friction and Heat Transfer

Removal of the conditions of adiabatic flow and a duct of constant cross-section brings about a further escalation in model complexity. The terms involving channel cross-section must be altered in appropriate fashion and a heat transfer term $q = \pm$ h dA $(T_{ext} - T)$ incorporated in the energy Equations 3.6.9 or 3.6.15. T_{ext} will either have to be known as a function of longitudinal distance z or must alternatively be

TABLE 3.23
Coefficients of Compressible Flow Model Equations

	$dq/C_p T$	dA/A	$dh_f\, M/RT$
$\dfrac{dN}{N}$	$\dfrac{1+\gamma N}{1-N}$	$-\dfrac{[2+(\gamma-1)N}{1-N}$	$\dfrac{2+(\gamma-1)N}{1-N}$
$\dfrac{dp}{p}$	$-\dfrac{\gamma N}{1-N}$	$\dfrac{\gamma N}{1-N}$	$-\dfrac{(\gamma-1)N+1}{1-N}$
$\dfrac{dT}{T}$	$\dfrac{1-\gamma N}{1-N}$	$\dfrac{(\gamma-1)N}{1-N}$	$\dfrac{(\gamma-1)N}{1-N}$
$\dfrac{d\rho}{\rho}$	$-\dfrac{1}{1-N}$	$\dfrac{N}{1-N}$	$-\dfrac{1}{1-N}$
$\dfrac{dv}{v}$	$\dfrac{1}{1-N}$	$-\dfrac{1}{1-N}$	$\dfrac{1}{1-N}$

Source: R.C. Binder, *Fluid Mechanics,* 4th ed., Prentice Hall, Upper Saddle River, NJ, 1962. With permission.

established by the addition of a differential energy balance over the external phase. The manipulations necessary to arrive at a particular set of profiles or some functional relation among the dependent variables (say Ma = f(p)) now become exceedingly tedious. Some relief may be obtained through the use of a compilation based on determinants of the coefficients of the model, shown in Table 3.23. It provides a *simple and systematic procedure for arriving at any desired set of differential interrelations among the variables* which can be integrated numerically or in some important cases even analytically. Use of the table follows.

The terms in the left-hand column are placed individually on the left side of each equation. The *sum* of the terms indicated by the top row makes up the right-hand side of the equations with the coefficients of each term drawn from the tabulation. Note that these coefficients are a function of Mach number and γ only.

dq is the differential heat transfer rate, $dh_f = \dfrac{2fv^2}{D}\,dz$ the differential frictional head, and $N = Ma^2$.

For example, the equation for dN/N takes the form:

$$\frac{dN}{N} = \frac{\dfrac{dq}{C_pT}(1+\gamma N)-\dfrac{dA}{A}[2+(\gamma-1)N]+\dfrac{Mdh_f}{RT}[2+(\gamma-1)N]}{1-N} \qquad (3.6.22)$$

or in terms of axial distance derivatives

$$\frac{dN}{dz} = \frac{\dfrac{dq}{dz}(1+\gamma N)\dfrac{N}{Cp\,T} - \dfrac{dA}{dz}[2+(\gamma-1)N]\dfrac{N}{A} + \dfrac{dh_f}{dz}[2+(\gamma-1)N]\dfrac{MN}{RT}}{1-N} \tag{3.6.23}$$

Four additional equations in dp/p, dT/T, $d\rho/\rho$, and dv/v, derived in similar fashion, complete the model in the five state variables N (i.e., Ma^2), pressure p, temperature T, density ρ, and velocity v.

It is not always necessary to solve the entire set which must be done numerically. Analytical solutions are possible in restricted cases (see Practice Problem 3.6.5), and single equations may be scanned in simple fashion to establish qualitative trends with respect to heat addition, friction, or area variation. For example, Equation 3.6.23 shows that in subsonic flow, N < 1, the effect of heat addition, friction, and an area *decrease* is to increase the Mach number. As another example, we consider frictionless compressible flow in a pipe of constant diameter. Application of Table 3.23 then yields:

$$\frac{dN}{dz} = \frac{N}{Cp\,T}\left(\frac{1+\gamma N}{1-N}\right)\frac{dq}{dz} \tag{3.6.24}$$

$$\frac{dp}{dz} = -\frac{\gamma N}{1-N}\frac{p}{Cp\,T}\frac{dq}{dz} \tag{3.6.25}$$

$$\frac{dT}{dz} = \frac{1-\gamma N}{1-N}\frac{1}{Cp}\frac{dq}{dz} \tag{3.6.26}$$

These equations show that in subsonic flow, an addition of heat along the pipe will increase the Mach number and reduce the pressure. When $\gamma N < 1$ the result of heat addition is an increase in temperature. However, for $\gamma N > 1$ and with the flow still subsonic, heat addition will, paradoxically, cause a *decrease* in temperature. The reason for this is that in this narrow range of flow, the expansion and the attendant cooling of the gas outstrips the heating effect.

Illustration 3.6.6   The Converging-Diverging Nozzle

An interesting use of Table 3.23 is the analysis of flow in a converging-diverging duct, shown in Figure 3.29. Two cases arise: for adiabatic frictionless flow, the table yields, after rearrangement, the following relation:

$$\frac{dA}{dz} = -\frac{A(1-N)}{N[2+(\gamma-1)N]}\frac{dN}{dz} \tag{3.6.27}$$

This equation shows that for the converging segment and $dN/dz > 0$, the flow will be subsonic. At the throat, $dA/dz = 0$ and, hence, sonic flow prevails, N = 1.

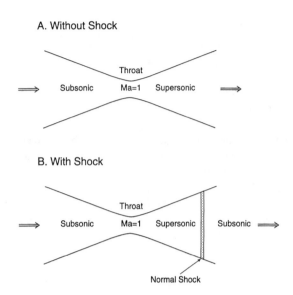

FIGURE 3.29 Flow in a converging-diverging duct: (A) frictionless, adiabatic flow with no shock formation, (B) flow with friction and/or heat transfer. Formation of shock.

Beyond that point, the condition $dA/dz > 0$ requires $N > 1$, i.e., the flow becomes supersonic.

In flow with friction and/or heat transfer, smooth transitions do not usually occur and we see instead the formation of a jump transition in the form of a normal shock from supersonic to subsonic flow (Figure 3.29B). The relation between upstream and downstream Mach numbers, known as the Rayleigh line, also can be derived through the use of Table 3.23 (see Practice Problem 3.6.5). Note that the case of adiabatic frictionless flow for constant cross-section, seemingly not covered by the table, can be accommodated by retaining an extra term, say dq, eliminating it subsequently by division of the resulting equations.

Illustration 3.6.7 Forced Convection Boiling: Vaporizers and Evaporators

We previously had seen in Illustration 3.3.8 the complexities that can arise when a liquid is boiled in a tank with no in or outflow, also known as pool boiling. No net production of vapor was considered there and the principal parameter effect examined was that of the temperature driving force $\Delta T = (T_{ext} - T)$. In a flow system, such as horizontal or vertical vaporizers and evaporators, a net production of vapor is involved which gives rise to additional phenomena. These phenomena and the phase changes and heat transfer mechanisms associated with them are illustrated for a vertical tube in Figure 3.30. The feed which typically enters as a liquid below its boiling point undergoes convective heating near the inlet until it comes to a boil. A period of nucleate boiling then ensues, similar to that encountered in pool boiling in which vapor bubbles formed at the wall pass into the liquid where they ultimately

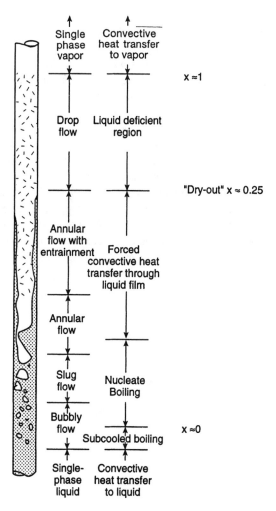

FIGURE 3.30 Flow regimes and modes of heat transfer during boiling of a liquid in a vertical vaporizer.

coalesce into slugs ("slug flow"). A considerable reduction in liquid volume occurs until a point is reached where the liquid is confined to an annular film at the wall and droplets in the vapor core. In this region, the so-called annular flow regime, evaporation at the surface of the annulus takes place by convective heat transfer through the liquid film. The entrained droplets also undergo evaporation and a further reduction in liquid volume occurs. Eventually the annular film completely disappears and we enter the region of drop or mist flow. This phenomenon which occurs at vapor fractions of about 0.25 is referred to as "dry-out" or "burn-out" since there is an immediate increase in wall temperature and an attendant risk of damaging or "burning" the tubes. This temperature rise is caused by the sudden drop in heat transfer coefficient from liquid to gas film values, and is to be avoided in practical operations. One way of doing this is to identify a critical heat flux $(q/A)_c$ at which the transition occurs, but the correlations of this quantity with system parameters are still somewhat tentative and incomplete. An alternative is to model the process and identify the distance from the inlet at which vapor fraction exceeds a certain prescribed value, say 0.2. This fraction is termed the vapor quality $x = V/(L + V)$ where V and L are the vapor and liquid mass flow rates, respectively. Thus, $x \approx 1$ in the mist flow region and $x \cong 0$ at the tube inlet (see Figure 3.30).

Several different models have been proposed for this highly complex system of which we adopt the so-called separated flow model. In it, vapor and liquid are considered as separate entities moving at constant but not necessarily equal velocities and in thermodynamic equilibrium with each other.

Let us consider the case of a pure liquid being vaporized. In setting up the model, all three conservation laws have to be invoked since pressure drop will affect the boiling point and must be taken into account. This calls for the use of a mechanical energy balance. Note again that vapor and liquid are everywhere in equilibrium, i.e., the vapor is saturated and at the boiling point corresponding to the pressure at a particular point. We obtain:

Total mass balance:

$$\text{Rate of mass in} - \text{Rate of mass out} = 0$$

$$(L + V) - \left(\begin{matrix} L + \Delta L \\ +V + \Delta V \end{matrix} \right) = 0 \qquad (3.6.28)$$

Cancelling terms and going to the limit we obtain:

$$\frac{dV}{dL} + 1 = 0$$

or equivalently,

$$dV/dz + dL/dz = 0 \qquad (3.6.29)$$

Energy balance:

$$\text{Rate of energy in} - \text{Rate of energy out} = 0$$

$$(H_L + H_v)|_z + q_{avg} - (H_L + H_v)|_{z+\Delta z} = 0 \qquad (3.6.30)$$

We use the inlet temperature as reference so that H (J/s) is made up of sensible and latent heat terms as follows:

$$H_L = L \, Cp_L \, (T - T_o) \qquad (3.6.31)$$

$$H_v = V \, C_{pL} \, (T - T_o) + V \Delta H_v \qquad (3.6.32)$$

We note that in these expressions, both temperature and flow rates L, V are state variables and have to be differentiated. Upon introducing the auxiliary relations into Equation 3.6.30, dividing by Δz, and going to the limit, we obtain:

$$L \, Cp_L \frac{dT}{dz} + V \, Cp_L \frac{dT}{dz} + \Delta H_v \frac{dV}{dz} - \pi dU(T_{ext} - T) = 0 \qquad (3.6.33)$$

Mechanical energy balance:

We note at the outset that in this balance three terms will in principle vary with distance — kinetic energy, potential energy (vertical devices), and friction. To reduce the complexity of the model we confine ourselves to friction only. Even then, however, the model is difficult to formulate because of the complexity of the different flow regimes and their impact on pressure drop. We limit ourselves for the time being to a general formulation and write:

$$\left(\frac{dp}{dz}\right)_f = f(L, V) \qquad (3.6.34)$$

The model then can be completed with an appropriate vapor pressure expression such as the Clausius-Clapeyron or Antoine Equations.

Equilibrium relation:

$$p = f(T) \qquad (3.6.35)$$

It consists of the four equations (3.6.29, 3.6.33, 3.6.34, and 3.6.35) in the four-state variables p, T, V, and L.

The heat transfer coefficient U and the frictional pressure drop $(dp/dz)_f$ now need to be addressed. Both are complex entities and numerous expressions, often related to a particular flow regime or system, have been suggested. One can avoid generalizations by fitting test data for a particular system to a simple but logical relation between film coefficient and vapor quality. One suggested relation has the form:

$$h = \frac{h_L}{1 + K_2 x^{K_3}} \qquad (3.6.36)$$

which reflects in simple fashion the decrease in heat transfer coefficient h_L, taken to be the normal liquid film coefficient, with increased vapor quality x.

Complexities also are encountered in the correlations of pressure drop with liquid and vapor flow rates and physical properties of the system. Here again, as in the case of heat transfer coefficients, empirical simplification is often used, of which a preferred version is

$$-\frac{dp}{dz} = K_1 L^{K_2} V^{K_3} \qquad (3.6.37)$$

The full model need not always be solved. Simpler correlations and simpler demands can also yield useful information. For example, for nucleation boiling of water in a vertical tube, the following heat transfer coefficient has been recommended:

$$h = 2.54 \, (\Delta T_b)^3 \exp (p/1.551) \qquad (3.6.38)$$

where $\Delta T_b = T_{surface} - T_{saturation}$, p is in units of MPa, and h in units of kJ/m^2sK.

Consider now the case of water entering a 1 m-long tube of diameter 2.54 cm at 5 atm and at its boiling point which is assumed constant, i.e., pressure drop is neglected. The flow rate F is 10^{-2} kg/s and it is desired to calculate the fraction evaporated, i.e., the quality of the steam at the exit, $x = V/F$. ΔT_b is set at 10°C. We obtain:

$$h = 2.54 \, (10)^3 \exp (0.507/1.551) = 3.52 \, kJ/m^2sK$$

and

$$q = h\pi DL \, \Delta T = (3.52)(\pi)(0.0254)(1)(10) = 2.81 \, kJ/s$$

With a given latent of evaporation of $\Delta H_v = 2,100$ kJ/kg at 5 atm, vapor exits at a rate:

$$V = q/\Delta H_v = 2.81/2100 = 1.34 \times 10^{-3} \, kg/s$$

The fraction evaporated is then:

$$x = V/F = 1.34 \times 10^{-3}/10^{-2} = 0.134$$

i.e., the quality of the exiting fluid is 13.4%.

We note that the heat transfer coefficient given by Equation 3.6.38 shows the usual strong dependence on ΔT_b associated with boiling and is quite dissimilar in form from other proposed relations including Equation 3.6.36. Such seemingly contradictory expressions are quite commonplace in the formulation of boiling heat transfer coefficients. This is unfortunate but has to be accepted as an unavoidable factor in modeling.

Illustration 3.6.8   Film Condensation on a Vertical Plate

Although condensation is, like evaporation, a two phase phenomenon, it has considerably simpler heat transfer characteristics than those seen in boiling. A distinction is made between *dropwise condensation* in which the liquid does not wet the cooled surface, and *film condensation* in which a smooth continuous film of liquid is formed.

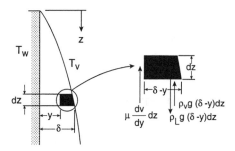

FIGURE 3.31   Variables and forces in filmwise condensation on a vertical plate.

The former process has much higher heat transfer rates than film condensation because of the direct exposure of the vapor to the cold surface and would, thus, be the preferred mode of operation. In practice, however, dropwise condensation is difficult to maintain since the droplets tend to coalesce into a more or less coherent film before dropping off the surface. Film condensation is the principal mode to be dealt with and has the advantage of being amenable to a relatively simple treatment.

An elegant analysis of film condensation on a vertical surface was first given by Nusselt in 1916. The physical process considered is shown in Figure 3.31, and the aim is to derive an expression for the local heat transfer coefficient which is a function of film thickness $h = k/\delta(z)$.

A preliminary analysis is needed here to establish the variables and the balances which make up the model. We argue as follows:

- A primary variable will be the flow rate L of the condensate, since it will determine the thickness of the falling film. That flow rate is derived by a balance of the shear and gravity forces acting on the descending condensate and yields in the first instance the *velocity distribution* which can be integrated to obtain the local flow rate $L(z)$. The expression will contain $\delta(z)$ as a second state variable as a result of the integration and a second equation, at the very least, will be required.
- We turn to a mass balance, taken over an increment dz, as the logical source for a second equation. That balance will contain the rate of condensation, dN, which is a new state variable since it depends on conduction through the film thickness δ that is in turn a function of vertical distance. Therefore, a third relation is required.
- We draw on the last available balance, that of energy, which equates the liberated heat of condensation of dN to the rate of conduction through the film thickness $\delta(z)$. No new variables are brought in and the model is consequently complete.

The detailed sequence is as follows.

Force balance:
  Here the diagram of Figure 3.31 reveals a subtlety which is not immediately apparent. In addition to the obvious forces of gravity and the opposing viscous shear,

a third force, that of the buoyancy of the displaced vapor needs to be taken into account. We obtain:

$$\text{Gravity} - (\text{viscous force} + \text{buoyancy}) = 0$$

$$\rho_L g(\delta - y)dx - \mu \frac{dv}{dy}dx - \rho_v g(\delta - y)dx = 0 \qquad (3.6.39)$$

which upon integration between $y = 0$ ($v = 0$) and y leads to the distribution:

$$v(y) = \frac{(\rho_L - \rho_v)g}{\mu}\left(\delta y - \frac{1}{2}y^2\right) \qquad (3.6.40)$$

A second integration of this expression over the cross-sectional area of the film assuming unit depth yields the local mass flow rate $L(\delta)$:

$$L(kg/s) = \rho_L \int vdA = \rho_L \int_0^\delta (\rho_L - \rho_v)g\left(\delta y - \frac{1}{2}y^2\right)dy \qquad (3.6.41)$$

$$L = \rho_L(\rho_L - \rho_v)g\delta^3/3\mu \qquad (3.6.42)$$

Mass balance:

$$\text{Rate of liquid in} - \text{Rate of liquid out} = 0$$

$$(L_z + dN) - L_{z+dz} = 0$$

or

$$dL = d[\rho_L(\rho_L - \rho_v)g\delta^3/3\mu] = dN \qquad (3.6.43)$$

We refrain from integrating this expression since it is dN which will be required in the energy balance and instead evaluate the differential. We obtain:

$$d[\rho_L(\rho_L - \rho_v)g\delta^3/3\mu] = [\rho_L(\rho_L - \rho_v)g\delta^2/\mu]d\delta = dN \qquad (3.6.44)$$

Energy balance:

$$\text{Rate of energy in} - \text{Rate of energy out} = 0$$

$$dN \, \Delta H_v - kdz \, (T_v\text{-}T_w)/\delta = 0$$

$$\text{Latent heat} \qquad \text{Conductive cooling} = 0$$

Upon introducing dN from Equation 3.6.43 and assuming a linear temperature distribution in the film, there results:

$$[\rho_L(\rho_L - \rho_v)g\delta^2/\mu]d\delta\Delta H_v = kdz\,(T_v - T_w)/\delta \tag{3.6.45}$$

When this expression is integrated over z with the film thickness of the inlet $\delta(0)$ set equal to zero, we obtain the desired film thickness distribution and, hence, the local heat transfer coefficient $h(z)$:

$$\delta(z) = \left[\frac{4\mu kz(T_v - T_w)}{g\Delta H_v\rho_L(\rho_L - \rho_v)}\right]^{1/4} \tag{3.6.46}$$

$$h(z) = \frac{k}{\delta(z)} = \left[\frac{\rho_L(\rho_L - \rho_v)g\Delta H_v k^3}{4\mu z(T_v - T_w)}\right]^{1/4} \tag{3.6.47}$$

Nusselt also considered horizontal tubes and reported both results in terms of mean integral film coefficients $\bar{h} = \dfrac{1}{z}\displaystyle\int_0^L h(z)d(z)$:

Vertical plate:

$$\bar{h} = 0.943\left[\frac{\rho_L(\rho_L - \rho_v)g\Delta H_v k^3}{\mu L(T_v - T_w)}\right]^{1/4} \tag{3.6.48}$$

Horizontal tube:

$$\bar{h} = 0.725\left[\frac{\rho_L(\rho_L - \rho_v)g\Delta H_v k^3}{\mu d(T_v - T_w)}\right]^{1/4} \tag{3.6.49}$$

Because ripples in the vertical film enhance heat transfer by about 20%, the recommended coefficient for Equation 3.6.48 is 1.13.

Of note here is the dependence in both cases of $\bar{h}$ on $(T_v - T_w)^{1/4}$. It is an inverse dependence, in contrast to the free convection coefficient (see Illustration 3.3.7) which varied directly with $\Delta T^{1/3}$.

Illustration 3.6.9   The Nonisothermal, Nonisobaric Tubular Gas Flow Reactor

Reaction rates of gases usually depend on the partial pressures of the components and, hence, on their mole fractions y_i and on total pressure P_T. When this is the case and pressure drop in the tubular reactor is significant, a mechanical energy balance has to be added to the usual mass and thermal energy balances. This balance contains velocity v and density ρ as additional state variables so that a model of considerable complexity may be expected. A systematic approach is needed to reduce the model to more manageable proportions. We illustrate this with the following example.

Consider the reaction $2A \rightarrow B + C$, representative of the thermal cracking of a hydrocarbon. The reaction rate has been reported as $r_A = k_r(T) \, y_A^2 \, P_T^2$ (mol/m^{3}s) and the reaction itself is endothermic. The model is expected to yield the distribution in the reactor of reactant mole fraction $y_A(z)$. Some useful preliminary work can be done to reduce the number of variables by using the stoichiometric relations.

Molar flow rates and molar masses:

Let $n_A(z)$, $n_B(z)$ and $n_C(z)$ represent the molar flow rates (mol/s) of the components. We have from the stoichiometry of the reaction:

$$\text{Total molar flow rate } n_T = n_A^0 \text{ (feed rate)}$$

and

$$n_A = y_A n_T = y_A n_A^0$$

$$n_B = \frac{1}{2}(n_A^0 - n_A) = (n_A^0/2)(1 - y_A)$$

$$n_C = \frac{1}{2}(n_A^0 - n_A) = (n_A^0/2)(1 - y_A) \qquad (3.6.50)$$

$$n_T = n_A^0$$

An average molar mass M_{avg} is required for the mass density ρ contained in the mechanical energy balance. We obtain:

$$M_{avg} = y_A M_A + y_B M_B + y_C M_C \qquad (3.6.51)$$

Since $2M_A = M_B + M_C$ and $y_B = y_C = \frac{1}{2}(1 - y_A)$, this converts to

$$M_{avg} = M_A \qquad (3.6.52)$$

The model can now be developed further by setting up the balances, starting with the mass balances.

Total mass balance:

$$n_A^0 M_A = \rho v A \qquad (3.6.53)$$

or equivalently,

$$v = 4 \frac{n_A{}^0 M_A}{\rho \pi d^2} \tag{3.6.54}$$

Reactant mass balance:

$$\text{Rate of A in} - \text{Rate of A out} = 0$$

$$y_A n_A{}^0 \big|_z - \left[\begin{matrix} y_A n_A{}^0 \big|z + \Delta Z \\ + r_{avg} A \Delta z \end{matrix} \right] = 0 \tag{3.6.55}$$

and upon going to the limit

$$n_A{}^0 \frac{dy_A}{dz} + k_r(T) A y_A{}^2 P_T{}^2 = 0 \tag{3.6.56}$$

Mechanical energy balance:

Since we are dealing with compressible flow, we draw on the differential form of this balance given in Illustration 3.6.1:

$$\frac{dP_T}{\rho} + v dv + 4f \frac{v^2}{2} \frac{dz}{d} = 0 \tag{3.6.57}$$

ρ and v can be expressed in terms of the principal state variables T and P_T by assuming ideal gas behavior $\rho = \dfrac{P_T M_{avg}}{RT}$ and using Equation 3.6.64. We obtain:

$$v = \frac{4 n_A{}^0 R}{\pi d^2} \frac{T}{P_T} \tag{3.6.58}$$

and

$$dv = \frac{4 n_A{}^0 R}{\pi d^2} \left(\frac{dT}{P_T} - \frac{T}{P_T{}^2} dP_T \right) \tag{3.6.59}$$

The mechanical energy balance then takes the form:

$$\frac{dP_T}{dz} + 16 \frac{(n_A{}^0) M_A R}{\pi d^4} \left(\frac{1}{P_T} \frac{dT}{dz} - \frac{T}{P_T{}^2} \frac{dP_T}{dz} \right) + \frac{32 f (n_A{}^0)^2 M_A R}{\pi^2 d^5} \frac{T}{P_T} = 0 \tag{3.6.60}$$

One notes here the dependence of pressure drop on both T and P_T brought about by the effect of these variables on local velocity.

Energy balance:

Here we obtain in the first instance:

$$\text{Rate of energy in} - \text{Rate of energy out} = 0$$

$$(\tilde{H}\,|_z + q_{avg}) - (\tilde{H}\,|_{z+\Delta z}) = 0 \tag{3.6.61}$$

Instead of making the necessary substitutions into the difference form, we show the reader a slightly different approach by using the differential form dH − dq = 0, and then decomposing dH into sensible heat and heat of reaction terms as usual. Note that the kinetic energy term is omitted here — but not in the mechanical energy balance — because of its small value relative to the thermal energy terms. We obtain:

$$dH = d\sum n_i \tilde{H}_i \tag{3.6.62}$$

where both the molar flow rates n_i and the component molar enthalpies $\tilde{H}_i$ are to be differentiated. This yields:

$$dH(J/s) = (n_A d\tilde{H}_A + n_B d\tilde{H}_B + n_C d\tilde{H}_C) + (\tilde{H}_A dn_A + \tilde{H}_B dn_B + \tilde{H}_C dn_C) \tag{3.6.63}$$

$$\text{Sensible Heat} \qquad\qquad\qquad \text{Heat of Reaction}$$

where the molar flow rates are given by Equation 3.6.50 and their differentials by the expressions:

$$dn_A = n_A{}^0 dy_A, \quad dn_B = -\frac{1}{2}n_A{}^0 dy_A, \quad dn_C = -\frac{1}{2}n_A{}^0 dy_A \tag{3.6.64}$$

Hence, the heat of reaction term becomes:

$$\tilde{H}_A dn_A + \tilde{H}_B dn_B + \tilde{H}_C dn_C = n_A{}^0 dy_A(\tilde{H}_A - \tilde{H}_B - \tilde{H}_C) = -n_A{}^0 dy_A \Delta H_r \tag{3.6.65}$$

For the enthalpy differential, we have the usual form:

$$d\tilde{H}_i = \tilde{C}_{pi} dT \tag{3.6.66}$$

Combining Equations 3.6.62 to 3.6.66 and introducing the result together with the auxiliary relation for dq into the energy balance (Equation 3.6.61), we obtain the limit:

$$\left[y_A \tilde{C}_{PA} + \frac{1}{2}(1 - y_A)(\tilde{C}_{PB} + \tilde{C}_{PC}) \right]\frac{dT}{dz} - n_A{}^0 \Delta H_r \frac{dy_A}{dz} - \pi dU(T_{ext} - T) = 0 \tag{3.6.67}$$

In compact form, the total model now consists of the following three equations in the three state variables: y_A, T, and P_T.

Mass balance:

$$\frac{dy_A}{dz} + K_1 \exp(-E_a / RT) P_T^2 y_A^2 = 0 \qquad (3.6.68)$$

Energy balance:

$$\left[y_A \tilde{C}_{PA} + \frac{1}{2}(1 - y_A)(\tilde{C}_{PB} - \tilde{C}_{PC}) \right] \frac{dT}{dz} - \Delta H_r \frac{dy_A}{dz} - K_2(T_{ext} - T) = 0 \quad (3.6.69)$$

Mechanical energy balance:

$$(1 - K_3 T P_T^{-2}) \frac{dP_T}{dz} + K_3 P_T^{-1} \frac{dT}{dz} + K_4 T^2 P_T^{-2} = 0 \qquad (3.6.70)$$

with

$$K_1 = \frac{A_r \pi d^2}{4 n_4^0}$$

$$K_2 = \frac{\pi d U}{n_A^0}$$

$$K_3 = \frac{16(n_A^0) M_A R}{\pi^2 d^4}$$

$$K_4 = \frac{2 f K_3}{d}$$

where A_r is the pre-exponential factor of the Arrhenius equation.

We note that the product distributions $y_B(z)$ and $y_C(z)$ can, if desired, be recovered from the relations:

$$y_B = y_C = \frac{1}{2}(1 - y_A) \qquad (3.6.71)$$

and that partial pressures are obtained by multiplication of these quantities by total pressure $P_T(z)$.

Temperature dependence of heat capacities and the heat of reaction can be incorporated directly into the algebra of these expressions without the need for differentiation. Friction factor f, on the other hand, can be considered constant since G is constant and viscosity changes can usually be neglected. Similarly, the heat transfer coefficient undergoes only minor variations, since changes in the Prandtl number with composition are usually small.

Practice Problems

3.6.1 Sonic Velocity in Steam: Discharge of Superheated Steam —

(a) Calculate the velocity of sound of saturated steam at 150°C, 475 kPa, assuming ideal gas behavior. Cp = 34.8 J/molK under these conditions.
(b) Using the compressible flow chart, Figure 3.28, and assuming frictionless flow, calculate the initial discharge mass velocity of steam from a tank through a valve.

Answer: (a) 506 m/s

3.6.2 Propagation of an Explosion Pressure Wave — An explosion known to generate a pressure of 15 atm creates a pressure shock wave that travels through air with a given $\gamma = 1.4$, $\rho = 1.2$ kg/m³. Calculate the velocity of the shock.

Comments:

The pressure generated by the explosion, which was given here, can in principle be derived from gas laws and the change in moles and volume that occur in the course of the reaction. The resulting temperature, which also is required, is obtained from an energy balance involving the heat of reaction.

3.6.3 Compressor Stations in Long Distance Natural Gas Transmission Lines — Natural gas is transmitted through a 1 m diameter pipe at the rate of G = 200 kg/m²s. Pressure at the inlet is 50 atm. Calculate the maximum possible length of pipe which will accommodate this flow before it has to be recompressed. Friction factor is estimated at f = 0.002, and $\gamma \approx 1.4$ for methane. What is the pressure at the outlet?

Answer: $L_{Max} = 100$ km; $p_2 \cong 2.5$ atm

3.6.4 Alternative Forms of the Energy Equation — Derive the alternative energy balance (Equation 3.6.9) for gas flow in a medium of constant cross-section.

(Hint: Show that $H = p/\rho + C_v T$ and use the relations $\rho = pM/RT$, $C_p - C_v = R$.)

3.6.5 Derivation of the Rayleigh Line — The Rayleigh Line relates upstream and downstream pressures and Mach numbers across a normal shock and is given by:

$$\frac{p_2}{p_1} = \frac{1 + \gamma Ma_1^2}{1 + \gamma Ma_2^2} \tag{3.6.72}$$

Derive this expression using Table 3.23. Note that the shock is of constant cross-section and frictionless as well as adiabatic.

(Hint: Retain dq terms initially and then eliminate by division.)

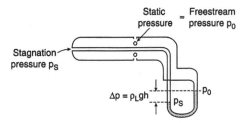

FIGURE 3.32 The pitot tube for the measurement of gas velocities.

3.6.6 The Pitot Tube and Compressible Flow — The pitot tube is a device for measuring gas velocities and utilizes the difference in pressure at the nose of the tube (the so-called stagnation pressure p_s), and that of the free stream p_0, see Figure 3.32). For incompressible flow, application of the Bernouilli equation leads to the relation:

$$v_0 = \left[\frac{2(p_s - p_0)}{\rho_0}\right]^{1/2} \tag{3.6.73}$$

When the flow exceeds $Ma = 0.2$, and while the flow is still subsonic, compressibility effects must be taken into account. Show that under these conditions the following revised expression applies:

$$v_0 = \left\{\frac{2}{\gamma}\frac{p_0}{\rho_0}\left[1-\left(\frac{p_0}{p_s}\right)^{(\gamma+1)/\gamma}\right]\right\}^{1/2} \tag{3.6.74}$$

3.6.7 Enthalpy Change Across a Normal Shock: The Rankine-Huguenot Relation — Show that the enthalpy change $\Delta H = Cp\Delta T$ across a normal shock is given by the following expression, known as the Rankine-Huguenot relation:

$$H_2 - H_1 = \frac{1}{2}(p_2 - p_1)\left(\frac{1}{\rho_2} + \frac{1}{\rho_1}\right) \tag{3.6.75}$$

3.6.8 Electrical Boiler — Water entering a tube at 105°C and a flow rate of 0.1 kg/s is to be brought to a boil and converted to steam with a quality of $x = 10\%$. Heat is supplied by an electrical coil wrapped around the tube and powered by 110 V. What is the total resistance of heating wire required? Assume a constant boiling point of 105°C throughout the tube and $\Delta H_r = 2100$ kJ/kg.
    Answer: 0.58 Ω

3.6.9 Estimation of Water Boiler Length — A refined examination of the early stages of forced convection boiling shows that initial bubble formation occurs when the bulk fluid is still subcooled, i.e., below the boiling point. Once saturated boiling conditions are reached in the bulk fluid, fully developed nucleate boiling takes place which is independent of the flow velocity. Simple correlations of h_b then apply that depend only on the physical properties of the fluid and the temperature driving force. For low pressure boiling of water up to 6.7 MPa and with constant physical properties assumed, the suggested expression for heat flux is given by:

$$q/A = 2.253 \ (\Delta T_b)^{3.86} \ J/m^2 s \qquad (3.6.76)$$

Water enters a 2.54 cm tube at a flow rate of 0.1 kg/s, 25°C and 0.12 MPa pressure. It is desired to estimate the length of tube required to produce steam of 5% quality at the exit, assuming that the subcooled boiling region is short and can be neglected. Thus, only convective heating and nucleate boiling are to be considered. ΔT_b is set at 10°C and pressure drop is assumed negligible. $\Delta H_v = 2050$ kJ/kg.
    (Hint: Use the correlation given in Table 3.10 to calculate the length of the heat-up section and Equation 3.6.76 for the boiling section.)

3.6.10 Annular Condensation in a Vertical Tube — Use the Nusselt film condensation model to derive the local heat transfer coefficient for condensation inside a small tube where the film builds up as an annulus.

3.6.11 Condensation on a Bank of Horizontal Tubes — A square array of 10 × 10 1 m long tubes of 1.27 cm diameter is to be used to condense atmospheric steam on the exterior surface of the tubes. The wall temperature is 98°C. Calculate the mass of steam condensed per unit length. Use 10 d in Nusselt equation.
    Answer: 100

3.6.12 Cracking of Acetone Vapor — Acetone is cracked in the first stage of acetic anhydride manufacture forming methane and gaseous ketene.

$$(CH_3)CO = CH_4 + CH_2 = CO$$

The reaction is endothermic and is to be carried out in a furnace held at T_{ext}. Set up the appropriate mass and energy balances.

REFERENCES

General
Tabulations of transport coefficients and methods for their prediction appear in the excellent text:
R.C. Reid, J.M. Prausnitz, and B.E. Poling. *The Properties of Gases and Liquids, 4th ed.* McGraw-Hill, New York, 1987.

Correlations of transport coefficient are taken up in most texts dealing with mass, energy, and momentum transport cited at the end of Chapter 2. See also:

C.J. Geankoplis. *Transport Processes and Unit Operations, 3rd ed.,* Allyn and Bacon, Boston, 1993.

Transport coefficients applicable to external flows are covered in the monograph:
R. Clift, J.R. Grace, and M.E. Weber. *Bubbles, Drops and Particles,* Academic Press, New York, 1978.

The early text,
W.H. McAdams. *Heat Transmission, 3rd ed.,* McGraw Hill, New York, 1954, *contains a rich compilation of heat transfer correlations which remain in use to this day.*

Mass Balances
A useful discussion of the various mass transfer coefficients and flux equations, as well as film theory, can be found in various editions of the text by Treybal.
R.E. Treybal. *Mass Transfer Operations, 3rd ed.,* McGraw-Hill, New York, 1979.

There is a plethora of monographs dealing with chemical reactor kinetics and engineering, among which the following stands out:
O. Levenspiel. *Chemical Reactor Engineering,* 3rd ed., John Wiley & Sons, New York, 1999.

See also:
E.B. Naumann. *Chemical Reactor Design,* John Wiley & Sons, New York, 1987.

Specialized texts dealing with catalysis, catalytic reactors, and the attendant transport phenomena include:
C.N. Satterfield. *Mass Transfer in Heterogeneous Catalysis,* MIT Press, Cambridge, MA, 1970.
J.J. Carberry and A. Varma. *Chemical and Catalytic Reaction Engineering,* McGraw-Hill, New York, 1986.
C.N. Satterfield. *Heterogeneous Catalysis in Industrial Practice, 2nd ed.,* McGraw-Hill, New York, 1980.

Diffusion in catalyst particles and the associated effectiveness factors, both isothermal and nonisothermal, are treated exhaustively in the outstanding treatise by Aris.
R. Aris. *The Mathematical Theory of Diffusion and Reaction in Permeable Catalysts,* vol. 1 and 2, Oxford University Press, U.K., 1974.

Distillation of binary mixtures in packed columns is treated by Treybal, cited above. The more complex case of multicomponent distillation is well covered in:
C.J. King. *Separation Processes, 2nd ed.,* McGraw-Hill, New York, 1980.

Additional information on distillation in both staged and packed columns with emphasis on industrial practice can be found in:
E.J. Henley and J.D. Seader. *Equilibrium Stage Separation Operations in Chemical Engineering,* John Wiley & Sons, New York, 1981.

Energy Balances
Heat exchanger design and performance is treated in all heat transfer texts (see Chapter 2 references) as well as in the specialized monograph:

H. Hausen. *Heat Transfer in Counter Flow, Parallel Flow and Cross Flow,* McGraw-Hill, New York, 1982.

Heat exchanger efficiency is covered here as well, and in greater detail and scope in:
W.M. Kays and A.L. London, *Compact Heat Exchangers,* McGraw-Hill, New York, 1964.

A useful general reference source for these and other topics in heat transfer is:
W.M. Rohsenow and J.P. Hartnett (Eds.). *Handbook of Heat Transfer Fundamentals, 2nd ed.,* McGraw-Hill, New York, 1985.

Finned heat exchangers are the subject of the monograph:
D.Q. Kern and A.D. Kraus. *Extended Surface Heat Transfer,* McGraw-Hill, New York, 1972.
See also Kays and London cited above.

Boiling heat transfer is covered in standard heat transfer texts, as well as in specialized treatises, among them:
E. Hahne and U. Grigull. *Heat Transfer in Boiling,* Academic Press, New York, 1977.
J.G. Collier. *Convective Boiling and Condensation, 2nd ed.,* McGraw-Hill, New York, 1981.

See also:
K. Nishikawa and Y. Fujita. Nuclear Boiling Heat Transfer and its Augmentation, in *Advances in Heat Transfer,* vol. 20, Academic Press, New York, 1990.

Freezing phenomena and heat transfer with phase changes in general are also addressed in standard heat transfer texts. A contemporary review is found in:
L.S. Yao and J. Prana. Melting and Freezing, in *Advances in Heat Transfer,* vol. 19, Academic Press, New York, 1981.

The specialized topic of freeze-drying is well covered in the monograph:
C.J. King. *Freeze-Drying of Foods,* CRC Press, Boca Raton, FL, 1971.

Force and Momentum Balances
The topics covered in this section, including fluid statics and dynamics and the pertinent energy equations, are the domain of fluid mechanics texts. Particularly thorough treatments can be found in:
V.L. Streeter, E.B. Wylie, and K.W. Bedford. *Fluid Mechanics, 9th ed.,* McGraw-Hill, New York, 1998.
F.M. White. *Fluid Mechanics, 2nd ed.,* McGraw-Hill, New York, 1986.

See also:
A.E. Fuhs and J.A. Schetz (Eds.). *Handbook of Fluid Dynamics and Fluid Machinery,* McGraw-Hill, New York, 1995.
which is an excellent up-to-date reference source.

Simultaneous Mass and Energy Balances
Heat effects in chemical reactions and chemical reactors are addressed in the monographs on these topics cited under Mass Balances. A very thorough treatment of nonisothermal effectiveness factors can be found in the aforementioned treatise by Aris.

Humidification, dehumidification, and water cooling, and the use of humidity charts in deriving variables of interest in these operations is well covered in:
R.E. Treybal. *Mass Transfer Operations, 3rd ed.*, McGraw-Hill, New York, 1979.

Also covered in this text are single stage vaporization and condensation processes. For compilations of vapor–liquid equilibria relevant to these operations, and to distillation in general, see:
S. Ohe. *Vapour-Liquid Equilibrium Data*, Elsevier, New York, 1989.
S. Ohe. *Vapour-Liquid Equilibrium Data at Elevated Pressures*, Elsevier, New York, 1990.
Optimum temperatures in reversible and parallel reactions, as well as the van Heerden diagram are addressed in the reactor texts cited previously.

For definitive treatments of cryogenic liquefaction and cryogenics in general, see:
R.F. Barron. *Cryogenic Systems, 2nd ed.*, Oxford University Press, U.K., 1985.
K.D. Timmerhaus and T.M. Flynn. *Cryogenic Process Engineering*, Plenum Press, New York, 1990.

A useful compilation of physical properties of gases of relevance in cryogenic operations appears in:
L'Air Liquide: Gas Encyclopedia, Elsevier, New York, 1976.

Simultaneous Mass, Energy, and Momentum Balances
Much of what appears in this section deals with compressible flow which is covered in standard fluid mechanics texts (see Streeter and Wylie, and White, cited previously). An excellent monograph, entirely devoted to that topic, is by:
J.D. Anderson Jr. *Modern Compressible Flow with Historical Perspective*, McGraw-Hill, New York, 1987.

For a good treatment of compressible flow in ducts with variable cross-section as well as with friction and heat transfer, see:
R.C. Binder. *Advanced Fluid Mechanics*, Prentice-Hall, Upper Saddle River, NJ, 1958.
R.C. Binder. *Fluid Mechanics, 4th ed.*, Prentice-Hall, Upper Saddle River, NJ, 1962.

Shock waves due to explosions are taken up in:
B. Lewis and G. von Elbe. *Combustion, Flames and Explosion of Gases, 3rd ed.*, Academic Press, New York, 1987.

Treatments of forced convection vaporizers can be found in the monographs on boiling cited under Energy Balances. The related topic of multiphase flow is covered in:
G.W. Govier and K. Aziz. *The Flow of Complex Mixtures in Pipes*, van Nostrand, New York, 1977.

The classical treatment of condensation on a vertical plate can be found in most heat transfer texts, including:
F. Kreith and M.S. Bohn. *Principles of Heat Transfer, 4th ed.*, Harper and Row, New York, 1986.
J.P. Holman. *Heat Transfer, 8th ed.*, McGraw-Hill, New York, 1991.

4 Ordinary Differential Equations

*There is no Applied Mathematics, without
Mathematics to Apply.*

Anonymous

Differential equations arise, as we had seen, whenever a state variable such as temperature, concentration, pressure, or velocity varies in time or space. The state variables are usually the dependent variables in such systems, while time or distance become the independent variables. Some exceptions to this rule may occur, e.g., when distance is used to describe the time varying mass or volume of an entity (see Chapter 2, Illustration 2.6 and Chapter 3, Illustration 3.3.12). Or one may eliminate time or distance by dividing two differential equations so that one of the previously dependent variables now becomes, in form at least, an independent variable (see Chapter 3, Illustration 3.3.2). These exceptions are few in number and in general the original definitions given above apply.

A distinction also is made between ordinary differential equations (ODEs) which contain only one independent variable, and partial differential equations (PDEs) which have two or more such variables. The latter are addressed in Chapters 7 to 9.

The present chapter starts with a classification of ODEs as to order, linearity, homogeneity, and other properties. The boundary and initial conditions that are an indispensable part of a differential equation are examined next and related to the underlying physics of the ODEs. We take up some classical analytical solution methods for both linear and nonlinear ODEs followed by a brief survey of numerical methods. The important solution method of the Laplace transformation is dealt with in Chapter 5.

We conclude Chapter 4 by introducing the reader to some important tools of nonlinear analysis and examine some associated topics such as bifurcations, multiple solutions, and attractors. As usual each section is amplified with Illustrations and Practice Problems.

4.1 DEFINITIONS AND CLASSIFICATIONS

4.1.1 ORDER OF AN ODE

The order of a differential equation is that of its *highest* derivative. Thus, the equation which arose in connection with isothermal diffusion and reaction in a catalyst pellet:

$$\frac{d^2C_A}{dr^2} + \frac{2}{r}\frac{dC_A}{dr} - k_r C_A / D_{eff} = 0 \qquad (3.2.41)$$

is a second order ODE in the concentration variable C_A.

Our task is considerably eased by the fact that most ODEs which arise in engineering and the physical sciences are either first or second order. In particular are

- All unsteady integral balances and all steady-state differential balances *without* molecular or diffusive transport lead to first order ODEs.
- Steady-state balances *with* molecular transport, i.e., those involving Fick's law, Fourier's law, or Newton's viscosity law, usually yield second order ODEs. In general, whenever the auxiliary relations already contain a derivative, incorporation in a differential balance will increase their order by one, thus resulting in an ODE of higher order.
- Second and higher order ODEs also arise when combining several first order ODEs. We had seen this in the case of the countercurrent heat exchanger where the model initially took the form:

$$F_t C_{pt}\frac{dT_t}{dz} - U\pi d(T_s - T_t) = 0 \qquad (3.3.7)$$

and

$$F_t C_{ps}\frac{dT_s}{dz} - U\pi d(T_s - T_t) = 0 \qquad (3.3.8)$$

Solving Equation 3.3.7 for the shell-side temperature T_s and substituting the result into Equation 3.3.8 enabled us to reduce the system to a single, but higher order ODE of the form:

$$\frac{d^2T_t}{dz^2} + K\frac{dT_t}{dz} = 0 \qquad (3.3.15)$$

We note in this connection that whenever an *analytical* solution is being sought, combining lower order ODEs in this fashion is a fruitful approach. In *numerical* work, on the other hand, the reverse procedure is often preferred, i.e., one decomposes higher order equations to a set of equivalent first order equations. This is done in order to take advantage of Standard ODE Solver Packages (e.g., Runge-Kutta Routines) which are specifically designed to solve sets of first order ODEs.

- ODEs of order higher than 2, although less common, also arise in certain areas of fluid and solid mechanics. Some examples of these are taken up in Chapters 5 and 7.

4.1.2   LINEAR AND NONLINEAR ODES

This distinction and categorization is of great importance in determining the method of solution and indeed the ease of solution of an ODE by analytical means. Thus, a host of methods exist and can be applied without undue difficulty to solve linear ODEs. This is primarily due to the fact that one can make use of the important Superposition Principle which in essence states that the general solution of a linear ODE can be composed of the sum of all *independent* particular solutions. In systems of nonlinear ODEs, this important principle is lost and one must resort to ad hoc methods that lack generality and are relatively few in number.

An *informal* definition of linear ODEs is that all *dependent* variables and their derivatives must appear in linear form, i.e., they are not multiplied or divided by each other, or raised to a power other than 1. A more *formal* definition consists of the requirement that the ODE must satisfy the following two conditions.

Given an ODE $f(y^{(n)} \ldots y^1, y, x) = 0$ and two particular solutions y_1 and y_2. Then if

$$f[y_1(x) + y_2(x)] = f(y_1) + f(y_2) \tag{4.1.1}$$

and

$$f(ky) = kf(y) \tag{4.1.2}$$

the ODE is said to be linear.

Note that these definitions do not require the *independent* variable to be linear. In fact, the latter can be as complex as one likes without violating the Superposition Principle. Some examples:

Linear ODE
$$\frac{d^2y}{dx^2} + e^x \frac{dy}{dx} + y = x^3$$

Nonlinear ODE
$$y\frac{d^2y}{dx^2} + \frac{1}{x}\frac{dy}{dx} + y = 0$$

Set of linear ODEs
$$\frac{dy}{dx} = x + z$$
$$\frac{dz}{dx} = y - z$$

Set of nonlinear ODEs
$$\frac{dy}{dx} + y/z = 0$$
$$\frac{dz}{dx} - y^2 = 0$$

In physical systems, nonlinearities are most often brought into the model by nonlinear auxiliary relations and physical properties. We have summarized those of most common occurrence and their sources in Table 4.1.

TABLE 4.1
Some Sources of Nonlinear Terms

Sources and Systems	Examples of Nonlinear Terms
Chemical reaction of order $\neq 1$, nonisothermal chemical reaction	$r = kC^n$ $r = A \exp(-E_a/RT)f(c)$
Nonlinear phase equilibria	$y = \dfrac{\alpha x}{1 + (\alpha - 1)x}$ $\ln p = aT + b$
Nonlinear drag or friction	$F_D = C_D A \rho \dfrac{v^2}{2}$ $h_f = 4f \dfrac{v^2}{2} \dfrac{L}{D}$
Nonlinear transport coefficient	$k(T), \mu(T), D(C)$
Radiation heat transfer	$q = \varepsilon \sigma (T_2^4 - T_1^4)$
Variable hold-up	$\dfrac{d(VC)}{dt}, \rho C_p \dfrac{d(VT)}{dt}$
Compressible flow, flow through ducts of variable cross-section	$F = \rho v A$
Nonlinear spring	$F_s = kx^2$
Pendulum	$\dfrac{d^2\theta}{dt^2} + \dfrac{g}{L}\sin\theta = 0$

Two additional points are worth noting. In our previous illustrations, we were able to arrive at analytical solutions even when the underlying equations were nonlinear (see, e.g., Chapter 3, Illustration 3.2.8 and Equations 3.2.76 and 3.2.78). The reason for this was that we were able to integrate the ODEs by separation of variables which applies quite generally to both linear and nonlinear separable and first order ODEs. The second point concerns numerical solution methods. These are usually unaffected by nonlinearities and are capable in principle of solving both linear and nonlinear ODEs with almost equal ease. They are, however, more prone in the nonlinear case to instabilities and other aberrations. Modern software packages are often able to overcome these difficulties.

4.1.3 ODEs with Variable Coefficients

This classification denotes differential equations in which the coefficients of the *derivatives* are functions of the *independent* variable, i.e., not constant. The classification is usually only applied to linear ODEs of order greater than one.

The reason for making a distinction between ODEs with constant and variable coefficients lies in the difference in analytical solution techniques which have to be applied. In the former case, the classical D-Operator Method, the Laplace Transformation or the Method of Eigenvalues are the tools of choice, and the solutions are usually expressed in terms of simple trigonometric or exponential functions. In the case of ODEs with variable coefficients, these methods become inconvenient or inapplicable. One then resorts to a solution in infinite power series that give rise to new classes of functions, such as the Bessel and Legendre functions.

Variable coefficient differential equations most commonly arise in mass or energy balances involving molecular or diffusive transport through a *variable* area, e.g., radially in a cylinder, sphere, or circle. Both area A and the gradient du/dr have to be differentiated in this case yielding coefficients which vary with radial distance. Thus, for diffusion and reaction in a spherical catalyst pellet we had (Chapter 3, Illustration 3.2.3):

$$\frac{d^2C_A}{dr^2} + \frac{2}{r}\frac{dC_A}{dr} - k_rC_A / D_{eff} = 0 \qquad (3.2.41)$$

Note that this equation is still linear since the nonlinear term 1/r is a function of the independent, not the dependent variable. However, if the order of the reaction rate k_rC_A is changed, e.g., to $k_rC_A^2$, the equation becomes nonlinear.

4.1.4 HOMOGENEOUS AND NONHOMOGENEOUS ODEs

A *linear* ODE that does not contain an isolated function of the independent variable, f(x) or an isolated constant, is termed *homogeneous*. When this is not the case, the equation is said to be *nonhomogeneous*. Thus,

$$\frac{dy}{dt} + k\,y = 0 \qquad (4.1.3)$$

and

$$\frac{d^2y}{dx^2} + K\frac{dy}{dx} + xy = 0 \qquad (4.1.4)$$

are homogeneous ODEs.

Examples of nonhomogeneous equations are

$$\frac{dy}{dt} + K_1y = K_2 \qquad (4.1.5)$$

$$\frac{dy}{dt} + K_1y = K_2 \sin K_3t \qquad (4.1.6)$$

and more generally,

$$\frac{d^2y}{dt^2} - K_1\frac{dy}{dt} - K_2y = f(t) \qquad (4.1.7)$$

The nonhomogeneous terms appearing on the right side of these equations are commonly referred to as *forcing functions* and their functional form has a direct impact on the form of the solution. They are usually associated with time-dependent models and, hence, appear extensively in Process Control Theory and other areas dealing with dynamic systems.

The preferred solution method of nonhomogeneous as well as homogeneous time-dependent equations is the Laplace Transformation. Nonhomogeneous ODEs also can be solved by adding a particular integral to the solution of the homogeneous ODE. This latter method is taken up in a subsequent section while the Laplace Transformation is deferred to Chapter 5.

4.1.5 AUTONOMOUS ODEs

These equations can be linear or nonlinear and are characterized by an absence of terms in the independent variable other than the derivatives themselves. When this is not the case, they are said to be *nonautonomous*. Examples of both classes which are usually converted to first order systems, appear below:

$$\text{Autonomous ODEs}: \quad \frac{dy}{dx} = f(y) \tag{4.1.8}$$

or for a set:

$$\dot{y} = f(y) \tag{4.1.9}$$

$$\text{Nonautonomous ODEs}: \quad \frac{dy}{dx} = f(x, y) \tag{4.1.10}$$

or for a set:

$$\dot{y} = f(x, y) \tag{4.1.11}$$

where we use a vector-matrix notation to generalize the classes to sets of simultaneous equations.

What prompts this classification is again a marked difference in the form of the solutions, as well as in the analytical solution methods. Thus, single autonomous ODEs are immediately integrable by separation of variables and, if linear, by Laplace Transformation as well. Nonautonomous equations are solved by special analytical techniques unless separable or by numerical techniques.

Illustration 4.1.1   Classification of Model ODEs

We undertake here the classification of model ODEs which were encountered in previous illustrations. We establish their order and distinguish between linear/non-linear equations, homogeneous and nonhomogeneous forms, second order ODEs with constant and variable coefficients, and autonomous/nonautonomous behavior. From Chapter 2 we have

The surge tank:

$$F_1(t) - F_2(t) = \frac{dW}{dt} \tag{2.2}$$

The equation is first order in the tank contents W and is linear with nonhomogeneous terms $F_1(t)$ and $F_2(t)$. $F_1(t)$ can be viewed as a forcing function and the equation is seen to be nonautonomous.

The steam-heated tube:

$$F_c C_p \frac{dT_t}{dz} - U\pi d(T_s - T_\tau) = 0 \tag{2.15}$$

This is a linear first order ODE in the tube temperature T_t. It is nonhomogeneous because of the steam-side term $U\pi DT_s$, but autonomous since no terms in z appear in it.

From Chapter 3 we have:

The isothermal catalyst pellet:

$$\frac{d^2 C_A}{dr^2} + \frac{2}{r}\frac{dC_A}{dr} - kC_A / D_{eff} = 0 \tag{3.2.41}$$

The nonisothermal catalyst pellet:

$$\frac{d^2 C_A}{dr^2} + \frac{2}{r}\frac{dC_A}{dr} - k_r(T)C_A / D_{eff} = 0 \tag{3.5.12}$$

Both of these equations are second order ODEs in C_A, homogeneous and with variable coefficients. The principal difference in the two is that Equation 3.2.41 is linear, while Equation 3.5.12 is nonlinear by virtue of the exponential dependence of k_r on temperature (Arrhenius equation) and because of the term $k_r(T)C_A$ which is the (nonlinear) product of functions of two state variables.

4.2 BOUNDARY AND INITIAL CONDITIONS

Boundary and initial conditions (BCs and ICs), usually expressed as equations, are needed to evaluate integration constants and to provide starting values for numerical integration procedures. The number of such conditions required equals the order of the ODE.

For first order ODEs, these conditions are usually identified from the prevailing values of the state variables at position z = 0 or time t = 0. Some typical examples of the information used to obtain these conditions are the following:

- Concentration, pressure, and temperature of the feed to a tubular reactor
- Initial level, concentration, or temperature of a stirred tank
- Initial velocity and position of a falling or rising particle
- Initial velocity and position of an oscillating system (pendulum, mass on spring)
- Inlet pressure, velocity, and temperature in compressible duct flow

When all the conditions required for a set of first order ODEs are given *at the same point in time or space*, one speaks of the problem as being an initial value problem, or IVP. All of the examples cited above are related to initial value problems. Also in this category are multiphase contacting devices in co-current flow, such as co-current heat exchangers. When flow is counter-current, the boundary conditions are generally given at opposite ends of the device. In these cases, i.e., when the required boundary conditions are only known at different locations, one speaks of a *boundary value problem,* or BVP. Such problems arise in a good many other physical processes. Analytical solution methods do not make a special distinction between IVPs and BVPs and can be applied with equal ease to either case. In numerical work, one generally has to know the value of *all* state variables at $z = 0$ or $t = 0$ in order to initiate the integration procedure. Hence, most standard ODE solver packages are designed to handle IVPs only. To solve BVPs, special solution methods must be resorted to which are discussed in greater detail in Section 4.4.

For second order ODEs, one requires two boundary conditions and these are frequently given at a different location, resulting in a BVP. A typical example is the ODE which describes diffusion and reaction in a catalyst pellet, Equation 3.2.41. Figure 4.1A shows the boundary conditions for a spherical pellet with no external film resistance. A first boundary condition (BC) is immediately obtained at the pellet surface where $C_A(R) = C_{Ab}$, the prescribed or known surface or bulk fluid concentration, C_{Ab}. For the second BC, one argues that since the concentration profile must be symmetrical about the center, the derivative dC_A/dr at that point will be zero. Alternatively the same condition may be deduced from the fact that the mass flux at the center is zero, hence $(dC_A/dr)_{r=0} = 0$.

The type of BCs used has a significant impact on the form of the solution and this has led to a formal classification of boundary conditions depending on whether they contain the state variable, its derivative alone, or a combination of the two. The resulting classes of BCs, their nomenclature, and their occurrence are tabulated in Table 4.2.

Using this table and the example of the catalyst pellet shown in Figure 4.1A, we see that it has a Type I boundary condition at the surface and a Type II condition at the center. For the catalyst pellet with film resistance, shown in Fig 4.1B, the center boundary condition is retained while the surface BC now becomes a Mixed-Type or Type III condition. Note that the latter is obtained by equating convective transport of reactant through the film to diffusive transport away from the surface and into the interior. Thus,

Type III BC:

A. No Film Resistance

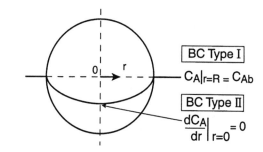

B. With Film Resistance

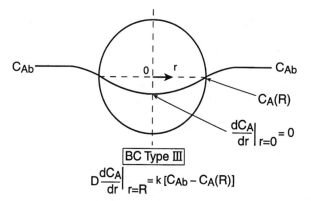

FIGURE 4.1 Example of a physical system with BCs of Type I, II, and III.

$$k_C 4\pi R^2 (C_{Ab} - C_{k=r}) = kD_{eff} 4\pi R^2 \frac{dC_A}{dr}\bigg|_{r=R}$$

$$(4.2.1)$$

<table>
<tr><td>Rate of transport
through film</td><td>Rate of diffusion
into interior</td></tr>
</table>

4.2.1 SOME USEFUL HINTS ON BOUNDARY CONDITIONS

It is frequently sufficient to formulate a Boundary Condition as "y is finite at $z =$ L" or "y is bounded at $y = L$," rather than specifying actual values of the state variable or its derivatives at that position. For example, in the frequently encountered solution for a bounded state variable y:

$$y = C_1 \exp (kx) + C_2 (\exp - kx) \qquad (4.2.2)$$

the integration constant C_1 can be easily evaluated by invoking the boundedness condition:

TABLE 4.2
Types of Boundary Conditions

Type	Nomenclature	Property	Occurrence
I	BC of type I	Contains y only	y specified at a particular location
II	BC of type II	Contains dy/dx only	Profile symmetrical; constant or zero diffusional flux
III	BC of type III or mixed type	Contains dy/dx and y	Diffusional flux with film resistance

$$y|_{x \to \infty} = \text{finite} \qquad (4.2.3)$$

i.e., C_1 must perforce be zero.

The boundary condition dy/dx = 0 arises, as we have seen, whenever *a profile is symmetrical or when the diffusive flux is zero*. There are numerous physical situations in which one or the other of these conditions applies including:

- $dv/dr|_{r=0} = 0$ in viscous flow of a fluid in a pipe (symmetry)
- $dC/dr|_{r=0} = 0$ in a cylindrical or spherical catalyst pellet (symmetry)
- $dT/dr|_{r=0} = 0$ in a cylindrical or spherical nonisothermal catalyst pellet (symmetry)
- $dT/dz|_{z=L} = 0$ at an insulated surface (zero flux)
- $dp/dz|_{z=L} = 0$ in a porous duct with one end sealed (zero flux)

Application of boundary conditions of Type III leads to awkward and lengthy expressions involving both state variables and their derivatives. This can be avoided by "bracketing" the exact solution with a Type I BC representing zero film resistance and a Type II condition dy/dx = 0 representative of infinite resistance. The technique is often invoked when the only solutions available are those for Type I and Type II conditions.

Boundary conditions involving higher order derivatives arise in certain problems of Solid Mechanics. An example of these appears in Chapter 5, Illustration 5.2.5.

Illustration 4.2.1 Boundary Conditions in a Conduction Problem: Heat Losses from a Metallic Furnace Insert

A cylindrical metallic rod, such as a bolt or a sampling port, extends from the exterior metal sheet cover of a furnace, well into its interior where it is exposed to high temperatures. Heat is conducted from the hot end of the insert to the heat at the exterior of the furnace. Some heat is lost from the head itself to the surrounding air, but a more important cumulative loss occurs due to conduction radially through the metal sheet cover and from there by convection and radiation to the atmosphere. The aim here is to set up the model equation and establish the associated boundary conditions.

We consider a circular difference element r, r+Δr and write:

$$\text{Rate of energy in} - \text{Rate of energy out} = 0$$

$$q_{cond} \big|_r - \left[\begin{array}{c} q_{cond}\big|_{r+\Delta r} + q_{conv} \\ + q_{rad} \end{array} \right] = 0$$

$$\left[-k2\pi rL \frac{dT}{dr}\bigg|_z \right] - \left[\left(-k2\pi rL \frac{dT}{dr} \right)_{r+\Delta r} + h2\pi r\Delta r(T - T_a) + \varepsilon\sigma 2\pi r\Delta r(T^4 - T_a^{\ 4}) \right] = 0$$

(4.2.4)

where L = metal sheet thickness. Upon dividing by $2\pi kL\Delta r$ and going to the limit $\Delta r \to 0$, we obtain:

$$\frac{d^2 T}{dr^2} + \frac{1}{r}\frac{dT}{dr} - \frac{h}{kL}[(T - T_a) + \varepsilon\sigma(T^4 - T_a^{\ 4})] = 0 \qquad (4.2.5)$$

Note that in arriving at this result, the *product* of conductive area and temperature gradient has to be differentiated.

Consider next the two boundary conditions required to solve the problem. A first condition is obtained at the *rim* r = R of the insert head. The exact value of the temperature at this location is not known but will be set equal to the temperature in the interior of the furnace. This procedure yields the *maximum* possible heat loss and avoids setting up a second energy balance *along* the bolt with uncertain values for the heat loss to the surrounding firebrick insulation.

The second boundary condition must be established at a location away from the insert head, and here we enter somewhat uncertain territory. An attractive argument is to say that at a sufficiently large distance from the bolt head the cover sheet temperature will approach that of the ambient air — unless another bolt intervenes! Alternatively we could content ourselves with the statement that the temperature remains *bounded,* i.e., $T_{r\to\infty}$ = finite. Whether this is sufficient information to evaluate the integration constant can only be established from the actual solution of the equation.

4.3   ANALYTICAL SOLUTIONS OF ODES

While numerical methods have by now become the standard tool for the solution of ODEs, particularly of nonlinear sets, analytical techniques are far from being obsolete and continue to maintain a strong presence and hold in the field. There are several reasons for this. Foremost among them is the fact that analytical methods are unsurpassed in providing a general and precise sense of solution behavior and in linking it to the physics of a process. An important example is the solution of second order linear and nonautonomous (i.e., forced) systems. Here the analysis and solution of a single ODE gives us a clear picture of the transition of exponentially decaying solutions to oscillatory behavior and provide precise criteria for the occurrence, usually undesirable, of exponential growth in the state variable (see Section

4.3.2). Such linear responses, as they are often called, are the logical starting point for the analysis of more complex nonlinear phenomena. In nonlinear analysis, to be taken up in Section 4.5, one dispenses with precise solutions of the ODEs and attempts instead to define domains in which certain types of behavior occur. This is often of greater interest and benefit than precise numerical response data for a specific set of initial or boundary conditions.

Analytical solutions and criteria also are indispensable in numerical work. Here they provide precise and proven expressions against which the numerical solution to a particular problem can be tested. This is a sound practice, given that numerical methods can, in spite of all refinements and safeguards, lead to unstable and other aberrant behavior.

We commence this section by providing the reader with a list, shown in Table 4.3 of the more important classical ODEs which arise in various fields of science and engineering and are associated with the names of famous mathematicians. They have been the subject of detailed analyses and a good deal of their general behavior is well known. In Table 4.4, we have added a summary of classical analytical

---

TABLE 4.3
Important ODEs

Name	Form	Occurrence
A. Linear ODEs		
1. Airy equation	$y'' + xy = 0$	Quantum mechanics, diffraction of waves
2. Cauchy-Euler equation	$x^2 y'' + bxy + cy = 0$	Solution of PDEs
3. Bessel equation	$y'' + \dfrac{1}{x} y' + \left(1 + \dfrac{n^2}{x^2}\right) y = 0$	Radial diffusive transport in circle or cylinder, vibrations of circular membranes
4. Legendre equation	$(1 - x^2)y'' - 2xy' + n(n + 1)y = 0$	Diffusive transport in sphere
5. Laguerre equation	$xy'' + (1 - x)y' + cy = 0$	Solution of PDEs
6. Hermite equation	$y'' - 2xy' + \lambda y = 0$	Wave mechanics
B. Nonlinear ODEs		
7. Bernoulli equation	$y' + f(x)y - g(x)y^n = 0$	Nonlinear electrical circuits
8. Riccati equation	$y' + f(x)y + g(x)y^2 = h(x)$	Intermediate result in various engineering problems
9. Duffing equation	$\ddot{y} + a\dot{y} + by + cy^3 = d\cos\omega t$	Electrical oscillations
10. van der Pol equation	$\ddot{y} - \lambda(1 - y^2)\dot{y} + y = 0$	Electrical and biological oscillations
11. Lotka-Volterra (predator-prey) model	$\dot{x} = x(a - by)$ $\dot{y} = y(-c + dx)$	Population growth
12. Lorenz attractor	$\dot{x} = 10(y - x)$ $\dot{y} = -xz + 28x - y$ $\dot{z} = xy - (8/3)x$	Free convection flow, chaos

TABLE 4.4
Analytical Solutions of ODEs

System	Solution

A. Major Methods

1. Separable ODEs

$y' = f(x)/g(y) = 0$

$y'' + f(x)/g(y') = 0$

By separation of variables

$\int g(y)dy = \int f(x)dx + C$

$\int g(y')dy' = \int f(x)dx + C$

2. Linear homogeneous second order ODEs with constant coefficients

$y'' + ay' + by = 0$

By D-operator method

$y = C_1 \exp(D_1 x) + C_2 \exp(D_2 x)$

3. Linear nonhomogeneous second order ODEs with constant coefficients

$ay'' + by' + cy = f(x)$

Solution of homogeneous ODE + particular integral y_p (see Table 4.7 for listing of y_p)

4. Linear homogeneous second order ODEs with variable coefficients

$a(x)y'' = b(x)y' + c(x)y = 0$

By power series

$$y = C_1 \sum_1^\infty a_n x^{n+k_1} + C_2 \sum_1^\infty b_n x^{n+k_2}$$

5. Sets of linear first order initial value ODEs with constant coefficients

By Laplace transformation (see Chapter 5)

B. Other Methods

6. Linear first order nonhomogeneous ODE with variable coefficients

$y' + f(x)y = g(x)$

Directly given by formula

$y = \exp \int -f(x)dx$

$[\int g(x) \exp \int f(x)dxdx + C]$

7. General first ODEs

$$y' + \frac{f(x,y)}{g(x,y)} = 0$$

Various solutions arise depending on the method used:

(a) by substitution $y = v\,x$

If substitution yields ODE in v,x only, the solution is

$$\ln x = C - \int \frac{g(1,v)dv}{f(1,v) + vg(1,v)}$$

(b) ODE is exact, i.e.,

$$\frac{\partial f}{\partial y} = \frac{\partial g}{\partial x}$$

Directly given by formula

$$\int f(x,c)dx + \int g(c,y)\partial y - \frac{\partial}{\partial y}\int f(x,c)dx = C$$

(c) ODE is *made* exact by multiplication by an integrating factor

See Table 4.9 for list of integrating factors

8. Nonlinear second order ODE with first derivative and terms in x missing.

$y'' = f(y)$

Multiply equation by $w(dy/dx)dx = 2dy$ to obtain

$y' = [2 \int f(y)dy + C]^{1/2}$

then apply separation of variables

TABLE 4.4 *(continued)*
Analytical Solutions of ODEs

System	Solution
9. Nonlinear second order ODE with missing dependent variable $f(y'', y', x) = 0$	Reduce to first order ODE by "p-substitution" $p = \dfrac{dy}{dx}$, and attempt integration by one of preceding methods, followed by a second integration
10. Nonlinear second order ODE with missing independent variable $f(y'', y', y) = 0$	As under 9, note that second derivative becomes $\dfrac{d^2 y}{dx^2} = \dfrac{dp}{dx} = \dfrac{dp}{dy}\dfrac{dy}{dx} = p\dfrac{dp}{dy}$

solutions of various types of *single* ODEs. A distinction is made between Major Methods which are encountered with great frequency in the sciences and in engineering, and Other Methods of somewhat less frequent occurrence. Among the Major Methods, Laplace transformation has been singled out for separate treatment in Chapter 5 because of its overriding importance and wide scope in the treatment of linear first order initial value problems.

4.3.1 Separation of Variables

This is a powerful and sometimes underrated method for solving both linear and nonlinear first order ODEs. It is the only method used so far in this text to solve a wide range of physical problems, a fact which attests to its power and versatility. In particular, we were able to solve the following by separation of variables.

- Stirred tank problems of various types, see Illustrations 2.4, 2.6, 3.2.3, 3.2.6, and 3.2.7, among those in early chapters.
- Steady-state differential balances: Thermal Treatment of Steel Strapping (Illustration 2.5), Drying of Plastic Sheets (Illustration 2.7), Tubular Reactor (Illustration 3.2.4), and Solute Release from a Tubular Wall (Illustration 3.2.9).

The following points and recommendations are submitted to the attention of the reader:

- Separation of variables is the preferred method of solving single ODEs and is always to be tried first.
- Single second order ODEs may be amenable to solution by separation of variables provided one of the boundary conditions is given in terms of the first derivative (see Item 1 in Table 4.4).

- ODEs which at first glance appear to defy separation of the variable may by proper manipulation be reduced to separable form. An example of this is given in the following illustration.

Illustration 4.3.1 Solution of Complex ODEs by Separation of Variables

Consider the following first order ODE:

$$x \sin y \frac{dy}{dx} + \frac{ye^x}{1-y} = e^x(y^3 + y) \qquad (4.3.1)$$

This equation is highly nonlinear, not because of the exponential terms which are in x, but by virtue of the y^3 term as well as the expression sin y(dy/dx). The equation does not at first sight appear to be separable. The situation is improved, however, by factoring out e^x and collecting terms. We obtain:

$$e^x \left(y^3 + y - \frac{y}{1-y} \right) = x \sin y \frac{dy}{dx} \qquad (4.3.2)$$

which is clearly separable. Formal integration leads to the result:

$$\int \frac{e^x}{x} dx = \int \frac{\sin y \, dy}{y^3 + y - y/(1-y)} + C \qquad (4.3.3)$$

Analytical evaluation of the left side is easily accomplished; that of the right side is more problematical. One has to resort to numerical methods and the question then arises whether these are not better applied at the source, i.e., at the ODE level. The answer here is no. The integrated form (Equation 4.3.3), although not fully evaluated, provides a better picture of the solution. In particular, it enables us to identify conditions on y which leads to a divergence of the integral. These may occur when $y^3 + y - y/1 - y$ goes to zero. In practice it is preferable to deal with integrated expressions, if attainable, rather than the ODE itself.

In Chapter 6, Illustration 6.1.7, we encounter a nonlinear ODE of the form:

$$du/d\tau = au^2 - bu + c \qquad (6.1.56)$$

Literature treatments of this equation identify it as a Riccati equation (Item 8, Table 4.3) and apply the solution methods pertinent to that form. In fact the equation is easily integrated by separation of variables. Furthermore, the solution which involves the roots of the quadratic in Equation 6.1.56 is amenable to simple asymptotic analysis. It is, of course, more impressive and fashionable to identify the ODE (Equation 6.1.56) as a Riccati equation, but in the end less fruitful.

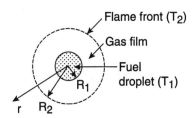

FIGURE 4.2   Configuration of a burning liquid fuel droplet.

Illustration 4.3.2   Repeated Separation of Variables:
The Burning Fuel Droplet as a Moving Boundary Problem

In the combustion of liquid fuels, the rate-determining step is frequently taken to be the rate of heat transfer through the stagnant gas film. Heat is conducted through this film to the drop surface where it vaporizes the fuel. Fuel vapor in turn diffuses to the flame front where the actual combustion takes place. The fuel droplet is assumed to be at its boiling point T_1, the flame front at a constant and known temperature, T_2 (see Figure 4.2).

The droplet size variation with time has been established experimentally to be of the form:

$$R_1^2 = (R_1^0)^2 - \alpha t \tag{4.3.4}$$

where R_1^0 is the initial droplet radius.

The model solution is to be used to verify this expression and to relate the constant α to physical parameters of the system.

An outline of the preferred procedure for solving moving boundary problems was given in Illustration 3.3.12. Typically one starts with a mass or energy balance about the core which is assumed to have uniform properties and proceeds outward into the film which is assumed to be at quasi-steady-state conditions. We obtain:

Core mass balance:

$$\text{Rate of fuel in} - \text{Rate of fuel out} = \begin{array}{c} \text{Rate of change} \\ \text{of fuel content} \end{array}$$

$$0 - F = \frac{d}{dt} m = \rho_L \, 4\pi R_1^2 \, \frac{dR_1}{dt} \tag{4.3.5}$$

Core energy balance:

$$\text{Rate of energy in} - \text{Rate of energy out} = \begin{array}{c} \text{Rate of change of} \\ \text{energy contents} \end{array}$$

$$q - FH_v = \frac{d}{dt} H_L \tag{4.3.6}$$

where F = rate of vapor formed (kg/s), and H_{VL} = vapor and liquid fuel enthalpies.

Taking the liquid enthalpy H_L as the reference state and using the appropriate auxiliary relation for q, we obtain from Equation 4.3.6:

$$k_v 4\pi R_1^2 \left(\frac{dT}{dr}\right)_{R_1} - F\Delta H_v = 0 \tag{4.3.7}$$

Quasi-steady-state differential energy balance in gas film:

$$\text{Rate of energy in} - \text{Rate of energy out} = 0$$

$$[H|_r + q|_{r+\Delta r}] - [H|_{r+\Delta r} + q_r] = 0$$

or equivalently,

$$dq - dH = 0 \tag{4.3.8}$$

which upon introduction of the relevant auxiliary relations yields:

$$d\left(--k_v 4\pi r^2 \frac{dT}{dr}\right) - d[FC_{pv}(T - T_0)] = 0 \tag{4.3.9}$$

Note that conduction takes a double negative sign since it takes place in the negative direction.

This expression can be directly integrated from the surface of the droplet (R_1, T_1) to some arbitrary position (r, T). We obtain:

$$k_v 4\pi r^2 \frac{dT}{dr} - k_v 4\pi R_1^2 \left(\frac{dT}{dr}\right)_{R_1} = FC_{pv}(T - T_1) \tag{4.3.10}$$

A second integration is performed, this time by separation of variables. This yields the result:

$$\int_{R_1}^{R_2} \frac{dr}{r^2} = \int_{T_1}^{T_2} \frac{dT}{K(T - T_1) + R_1^2 \left(\dfrac{dT}{dr}\right)_{R_1}} \tag{4.3.11}$$

and

$$\frac{1}{R_1} - \frac{1}{R_2} = \frac{1}{K}\ln\left[\frac{T_2 - T_1}{(R_1^2 / K)\left(\dfrac{dT}{dr}\right)_{R_1}} + 1\right] \tag{4.3.12}$$

where $K = FC_{pv}/4\pi k_v$. Note that in this integration both R_1 and $(dT/dr)_{R_1}$ are held constant by virtue of the steady-state assumption.

We pause at this point for a brief inventory. The model equations on hand are now three in number: the core mass balance (4.3.5), the core energy balance (4.3.7), and the integrated steady-state gas film energy balance (4.3.12). The associated unknown state variables are F, $(dT/dr)_{R_1}$ and R_1 of which we wish to retain only R_1. Elimination of F and $(dT/dr)_{R_1}$ from these three equations and a formal second integration by separation of variables leads us to:

$$\ln\left[1 + \frac{C_{pv}}{\Delta H_v}(T_2 - T_1)\right]\int_0^t dt = -\frac{C_{pv}\rho_L}{k_v}\int_{R_1^0}^{R_1} R_1(1 - R_1/R_2)dR_1 \quad (4.3.13)$$

One notes that in order to satisfy the experimental finding, Equation 4.3.4, the right-side integral must yield the form R_1^2, i.e., the ratio of inner to outer radius R_1/R_2 has to be a constant. This is an acceptable assumption, given that the flame front recedes in proportion to the shrinking fuel core.

We now finalize the result by carrying out the indicated integration and obtain after rearrangement:

$$R_1^2 = (R_1^0)^2 - \alpha t = (R_1^0)^2 - \frac{2k_v}{\rho_L C_{pv}(1 - R_1/R_2)}\ln\left[1 + \frac{C_{pv}}{\Delta H_v}(T_2 - T_1)\right]t \quad (4.3.14)$$

where k_{pv}, C_{pv} = thermal conductivity and heat capacity of the vapor, ΔH_v = latent heat of vaporization, and T_1, T_2 = boiling point of fuel and temperature of the flame front, respectively. Most of these physical parameters are readily available. The unknown flame temperature T_2 is arrived at by equating heat of vaporization and sensible heat of fuel vapor to the heat of combustion, i.e., by performing an integral energy balance. This leaves the ratio of radii R_1/R_2 which has to be obtained by fitting at least one set of experimental data to the Equation 4.3.14. This has in one case yielded a value of $R_1/R_2 = 0.48$, an acceptable number for the geometry in question.

Comments:

We have succeeded in this example in modeling a process that, to the uninitiated at least, is one of considerable complexity. Let us summarize the features which led to a successful solution of the problem.

1. The principal simplifying step was the use of the combination of a uniform shrinking core tied to an external vapor film taken to be at a quasi-steady state. This resulted in a decoupling of the process into three ODEs, two of them in time t (Equations 4.3.5 and 4.3.6) and one in distance r_1 (Equation 4.3.9).

2. A second step was the recognition that the ODEs could be solved in succession and independent of each other, and that this could be done by a double application of the method of separation of variables. Note that

inner and outer radii R_1 and R_2 were quasi steady-state variables in this process and that the initial radius $R_1{}^0$ was only brought in at the last integration step, Equation 4.3.13.

3. The solution was aided considerably by adopting a systematic procedure that started with balances around the core and then moved outward into the gas film. Along the way we kept a running account of the number of dependent variables and the number of equations. When the two were equal, we stopped adding new equations and decided which variables to eliminate. This process led to the final result, Equation 4.3.14.

4. The solution we obtained, (Equation 4.3.14), can be adapted to other fuel systems as well, using the relevant physical parameters and flame temperature. Although the ratio R_1/R_2 may differ among systems, the change is not expected to be major so that the value of ~0.5 can be used as a good first approximation.

4.3.2 THE D-OPERATOR METHOD: SOLUTION OF LINEAR NTH ORDER ODES WITH CONSTANT COEFFICIENTS

We start this section with an example that we use to introduce the reader to the concept of characteristic roots or eigenvalues of a linear ODE, and to the important superposition principle. Consider the equation:

$$\frac{d^2y}{dx^2} - y = 0 \qquad (4.3.15)$$

A relative novice to the field might attempt a solution by substituting trial functions into the ODE and seeing whether the ODE is satisfied. It might further be argued that since the equation is a second order one, two boundary conditions will have to be satisfied, hence, two integration constants will have to be evaluated. These integration constants must be associated with two *independent* functions, for if they were not, the two constants would coalesce into a single one and we would be unable to satisfy the two boundary conditions.

Let us attempt a solution with some simple trial functions. Neither sin x nor cos x satisfy Equation 4.3.15. However, both e^x and e^{-x} do, and furthermore they are independent of each other. One might, therefore, formulate a general solution of the form:

$$y = C_1 e^x + C_2 e^{-x} \qquad (4.3.16)$$

This sum also satisfies the ODE. Thus, we have, somewhat inadvertently, discovered the superposition principle, at least as it applies to this example. That principle in essence states that the general solution to a nth order *linear* ODE is composed of the *sum* of n independent functions. Uniqueness of the solution is guaranteed by uniqueness theorems which are described in most texts dealing with ODEs.

If one were to conduct extensive trials of this type, one would discover that the solution of any linear homogeneous ODE with constant coefficients, of whatever order, is always composed of the sum of exponential functions with either real or imaginary arguments. Early workers in the field were well aware of this fact. They also had noted a precise connection between the (constant) coefficients of the ODE and those of the arguments of the exponential functions. This led to the development of a formalism known as the D-Operator Method. In it, the operational part of a derivative, that is d/dx, is replaced by the operator symbol D, and that symbol treated as an *algebraic* entity, subject to the usual rules of algebra. Equation 4.3.15 can then be written in the form:

$$(D^2 - 1)y = 0 \tag{4.3.17}$$

Equivalently,

$$D^2 - 1 = 0 \tag{4.3.18}$$

with the solutions:

$$D_1 = 1, D_2 = -1 \tag{4.3.19}$$

The Equation 4.3.18 is termed the characteristic equation of the ODE and its solution its characteristic roots. These roots are *identical* to the coefficients of the arguments of the exponential functions in Equation 4.3.16.

Table 4.5 lists a compilation of characteristic roots and the corresponding solutions for the most frequently encountered case of a second order ODE. For real and

---

TABLE 4.5
Solutions of the Second Order ODE $ay'' + by' + cy = 0$

Characteristic Roots or Eigenvalues	Solution
1. Distinct and real: $D_{1,2}$	$y = C_1 e^{D_1 x} + C_2 e^{C_2 x}$
	or $\quad y = C_1' \sinh D_1 x + C_2' \cosh D_2 x$
2. Identical and real: $D_1 = D_2 = D$	$y = C_1 e^{Dx} + C_2 x e^{Dx}$
3. Imaginary: $C_{1,2} = \pm bi$	$y = C_1 e^{bix} + C_2 e^{-bix}$
	or $\quad y = C_1' \cos bx + C_2' \sin bx$
4. Complex conjugate: $D_{1,2} = a \pm bi$	$y = C_1 e^{(a+bi)x} + C_2 e^{(a-bi)x}$
	or $\quad y = (C_1' \cos bx + C_2' \sin bx)e^{ax}$
	Euler's formula
$\sin x = \dfrac{1}{2}(e^x - e^{-x})$	$e^{ix} = \cos x + i \sin x$
$\cosh x = \dfrac{1}{2}(e^x - e^{-x})$	

---

distinct roots, the solution is the sum of the corresponding exponential functions which also can be expressed in terms of equivalent hyperbolic functions. When the roots are identical, one of the exponential functions is premultiplied by the independent variable. Exponential functions with imaginary arguments that result from complex conjugate characteristic roots are converted to trigonometric functions with real arguments using the Euler formula given in the table.

These characteristic roots also can be obtained by matrix methods. To accomplish this we decompose the nth order equation into an equivalent set of n first order ODEs and evaluate the eigenvalues λ_i of the coefficient matrix. For Equation 4.3.15, we obtain the equivalent set:

$$\frac{dy}{dx} = 0 + z$$

$$\frac{dz}{dx} = y + 0 \tag{4.3.20}$$

for which the coefficient matrix is given by:

$$\underset{\sim}{A} = \begin{matrix} 0 & 1 \\ 1 & 0 \end{matrix} \tag{4.3.21}$$

The eigenvalues follow from the relation:

$$\det(\underset{\sim}{A} - \lambda \underset{\sim}{I}) = 0 \tag{4.3.22}$$

or equivalently,

$$\begin{vmatrix} 0 - \lambda & 1 \\ 1 & 0 - \lambda \end{vmatrix} = 0 \tag{4.3.23}$$

Hence, $\lambda^2 - 1 = 0$ and $\lambda_{1,2} = \pm 1$. The eigenvalues of the coefficient matrix of the set of two first order ODEs (Equation 4.3.21) are thus seen to be identical to the characteristic roots of the corresponding second order ODE (Equation 4.3.14).

Illustration 4.3.3   The Longitudinal Heat Exchanger Fin Revisited

We return here to the lengthwise heat exchanger fin we had first considered in Illustration 3.3.4. The ODE for the temperature distribution we derived there was given by:

$$\frac{d^2}{dx^2}(T_h - T_f) - \frac{2h_f}{kW}(T_h - T_f) = 0 \tag{3.3.31}$$

where T_h and T_f were the (hot) shell side and the fin temperature, respectively.

This is a linear and homogeneous second order ODE with constant coefficients that can be solved by the D-operator or eigenvalue methods. We choose the former and write, in equivalent operator notation,

$$(D^2 - m^2)y = 0 \qquad (4.3.24)$$

where $m^2 = 2h_f/kW$ and the characteristic roots are given by $D_{1,2} = \pm m$. These are real and distinct and lead to the general solution (see Table 4.5):

$$T_h - T_f = C_1 \exp(mx) + C_2 \exp(-mx) \qquad (4.3.25)$$

The two boundary conditions were discussed in the original illustration and are given by:

BC1 $\left. \dfrac{d}{dx}(T_h - T_f) \right|_{x=0} = 0$ (Neglibible heat transfer at fin edge)

$$(4.3.26)$$

BC2 $(T_h - T_f |_{x=L} = (T_h - T_t)$ (Fin temperature at base equals tube temperature)

We obtain, from BC 1

$$[-mC_1 \exp(-mx) + mC_2 \exp(mx)]_{x=0} = 0 \qquad (4.3.27)$$

$$\therefore C_1 = C_2 \qquad (4.3.28)$$

From BC 2, we have

$$T_h - T_f = C_1[\exp(-mL) + \exp(mL)] = 2\,C_1 \cosh mL \qquad (4.3.29)$$

and, hence,

$$C_1 = C_2 = (T_h - T_t)/2 \cosh mL \qquad (4.3.30)$$

Substitution into the general solution (Equation 4.3.25) then yields the fin temperature profile $T_f(x)$:

$$\frac{T_h - T_f}{T_h - T_t} = \frac{\cosh mx}{\cosh mL} \qquad (4.3.31)$$

We now proceed to evaluate the fin effectiveness E which was defined in Illustration 3.3.4 as:

$$E = \frac{\text{Actual heat transferred } q_a}{\text{Ideal heat transferred } q_i} \tag{3.3.32}$$

q_a equals the heat leaving the base of the fin $-kW\Delta z \dfrac{dT_f}{dx}\bigg|_{x=L}$ and can be evaluated with the aid of the hyperbolic relations given in Table 4.6, Items 12 and 3. We have

$$q_a = -kW\Delta z \frac{dT_f}{dx} = kW\Delta z \frac{d}{dx}(T_h - T_f) = kW\Delta z \frac{T_h - T_t}{\cosh mL}\frac{d}{dx}\cosh mx \mid_L$$

$$\tag{3.3.33}$$

$$q = kW\Delta z(T_h - T_t)m\frac{\sinh mL}{\cosh mL} = kW\Delta z(T_h - T_t)m \tanh mL$$

From this we obtain:

$$E = \frac{kW\Delta z(T_h - T_t)}{h_f 2L\Delta z(T_h - T_t)}m \tanh mL \tag{4.3.34}$$

or, since $2h_f/kW = m^2$:

$$E = \frac{\tanh(mL)}{mL} \tag{4.3.35}$$

Illustration 4.3.4   Polymer Sheet Extrusion: The Uniformity Index

In this example we consider the performance of a simple device used in the extrusion of polymer sheets. The molten polymer is forced with an inlet pressure p^0 into a pipe with a lateral slit or lip extending some distance away from the pipe wall (Figure 4.3). The polymer flows into the pipe axially and exits radially through the extruder lip. A problem that arises in these devices is that the pressure driving the melt through the slit diminishes in the axial direction causing nonuniformity in the thickness of the extruded sheet. A model is required to relate sheet thickness to the system parameters and to axial distance so that these can be properly modified to ensure high uniformity. This is done by considering the ratio of radial flow at the inlet, $Q_r(0)$ and the corresponding flow $Q_r(L_p)$ at the pipe end which is sealed off. The ratio of the two quantities is known as the uniformity index $E = Q_r(L_p)/Q_r(0)$. Thus, for complete uniformity, $E = 1$, and for nonuniform sheets, $E < 1$. In analyzing the system, we shall assume that flow is Newtonian, so that standard flow-pressure drop relations may be applied.

We start by considering a mass balance over the difference element shown in Figure 4.3B. Axial flow Q_a enters and leaves the element at position z and z + Δz, while at the same time there is a radial outflow over the distance Δz. Flow rate Q

TABLE 4.6
Table of Hyperbolic Functions

1. Hyperbolic sine of u

$$\sinh u \frac{1}{2}(e^u - e^{-u}) = \frac{1}{\operatorname{csch} u}$$

2. Hyperbolic cosine of u

$$\cosh u = \frac{1}{2}(e^u + e^{-u}) = \frac{1}{\operatorname{sech} u}$$

3. Hyperbolic tangent of u $\tanh u = (e^u - e^{-u})/(e^u + e^{-u})$
4. Hyperbolic cotangent of u $\coth u = (e^u + e^{-u})/(e^u - e^{-u})$

Relation to Trigonometric Functions

5. $\sinh iu = i \sin u$
6. $\cosh iu = \cos u$
7. $\tanh iu = i \tan u$
8. $\sinh u = -i \sin iu$
9. $\cosh u = \cos iu$
10. $\tanh u = i \tan iu$

Derivatives

11. $\dfrac{d}{dx}\sinh x = \cosh x$

12. $\dfrac{d}{dx}\cosh x = \sinh x$

13. $\dfrac{d}{dx}\tanh x = \operatorname{sech}^2 x$

14. $\dfrac{d}{dx}\coth x = \operatorname{csch}^2 x$

Integrals

15. $\int \sinh x \, dx = \cosh x$
16. $\int \cosh x \, dx = \sinh x$
17. $\int \tanh x \, dx = \ln(\cosh x)$
18. $\int \coth x \, dx = \ln(\sinh x)$

Other Relations

19. $\cosh^2 u - \sinh^2 u = 1$
20. $\sinh(-u) = -\sinh u$
21. $\cosh(-u) = \cosh u$
22. $\tanh(-u) = -\tanh u$
23. $\coth(-u) = -\coth u$

---

in these terms can be related to pressure drop via the relations given in Table 3.20, suitably transformed to the conditions and symbols used here:

Axial flow:

$$Q_a = -\frac{\pi R^4}{8\mu}\frac{dp}{dz} \tag{4.3.36}$$

A. Device

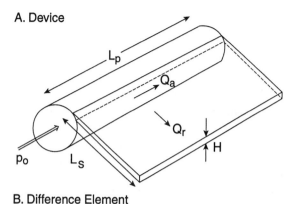

B. Difference Element

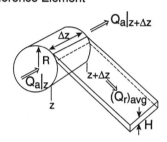

FIGURE 4.3 (A) Schematic diagram of a polymer sheet extruder, (b) difference element for the mass balance.

Radial flow:

$$(Q_r)_{avg} = \frac{H^3 \Delta z}{12\mu} \frac{(\Delta p_r)_{avg}}{L_s} \tag{4.3.37}$$

Note that for axial flow the pressure derivative rather than $\Delta p/L$ is used since p varies nonlinearly with z. For radial flow, the variation is linear and we can write $\frac{dp}{dr} = (p - p_{atm})/L_s$.

We have:

$$\text{Rate of flow in} - \text{Rate of flow out} = 0$$

$$Q_a \big|_z - [(Q_a \big|_{z+\Delta z}) + (Q_r)_{avg}] = 0 \tag{4.3.38}$$

$$\frac{\pi R^4}{8\mu} \Delta\left(\frac{dp}{dz}\right) - \frac{H^3 \Delta z}{12\mu} \frac{(\Delta p_r)_{avg}}{L_s} = 0$$

Dividing by Δz and going to the limit yields the second order ODE:

$$\frac{d^2p}{dx^2} - m^2p = 0 \tag{4.3.39}$$

where $m^2 = \frac{2}{3}\frac{H^3}{\pi R^4 L_s}$ and p_{ext} has been set $= 0$.

Solution of this equation by the D-operator method yields:

$$p = C_1 \sinh mx + C_2 \cosh mx$$

where we use the hyperbolic rather than exponential form for later convenience. Two boundary conditions are required which are as follows:

$$\text{BC1} \quad \left.\frac{dp}{dz}\right|_{z=L_p} = 0 \quad \text{(No flow at sealed end)} \tag{4.3.40}$$

$$\text{BC2} \quad p(0) = p^0 \quad \text{(Inlet pressure above atmospheric)}$$

We obtain, from BC 1, using the derivatives of hyperbolic functions listed in Table 4.6:

$$C_1 = -C_2 \tanh (mL_p) \tag{4.3.41}$$

and from BC 2:

$$C_2 = p^0$$

The resulting axial pressure profile is given by the relation:

$$p = p^0[(\cosh mx - \tanh (mL_p) \sinh (mx)] \tag{4.3.42}$$

A quick look at the uniformity index is warranted. We have:

$$E = \frac{Q_r(L_p)}{Q_r(0)} = \frac{p(L_p)}{p(0)}$$

and, hence,

$$E = \cosh(mL_p) - \frac{\sinh^2(mL_p)}{\cosh(mL_p)} \tag{4.3.43}$$

Using the hyperbolic relations of Table 3.20, Items 19 and 2, this reduces to the simple expression:

$$E = \text{sech}(mL_p) = \text{sech}\left(\frac{2H^3L_p^{\,2}}{3\pi L_s R^4}\right)^{1/2} \qquad (4.3.44)$$

mL_p is usually much less than one, so that one can use a truncated series expansion of the hyperbolic secant found in standard mathematical handbooks:

$$E = \text{sech}(mL_p) \cong 1 - \frac{(mL_p)^2}{2} = 1 - \frac{H^3L_p^{\,2}}{3\pi L_s R^4} \qquad (4.3.45)$$

To obtain a sense of parameter sensitivity, suppose that for a given configuration, E was found to be 0.95, i.e., $H^3L_p^{\,2}/3\pi L_s R^4 = 0.05$. It is now proposed to double the sheet thickness H. How will this affect the sheet uniformity? We find $H^3_{new}/H^3_{old} = 8$, which translates into a new index value of $E_{new} = 0.60$. Thus, E has dropped from an acceptable value of 95% to a low and usually unacceptable level of 60%.

Comments:

The first impression one gains from the formulation of the problem is that it calls for a PDE model. Velocities vary in a complex way both *radially* and *axially*, and it is likely that an *angular* component has to be contended with as well. As in the preceding example of the finned heat exchanger, the geometry is a discontinuous one, leading to discontinuous boundary conditions which add to the complexity of the problem. We are, thus, dealing with a fairly difficult application of the Navier-Stokes and continuity equations. Non-Newtonian behavior would further aggravate the situation.

The principal tool in side-stepping these difficulties was the tacit assumption that the opening width of the lip is small in comparison to the circumference of the pipe and, consequently, the normal parabolic velocity profile remains essentially undisturbed. This is a reasonable simplification in view of the small thickness of normal polymer sheets. Its consequences, however are quite considerable since we can now lump the radial flow into the axial mass balance as a "rate out" term which is determined solely by the local radial pressure drop and the geometry of the slit. Thus, we have reduced the number of state variables from *four* (three velocities and pressure) to only one, i.e., pressure, and the number of independent variables from three to one, the axial distance. Note that the model can easily accommodate non-Newtonian flow, but this requires the use of an appropriate non-Newtonian Q – dp/dz relation to replace Poiseuille's law, Equation 4.3.36.

There is another parallel to the finned heat exchanger. In both cases the primary profiles, here given by Equation 4.3.42, are converted to criteria which serve to compare *actual* performance to an established *ideal*. For the heat exchanger, the criterion was the fin effectiveness which conveyed a sense of the degree of nonuniformity in fin temperature. In a similar way, the uniformity index in polymer extrusion establishes the degree of nonuniformity of tubular pressure and, hence, sheet thickness.

The reason for choosing the hyperbolic form of solution of the ODE becomes apparent when we reach Equation 4.3.44. The uniformity index E can now be expressed in compact form as the hyperbolic secant of a single dimensionless group $H^3L_p^2/3\pi L_s R^4$. Never content to stop simplifying, we reached back to first year calculus, an often neglected area, to expand the hyperbolic secant into the simple truncated algebraic Equation 4.3.45. This equation related the uniformity index in revealing fashion to the geometry of the system. Of particular note is the dependence of E on H^3/R^4 which indicates that any adverse effect on E caused by an increase in polymer sheet thickness H can be easily compensated for by an increase in pipe radius R. An increase in slit length L_s can be used to similar good effect. Thus, the simple Equation 4.3.45 manages to illuminate the entire problem and enables us to quickly address important design questions.

4.3.3 NONHOMOGENEOUS LINEAR SECOND ORDER ODEs WITH CONSTANT COEFFICIENTS

We consider here systems of the form

$$L(y) = ay'' + by' + cy = f(x) \qquad (4.3.46)$$

where a, b, c are constants, and f(x) is the nonhomogeneous term. It can be shown by the superposition principle that the solution will in this case be made up of the sum of the solution of the homogeneous form of Equation 4.3.46, termed the *complementary function,* and a particular integral y_p which has the same functional form as the nonhomogeneous term f(x). Thus,

$$\text{General solution} = \text{Complementary solution} + \text{Particular integral} \quad (4.3.47)$$

Methods for the evaluation of the complementary solution were given in Section 4.3.2. Evaluation of the particular integral is by the so-called *method of undetermined coefficients.* It consists of substituting the known form of y_p which is identical to that of f(x), into the ODE 4.3.46 and evaluating the undetermined coefficients by setting the sum of coefficients of a particular function equal to zero. This method, which also finds use in series solutions taken up in the next section, will be discussed in more detail there. For our present purposes, we content ourselves with a listing of the most frequently required particular integrals shown in Table 4.7. These can be used directly in the Formulation 4.3.47 to arrive at a general solution of the nonhomogeneous ODE. We demonstrate its application in the example below.

Illustration 4.3.5 Vibrating Spring with a Forcing Function

Vibrating systems give rise to a host of interesting solutions. We consider only the simplest of these, that of a mass suspended from a spring and vibrating under its own weight. A full analysis of such systems is deferred to the next chapter dealing with the Laplace transformation which is the preferred method of solution in these cases.

Applying Newton's law to the system we obtain, in the first instance:

TABLE 4.7
Particular Integrals y_p of the Second Order ODE $ay'' + by' + cy = f(x)$

$f(x)$	Form of y_p	Coefficients of y_p
a_0	K	$K = a_0/c$
$a_0 + a_1x + ... \, a_nx^n$	$A_0 + A_1x + ... \, A_nx^n$	Determined by substituting into ODE and equating coefficients
a_0e^{rx}	A_0e^{rx}	$A_0 = \dfrac{a_0}{ar^2 + br + c}$
$a_0 \sin nx$	$A_0 \sin nx$	$A_0 = \dfrac{(c - n^2a)a_0}{(c - n^2a)^2 + n^2b^2}$
$a_0 \cos nx$	$A_0 \cos nx$	$A_0 = \dfrac{(c - n^2a)a_0}{(c - n^2a)^2 + n^2b^2}$
$a_0 \sin nx + b_0 \cos nx$	$A_0 \sin nx + B_0 \cos nx$	$A_0 = \dfrac{(c - n^2a)a_0 + nbb_0}{(c - n^2a)^2 + n^2b^2}$
		$B_0 = \dfrac{(c - n^2a)b_0 + nba_0}{(c - n^2a)^2 + n^2b^2}$

$$\sum \text{Forces} = m\frac{d^2x}{dt^2}$$

or

$$F_g - F_s = m\frac{d^2x}{dt^2} \tag{4.3.48}$$

where F_g and F_s are the gravity force and the restoring force of the spring, respectively. The latter varies directly with the extension x, and for linear behavior is expressed by Hooke's law

$$F_s = kx \tag{4.3.49}$$

Equation 4.3.47 then becomes, after substitution and rearrangement:

$$\frac{d^2x}{dt^2} + (k/m)x = g \tag{4.3.50}$$

where the gravitational constant g is the nonhomogeneous term.

Although other solution methods for this equation exist, including the Laplace transformation, we shall use the example to demonstrate the use of the particular integral and its superposition on the complementary solution. The latter is obtained by the D-operator method. We write:

$$(D^2 + k/m)x = 0 \tag{4.3.51}$$

which has the characteristic roots:

$$D_{1,2} = \pm i(k/m)^{1/2} = \pm bi \tag{4.3.52}$$

so that the complementary solution becomes (see Table 4.5):

$$x_c = C_1 \sin bt + C_2 \cos bt \tag{4.3.53}$$

The particular integral y_p is established with the aid of Table 4.7, yielding:

$$y_p = g(k/m) \tag{4.3.54}$$

Hence, the general solution is given by:

$$x = C_1 \sin bt + C_2 \cos bt + g(k/m) \tag{4.3.55}$$

We now introduce the boundary conditions (initial conditions here) by specifying that the mass is initially extended to a position x_0 and that the velocity at $t = 0$ is zero. Note that these conditions have to be applied to the *full* Equation 4.3.55, not just the complementary solution (Equation 4.3.53). We obtain:

From IC 2 $\qquad\qquad\qquad C_1 = 0 \tag{4.3.56}$

From IC 1 $\qquad\qquad\qquad C_2 = x_0 - g(k/m)$

The general solution then takes the form:

$$x = (x_0 - mg/k) \cos [(k/m)^{1/2}t] \tag{4.3.57}$$

The equation reveals that the response of the system to the forcing function g is an oscillatory one with amplitude $(x_0 - mg/k)$ and frequency $(k/m)^{1/2}$ s^{-1}. The oscillations persist indefinitely without any decay in the amplitude. Time dependent amplitudes arise when the forcing function is itself time-dependent or when friction exercises a dampening effect. These cases that arise in the classical analysis of second order linear systems are taken up in greater detail in Chapter 5.

4.3.4 SERIES SOLUTIONS OF LINEAR ODEs WITH VARIABLE COEFFICIENTS

When the coefficients of a linear ODE themselves become functions of the independent variable, the D-operator method can no longer be applied. One must turn to alternative methods which have led to the development of series solutions. The series solutions belong to a wider class of solution techniques in which a specific *form* of the solution is *guessed* or *assumed*, for example y = a sin x + b cos x. The unknown coefficients, here a and b, are evaluated by substituting the solution into the ODE and setting the coefficients of like terms equal to zero. This procedure is known as the *method of undetermined coefficients* which was encountered briefly in connection with particular integrals.

The solution form we shall assume here is a power series in x, i.e.,

$$y = a_0 + a_1 x^{1+k} + a_2 x^{2+k} + \dots \qquad (4.3.58)$$

This is not an unreasonable guess to make since the solution to the *constant* coefficient case also can be expressed in terms of power series in x, for example:

$$e^{ax} = 1 + \frac{ax}{1!} + \frac{(ax)^2}{2!} + \dots \qquad (4.3.59)$$

It then can be argued that variable coefficients, particularly those of a polynomial form, will merely alter the coefficients and the exponents of x but will not otherwise deviate from the power series forms. To allow for this effect, we have included an undetermined parameter k in the exponent which will be a function of the variable coefficients contained in the ODE.

We start by demonstrating these concepts and their validity with a simple example.

Illustration 4.3.6   Solution of a Linear ODE With Constant Coefficients by a Power Series Expansion

We consider the first order ODE:

$$y' + y = 0 \qquad (4.3.60)$$

and assume a series solution of the form:

$$y = a_0 + a_1 x + a_2 x^2 + a_3 x^3 + \dots = 0 \qquad (4.3.61)$$

Note that a solution also can be arrived at by separation of variables which we can use to validate the series solution.

Substitution of Equation 4.3.61 into Equation 4.3.60 yields:

$$y = (a_0 + a_1) + (2a_2 + a_1)x + \dots = 0 \qquad (4.3.62)$$

We now proceed to evaluate a_0, a_1, and a_2 by the method of undetermined coefficients, setting the aggregate coefficient of each power of x equal to zero. This is justified by the fact that the series expansion (Equation 4.3.61) must equal zero for any arbitrary value of x. We obtain:

$$a_1 = -a_0$$

$$a_2 = -\frac{1}{2}a_1 = \frac{1}{2}a_0 \qquad (4.3.63)$$

and the series solution becomes:

$$y = a_0\left(1 - x + \frac{1}{2}x^2 - \ldots\right) \qquad (4.3.64)$$

where a_0 will evidently play the role of an integration constant.

Let us compare this with the solution obtained by separation of variables which has the exponential form and associated series expansion:

$$y = C\exp(-x) = C\left(1 - x + \frac{x^2}{2} - \ldots\right) \qquad (4.3.65)$$

This is proof, at least for the initial three terms, of the validity of the series solution.

We now turn to the more general case of a second order ODE with variable coefficients:

$$a(x)y'' + b(x)y' + c(x)y = 0 \qquad (4.3.66)$$

where the coefficients are assumed to be of polynomial form:

$$a(x) = a_0 + a_1 x + a_2 x^2 \ldots$$

$$b(x) = b_0 + b_1 x + b_2 x^2 \ldots \qquad (4.3.67)$$

$$c(x) = c_0 + c_1 x + c_2 x^2 \ldots$$

For this case it can be shown that the solution takes the form:

$$y = C_1 \sum_{n=0}^{\infty} a_n x^{n+k_1} + C_2 \sum_{n=0}^{\infty} b_n x^{n+k_2} \qquad (4.3.68)$$

Evaluation of the coefficients is cumbersome, but can be accelerated by the so-called Method of Frobenius which is described in standard texts on ODEs. We shall not go into the details of this procedure but will examine instead the functions which arise in this solution. The following points are of note.

- The functions which result from the series solution of linear second order ODEs with polynomial coefficients are either finite polynomials or infinite power series in x.
- A series of new functions arise as a result which are denoted by the name of the associated ODEs, in particular: Bessel functions, Legendre polynomials, Laguerre polynomials, and Hermite polynomials.

Other classes of functions include Chebyshev polynomials and Hypergeometric functions.

- These functions do not differ in their general properties from the classical exponential, circular, or hyperbolic functions. They are usually exponential or periodic in behavior, can be differentiated or integrated, and are either bounded or unbounded at the origin and at infinity.
- Extensive tabulations for most functions appear in various mathematical handbooks (see References). The reassuring fact emerges that for each value of x, a corresponding value of the function can be looked up or deduced from certain relations (recursion formulae). In this and other respects, these seemingly exotic functions with forbidding German, French, and Russian names are no different from their more conventional counterparts.

We focus our attention here on Bessel functions which arise in conduction and diffusion in circular and cylindrical geometries, particularly at the PDE level. In order to acquaint the reader with their general behavior, we list in Table 4.8 some of their more important properties, including their integrals and derivatives which are used to derive expressions for diffusional flux from the primary profiles. The list of derivatives also contains the so-called recursion formulae, i.e., relations between Bessel functions of different orders. We note in this connection that the order of a Bessel function, denoted by a subscript, is related to and determined by the form of the variable coefficients of the ODE, and resides in the exponent k of the series expansion (Equation 4.3.68). Both fractional and integer orders can arise, each order being associated with a *distinct* function. Thus, a zero order Bessel function is not identical to a first order Bessel function, but may be similar in *form*, i.e., periodic or exponential. The recursion formulae serve to interrelate them.

The four Bessel functions listed in Table 4.8 are infinite power series which give rise to both periodic and exponential behavior. This is demonstrated for zero order Bessel functions ($k = 0$) in the plots shown in Figure 4.4. One notes that the modified Bessel function $K_0(x)$ and $Y_0(x)$ are unbounded at the origin. This rules out their use in domains which include the origin of a radial geometry.

We now present three illustrations involving the derivation and use of such Bessel functions.

Illustration 4.3.7   Evaluation of a Bessel Function

Let us consider the evaluation of a second order Bessel function of the first kind at a value of $x = 5$, i.e., we wish to determine the value of $I_2(5)$. We note that tabulations

TABLE 4.8
Properties of Bessel Functions

A. Types and Designation

Symbol		Designation
$J_k(x)$		Bessel function of the first kind and order k
$Y_k(x)$		Bessel function of the second kind and order k
$I_k(x)$	Modified	Bessel function of the first kind and order k
$K_k(x)$	Modified	Bessel function of the second kind and order k

B. Functional Form

Bessel Function	Functional Form
$J_k(x)$	Damped periodic
$Y_n(x)$	Damped periodic
$I_k(x)$	Exponential
$K_n(x)$	Exponential

In particular

$J_{1/2}(x)$	$(2/\pi x)^{1/2} \sin x$
$J_{-1/2}(x)$	$(2/\pi x)^{1/2} \cos x$
$I_{1/2}(x)$	$(2/\pi x)^{1/2} \sinh x$
$I_{-1/2}(x)$	$(2/\pi x)^{1/2} \cosh x$

C. Values of Various Functions at x = 0 and x = ∞

	$x = 0$	$x = \infty$
$J_k(x)$	0*	0
$I_k(x)$	0*	∞
$Y_k(x)$	$-\infty$	0
$K_k(x)$	∞	0
sin (x)	0	—
cos (x)	1	—
sinh (x)	0	∞
cosh (x)	1	∞

(Note, however, the special cases $J_0(0) = I_0(0) = 1$ and $J_{-k}(0) = I_{-k}(0) = \pm \infty$.)

D. Derivatives of Bessel Functions and Recursion Formula

$$x \frac{d}{dx} J_k(\alpha x) = k J_k(\alpha x) - \alpha x J_{k+1}(\alpha x)$$
$$= \alpha x J_{k-1}(\alpha x) - k J_k(\alpha x)$$
$$x \frac{d}{dx} Y_k(\alpha x) = k Y_k(\alpha x) - \alpha x Y_{k+1}(\alpha x)$$
$$= \alpha x Y_{k-1}(\alpha x) - k Y_k(\alpha x)$$
$$x \frac{d}{dx} I_k(\alpha x) = k I_k(\alpha x) + \alpha x I_{k+1}(\alpha x)$$
$$= \alpha x I_{k-1}(\alpha x) - k I_k(\alpha x)$$
$$x \frac{d}{dx} K_k(\alpha x) = k K_k(\alpha x) - \alpha x K_{k+1}(\alpha x)$$
$$= -\alpha x K_{k-1}(\alpha x) - k K_k(\alpha x)$$

TABLE 4.8 *(continued)*
Properties of Bessel Functions

E. Integrals of Bessel Functions

$$\alpha \int x^k J_{k-1}(\alpha x)dx = x^k J_k(\alpha x) + C$$

$$\alpha \int x^k Y_{k-1}(\alpha x)dx = x^k Y_k(\alpha x) + C$$

$$\alpha \int x^k I_{k-1}(\alpha x)dx = x^k I_k(\alpha x) + C$$

$$\alpha \int x^k K_{k-1}(\alpha x)dx = -x^k K_k(\alpha x) + C$$

F. Values of Bessel Functions for Small Arguments

$$J_n = I_n \cong \left(\frac{x}{2}\right)^n$$

in handbooks usually list values only for zeroth and first order functions. To obtain values for higher order Bessel functions, use must be made of the recursion formulae listed under Table 4.8D. Setting k = 1, we obtain:

$$I_2(x) = I_0(x) - \frac{2}{x}I_1(x) \tag{4.3.69}$$

or

$$I_2(5) = I_0(5) - \frac{2}{5}I_1(5)$$

Tabulations for $I_0(5)$ and $I_1(5)$ give values of 27.24 and 24.34, respectively. There results:

$$I_2(5) = 27.24 - \frac{2}{5}24.34 = 17.50$$

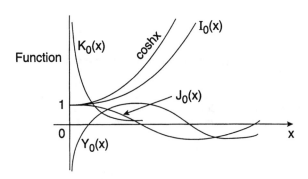

FIGURE 4.4   Graphical representation of zero order Bessel functions. $J_0(x)$ and $Y_0(x)$ are Bessel functions of the first and second type; $I_0(x)$ and $K_0(x)$ are *modified* Bessel functions of the first and second type.

Illustration 4.3.8   Solution of a Second Order ODE with Variable Coefficients by the Generalized Formula

Procedures for obtaining power series solutions of ODEs are fairly lengthy and cumbersome. Fortunately, these procedures may be avoided in most problems by making use of the following generalized formula. The accompanying illustration will demonstrate its use.

The differential equation:

$$x^2 \frac{d^2y}{dx^2} + x(a+2bx^r)\frac{dy}{dx} + [c + dx^{2s} - b(1-a-r)x^r + b^2x^{2r}]y = 0 \quad (4.3.70)$$

has the generalized solution:

$$y = x^{(1-a)/2} \exp(-bx^r/r) [C_1 Z_k(d^{1/2} x^s/s) + C_2 Z_{-k}(d^{1/2}x^s/s)] \quad (4.3.71)$$

where

$$k = \frac{1}{s}\left[\left(\frac{1-a}{2}\right)^2 - c\right]^{1/2}$$

Z_k denotes one of the Bessel functions. If $\sqrt{d}/s$ is real and k is not zero or an integer, Z_k denotes J_k; if k is zero or an integer n, Z_k denotes J_n, Z_{-k} denotes Y_n. If $\sqrt{d}/s$ is imaginary and k is not zero or an integer, Z_k denotes I_k, Z_{-k} denotes I_{-k}; I and K then assume *real* arguments. If k is zero or an integer n, Z_k denotes I_n, and Z_{-k} denotes K_n.

Suppose the solution is to be established of the following ODE, using Equations 4.3.70 and 4.3.71:

$$x^2 \frac{d^2y}{dx^2} + x(1-2\beta)\frac{dy}{dx} + \beta^2 x^{2\beta}y = 0 \quad (4.3.72)$$

When comparing with the generalized equation given previously, the following will be observed:

1. $1 - 2\beta$ will equal $a + 2bx^r$ if $b = 0$ and $a = 1 - 2\beta$.
2. $\beta^2 x^{2\beta}$ will equal $c + dx^{2s} - b(1 - a - r)x^r + b^2x^{2r}$ if 1 above is granted and $c = 0$, $d = \beta^2$, and $s = \beta$.

Consequently, $a = 1 - 2\beta$, $b = 0$, $c = 0$, $d = \beta^2$, $s = \beta$. Then $k = (1/\beta)\sqrt{\beta^2} = 1$, $\sqrt{d}/s = 1$. The solution is then:

$$y = x\beta[C_1 J_1(x^\beta) + C_2 Y_1(x^\beta)] \tag{4.3.73}$$

Illustration 4.3.9   Concentration Profile and Effectiveness Factor of a Cylindrical Catalyst Pellet

We return here to the problem of diffusion and reaction in a catalyst particle. This time the process is assumed to take place in a cylindrical pellet of sufficient length L that only radial diffusion needs to be considered, i.e., the flux through the ends of the cylinder is neglected. The reaction is assumed to be first order. A mass balance over a radial difference element then yields the expression:

$$\text{Rate of reactant in} - \text{Rate of reactant out} = 0$$

$$-- D_{eff} 2\pi r L \frac{dC}{dr}\bigg|_{r+\Delta r} - \begin{bmatrix} -- D_{eff} 2\pi r L \frac{dC_A}{dr}\bigg|_r \\ + k_r (C_A)_{avg} 2\pi r L \Delta r \end{bmatrix} = 0 \tag{4.3.74}$$

Upon dividing by $2\pi L \Delta r$ and letting $\Delta r \to 0$, we obtain:

$$r \frac{d^2 C_A}{dr^2} + \frac{dC_A}{dr} - (k_r / D_{eff}) r C_A = 0$$

or equivalently,

$$r^2 \frac{d^2 C_A}{dr^2} + r \frac{dC_A}{dr} - \alpha^2 r^2 C_A = 0 \tag{4.3.75}$$

where $\alpha^2 = k_r/D_{eff}$.

Comparison with the generalized Equations 4.3.70 and 4.3.71 yields the following parameter values:

$$a = 1, b = c = 0, d = -\alpha^2, s = 1$$

The solution is then immediately given as

$$C = A\, I_0(\alpha r) + B\, K_0(\alpha r) \tag{4.3.76}$$

with BC 1: $\dfrac{dC}{dr}(0) = 0$ (symmetry) or $C(0) = $ finite

BC 2: $C(R) = C_s$ (surface concentration of reactant)

Since $K_0(0) = \infty$ (Table 4.8C), it follows from BC 1 that the integration constant B must be zero. Together with BC 2 this yields the final result:

$$\frac{C}{C_s} = \frac{I_0(\alpha r)}{I_0(\alpha R)} \tag{4.3.77}$$

The plot in Figure 4.4 shows that $I_0(r)$ increases exponentially with r and has a zero slope at the origin. This is in qualitative agreement with the concentration profile one would expect to see.

The effectiveness factor E can be determined from the expression:

$$E = \frac{\int_0^R k_r C_s 2\pi r L I_0(\alpha r) dr}{I_0(\alpha R) k_r C_s \pi R^2 L} \tag{4.3.78}$$

Use of the Table 4.8E of integrals of Bessel functions then yields, with k set = 1:

$$\int_0^R r I_0(\alpha r) dr = (r/\alpha) I_1(\alpha r)\Big|_0^R = (R/\alpha) I_1(\alpha R) \tag{4.3.79}$$

and the final effectiveness factor becomes, after cancellation of terms:

$$E = \frac{2 I_1(\alpha R)}{\alpha R I_0(\alpha R)} \tag{4.3.80}$$

Comments:

The appearance of Bessel functions in the final expression (Equation 4.3.80) need not deter us from evaluating E. As noted previously, convenient tabulations of zero and first order Bessel functions are available in handbooks of mathematical functions (see References). Alternatively, use can be made of graphs of E for various geometries which appear in monographs dealing with porous catalysts (see References at the end of Chapter 3).

For small values of the argument αR, the effectiveness factor E should approach unity. It can be shown that this is indeed the case. Using the tabulations of Table 4.8 (Item F), we find $I_1(\alpha R) \to (\alpha R/2)$ and $I_0(\alpha R) \to 1$, so that $2 I_1(\alpha R)/\alpha R I_0(\alpha R) \to 1$, as required.

4.3.5 OTHER METHODS

Methods in this category, though less sweeping in scope than those discussed in the previous sections, nevertheless find their use in the solution of a host of special problems. These techniques, listed in Table 4.4, are capable of solving both linear and nonlinear first and second order ODEs. We mention in particular the use of various transformations, the p-substitution, the solution of exact equations, and the use of integrating factors to make them exact. A partial listing of such factors appears in Table 4.9. Techniques for their derivation can be found in standard texts on ODEs (see References). Our purpose here is confined to the presentation of several illustrative examples dealing with physical models which are amenable to solution by these techniques.

TABLE 4.9
Short List of Integrating Factors

Equation	Integrating Factor
1. $y' - f(y/x) = 0$	$[y - xf(y/x)]^{-1}$
2. $y' - \dfrac{y + xf(x^2 + y^2)}{x - yf(x^2 + y^2)} = 0$	$[x^2 + y^2]^{-1}$
3. $y' + \dfrac{p(x,y)}{q(x,y)} = 0$	Various forms:
(a) $(\partial p/\partial y - \partial q/\partial x)/q = f(x)$	$\exp \int f(x)dx$
(b) $(\partial p/\partial y - \partial q/\partial x)/p = g(y)$	$\exp \int -g(y)dy$
(c) $p = yf(xy); q = xg(xy)$	$[xp - yq]^{-1}$
(d) $\partial p/\partial x = \partial q/\partial y; \partial p/\partial y = -\partial q/\partial x$	$[p^2 + q^2]^{-1}$

Illustration 4.3.10   Product Distributions in Reactions in Series: Use of the Substitution y = vx

The following consecutive reactions give a good representation of many organic reactions such as the chlorination, nitration, and sulfonation of aromatics:

$$A + B \overset{k_1}{\rightarrow} R$$

$$R + B \overset{k_2}{\rightarrow} S$$

(4.3.81)

The calculation of the variation of these species with time or distance (stirred tank or plug flow reactors) is usually achieved numerically but the important product distributions $R/A_0 = f(A)$ and $S/A_0 = g(A)$ can, for a batch reactor, be obtained in easy fashion analytically from the rate laws and the stoichiometry of the reactions. If the intermediate R is the desired product, the distributions can be used to calculate optimum conversion of A to achieve a maximum yield in R.

We assume the rate laws to correspond to the stoichiometry of the reaction, the process to be isothermal, and carried out in a batch reactor. We obtain:

Mass balances or rate laws:

$$-k_1 C_A C_B = dC_A/dt$$

(4.3.82)

$$k_1 C_A C_B - k_2 R C_B = dC_R/dt$$

(4.3.83)

Division of the two equations eliminates dt (our favorite trick) and we obtain:

$$\frac{dC_R}{dC_A} + \frac{k_1 C_A - k_2 C_R}{k_1 C_A} = 0$$

(4.3.84)

We try the substitution $C_R = vC_A$ (Item 7a in Table 4.4) and obtain:

$$(v + C_A(dv/dC_A) + (1 - k_2 v) = 0 \tag{4.3.85}$$

Thus, the substitution has successfully reduced the ODE to one in v, C_A only, which has the solution (see Table 4.4, Item 7a):

$$\ln C_A = C - \int \frac{g(1, C_R/C_A)d(C_R/C_A)}{f(1, C_R/C_A) + (C_B/C_A)g(1, C_R/C_A)}$$

with $g = k_1$ and $f = k_1 - k_2 (C_R/C_A)$.

Evaluation of the integral leads to the expression:

$$C_A = C[1 + (1 - (k_2/k_1)(C_R/C_A))]^{k_1/(k_2-k_1)} \tag{4.3.86}$$

where C = integration constant. It is evaluated from the initial condition $C_R(C_{A0}) = 0$ and yields:

$$C = C_{A0}$$

The solution then becomes:

$$C_A/C_{A0} = [1 + (1 - (k_2/k_1)(C_R/C_A))]^{k_1/(k_2-k_1)} \tag{4.3.87}$$

Alternatively, solving for C_R one obtains:

$$C_R/C_{A0} = \frac{1}{1 - k_2/k_1}[(C_A/C_{A0})^{k_2/k_1} - (C_A/C_{A0})] \tag{4.3.88}$$

which is the distribution of the intermediate R.

If R is the desired product, it is useful to know at which point the reaction should be stopped before C_R begins to decline. We find this by maximizing the yield of C_R, i.e., we write, using Equation 4.3.88

$$d(C_R/C_{A0})/d(C_A/C_{A0}) = 0 = \frac{1}{1 - k_2/k_1}\left[\frac{k_2}{k_1}\left(\frac{C_A}{C_{A0}}\right)^{(k_2/k_2)-1} - 1\right] \tag{4.3.88}$$

and hence,

$$(C_A/C_{A0}) = (k_1/k_2)^{k_1/(k_2-k_1)} \tag{4.3.90}$$

This means that in order to maximize the yield of C_R, the reaction should be stopped when the conversion X of C_A has reached the value:

$$X = 1 - (C_A / C_A^0) = 1 - (k_1 / k_2)^{k_1/(k_2 - k_1)}$$ (4.3.91)

Illustration 4.3.11 Path of Pursuit

We examine here a topic quite removed from our usual concerns. A prey, in the form of an enemy in warfare or an animal, is moving in a straight line along the y-axis with a velocity a, and is to be intercepted by a pursuer moving at velocity b and starting up on the x-axis. A pathway is traced out by the pursuer, the tangent of which must always pass through the location of the prey. It can be shown that such a pathway leading to interception is described by the ODE:

$$1 + \left(\frac{dy}{dx}\right)^2 = k^2 x^2 \left(\frac{d^2 y}{dx^2}\right)^2$$ (4.3.92)

where $k^2 = b^2/a^2$ and the boundary conditions are given by $y = dy/dx = 0$ at $x = x_0$.

We recognize this as a second order nonlinear ODE with missing terms in y, which calls for the use of the p-substitution (see Item 9 in Table 4.4). We obtain, after substitution of p and separation of variables,

$$\int \frac{k \, dp}{(1 + p^2)^{1/2}} = \int \frac{dx}{x}$$ (4.3.93)

where the integral on the left is found in mathematical tables in the form:

$$\int \frac{dx}{(a^2 + x^2)^{1/2}} = \ln[x + (a^2 + x^2)^{1/2}]$$ (4.3.94)

A first integration is performed, yielding:

$$p = \frac{dy}{dx} = \frac{1}{2}\left[\left(\frac{C_1}{x}\right)^{-1/k} - \left(\frac{x}{C_1}\right)^{-1/k}\right]$$ (4.3.95)

followed by a second integration which leads to the result:

$$y(x) = \frac{1}{2}\left[\frac{k}{1-k}\left(\frac{C_1}{x}\right)^{(k-1)/k} + \frac{k}{(k+1)}\left(\frac{x}{C_1}\right)^{(k+1)/k}\right] + C_2$$ (4.3.96)

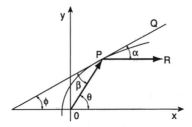

FIGURE 4.5 Geometry of the mirror.

The integration constants C_1 and C_2 are evaluated from the boundary conditions given at the start which results in:

$$C_1 = x_0, \; C_2 = 0 \tag{4.3.97}$$

Introduction of these constants leads, with some rearrangement, to the final result:

$$y(x) = \frac{1}{2}\left[\frac{k}{1-k}\left(\frac{x_0}{x}\right)^{(k-1)/k} + \frac{k}{1+k}\left(\frac{x}{x_0}\right)^{(k+1)/k} \right] \tag{4.3.98}$$

This is the equation for the path of pursuit leading to interception of the prey.

Illustration 4.3.12   Design of a Parabolic Mirror

In yet another unusual problem, we consider the design of a curved mirror such that the light from a point source at the origin O is reflected as a beam parallel to the x-axis (see Figure 4.5).

Let the ray of light OP strike the mirror at P and be reflected along PR. If PQ is the tangent at P and α, β, ϕ, and θ are the angles indicated, $\alpha = \beta$ by the optical law of reflection and $\alpha = \phi$ by geometry. Hence, $\beta = \phi$. The equation:

$$\tan\theta = \tan(\beta + \phi) = \tan 2\phi = \frac{2\tan\phi}{1-\tan^2\phi} \tag{4.3.99}$$

gives

$$\frac{y}{x} = \frac{2y'}{1-(y')^2} \tag{4.3.100}$$

since $y' = \tan\phi$. Solution of this quadratic equation for y' gives:

$$yy' = -x \pm \sqrt{x^2 + y^2} \tag{4.3.101}$$

or

$$xdx - ydy = \pm\sqrt{x^2 + y^2}\,dx$$

The equation admits an integrating factor $(x^2 + y^2)^{-1/2}$ as we see by multiplying it by that factor into the form:

$$\frac{x\,dx + y\,dy}{\pm\sqrt{x^2 + y^2}} = \frac{1}{2}\frac{d(x^2 + y^2)}{\pm\sqrt{x^2 + y^2}} = dx \qquad (4.3.102)$$

Both sides are now exact differentials and the equation gives, on integrating,

$$\pm\sqrt{x^2 + y^2} = x + c \qquad (4.3.103)$$

or, on squaring, $y^2 = 2cx + c^2$. The curves form a family of parabolas with the focus at the origin.

Comments:

A number of features are of note here. The geometrical construction and the relations derived from it, require conversion of a double-angle tangent tan 2ϕ to tan ϕ. The formula for this conversion, given above, can be found in standard mathematical tables.

The original ODE 4.3.101 is not exact, nor does the Table 4.9 immediately reveal an appropriate integrating factor. However, upon rearrangement into the form (Equation 4.3.102), one recognizes the left-side differential to be exact, since it satisfies the criterion $\dfrac{\partial f}{\partial y} = \dfrac{\partial g}{\partial x}$. Furthermore, there is no need for the integration formula given in Table 4.9 since the alternative form given in Equation 4.3.96 is immediately integratable. The curse of this problem lies in the requirement to make an inspired guess. Although this is usually the realm of mathematicians, ordinary mortals should not be excluded from trying. A less trying example of the application of integrating factors is given in Practice Problem 4.7.

4.4 NUMERICAL METHODS

We address this topic only briefly wishing merely to acquaint the reader with the methodology which underlies the numerical ODE solver packages. A first distinction to be made is between initial value and boundary value problems. We already saw that the choice of analytical solutions depended to some extent on which of these two classes was being addressed. Thus, the Laplace transformation is capable of handling IVPs but becomes somewhat cumbersome for BVPs, while the D-operator method can handle both classes with equal ease. Numerical packages are usually designed for IVPs. BVPs require special techniques which we take up first. This is followed by a discussion of various numerical techniques available for IVPs.

4.4.1   BOUNDARY VALUE PROBLEMS

These problems are usually associated with second and higher order ODEs or equivalent sets of first order ODEs, with boundary conditions specified at different points in space. Countercurrent heat exchangers are of this type, but the classical example is that of diffusion and reaction in a catalyst pellet which for the isothermal case *in* a sphere was given by:

$$\frac{d^2C_A}{dr^2} + \frac{2}{r}\frac{dC_A}{dr} - k_r C_A / D_{eff} = 0 \qquad (3.2.41)$$

with boundary conditions $C_A(R) = C_S$ and $\left.\dfrac{dC_A}{dr}\right|_{r=0} = 0$.

For numerical work, higher order ODEs are usually first decomposed into sets of first order ODEs since most packages handle just such systems. For the above equation, this yields the simultaneous set in p and C_A:

$$p = \frac{dC_A}{dr}$$

$$\frac{dp}{dr} + \frac{p}{r} - (k_r / D_{eff})C_A = 0 \qquad (4.4.1)$$

with the BC $C_A(R) = C_{AS}$ and $p(0) = 0$. We are still left with the problem of how to use the given BCs to initiate the integration procedure. We briefly describe two methods to achieve this.

1. The Shooting Method. In this procedure one starts the integration at the center of the pellet, using the given boundary condition $p(0) = 0$ and an *assumed* value of the concentration $C_A(0)$. Integration is carried out by "shooting" — in a stepwise fashion — at the given surface concentration $C_A(R)$. If a match between numerical and given values is obtained, the integration is terminated. If not, a new value of $C_A(0)$ is assumed and the procedure repeated. This is evidently a rough-and-ready method which does, however, finds its advocates and users. A more refined technique is the following.
2. Method of Polynomial Approximation. Here the original boundary conditions are retained and the interval $(0,R)$ spanned by a polynomial with unknown coefficients, usually of the Legendre type. The unknown coefficients are evaluated by substitution into the boundary value ODE. Various refinements to the method have been developed which are treated in the references cited at the end of the chapter.

4.4.2   INITIAL VALUE PROBLEMS

A simple sketch of the procedure applicable to these problems is shown in Figure 4.6. The method essentially consists of marching forward in incremental steps Δx

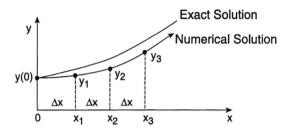

FIGURE 4.6 Step size and solution generated by the numerical integration of an ODE.

starting from the initial values of the ODE. The smaller the step size, the closer the agreement between numerical and exact solution.

For the purposes of the computation, the ODE is cast in the form:

$$\frac{dy}{dx} = f(x, y) \tag{4.4.2}$$

or the equivalent incremental form:

$$\Delta y = y_{j+1} - y_j = \int_{x_1}^{x_2} f(x, y)dx \cong f_{avg}(x, y)\Delta x \tag{4.4.3}$$

The choice of $f_{avg}(x,y)$ determines the type of method as well as its quality and computational efficiency. The more elaborate the form $f_{avg}(x,y)$, the closer we will come to the true solution. The price one pays is in the greater complexity of the computational procedure. Depending on the form of $f_{avg}(x,y)$ chosen, the following distinction is made among the various integration method.

1. Single Step Method. No y other than that at the previous position x_j is required for the evaluation of $f_{avg}(x,y)$, i.e., y and $f_{avg}(x,y)$ will always be known or computable from the immediately preceding step. The simplest of these is the Euler method which has the form:

$$y_{j+1} - y_j = f(x_j, y_j)\Delta x = f_{avg}(x,y)\Delta x \tag{4.4.4}$$

Thus, the new value of the dependent variable, y_{j+1}, is calculated from the value of $f(x,y)$ of the previous step.

2. Multistep Methods. Here y and $f_{avg}(x,y)$ values other than those at position x_j are required. One may reach backwards beyond the last step to improve on y and $f_{avg}(x,y)$ obtained in single-step methods, or venture forward into unknown territory to obtain additional improvement in the values of y and $f(x,y)$. Multistep methods fall into the following three broad classes:
   (a) Open or Explicit Method. Although $f_{avg}(x,y)$ and y are required at values other than x_j, these are known from previous steps (except at the start) and y_{j+1} therefore can be calculated. A typical formula, due to Adams, is

$$y_{j+1} - y_j = [3/2\, f_j - 1/2\, f_{j-1}]\Delta x = f_{avg}(x,y)\Delta x \qquad (4.4.5)$$

Here f_{avg} is seen to make up off-values of the *two* immediately pre-ceding steps. Note that the method is not self-starting since f_{j-1} is unknown at x_0; hence, one uses a single step method to initiate the integration and switches to multistep procedures after the first few increments.

(b) Closed or Implicit Method. An example of an algorithm of this type, due to Adams-Moulton, is the expression:

$$y_{j+1} - y_j = \left[\frac{1}{2}f_{j+1} + \frac{1}{2}f_j\right]\Delta x \qquad (4.4.6)$$

Here unknowns occur on both sides of the equation, y_{j+1} and f_{j+1}; hence, an iterative process must be resorted to. However, the method is very accurate because it incorporates features of what has gone before (f_j) as well as what is to come (f_{j+1}). (a) and (b) are rarely used alone. Instead they are combined into method (c).

(c) Predictor-Corrector Method. In this procedure, the open method is used to arrive at a first estimate of y_{j+1} ("predictor"), which is then refined by using a closed method ("corrector").

A listing of the more important numerical integration procedures and associated algorithms appears in Table 4.10.

TABLE 4.10
Numerical Integration Methods

Name and Type	Algorithm
A. Single-Step	
1. Euler	$y_{j+1} - y_j = f(x_j, y_j)\Delta x$
2. Runge-Kutta	$y_{j+1} - y_j = 1/6[K_1 + 2\,K_2 + 2\,K_3 + K_4]\Delta x$
Various orders available of which the fourth order is the most frequently used	$K_1 = f(x_j, y_j)$
	$K_2 = f[(x_j + \Delta x/2), y_j + K_1/2]$
	$K_3 = f[(x_j + \Delta x/2), y_j + K_2/2]$
	$K_4 = f(x_j + \Delta x, y_j + K_3)$
B. Multistep Methods	
1. Adams-Bashforth (second order)	$y_{j+1} - y_j = [3/2\, f_j - 1/2\, f_{j-1}]\Delta x$
2. Adams-Moulton (second order)	$y_{j+1} - y_j = 1/2\,[f_{j+1} - f_j]\Delta x$
3. Predictor-corrector	Combination of 1 and 2.
4. Gear package	Uses Adams predictor-corrector; provisions for adjusting step-size and order of difference formula

4.4.3 Sets of Simultaneous Initial Value ODEs

Here it becomes convenient to express both the ODEs and the integration procedure in vector form. This merely means that after each integration step Δx, one stores a vector array of new values y_{j+1}, rather than a *single* value. Runge-Kutta and similar constants also now become vector arrays. None of this involves new types of computations, but does increase storage requirements. A fourth-order Runge-Kutta procedure applied to a set of initial value ODEs now looks as follows:

ODEs:

$$\underset{\sim}{y}' = \underset{\sim}{f}(x, \underset{\sim}{y}) \tag{4.4.7}$$

Initial conditions:

$$\underset{\sim}{y}(a) = \underset{\sim}{A}$$

Runge-Kutta constants:

$$\underset{\sim}{K}_{1j} = \underset{\sim}{f}(x_j, \underset{\sim}{y}_j)$$

$$\underset{\sim}{K}_{2j} = \underset{\sim}{f}[(x_j + 1/2\,\Delta x), \underset{\sim}{y}_j + 1/2\,\Delta x\,\underset{\sim}{K}_{1j})]$$

$$\underset{\sim}{K}_{3j} = \underset{\sim}{f}[(x_j + 1/2\,\Delta x), \underset{\sim}{y}_j + 1/2\,\Delta x\,\underset{\sim}{K}_{2j})] \tag{4.4.8}$$

$$\underset{\sim}{K}_{4j} = \underset{\sim}{f}[(x_j + \Delta x), \underset{\sim}{y}_j + \Delta x\,\underset{\sim}{K}_{3j})]$$

Difference algorithm:

$$\underset{\sim}{y}_{j+1} - \underset{\sim}{y}_j = 1/6[\underset{\sim}{K}_{1j} + 2\underset{\sim}{K}_{2j} + 2\underset{\sim}{K}_{3j} + \underset{\sim}{K}_{4j}]\Delta x \tag{4.4.9}$$

An example of the application of these equations appears in Illustration 4.4.2.

4.4.4 Potential Difficulties: Stability

Difficulties which arise in the numerical integration of ODEs usually come under the general heading of "stability" which is a joint property of the ODEs and the solution technique used. The ODEs that are prone to unstable behavior are often referred to as being "stiff."

One source of instability which resides mainly in the numerical procedure is due to round-off errors and truncation errors. One can remedy these relatively easily by reducing the step size Δx and/or using higher order integration routines.

A second and more serious source of difficulty arises in cases where f(x,y) has multiple values along the x-axis which results in multiple solutions to the difference equation. Only one of these, the *fundamental equation,* leads to the proper result. The other solutions are termed *parasitic* which feed on errors in the numerical solution, such as round-off and truncation errors. The growth of parasitic solutions is usually exponential and often oscillatory as well and soon overwhelms the fundamental solution.

A third source of instability or stiffness is due to the form of the ODEs. It arises principally in systems which contain widely differing functions, e.g., exp (100 t) and exp (0.1 t). Such disparate functional forms are seen, for example, in reaction networks involving both fast and very slow reactions.

One remedy is to remove the fast reaction terms or equations and assume that the slow reactions are rate determining. This is often done. Another remedy is to use a very small step size initially and increase it further along the solution path to accommodate the "slow" terms.

The gear package or method cited in Table 4.10 is widely used to overcome instabilities and stiffness. It does this in part by using predictor-corrector methods, and making provision for changing step size and the order of the integration routine.

Illustration 4.4.1   Example of a Solution by Euler's Method

Given the ODE system:

$$\frac{dy}{dx} = f(x, y) = -y^2 \quad y(0) = 1 \tag{4.4.10}$$

with an analytical solution given by

$$y = 1/(1 + x) \tag{4.4.11}$$

We solve the same system numerically by Euler's method:

$$\Delta y = f(x,y)_{avg}\, \Delta x, \text{ using } \Delta x = 0.1 \tag{4.4.12}$$

	y values	
	Numerical	**Analytical**
First step		
$y_1 - 1 = -(1)^2\, 0.1 = -0.1$	0.9	0.909
Second step		
$y_2 - 0.9 = -(0.9)^2\, 0.1 = -0.081$	0.819	0.833
Third step		
$y_3 - 0.819 = -(0.819)^2\, 0.1 = -0.067$	0.752	0.769

Agreement is seen to be good initially but becomes less so as the integration progresses. This is due to the rudimentary nature of the method.

Illustration 4.4.2 Solution of Two Simultaneous ODEs by the Runge-Kutta Method

Consider the two nonlinear Volterra-Lotka predator-prey equations:

$$y_1' = y_1(3 - y_2) = f_1(x, y_1, y_2) \quad y_1(0) = 1 \tag{4.4.13}$$

$$y_2' = y_2(y_1 - 2) = f_2(x, y_1, y_2) \quad y_2(0) = 2 \tag{4.4.14}$$

where y_2 denotes the predator; y_1, the prey. We write the system equations in vector form obtaining:

$$\underset{\sim}{y}' = \underset{\sim}{f}(x, \underset{\sim}{y}) \quad \underset{\sim}{y}(0) = \underset{\sim}{A} \tag{4.4.15}$$

where

$$\underset{\sim}{y}' = \begin{matrix} y_1' \\ y_2' \end{matrix}, \quad \underset{\sim}{f} = \begin{matrix} 3y_1 - y_1 y_2 \\ y_1 y_2 - 2y_2 \end{matrix} \quad \underset{\sim}{A} = \begin{matrix} 1 = y_1(0) \\ 2 = y_2(0) \end{matrix} \tag{4.4.16}$$

Solution is by the second order Runge-Kutta method described in vector form by:

R-K constants:

$$\underset{\sim}{K}_{1j} = \underset{\sim}{f}(x_j, \underset{\sim}{y}_j)$$

$$\underset{\sim}{K}_{2j} = \underset{\sim}{f}(x_j + \Delta x, \underset{\sim}{y}_j + \underset{\sim}{K}_{1j}) \tag{4.4.17}$$

Difference equation:

$$\underset{\sim}{y}_{j+1} = \underset{\sim}{y}_j + 1/2(\underset{\sim}{K}_{1j} + \underset{\sim}{K}_{2j}) \tag{4.4.18}$$

We choose a step-size of $x = 0.25$ and proceed to calculate R-K constants and the resulting increment in y. *First step* (from $x = 0$ to $x = 0.25$):

First R-K constant:

For first ODE: $K_{11}(1) = 0.25[(3(1) - (1)2)]$ Store as: $\underset{\sim}{K}_{11} = \begin{matrix} 0.25 \\ -0.5 \end{matrix}$

$$\tag{4.4.19}$$

For second ODE: $K_{11}(2) = 0.25[(1(2) - 2(2))]$

(Note that the first subscript refers to the R-K number, the second subscript to the step number.)

Second R-K constant:

For first ODE: $K_{21}(1) = 0.25[3(1+0.25) - (1+0.25)(2-0.5)]$

For second ODE: $K_{21}(2) = 0.25[(1+0.25)(2-0.5) - 2(2-0.5)]$

$$\text{Store as: } \underset{\sim}{K}_{21} = \begin{matrix} 0.469 \\ -0.281 \end{matrix}$$

Substitution into the difference equation yields the following y values at the end of the first step:

$$\underset{\sim}{y}_1 = \begin{matrix} 1.36 & \text{Prey} \\ 1.61 & \text{Predator} \end{matrix}$$

and for the second step ($x = 0.25 \rightarrow 0.50$):

$$\underset{\sim}{K}_{12} = \begin{matrix} 0.473 \\ -0.258 \end{matrix} \quad \underset{\sim}{K}_{22} = \begin{matrix} 0.755 \\ -0.057 \end{matrix} \quad \underset{\sim}{y} = \begin{matrix} 1.973 \\ 1.452 \end{matrix}$$

Further steps are handled in similar fashion.

4.5 NONLINEAR ANALYSIS

The term analysis, as it is applied here, refers to the methodology of obtaining an understanding of the *qualitative* nature of the solution and identifying regions of unusual behavior without actually solving the equations, or by solving them only partially. Thus, we do not seek to derive a solution for a particular set of parameter values and boundary conditions but instead ask ourselves these equations. Under what conditions or set of values will the solution be periodic or when will it be exponentially decaying? When does it become unstable or become unbounded? Can there be more than one solution?

An analytical tool of sorts for *linear* systems had already been provided by the so-called characteristic roots of the D-operator method described in Section 4.3. Although this was not demonstrated explicitly, we were able to predict the *form* of the solution by a mere inspection of the characteristic roots without actually solving the ODE. Thus, when the roots were real, exponential solutions would result; when the roots were imaginary, they were purely oscillatory; and when they were complex, they became periodic with exponentially rising or decaying amplitudes (see Table 4.5). A more detailed examination of these phenomena and of linear analysis in general is deferred to Chapter 5 dealing with the Laplace transformation. That transformation is not only a highly useful solution method for linear initial value ODEs, but it also provides a convenient vehicle for an analysis of such systems.

What we wish to do in this section is to address systems of *nonlinear* ODEs and the associated subject of nonlinear analysis. This is a vast topic, of which we are able to give only a brief synopsis. We hope nevertheless to provide the reader with an understanding of the principal tools used in nonlinear analysis and to open the door for a glimpse of the exotic phenomena which can arise in nonlinear systems. These include multiplicities giving rise to catastrophe, bifurcations (including the Hopf bifurcations), period doubling, and chaos. Such phenomena arise only in nonlinear systems and were addressed early on in the development of mathematical analysis. Euler's calculation of the load which will buckle a beam is one of the first examples of catastrophe theory. The full development of the theories of nonlinear phenomena had to await the advent of the computer which aided immensely in the discovery of various forms of exotic nonlinear behavior. We now turn to the consideration of the principal tools for analysis and a description of the various phenomena of nonlinear systems.

4.5.1   PHASE PLANE ANALYSIS: CRITICAL POINTS

Phase plane analysis refers to the examination of the interrelation of the *dependent variables* of a system. That interrelation is established through a favorite algebraic trick of ours, the division of two first order ODEs to eliminate the independent variable, usually time t, resulting in the relation $y_1 = f(y_2)$. Although extensions to *sets* of equations exist — one then speaks of phase *space* analysis — the two-equation system is best suited for an illustration of the power of the method and the insight it provides.

We use as an introduction to the method the behavior of a pendulum considered to consist of a point mass m fixed to a rigid rod of length l. Both gravitational and frictional forces are involved. The latter is assumed to be proportional to the instantaneous velocity of the mass, or equivalently, the rate of change of the angle of deflection $d\theta/dt$. A force balance then leads to the expression:

$$ml\frac{d^2\theta}{dt^2} \quad + \quad kl\frac{d\theta}{dt} \quad + \quad mg\sin\theta \quad = 0$$

$$\underbrace{\qquad\qquad}_{\text{Acceleration}} \qquad \underbrace{\qquad}_{\text{Friction}} \qquad \underbrace{\qquad}_{\text{Gravity}}$$

$$(4.5.1)$$

or equivalently,

$$a_0\ddot{\theta} + a_1\dot{\theta} + a_2\sin\theta = 0$$

This is a second order nonlinear ODE in θ which can be decomposed into an equivalent set of two first order ODEs by defining the velocity $d\theta/dt$ as a new variable θ_2 and designating the angle of deflection as θ_1. We obtain the set:

$$\frac{d\theta_1}{dt} = \theta_2 = f_1(\theta_1, \theta_2)$$

$$(4.5.2)$$

and

$$\frac{d\theta_2}{dt} = -\frac{a_1}{a_0}\theta_2 - \frac{a_2}{a_0}\sin\theta_1 = f_2(\theta_1, \theta_2)$$

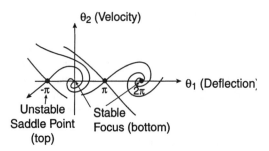

FIGURE 4.7   Phase plane representation of the trajectories of a pendulum with friction.

Division of the two equations eliminates dt and yields the result:

$$\frac{d\theta_2}{d\theta_1} = -\frac{a_1\theta_2 + a_2\sin\theta_1}{a_0\theta_2} \qquad (4.5.3)$$

The solution of this equation, usually done numerically, leads to a family of curves $\theta_2 = f(\theta_1)$ which can be plotted in the phase plane θ_2 vs. θ_1. The curves, a typical example of which is shown in Figure 4.7, are "trajectories" or "pathways" of the pendulum, each point representing its velocity θ_2 at a particular position or deflection θ_1. Each pair of initial conditions $\theta_1(0)$ and $\theta_2(0)$ is associated with a particular curve, leading to an infinite number of trajectories in (θ_1, θ_2) space.

The various points to which the trajectories converge are called "critical points," "equilibrium points," or "stationary points." They correspond to the steady states of the pendulum attained as $t \rightarrow \infty$ and can be calculated by setting the time derivatives in Equation 4.5.2 equal to zero. There is an infinite set of such points that occur at $\sin\theta_1 = 0$, i.e., at $\theta_1 = 0$, π, 2π, ..., as well as negative values of same.

A first set of critical points are those at $\pm\pi$, $\pm3\pi$, ..., etc. which are unstable and are referred to as *saddle points*. They correspond to the condition of the pendulum having come to rest in a vertically upward position. That position is clearly unstable since a slight deviation of θ_1 from it will cause the pendulum to resume swinging. The situation is depicted by arrows pointing away from the equilibrium point.

A second set of stationary points are located at 0, $\pm2\pi$, $\pm4\pi$, etc. and carry the designation *focus*. They correspond to the condition of the pendulum having come to rest in a vertically downward position. That state is clearly stable and is indicated by arrows pointing toward it.

Stationary points are always calculated by setting time derivatives of the ODEs equal to zero and solving the set of nonlinear algebraic equations, here given by:

$$f_1(\theta_1, \theta_2) = 0$$
$$f_2(\theta_1, \theta_2) = 0 \qquad (4.5.4)$$

A host of other interesting critical points may arise, depending on the form of the ODEs involved. To seek out these points and to characterize them in relation to the functional form of the model, use is made of the so-called Jacobian J of the set

Equation 4.5.4. J is a matrix whose components here are the four partial derivatives of the algebraic set Equation 4.5.4. Thus,

$$\underline{J}(\theta_1, \theta_2) = \begin{pmatrix} \partial f_1 / \partial \theta_1 & \partial f_2 / \partial \theta_1 \\ \partial f_1 / \partial \theta_2 & \partial f_2 / \partial \theta_2 \end{pmatrix} \tag{4.5.5}$$

The order of the Jacobian matrix equals the number of ODEs involved.

Characterization of the critical points is achieved by determining the eigenvalues μ of that matrix and examining their properties. That is to say we set:

$$\begin{vmatrix} \dfrac{\partial f_1}{\partial \theta_1} - \mu & \dfrac{\partial f_1}{\partial \theta_2} \\ \dfrac{\partial f_2}{\partial \theta_1} & \dfrac{\partial f_2}{\partial \theta_2} - \mu \end{vmatrix} = 0 \tag{4.5.6}$$

and examine the roots $\mu_{1,2}$ of the resulting quadratic equation in μ. Using our pendulum as an example, the entire procedure of critical point analysis is then made up of the following steps:

(1) Solve the set Equation 4.5.4 to establish the coordinates θ_1^e, θ_2^e of the stationary or equilibrium points.
(2) Derive expressions for the partial derivative in Equation 4.5.6 from the set Equation 4.5.4.
(3) With (2) having been established, expand the determinant Equation 4.5.6 and solve the resulting quadratic in μ. This yields the roots $\mu_{1,2}$ as a function of θ_1 and θ_2.
(4) Substitute θ_1^e and θ_2^e obtained in (1), into the expressions for $\mu_{1,2}$.
(5) Examine the nature of $\mu_{1,2}$ thus obtained.

It is the nature of these roots, i.e., whether they are positive or negative, real or complex, which determines the type of critical points involved. We have summarized the principal characteristic points in Figure 4.8 which reveals the existence of eight types of such points, depending on the properties of $\mu_{1,2}$. Thus, when $\mu_{1,2}$ are complex with a negative real part $\text{Re}(\mu)$, the critical point will be a stable focus (Figure 4.8D) with all trajectories converging to that critical point, but none emerging from it. This corresponds to a pendulum coming to rest in the bottom position. When one of the roots is real positive and the other real negative, the critical point will be an unstable saddle (Figure 4.8C) with trajectories leading into it, as well as away from it. This corresponds to a pendulum having come to a precarious rest in the top position. We now proceed to a more complete examination of this device.

Illustration 4.5.1 Analysis of the Pendulum

The operative equations in the state variables θ_1 (angle of deflection) and θ_2 (time derivative of θ_1) are given by the Expression 4.5.2. We start by establishing the stationary values of θ_1 and θ_2. To obtain these, we set:

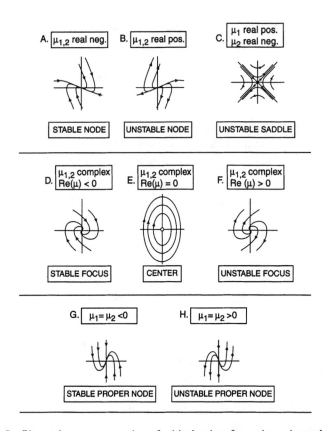

FIGURE 4.8 Phase plane representation of critical points for various eigenvalues $\mu_{1,2}$.

$$f_1 (\theta_1, \theta_2) = f_2 (\theta_1, \theta_2) = 0 \qquad (4.5.7)$$

so that

$$\begin{aligned}\theta_2 &= 0 \\ \sin \theta_1 &= 0\end{aligned} \qquad (4.5.8)$$

with roots $\theta_1 = \pm\, n\pi$, $n = 0, 1, 2, \ldots$.

We next evaluate the components of the Jacobian matrix Equation 4.5.5, obtaining:

$$\partial f_1 / \partial \theta_1 = 0 \quad \partial f_2 / \partial \theta_1 = -\frac{a_2}{a_0} \cos \theta_1$$

$$(4.5.9)$$

$$\partial f_1 / \partial \theta_2 = 0 \quad \partial f_2 / \partial \theta_2 = -\frac{a_1}{a_0}$$

and from Equation 4.5.6:

$$\begin{vmatrix} 0-\mu & -\dfrac{a_2}{a_0}\cos\theta_1 \\ 1 & -\dfrac{a_1}{a_0}-\mu \end{vmatrix} = 0 \tag{4.5.10}$$

Let us consider the two cases of the pendulum *with* and *without* friction.

Frictionless Pendulum — For this case we set $a_1 = 0$ and obtain from Equation 4.5.10

$$\mu_{1,2} = \pm\left(-\frac{a_2}{a_0}\cos\theta_1\right)^{1/2} \tag{4.5.11}$$

For the stationary points $\theta_1 = 0, \pm 2\pi, \pm 4\pi, \ldots$ (Equation 4.5.8), we have $\cos\theta_1 = 1$ and the eigenvalues are pure imaginary. Thus,

$$\mu_{1,2} = \pm\frac{a_2}{a_0}i = \pm bi \tag{4.5.12}$$

This corresponds to Case E in Figure 4.8, i.e., the critical point is a center and the pendulum swings indefinitely with a constant amplitude given by the abscissa intercepts.

The remaining stationary points in Equation 4.5.8, i.e., $\theta_1 = \pm\pi, \pm 3\pi, \pm 5\pi, \ldots$ lead to real values of $\mu_{1,2}$, since we now have $\cos\theta_1 = -1$. The characteristic roots become:

$$\mu_{1,2} = \pm\frac{a_2}{a_0} \tag{4.5.13}$$

that is they are real positive and real negative, respectively. This corresponds to Case C in Figure 4.8 and leads to an unstable saddle as critical point. We recognize this as the situation in which the pendulum points vertically upward.

Pendulum with Friction — Here the expansion of the full determinant, Equation 4.5.10, leads to the following quadratic in μ:

$$\mu^2 + \frac{a_1}{a_0}\mu + \frac{a_2}{a_0}\cos\theta_1 = 0 \tag{4.5.14}$$

with roots:

$$\mu_{1,2} = \frac{-a_1/a_0 \pm [(a_1/a_0)^2 - 4(a_2/a_0)\cos\theta_1]^{1/2}}{2} \tag{4.5.15}$$

One recognizes immediately that for $\cos \theta_1 = -1$, one always obtains a real positive and real negative root respectively, leading to the same unstable saddle point we had seen previously.

For $\cos \theta_1 = 1$, we distinguish three cases, depending on the value of the discriminant (bracketed term in Equation 4.5.15).

(1) $4\,a_2/a_0 > (a_1/a_0)^2$. Here the roots become complex, with a real negative part:

$$\mu_{1,2} = \frac{-a_1/a_0 \pm i[4\,a_2/a_0 - (a_1/a_0)^2]^{1/2}}{2} \qquad (4.5.16)$$

This corresponds to Case D of Figure 4.8, i.e., the critical point is a stable focus with the pendulum swinging repeatedly with decreasing amplitude until the friction brings it to a stop at the bottom of its trajectory.

(2) $4\,a_2/a_0 = (a_1/a_0)^2$. For this case, we have:

$$\mu_1 = \mu_2 = -a_1/2a_0 < 0 \qquad (4.5.17)$$

that is we are dealing with a stable proper node, Case H of Figure 4.8. The pendulum is *critically* damped and comes to rest with no oscillations.

(3) $4\,a_2/a_0 < (a_1/a_0)^2$. This condition always yields two real negative roots so that Case A of Figure 4.8 applies. The pendulum is overdamped and comes to rest with no oscillations.

We shall encounter this type of behavior again in the linear analysis to be undertaken in Chapter 5.

4.5.2 ANALYSIS IN PARAMETER SPACE: BIFURCATIONS, MULTIPLICITIES, AND CATASTROPHE

We turn here to an examination of a second important tool of nonlinear analysis in which *phase space* is replaced by *parameter space* as the domain of study. The topic is no longer the dependence of the state variables on time or their interdependence. Rather, we seek out interesting types of solution behavior which come about as a result of a change in parameter values. Parameters to be considered include various transport coefficients or reaction rate constants, the load on structures, properties of the components of electrical circuits, and the like.

We had already seen an example of parameter space analysis in Illustration 3.5.3 dealing with nonisothermal effectiveness factors E_{ni}. Here the parameter in question was the Thiele Modulus, which is in essence a nondimensionalized ratio of reaction and transport rate coefficients. An increase in modulus values at first saw a smooth, single-valued decline in the effectiveness factor E_{ni} (Figure 3.16). Further increases, however, ultimately led into a region with a multiplicity of three solutions, of which two were stable, one unstable. The system reacted to this by undergoing a jump change to higher E_{ni} values when a certain critical value of the modulus was attained.

A. Turning Point

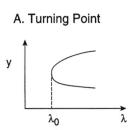

B. Bifurcations

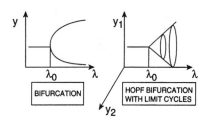

FIGURE 4.9 Nonlinear behavior in parameter space.

Similarly, a jump *decline* in E_{ni} occurred during the return journey of diminishing modulus values. The net result was a hysterisis effect resulting in different pathways of E_{ni} depending on whether one approached the multiplicity region from the high or low end of modulus values.

The study of multiplicities and the associated system behavior has become the domain of a number of mathematical subdisciplines, variously known as bifurcation theory, catastrophe theory, or singularity theory. The term *bifurcation* arises from the graphical representation of the transition of single values solutions to multiple solutions, leading to the formation of a "fork" in solution space. Examples of these graphs, known as bifurcation diagrams, appear in Figure 4.9. The term *catastrophe* refers to the jump changes in a state variable which occur in the region of multiplicities. These changes can be detrimental (e.g., buckling of a beam) as well as beneficial, in which case the term *anastrophe* would probably be more appropriate. *Singularity* is the mathematician's way of denoting points in space at which the state variable is not defined. This occurs, for example, when it assumes a value of infinity or when multiple values arise. All three theories are based on steady-state analyses, i.e., the systems under scrutiny are all algebraic in form even though they often originate from differential equations.

Let us consider the bifurcation diagrams of Figure 4.9 in greater detail. The feature they have in common is the onset of multiplicity at a certain critical parameter value λ_0. Beyond that point their behavior differs in detail. The simplest of them, aptly termed a *turning point,* is parabolic in form. A representative equation which produces this shape is the simple parabola:

$$y^2 = (\lambda - \lambda_0) \tag{4.5.18}$$

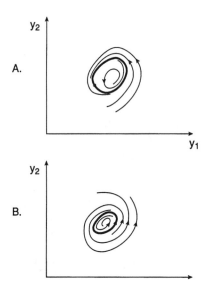

FIGURE 4.10   Phase plane representation of limit cycles: (A) stable cycle, (B) unstable cycle.

where the parameter value λ_0 is the turning point (Figure 4.9A). The simple bifurcation with three intersecting branches shown in Figure 4.9B, arises in systems of two algebraic equations with one vanishing eigenvalue of the Jacobian, the Hopf bifurcation in systems with pure imaginary eigenvalues of the same matrix. The latter have the additional distinctive feature of so-called limit cycles which are circular in shape and increase in their amplitude of oscillation, in y_1, y_2 space, as the value of the parameter λ is increased (Figure 4.9B). Two typical limit cycles are shown in Figure 4.10. Case A depicts the situations where the trajectories *outside* the cycle all converge toward it, while those within the cycle move away from it and converge to a focus. Both the cycle and the focus are termed *regular attractors*. In Case B, only the focus is an attractor, or attractive basin, since trajectories in the vicinity of the limit cycle all move away from it.

The following theorems give a more complete set of conditions for the genesis of various bifurcations:

(1) A *turning point* arises when the following conditions are satisfied:
   • The algebraic set $\underset{\sim}{f}$ vanishes at the critical point y_0, λ_0, i.e.,

$$f(y_0,\lambda_0) = 0$$

   • The Jacobian of the algebraic set, $\underset{\sim}{f_y}$, has an eigenvalue 0 at the critical

   point, i.e., $\underset{\sim}{f_y}(y_0,\lambda_0)$ has rank $n-1$, where n = number of algebraic

   equations

- The *augmented* Jacobian $f_y \mid f_\lambda$ has full rank n at (y_0, λ_0) where $f_y \mid f_\lambda$ is an "augmented matrix" obtained by adding the elements f_λ to those of f_y. The subscripts in these expressions denote partial derivatives.

(2) A *simple bifurcation* (three intersecting branches) arises when the following conditions are satisfied:

- $f(y_0, \lambda_0) = 0$

- $f(y_0, \lambda_0)$ has rank n − 1

- $f_y \mid f_\lambda$ *also* has rank n − 1 at y_0, λ_0

Thus, the only distinction between a turning point and a simple bifurcation point is that with the former, the augmented matrix has full rank n, while the latter case falls short with a rank of n − 1.

We recall here for the benefit of the reader that the rank of a matrix refers to the order of the first nonvanishing determinant. Thus, the matrix:

$$A = \begin{pmatrix} 0 & a & b \\ 0 & c & 0 \end{pmatrix} \qquad (4.5.19)$$

has rank n = 2, or full rank, since the first nonvanishing determinant is given by:

$$\begin{vmatrix} a & b \\ c & 0 \end{vmatrix} \neq 0 \qquad (4.5.20)$$

On the other hand, the matrix:

$$A = \begin{pmatrix} 0 & 0 & b \\ 0 & 0 & d \end{pmatrix} \qquad (4.5.21)$$

has rank n < 2 since all second order determinants formed from it vanish. These features will be demonstrated in the illustration which follows.

(3) A *Hopf bifurcation* arises when:

- $f(y_0, \lambda_0) = 0$

- $f_y(y_0, \lambda_0)$ has a pair of imaginary eigenvalues $\mu_{1,2} = \pm\, bi$ (4.5.22)
- $d[\text{Re } \mu(\lambda_0)/d\lambda] \neq 0$

All these criteria are somewhat tersely stated and it is best to demonstrate their use by means of some illustrations.

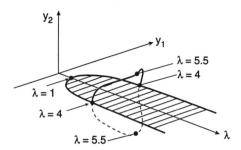

FIGURE 4.11 Turning points and bifurcation points for a nonlinear system of ODEs. (R. Seydel, *From Equilibrium to Chaos,* Elsevier Science Publishing Co., New York, 1988. With permission.)

Illustration 4.5.2   Bifurcation Points in a System of Nonlinear Algebraic Equations

We consider the system of equations:

$$f_1 (y_1, y_2) = \lambda (y_1^2 + y_2^2 - 1) + 1 = 0 \qquad (4.5.23)$$

$$f_2 (y_1, y_2) = 10 \, y_2 - \lambda y_2 (1 + 2y_1^2 + y_2^2) = 0 \qquad (4.5.24)$$

where λ is a variable parameter.

Equation 4.5.24 is satisfied for $y_2 = 0$, and substitution of this value into Equation 4.5.23 yields:

$$y_1^2 = \frac{\lambda - 1}{\lambda} \qquad (4.5.25)$$

A bifurcation can only occur for real values of y_1, that is for $\lambda > 1$. That bifurcation will lie in the $y_2 = 0$ plane, as shown in Figure 4.11, and starts at the critical value $\lambda_0 = 1$. It will have the coordinates $(y_1, y_2, \lambda) = (0, 0, 1)$, as can be verified by substitution of $\lambda_0 = 1$ into Equation 4.5.25 and satisfies the first criterion $f(\underset{\sim}{y}_0, \lambda_0) = 0$. We now proceed to show that this point is in fact a turning point as shown in Figure 4.11 by establishing the rank of the augmented matrix $f_y | f_\lambda$. This involves evaluating the partial derivatives $\partial f_1/\partial y_1$, $\partial f_1/\partial y_2$, $\partial f_2/\partial y_1$, and $\partial f_2/\partial y_2$ from Equations 4.5.23 and 4.5.24 and yields the Jacobian,

$$f_y(\underset{\sim}{y}, \lambda) = \begin{pmatrix} 2\lambda y_1 & 2\lambda y_2 \\ -4\lambda y_1 y_2 & 10 - \lambda - 2\lambda y_1^2 - 3\lambda_2^2 \end{pmatrix}$$

and

$$f_\lambda(\underset{\sim}{y}, \lambda) = \begin{pmatrix} y_1^2 + y_2^2 - 1 \\ -y_2(1 + 2y_1^2 + y_2^2) \end{pmatrix}$$

so that

$$f_{\underset{\sim}{y}} \mid f_{\underset{\sim}{\lambda}} \text{ at } (0,0,1) \text{ is given by}$$

$$\begin{pmatrix} 0 & 0 & -1 \\ 0 & 9 & 0 \end{pmatrix}$$

which has full rank $n = 2$. This is seen from the fact that the second order determinant 0 to 9 (-1) does not vanish. Thus, by the theorems previously stated, we are dealing with a turning point rather than a simple bifurcation point. The latter would have produced a rank of $n - 1$ for the augmented Jacobian.

Additional regions of multiplicity arise when we consider the case $y_2 \neq 0$. To show this, we recast Equation 4.5.23 in the form:

$$y_1^{\,2} + y_2^{\,2} = 1 - \frac{1}{\lambda} \tag{4.5.26}$$

and substitute it into Equation 4.5.24 to obtain:

$$\lambda y_1^2 + 2\lambda - 11 = 0 \tag{4.5.27}$$

Equations 4.5.26 and 4.5.27 together yield values of:

$$y_1 = \pm \left(\frac{11 - 2\lambda}{\lambda} \right)^{1/2} \tag{4.5.28}$$

and

$$y_2 = \pm \left(\frac{3\lambda - 12}{\lambda} \right)^{1/2} \tag{4.5.29}$$

It follows that in order to obtain real values of y_1 and y_2, the region of multiplicity will have to be restricted to the range $4 \leq \lambda \leq 5.5$. These regions that result are depicted in Figure 4.11. It will be left to the exercises to show that we obtain a pair each of bifurcation and turning points at the endpoints of the range.

Illustration 4.5.3   A System with a Hopf Bifurcation

We examine next the following system of nonlinear parametric algebraic equations:

$$f_1(y_1, y_2) = -y_2 + y_1(\lambda - y_1^2 + y_2^2) = 0 \tag{4.5.30}$$

$$f_2(y_1, y_2) = y_1 + y_2(\lambda - y_1^2 + y_2^2) = 0 \tag{4.5.31}$$

where λ = parameter.

We start by showing that the only stationary point occurs at $y_1 = y_2 = 0$. We do this by eliminating the bracketed expression, dividing, and solving the result for y_2. This yields:

$$y_2 = y_1 i \tag{4.5.32}$$

which, for real values of $y_{1,2}$, can only be true if $y_1 = y_2 = 0$.

We next establish the eigenvalues of the equations. The partial derivatives required are as follows:

$$\frac{\partial f_1}{\partial y_1} = \lambda + y_2{}^2 - 3y_1{}^2 = \lambda \tag{4.5.33}$$

$$\frac{\partial f}{\partial y_2} = -1 - 2y_1 y_2 = -1 \tag{4.5.34}$$

$$\frac{\partial f_2}{\partial y_1} = 1 - 2y_1 y_2 = 1 \tag{4.5.35}$$

$$\frac{\partial f_2}{\partial y_2} = \lambda - y_1{}^2 + 3y_2{}^2 = \lambda \tag{4.5.36}$$

The Jacobian determinant then becomes:

$$\begin{vmatrix} \lambda - \mu & -1 \\ 1 & \lambda - \mu \end{vmatrix} = 0 \tag{4.5.37}$$

which yields the eigenvalues:

$$\mu_{1,2} = \lambda \pm i \tag{4.5.38}$$

We distinguish three cases:

(1) $\lambda > 0$: The characteristic roots are a complex conjugate pair with $Re > 0$, hence an unstable focus results (Case F, Figure 4.8).

(2) $\lambda < 0$: The characteristic roots are a complex conjugate pair with $Re < 0$. A stable focus is the result (Case D).

(3) $\lambda = 0$: Two purely imaginary characteristic roots are obtained. To verify whether these lead to a center or a Hopf bifurcation, we take the derivative of $d[Re\ \mu\ (\lambda_0)/d\lambda]$ and find that it equals 1, i.e., $\neq 0$, so that we have indeed a Hopf bifurcation. It has its genesis in parameter space at the point $y_1 = y_2 = \lambda_0 = 0$.

4.5.3 CHAOS

Chaotic behavior arises in systems of nonlinear ODEs whose solutions are highly sensitive to the initial conditions, or systems of nonlinear algebraic equations with similar extreme sensitivity to parameter values. ODEs must be at least three in number, but in the case of algebraic systems, a single equation will suffice. We give two examples of such unstructured or chaotic behavior.

ODE systems are exemplified by the famous Lorenz equations, given in Table 4.3 and repeated here:

$$\frac{dx}{dt} = 10(y - x)$$

$$\frac{dy}{dt} = -xz + 28x - y \qquad\qquad (4.5.39)$$

$$\frac{dz}{dt} = xy - (8/3)x$$

They are a description of weather patterns which were being investigated by Lorenz, and their nonlinearities, resting in the terms xz and xy, are relatively mild. Yet on solving them numerically, Lorenz found a divergence of solutions for nearly identical initial conditions which were originally specified to four figures and later rounded off to two significant figures. This led to the divergent and quite dissimilar solutions shown in Figure 4.12.

A typical algebraic example is given by the so-called logistic equation which describes population growth with increments in time:

$$y_{n+1} = \lambda y_n [1 - y_n] \qquad\qquad (4.5.40)$$

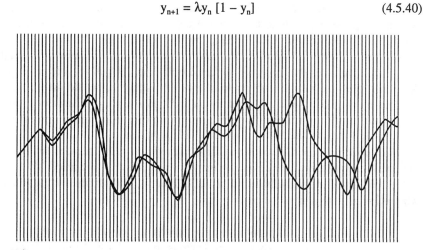

FIGURE 4.12   Output from the numerical solution of Lorenz's set of three nonlinear ODEs. (J. Gleick, *Chaos*, Viking Penguin Inc., New York, 1987. With permission.)

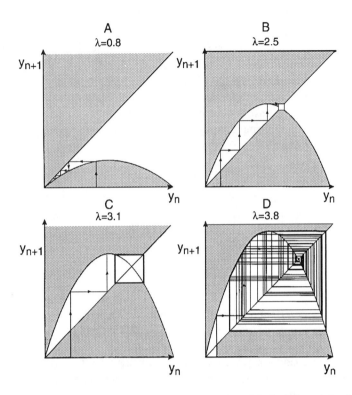

FIGURE 4.13 Phase plane portrait of the numerical solution of the logistic equation for various parameter values. (Adapted from J. Gleick, *Chaos,* Viking Penguin Inc., New York, 1987.)

One can think of y as the fraction of the population suffering from an epidemic and λ as the infection rate. The index n denotes an increment in time, say 1 year. A plot of y_{n+1} vs. y_n leads to the staircase construction shown in Figure 4.13 for various parameter values of λ. The solutions lie between the straight line $y = \lambda x$ and the parabola $y = \lambda x - \lambda x^2$. At low infection rates, $\lambda = 0.8$, the birth of healthy individuals overtakes the fraction of infected individuals which soon drops to zero. At higher rates, the parabola begins to intersect the straight line and the fraction of infected individuals rises and then stabilizes around the point of intersection in a mildly oscillatory form ($\lambda = 2.5$). An increase in λ to 3.1 leads to more pronounced oscillations which at $\lambda = 3.8$ become completely chaotic.

The subject of chaos has grown enormously over the last 3 decades and it is not our intention to address it here even in a marginal way. We draw the reader's attention to the specialized monographs listed in the References, and summarize the features which characterize chaotic behavior.

- Sensitivity to initial conditions or parameter values, already mentioned.
- Chaos is not completely random. There is some order within the disorder. For example, in Figure 4.13 the oscillations, though quite erratic, are centered on the point of intersection between parabola and straight line.

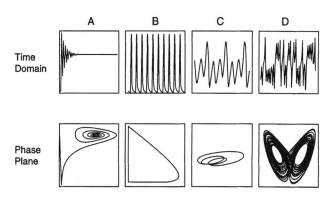

FIGURE 4.14 Time domain and phase plan portrait of the progression toward chaos: (A) stable behavior, (b) periodic behavior, (c) period doubling, (D) chaos. (Adapted from J. Gleick, *Chaos,* Viking Penguin Inc., New York, 1987.)

- Nonlinearity and some type of feedback are necessary ingredients. In the logistic equation, feedback takes place through the indexed variables y_n, y_{n+1}.
- All chaos hypotheses stipulate initiation by bifurcation, usually Hopf bifurcation. The criteria for the latter, Equations 4.5.20, therefore can be used as a guidepost for possible chaotic behavior. Evidently, the converse does not hold, i.e., not all bifurcations give rise to chaotic behavior.
- An intermediate stage on the way to chaos is the phenomenon of period doubling, shown in Figure 4.14C where a particular oscillation is successively joined by other oscillations of a different frequency and amplitude.
- Chaos may give rise to strange attractors, an example of which appears in Figure 4.14D as a projection onto the phase plane. One notes their "fuzziness," which contrasts with the clear delineation of regular attractors such as stable nodes or foci, and limit cycles. This has led to the following definition. An attractor is a strange attractor if the flow lines, i.e., trajectories, depend sensitively on the initial conditions.

We hope with this all-too-brief synopsis to have provided the reader with an incentive to dig further into this fascinating topic.

Historical Note:
The start of chaos studies is usually identified with Lorenz' 1963 paper: "Deterministic Non-Periodic Flow," which went unnoticed for several years. Earlier mathematicians seem to have been aware of the possibility of chaos without having actually discovered it. See in this connection the warning of Poincaré: "... small errors may produce enormous errors ..." at the turn of the century. The flourishing studies of the 1960s and 1970s are associated with the names of Benoit Mandelbrot, who discovered Fractals; Mitchell Feigenbaum and Robert May, both of whom studied the Logistic Equation; and a host of other mathematicians. The interest and thrust remain undiminished to this day.

Practice Problems

4.1 Classification of ODEs: Boundary Conditions —

(a) Classify the following ODEs
- $y'' + y' + (\sin x)y = 0$
- $y'' + y' + y = \sin x$
- $y'' + y' + (\sin^2 x)y = 0$
- $y'' + y' + \sin y = 0$
- $y'' + y' + y = 0$

(b) Give an example each of an autonomous ODE, a nonautonomous ODE, a homogeneous and a nonhomogeneous ODE. Are all autonomous ODEs homogeneous? Are all homogeneous ODEs autonomous?

(c) Give two physical examples each, other than those cited in the text, which give rise to Type II and Type III boundary conditions.

4.2 Tubular Reactors with Axial Diffusion. The Danckwerts Boundary Conditions —

(a) Show that for a tubular reactor with axial dispersion, conditions at the inlet and outlet are given by the so-called Danckwerts, or close boundary conditions:

$$vC(0^-) = vC(0^+) - D\frac{dC}{dz}\Big|_{0^+}$$

$$\frac{dC}{dz}\Big|_{x=L} = 0$$

(4.5.41)

(b) Using the D-operator method and the above boundary condition show that the outlet concentration for a first order reaction is given by:

$$C_{out} = C_{in}\frac{4s\exp(Pe/2)}{(1+s)^2 \exp(s\,Pe/2) - (1-s)^2 \exp(-s\,Pe/2)}$$

(4.5.42)

where $s = \left(1 + \dfrac{4k\tau}{Pe}\right)^{1/2}$, Pe = Peclet Number = vL/D.

4.3 The Countercurrent Heat Exchanger — Derive Equation 3.3.16 for the tube-side temperature profile of a single pass, shell-and-tube countercurrent heat exchanger.

4.4 The Shrinking-Core Model — Show by repeated application of the separation of variables method, that the relation between core radius r_C and time of reaction for a reacting spherical particle is given by:

$$t = \frac{\rho_p R^2}{6b\,D_{eff}\,C_{As}}\left[1 - 3\left(\frac{r_C}{R}\right)^2 + 2\left(\frac{r_C}{R}\right)^3\right]$$

(4.5.43)

where b = moles of solid reacting per mole of reactant gas A, D_{eff} = diffusivity through the ash layer. Assume diffusion through the ash layer is controlling. Use the systematic approach employed in Illustration 4.3.2.

4.5 The Airy Equation — Use a power series expansion to obtain a solution to the Airy equation $y'' - xy = 0$.

(Hint: Show that $a_2 = 0$ and that subsequent terms are given by the recursion formula.)

$$a_{n+2} = \frac{a_{n-1}}{(n+2)(n+1)}$$

4.6 Deflection of a Horizontal Beam — The deflection y of a horizontal beam subject to a restoring force which is proportional to the deflection is described by the fourth order ODE:

$$EI\frac{d^4y}{dx^4} + ky = 0 \tag{4.5.44}$$

where E = Modulus of Elasticity, I = Moment of Inertia.

Using the D-operator method, show that the solution to this problem is given by:

$$y = C_1\, e^{ax} \cos ax + C_2\, e^{ax} \sin ax + C_3\, e^{-ax} \cos ax + C_4\, e^{-ax} \sin ax \tag{4.5.45}$$

(Hint: Set $k/4EI = a^4$ and derive the characteristic equation $D^4 + 4a^4 = 0$ whose roots are $D = \pm a \pm ai$.)

4.7 Use of Integrating Factors — Show that the nonlinear ODE $xy(dy/dx) + \frac{1}{x} + 4^2 = 0$ has the integrating factor x and integrate the result.

(Hint: Consult Table 4.9.)

4.8 The Bernoulli Equation — Derive a closed form solution of the Bernoulli equation:

$$y' + f(x)y = g(x)y^n \tag{4.5.46}$$

using the substitution $u = y^{1-n}$.

(Hint: Use Item 6 of Table 4.4.)

4.9 The Pendulum — The equation of motion for a frictionless pendulum is given by:

$$\frac{d^2\theta}{dt^2} + \frac{g}{1}\sin\theta = 0 \tag{4.5.47}$$

where θ = angle of deflection. Show that the closed form solution of this problem is given:

$$\int \frac{d\theta}{\sqrt{g\cos\theta + C_1}} = \sqrt{\frac{2}{1}}t + C_2 \qquad (4.5.48)$$

4.10 The Nonlinear Countercurrent Heat Exchanger — When fluids with a strong temperature dependence of their viscosity are heated in an exchanger, the heat transfer coefficient becomes a function of T, resulting in a set of nonlinear model equations. Indicate how these equations would be solved numerically.

4.11 Path of Pursuit — Derive Equation 4.3.92.
(Hint: Sketch the paths.)

4.12 The Duffing Equation — For a Duffing-type equation of the form:

$$\ddot{y} + \dot{y} - y + y^3 = 0 \qquad (4.5.49)$$

derive the stationary solutions and analyze their character and stability.
Answer: Critical points consist of an unstable saddle and stable focus.

4.13 The van der Pol Equation — Deduce the nature and stability of the stationary solution of the van der Pol equation:

$$\ddot{y} - \lambda(1 - y^2)\dot{y} + y = 0 \qquad (4.5.50)$$

in the parameter range

$$3 > \lambda > -3$$

Partial answer: There is a center at $y_1 = y_2 = \lambda = 0$.

4.14 Identification of Turning and Bifurcation Points — Prove that two of the critical points in Figure 4.11 are bifurcation points.

REFERENCES

There are a host of texts on ODEs that treat the topic at an intermediate level and in an understandable manner, using numerous practical examples. Among them:
M.R. Spiegel. *Applied Differential Equations,* Prentice-Hall, Upper Saddle River, NJ, 1981.
E.J. Kostelich and D. Armbruster. *Introductory Differential Equations: From Linearity to Chaos,* Addison-Wesley, Reading, MA, 1996.
E.D. Rainville, P.E. Bedient and R.E. Bedient. *Elementary Differential Equations, 8th ed.,* Prentice-Hall, Upper Saddle River, NJ, 1997.

ODEs also are well covered in advanced treatments of Engineering Mathematics, see for example:

E. Kreyszig. *Advanced Engineering Mathematics, 7th ed.,* John Wiley & Sons, New York, 1992.

D. Zwillinger. *Handbook of Differential Equations, 2nd ed.,* Academic Press, New York, 1992. *This contains useful general information and compilations.*

Much more profound treatments dealing with theoretical aspects are to be found in:
E.L. Ince. *Ordinary Differential Equations,* Dover, New York, 1956.
V.I. Arnold. *Ordinary Differential Equations,* MIT Press, Cambridge, MA, 1980.

Functions which arise in series solutions are tabulated in mathematical handbooks including:
M.R. Spiegel. *Mathematics Handbook of Formulas and Tables,* Schaum, New York, 1968.

And the classic but less easily read:
M. Abramovitz and I.A. Stegun. *Handbook of Mathematical Functions,* Dover, New York, 1970.

An early treatment and readable text of nonlinear ODEs is by:
W.F. Ames. *Non Linear Ordinary Differential Equations in Transport Processes,* Academic Press, New York, 1968.

The last 2 decades have seen an explosion in books dealing with nonlinear ODEs and the associated exotic phenomena. A readable account focused primarily on numerical techniques is given in:
R. Seydel. *From Equilibrium to Chaos,* Elsevier, New York, 1988.

Somewhat more challenging is the oft-cited text:
J. Guckenheimer and P. Holmes. *Non-Linear Oscillations. Dynamical Systems and Bifurcations of Vector Fields,* Springer, New York, 1985.

See also:
E. Beltrami. *Mathematics for Dynamic Modeling, 2nd ed.,* Academic Press, New York, 1997.

Catastrophe theory is taken up in:
R. Gilmore. *Catastrophe Theory for Scientists and Engineers,* John Wiley & Sons, New York, 1981.

And in the more advanced text:
V.I. Arnold. *Catastrophe Theory, 3rd ed.,* Springer, New York, 1992.

A historical account and highly readable description of the mathematical background of nonlinear phenomena appears in the paperback:
J. Gleick. *Chaos,* Penguin, New York, 1987.

An up-to-date account of the topic with numerous lucid examples appears in:
H.-O. Pietgen, H. Jürgens, and D. Saupe. *Chaos and Fractals: New Frontiers of Science,* Springer, New York, 1992.

Of the many books on numerical methods we liked the elementary text:
R.W. Hornbeck. *Numerical Methods,* Quantum, New York, 1975.

Chapters on numerical methods for solving ODEs also appear in the advanced text:
W.H. Press, B.P. Flannery, S.A. Tukolsky, and W.T. Veltenling. *Numerical Recipes: The Art of Scientific Computing,* Cambridge, U.K., 1986.

Recent texts which come with diskettes for solving algebraic and ordinary differential equations are:
A. Constantinides. *Applied Numerical Methods with Personal Computers,* McGraw-Hill, New York, 1987.
D. Kahaner, C. Moler, and S. Nash. *Numerical Methods and Software,* Prentice-Hall, Upper Saddle River, NJ, 1989.

5 The Laplace Transformation

A theory should be as simple as possible, and no simpler.

Albert Einstein

The Laplace transformation (or Laplace transform, for short) belongs to a broader class of integral transform operations in which a function f(t) is multiplied by a "Kernel" K(s,t) and integrated between the limits a and b. Thus,

$$T\{F(t)\} = \int_a^b F(t)K(s,t)dt = f(s) \tag{5.1}$$

where T = operational symbol for the transformation and f(s) = transform of F(t).

F(t), the function operated on, is quite arbitrary in form and can be an ordinary function in t, such as sin at, a derivative d^2F/dt^2, or even an integral. The kernel and the integration limits (a,b) define the type of transform. Apart from Laplace transforms, there are Fourier transforms of various types, transforms including Bessel functions, and several others, all of which have their own special kernels and integration limits. These are taken up in more detail in Chapter 9. For the Laplace transform, the kernel K(s,t) is the function e^{-st} and the integration limits (a,b) are from zero to infinity. Thus, the Laplace transform of f(t) takes the form:

$$L\{F(t)\} = \int_0^\infty F(t)\exp(-st)dt = f(s) \tag{5.2}$$

where L is its operational symbol and L^{-1} is its inverse, i.e.,

$$L^{-1}\{f(s)\} = F(t) \tag{5.3}$$

This transformation, when applied to each term of an ordinary differential equation (ODE), has the effect of eliminating the independent variable t, thus reducing the ODE to an algebraic equation in the transformed state variable f(s). After solving for f(s), the AE is then translated back into the solution space by means of appropriate "dictionaries," the Laplace transform tables. The reader will note that this procedure bears a resemblance to the D-operator method which likewise transforms an ODE to an AE, and after solving the latter, translates the result back into the solution domain by means of an appropriate dictionary, Table 4.4.

The Laplace transform is generally used to solve linear initial value ODEs with constant coefficients. Although it can in principle be applied to boundary value problems, the procedure is somewhat cumbersome since the missing initial conditions have to be evaluated by substitution of given boundary conditions into the solution, much like integration constants (see Illustration 5.2.5). It is also of little help in solving variable coefficient ODEs and is generally inapplicable to nonlinear ODEs. Once these limitations are accepted, however, it becomes an extremely powerful tool both for the solution and the analysis of linear ODEs, as well as PDEs. It can directly solve many nonhomogeneous initial value problems without first finding the fundamental solution of the corresponding homogeneous problems. Second, it can handle a wide array of nonhomogeneous terms, including the important class of discontinuous or impulsive forcing functions. Third, the initial conditions appear automatically in the solution, thus obviating the need to evaluate integration constants.

Because of these properties, the Laplace transform has become an indispensable tool in linear control theory which deals extensively with nonhomogeneous initial value problems. It is there that it finds one of its most fruitful uses and it does this often by means of analysis rather than an actual solution of the ODEs.

The question then arises whether, given the attractive features of the Laplace transform, one need to retain the D-operator method. The answer is yes, since the latter is capable of handling the important class of boundary value problems that are not easily accessible to the Laplace transformation.

We proceed in this chapter by first discussing some general properties of the Laplace transform, followed by its application to the solution of some simple ODEs. This is followed by a survey of the response of first and second order systems to various types of forcing functions which provides an entry into linear control theory. We discuss there the use of the transfer function and block diagrams, and provide a glimpse of what is known as Laplace domain analysis. We conclude by taking up some of the less common applications of the transform.

5.1   GENERAL PROPERTIES OF THE LAPLACE TRANSFORM

We have tabulated in Table 5.1 some general properties of the Laplace transform and supplement this, in Table 5.2 and 5.3, with tabulations of transforms of some common Functions, as well as of some discontinuous functions. The Laplace transform is particularly powerful and unsurpassed in handling the latter. Our comments here are with respect to Table 5.1.

To begin with, we note that the table is akin to a table of integrals in that one can move from left to right or from right to left, depending on the information sought. In this instance, one moves from right to left to obtain the transform $f(s)$ of a function $F(t)$, and from left to right to obtain what is termed the inverse transform

TABLE 5.1
General Properties of the Laplace Transform

$f(s)$	$F(t)$

1. Laplace transform

$$\int_0^\infty F(t)e^{-st}dt$$

$F(t)$

2. Inverse transform

$f(s)$

$$\frac{1}{2\pi i}\lim_{\beta \to \infty}\int_{\gamma-i\beta}^{\gamma+i\beta} e^{tz}f(z)dz$$

3. Transform of a constant

C/s

C

4. Transform of a sum

$af(s) + bg(s)$

$aF(t) + bG(t)$

5. Transform of derivatives

$sf(s) - F(0)$ $F'(t)$

$s^2f(s) - sF(0) - F'(0)$ $F''(t)$

$s^nf(s) - s^{n-1}F(0) - s^{n-2}F'(0) \dots F^{(n-1)}(0)$ $F^{(n)}(t)$

6. Transform of an integral

$$\frac{1}{s}f(s)$$

$$\int_0^t F(\tau)d\tau$$

7. Inverse of a product: the convolution theorem

$f(s)\ g(s)$

$$\int_0^t F(\tau)G(t-\tau)d\tau = F(t) * G(t)$$

8. Inverse of a ratio of polynomials (Heaviside expansion)

$$\frac{p(s)}{q(s)}\text{(Order of }p(s) < q(s))$$

$$\sum_{n=1}^\infty \frac{(s-a_n)p(a_n)}{q(a_n)}e^{a_nt} = \sum_{n=1}^\infty \frac{p(a_n)}{q'(a_n)}e^{a_ny}$$

where a_n = roots of $q(s)$

9. Inverse of derivatives

$f'(s)$ $-t\ F(t)$

$f^{(n)}(s)$ $(-1)^n t^n\ F(t)$

10. Inverse of an integral

$$\int_0^\infty f(x)dx$$

$$\frac{1}{t}F(t)$$

11. Translation or shifting properties

(a) $f(s - a)$ $e^{at}\ F(t)$

(b) $e^{-as}\ f(s)$ $\begin{cases}F(t-a) & t > a \\ 0 & t < a\end{cases}$

12. Initial value theorem

$$\lim_{s \to \infty} sf(s)$$

$F(0)$

13. Final value theorem

$$\lim_{s \to 0} sf(s)$$

$$\lim_{t \to \infty} F(t)$$

TABLE 5.2
Laplace Transforms of Some Functions

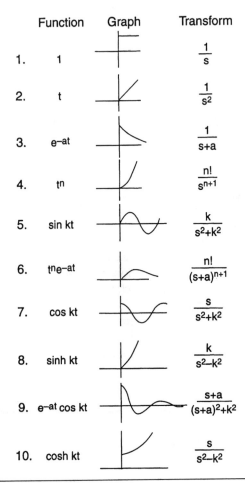

	Function	Graph	Transform
1.	1		$\dfrac{1}{s}$
2.	t		$\dfrac{1}{s^2}$
3.	e^{-at}		$\dfrac{1}{s+a}$
4.	t^n		$\dfrac{n!}{s^{n+1}}$
5.	$\sin kt$		$\dfrac{k}{s^2+k^2}$
6.	$t^n e^{-at}$		$\dfrac{n!}{(s+a)^{n+1}}$
7.	$\cos kt$		$\dfrac{s}{s^2+k^2}$
8.	$\sinh kt$		$\dfrac{k}{s^2-k^2}$
9.	$e^{-at}\cos kt$		$\dfrac{s+a}{(s+a)^2+k^2}$
10.	$\cosh kt$		$\dfrac{s}{s^2-k^2}$

of $f(s)$, i.e., the function $F(t)$ itself. The latter process is commonly referred to as an inversion. The formula given for the general inversion, Item 2, involves a line integral in the complex plane and requires some background knowledge of complex variable theory. It is used only sparingly and we shall here limit ourselves to making use of more convenient Items.

Item 5, the transform of derivatives requires special mention. Its main feature is that it converts the derivatives into algebraic expressions in s. In this it resembles the D-operator method and, as we shall see, also leads to a set of characteristic values termed *poles*. It has, however, the additional advantage of incorporating the initial conditions in the resulting algebraic expression. This was not the case in the D-operator method which required the somewhat cumbersome evaluation of integration constants.

TABLE 5.3
Laplace Transforms of Discontinuous Functions

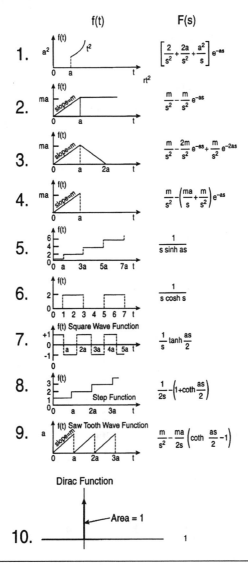

Two additional items call for special mention. One is the convolution integral, Item 7, which allows the inversion of the product of two arbitrary function $f(s)$ and $g(s)$. It is frequently used to carry a general and unspecified function, say $F(t)$, into the transformation process and return it upon inversion as an integrand of the convolution integral. The second item of special interest is the Heaviside expansion, Item 8. To use it in the inversion of a ratio of polynomials, one first has to evaluate the roots of the denominator $q(s)$ that are then substituted into the inversion formula given on the right side. That formula applies only to distinct roots. Extensions to repeated roots are available (see References). Alternatively, the ratio can be decomposed into partial fractions and each fraction thus obtained inverted on an individual basis. We demonstrate the use of these formula with some sample illustrations.

Illustration 5.1.1   Inversion of Various Transforms

1. Obtain the inverse $L^{-1}\left\{\dfrac{1}{(s^2+k^2)^2}\right\}$

Since the roots of the denominator are both repeated, one cannot use the Heaviside expansion shown in Item 8 of Table 5.1. We note, however, from Table 5.2, Item 5, that:

$$L^{-1}\left\{\frac{k}{(s^2+k^2)}\right\} = \sin kt \qquad (5.1.1)$$

so that we are in a position to apply the convolution theorem. We obtain:

$$L^{-1}\left\{\frac{1}{(s^2+k^2)^2}\right\} = \frac{1}{k^2}\sin kt * \sin kt$$

$$= \frac{1}{k^2}\int_0^t \sin k\tau \sin k(t-\tau)d\tau \qquad (5.1.2)$$

Expanding $\sin k(t-\tau)$ gives:

$$\sin (kt - k\tau) = \sin kt \cos (-k\tau) + \cos kt \sin (-k\tau) \qquad (5.1.3)$$

and using the following formula obtained from tables of integrals:

$$\int_0^t \sin^2 k\tau\, d\tau = \frac{1}{2k}\left[1 - \frac{1}{2}\sin^2 kt\right]$$

$$\int_0^t \sin k\tau \cos k\tau\, d\tau = \frac{1}{2k}\sin^2 kt \qquad (5.1.4)$$

as well as,

$$\sin 2 kt = 2 \sin kt \cos kt \qquad (5.1.5)$$

$$\sin^2 kt + \cos^2 kt = 1$$

There finally results:

$$L^{-1}\left\{\frac{1}{(s^2+k^2)^2}\right\} = \frac{1}{2k^3}\{\sin kt - kt\cos kt\} \tag{5.1.6}$$

2. Find $L^{-1}\left\{\dfrac{e^{-5s}}{(s-2)^4}\right\}$

Here some thought will reveal that application of the two shifting properties 11a and 11b to the polynomial and exponential terms in succession will accomplish the desired inversion. We first apply 11a, using Item 4 of Table 5.2 and obtain:

$$L^{-1}\left\{\frac{1}{(s-2)^4}\right\} = e^{2t}L^{-1}\left\{\frac{1}{s^4}\right\} = e^{2t}\frac{1}{6}t^3 \tag{5.1.7}$$

Knowing the inversion of the polynomial part, we then apply the shifting property 11b to the full expression. This yields:

$$L^{-1}\left\{\frac{e^{-5s}}{(s-2)^4}\right\} = \begin{cases} \dfrac{1}{6}(t-5)^3 e^{2(t-5)} & t > 5 \\[2mm] 0 & t < 5 \end{cases} \tag{5.1.8}$$

3. Invert $\left\{\dfrac{3s+1}{(s-1)(s^2+1)}\right\}$

We recognize this as a ratio of polynomials $p(s)/q(s)$ where $p(s) = 3s + 1$, $q(s) = (s - 1)(s^2 + 1) = s^3 - s^2 + s - 1$, and the roots of $q(s)$ are $a_1 = 1$, $a_2 = i$, $a_3 = -i$. Since the roots are not repeated and the order of $p(s)$ is less than that of $q(s)$, the Heaviside expansion, Item 8 of Table 5.1, may be applied.

We have:

$$q'(s) = 3s^2 - 2s + 1 \tag{5.1.9}$$

Expanding the sum of the Heaviside expression, we obtain:

$$\frac{p(1)}{q'(1)}e^t + \frac{p(i)}{q'(i)}e^{it} + \frac{p(-i)}{q'(-i)}e^{-it}$$

$$= 2e^t + \left(-1-\frac{1}{2}i\right)(\cos t + i\sin t) + \left(-1+\frac{1}{2}i\right)(\cos t - i\sin t) \tag{5.1.10}$$

Evaluation of the products reduces Equation 5.1.10 to the expression:

$$L^{-1}\left\{\frac{3s+1}{(s-1)(s^2+1)}\right\} = 2e^t - 2\cos t + \sin t \tag{5.1.11}$$

The same result also may be obtained by partial fractions. We write:

$$\frac{3s+1}{(s-1)(s^2+1)} = \frac{A}{s-1} + \frac{Bs+C}{s^2+1} = \frac{A(s^2+1)(Bs+C)(s-1)}{(s-1)(s^2+1)}$$

$$\qquad\qquad\text{I}\qquad\qquad\text{II}\qquad\qquad\text{III}\qquad\qquad\qquad\qquad (5.1.12)$$

Equating coefficients of equal powers in I and III, one obtains:

$$A + B = 0 \quad A - C = 1 \quad C - B = 3 \qquad\qquad (5.1.13)$$

and hence,

$$A = 2, \quad B = -2, \quad C = 1$$

The problem is then reduced to an inversion of the following sum:

$$2L\left\{\frac{1}{s-1}\right\} - 2L^{-1}\left\{\frac{s}{s^2+1}\right\} + L^{-1}\left\{\frac{1}{s^2+1}\right\} \qquad (5.1.14)$$

for which we use Items 3, 5, and 7 of Table 5.2. The final result is given by:

$$L^{-1}\left\{\frac{3s+1}{(s-1)(s^2+1)}\right\} = 2e^t - 2\cos t + \sin t \qquad (5.1.15)$$

which is identical to the previous result.

5.2   APPLICATION TO DIFFERENTIAL EQUATIONS

The Laplace transform has certain attractive features, some already noted, which makes it the preferred tool for solving linear initial value problems.

- It can be applied quite automatically to problems of this type.
- It directly incorporates initial conditions into the transforms of the derivatives of the ODE, thus dispensing with the need to evaluate integration constants.
- The transform is capable of handling a wide variety of different forcing functions, including those of a discontinuous nature (Table 5.3), and it does so with much greater ease then other procedures. We recall that the D-operator method would in this case require the evaluation of a particular integral which becomes difficult if not impossible to apply in the case of discontinuous functions.
- The method often provides qualitative information as to the *nature* of the solution by a mere inspection of the form and the coefficients of the ODE without having to proceed to an *actual* solution. In this it resembles the D-operator method that enables us to forecast the *shape* of the solution

curves from the coefficients of the ODE. The process of extracting such information without actually solving the ODE is sometimes referred to as *Laplace domain analysis.*

The details of the procedure for solving ODEs may be summarized as follows:

1. Apply the Laplace transform in turn to each term of the ODE in Y(t). If that term is a *derivative*, one obtains a composite of the transform of the unknown function, y(s) and its initial values (see Item 5 of Table 5.1). For example, dY/dt becomes, when transformed, y(s) – Y(0). Terms directly containing the unknown state function become the transform of that variable. Thus, L{kY(t)} will become ky(s). Finally, the nonhomogeneous terms or forcing functions are directly reduced to explicit functions of s. For example, the forcing function e^{at} is transformed directly into the explicit form 1/(s-a).
2. Solve the algebraic equation in y(s) that resulted from Step 1. This yields expressions of the form:

$$y(s) = G(s) \qquad (5.2.1)$$

where y(s) is the transformed state variable Y(t) and G(s) is an explicit function of s containing, among other things, the transforms of the forcing functions and the initial conditions. An example is

$$y(s) = G(s) = \frac{Y_0(s}{(s-1)}$$

3. Invert the Expression 5.2.1, i.e., apply the operator L^{-1} to each side. For y(s), this automatically yields the desired state variable Y(t). Inversion of the right-side term G(s) is accomplished by means of tables, such as Tables 5.2 and 5.3, and by one or more of the procedures listed in Table 5.1, such as the use of the convolution integral, the Heaviside expansion, or partial fractions. Together these two inversions yield the desired solution in the final form:

$$Y(t) = f(t, \text{Initial Conditions}) \qquad (5.2.2)$$

For simultaneous ODEs, the procedure is similar but requires an additional step. We proceed as follows:

1. Apply the Laplace transform to each term of each of the n ODEs of the system. Instead of a single algebraic equation in y(s), we now obtain n such equations containing n transforms, $y_1(s)$, $y_2(s)$ ... $y_n(s)$.
2. Eliminate algebraically n – 1 of the transforms, reducing the system to a *single* algebraic equation in $y_i(s)$.

3. Solve the equation which resulted in Step 2 for $y_i(s)$.
4. Invert the result from Step 3 to obtain $Y_i(t)$.
5. Repeat the procedure for the remaining $n - 1$ transforms.

In what follows we present two illustrations of the solution of *single* ODEs. Examples of simultaneous ODEs appear in Practice Problems 5.2 and 6.1.3.

Illustration 5.2.1   The Mass-Spring System Revisited: Resonance

We consider here the system previously seen in Illustration 4.3.5, that of a vibrating spring with a forcing function. The forcing function used there was the weight of the mass m attached to the spring so that gravity and the restoring force kx of the spring were the forces to be considered. We obtained, by application of Newton's law:

$$\frac{d^2x}{dt^2} + (k/m)x = g \tag{4.3.46}$$

where the gravitational constant g represented the forcing function. We now generalize this equation to apply to an arbitrary forcing function F(t) and specify more general initial conditions, so that:

$$\frac{d^2X}{dt^2} + \omega_0{}^2 X = F(t)/m \tag{5.2.3}$$

and $X(0) = X_0$ (initial position)
$\quad X'(0) = v_0$ (initial velocity)
$\quad \omega_0 \quad = (k/m)^{1/2}$

We carry the forcing function in unspecified form into the Laplace transformation process and obtain:

$$s^2\, x(s) - sX_0 - v_0 + \omega_0{}^2 x(s) = f(s)/m \tag{5.2.4}$$

Solving for x(s), we obtain:

$$x(s) = \frac{X_0 s + v_0}{s^2 + \omega_0{}^2} + \frac{v_0 s}{m}\frac{1}{s^2 + \omega_0{}^2} \tag{5.2.5}$$

This is the expression which now has to be inverted. Inversion of the first fraction is by Items 5 and 7 of Table 5.2, that of the second term by means of the convolution integral, Item 7 in Table 5.1. We obtain:

$$X(t) = X_0 \cos\omega_0 t + \frac{v_0}{\omega_0}\sin\omega_0 t + \frac{1}{m\omega_0}\int_0^t \sin\omega_0\tau\, F(t-\tau)d\tau \tag{5.2.6}$$

Note the appearance of the initial conditions X_0 and v_0 in this expression and that the forcing function $F(t)$ remains unspecified under the convolution integral. The advantage here of the convolution formulation is its ability to yield closed form solutions without the need to specify certain terms of the original ODE.

We consider the following two cases for $F(t)$: (1) $F(t)$ = constant = mg, and v_0 = 0. Under these conditions, the sine term drops out and the integral becomes:

$$\frac{1}{m\omega_0}\int_0^t \sin\omega_0 t F(t-\tau)d\tau = -\frac{g}{m\omega_0^2}\cos\omega_0 t \tag{5.2.7}$$

We, thus, recover the solution given in Illustration 4.3.5, i.e.;

$$X(t) = \left(X_0 - \frac{mg}{k}\right)\cos(k/m)^{1/2}t \tag{4.3.57}$$

or in equivalent form,

$$X(t) = (X_0 - g/\omega_0^2)\cos\omega_0 t \tag{5.2.8}$$

(2) $F(t) = F_0 \sin\omega t$. Here the expression to be inverted becomes:

$$x(s) = \frac{X_0 s + v_0}{s^2 + \omega_0^2} + \frac{F_0}{m}\frac{\omega}{(s^2 + \omega_0^2)(s^2 + \omega^2)} \tag{5.2.9}$$

The first term on the right is inverted via Items 5 and 7 of Table 5.2, the second term either by partial fractions or the Heaviside expansion. We obtain:

$$X(t) = X_0\cos\omega_0 t + \frac{1}{\omega_0}\left[v_0 + \frac{F_0\omega}{m(\omega^2 - \omega_0^2)}\right]\sin\omega_0 t - \frac{F_0}{m(\omega^2 - \omega_0^2)}\sin\omega t \tag{5.2.10}$$

where as before $\omega_0 = (k/m)^{1/2}$.

Here ω_0 is referred to as the *natural vibration frequency* and ω as the *forced vibration frequency* of the system. Let us now ask ourselves what happens when the two frequencies are identical. Intuitively one could argue that this superposition of two vibrations with the same frequency might lead to an *escalation* in the amplitude of the vibrations of the system. This is indeed the case, as is shown below.

(3) $F = F_0 \sin\omega_0 t$; resonance. The expression to be inverted now becomes:

$$x(s) = \frac{X_0 s + v_0}{s^2 + \omega_0^2} + \frac{F_0\omega_0}{m(s^2 + \omega_0)^2} \tag{5.2.11}$$

One notes here the appearance of a *repeated* term in the denominator of the second fraction. Its inversion was demonstrated in Illustration 5.1.1 and led to the

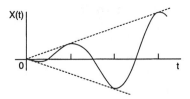

FIGURE 5.1   Solution of a second order nonhomogeneous ODE leading to resonance.

appearance of a term in t as kt cos kt, i.e., a *time dependent* amplitude. For the case in hand, we obtain in similar fashion:

$$X(t) = X_0 \cos \omega_0 t + \frac{1}{\omega_0^2}\left[v_0 \omega_0 + \frac{F_0}{2m} \right] \sin \omega_0 t - \frac{F_0}{2m\omega_0} t \cos \omega_0 t \quad (5.2.12)$$

In view of the last term, the amplitude of the oscillations increases indefinitely and one speaks of the forcing function F(t) as being in resonance with the system frequency. In particular, for $X_0 = 0$ and $v_0 = -F_0/(2m\omega_0)$, one obtains the expression:

$$X(t) = -\frac{F_0}{2m\omega_0} t \cos \omega_0 t \quad (5.2.13)$$

That expression clearly shows a linear increase in amplitude with t, as indicated in Figure 5.1, and would in time lead to a rupture of the mass spring system.

Illustration 5.2.2   Equivalence of Mechanical Systems and Electrical Circuits

We wish here to demonstrate the equivalence of the equations that describe mechanical vibrations on the one hand and the oscillations that arise in certain electrical circuits on the other.

We do this by first deriving a more general equation for forced mechanical vibrations which now includes a damper or dashpot in the system, as illustrated in Figure 5.2A. The damper has the effect of producing a countervailing force that is proportional to the *velocity* of the vibrating mass. This in turn leads to the appearance of a first-order derivative $k_1 dX/dt$ in the constitutive equation. We now obtain:

$$m\frac{d^2X}{dt^2} \quad + \quad k_1\frac{dX}{dt} \quad + \quad k_2 X \quad = F(t)$$

$$\text{Acceleration} \quad \text{Damper} \quad \text{Spring} \quad \text{Forcing Function}$$

$$(5.2.14)$$

where the forcing function is again kept in a general and unspecified form.

We next turn to the consideration of the simple electrical circuit shown in Figure 5.2B. It is made up of a coil with inductance L, a resistor with resistance R, a

A. Vibrating Mass

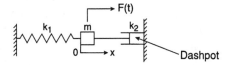

B. Oscillating Electrical Circuit

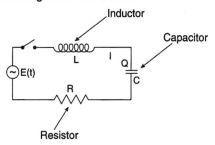

FIGURE 5.2 Two different physical systems which give rise to identical forms of second order ODEs.

capacitor with capacitance C, and a voltage supply E(t). From elementary electricity theory it is known that for the first three items, the voltage drop is given by:

Inductor	$V_I = L\, di / dt$	
Resistor	$V_R = iR$	(5.2.15)
Capacitor	$V_C = q / C$	

where i = current, q = charge.

The sum of three voltage drops must equal the imposed voltage E(t) so that:

$$L\frac{di}{dt} + \frac{q}{C} + iR = E(t) \tag{5.2.16}$$

Since current equals the rate of flow of charge q at any time, we have i = dq/dt. Introducing this relation into Equation 5.2.16, we obtain the second order ODE:

$$L\frac{d^2q}{dt^2} \;+\; R\frac{dq}{dt} \;+\; q/C \;=\; E(t)$$

$$\text{Inductor} \quad \text{Resistor} \quad \text{Capacitor} \quad \text{Imposed voltage} \tag{5.2.17}$$

The analogy to the vibrating mass and spring, Equation 5.2.14, is immediately evident. We note in particular that the inductor corresponds to the acceleration term, i.e., accelerates the charge, the resistor has a "damping" effect on charge flow, and the capacitor, likewise, resists charge flow much like the action of the spring.

The response of these systems to various forcing functions gives rise to some interesting phenomena. We had already given a partial analysis of this type in Illustration 5.2.1. In the following two illustrations, we shall first, by way of pre-amble, address the response of first order systems and ODEs (Illustration 5.2.3), and follow this up, in Illustration 5.2.4, with a more general analysis of second order systems of the type given above. We will show in particular, how these responses are related to the coefficients of the constituent equations, and how they are affected by the form of the forcing function.

Illustration 5.2.3   Response of First Order Systems

We use here, as an example of a first order system, a thermocouple or a thermometer which is exposed to a change in the ambient temperature. That change represents a forcing function $F(t)$. We treated this case in Illustration 3.3.3 where a step change in the ambient temperature was considered. Here we generalize the treatment to accommodate arbitrary forcing functions. A number of new features in both the form of the ODE and its transform are introduced which help in the generalization of the results.

The ODE was previously written in the form:

$$hA(T_a - T) = \rho V C_p \frac{dT}{dt} \tag{5.2.18}$$

Note that at steady-state, the relation becomes:

$$hA(T_{as} - T_s) = 0 \tag{5.2.18a}$$

where the subscript $_s$ denotes the (previous) steady-state. Subtraction of the two equations, 5.2.18 and 5.2.18a yields:

$$hA[(T_a - T_{as}) - (T - T_s)] = \rho V C_p \frac{d(T - T_s)}{dt} \tag{5.2.19}$$

or

$$[X - Y] = \tau \frac{dY}{dt} \tag{5.2.20}$$

where X and Y are so-called deviation variables, defined as:

$$X = T_a - T_{as}, \text{ the forcing function or input}$$

and

$$Y = T - T_s, \text{ the response function or output}$$

$\tau = \rho VC_p/hA$ is the so-called time constant, with units of time.

Noting that $Y(0) = 0$, the Laplace transform of Equation 5.2.20 yields the expression

$$x(s) - y(s) = \tau s y(s) \qquad (5.2.21)$$

or in rearranged form,

$$\frac{\text{Transform of output}}{\text{Transform of input}} = \frac{y(s)}{x(s)} = \frac{1}{\tau s + 1} \qquad (5.2.22)$$

The term on the right is referred to as the transfer function of the system and denoted by the symbol $G(s)$. It also can be viewed as the ratio of the transforms of the output to that of the input. Thus,

$$G(s) = \frac{y(s)}{x(s)} = \frac{1}{\tau s + 1} \qquad (5.2.23)$$

More about $G(s)$ will be given in Section 5.3.

We now consider various inputs X to the system and examine the resulting response Y.

(I) Step Input A — Here we have, from Item 3 of Table 5.1:

$$x(s) = A/s \qquad (5.2.24)$$

and the relation to be inverted becomes:

$$y(s) = \frac{A}{s} \frac{1}{\tau s + 1} \qquad (5.2.25)$$

Inversion can be accomplished by either the Heaviside expansion or by partial fractions and yields:

$$Y(t) = A(1 - e^{-t/\tau}) \qquad (5.2.26)$$

This expression depicts a smooth exponential rise to the new steady-state value A, as shown in Figure 5.3.

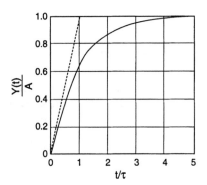

FIGURE 5.3   Response Y(t)/A of a first order ODE to a step change in input. (D.R. Cough-anowr, *Process Systems Analysis and Control, 2nd ed.,* McGraw-Hill, New York, 1991. With permission.)

(II) Unit Impulse Input — The input here consists of a pulse of magnitude 1 applied over a infinitesimally small time interval. The transform of such a pulse, also known as the *Dirac delta function,* equals 1, see Item 10 of Table 5.3. The transform of the ODE is then given by:

$$y(s) = \frac{1}{\tau s + 1} \tag{5.2.27}$$

with an inverse (see Item 3 of Table 5.2)

$$Y(t) = \frac{1}{\tau} e^{-t/\tau} \tag{5.2.28}$$

This expression is plotted in Figure 5.4.

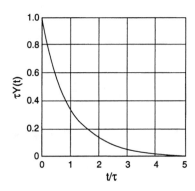

FIGURE 5.4   Response τY(t) of a first order system to an impulse input. (D.R. Coughanowr, *Process Systems Analysis and Control, 2nd ed.,* McGraw-Hill, New York, 1991. With permission.)

One notices that the response rises immediately to 1.0 and then decays exponentially. Such an abrupt rise is not physically possible but is closely approached by the response of the thermocouple to a pulse of narrow width.

(III) Sinusoidal Input — This is an interesting case in which the forcing function or input is of the form:

$$X(t) = A \sin \omega t \qquad (5.2.29)$$

The Laplace transform is now given by:

$$y(s) = \frac{A\omega}{s^2 + \omega^2} \frac{1}{\tau s + 1} \qquad (5.2.30)$$

which upon inversion by partial fraction or the Heaviside expansion yields:

$$Y(t) = \frac{A\omega\tau e^{-t/\tau}}{\tau^2\omega^2 + 1} - \frac{A\omega\tau}{\tau^2\omega^2 + 1} \cos \omega t + \frac{A}{\tau^2\omega^2 + 1} \sin \omega t \qquad (5.2.31)$$

This expression can be further consolidated by combining the two trigonometric terms using the identity:

$$p \cos A + q \sin A = r \sin (A + \phi) \qquad (5.2.32)$$

$$r = (p^2 + q^2)^{1/2}, \ \tan \phi = p/q$$

Application to Equation 5.2.31 leads to the transformed expression:

$$Y(t) = \frac{A\omega\tau}{\tau^2\omega^2 + 1} e^{-t/\tau} + \frac{A}{(\tau^2\omega^2 + 1)^{1/2}} \sin(\omega t + \phi) \qquad (5.2.33)$$

with $\phi = \tan^{-1}(-\omega t)$.

Several features of this expression are worth noting.

1. The solution is made up of an exponentially decaying term and a periodic term. This latter term, called the *ultimate periodic solution,* constitutes the response as $t \to \infty$, i.e.,

$$\frac{Y(t)}{t \to \infty} = \frac{A}{(\tau^2\omega^2 + 1)^{1/2}} \sin(\omega t + \phi) \qquad (5.2.34)$$

2. The output given by Equation 5.2.34 has the same frequency ω as the forcing function but lags behind it by an angle $|\phi|$.

3. The ratio of output amplitude to input amplitude of the ultimate periodic solution is $(\tau^2\omega^2 + 1)^{-1/2}$ which is always smaller than 1. The output signal is said to be *attenuated* with respect to the input amplitude.

We note that first order systems do not oscillate on their own and, hence, do not have a natural frequency ω_0 as do second order systems. Thus, resonance does not arise here. These and other features are discussed in the following illustration.

Illustration 5.2.4   Response of Second Order Systems

The genesis of second order ODEs in oscillating mechanical and electrical systems that yield to analysis and solution by the Laplace transformation was briefly discussed in Illustration 5.2.2. The ODEs involved were of the form:

$$K_1 \frac{d^2Y}{dt^2} + K_2 \frac{dY}{dt} + K_3 Y = F(t) \tag{5.2.35}$$

For the purpose of analyzing the solution behavior, it is convenient to recast the expression into the following form:

$$\tau^2 \frac{d^2Y}{dt^2} + 2\lambda\tau \frac{dY}{dt} + Y = X(t) \tag{5.2.36}$$

where τ = $(K_1/K_3)^{1/2}$ time constant (sec)

λ = $\dfrac{K_2}{2}(K_1 K_3)^{-1/2}$ characteristic parameter, dimensionless

$X(t) = F(t)/K_3$

Assuming initial conditions $Y(0) = Y'(0) = 0$, the transform of Equation 5.2.36 becomes:

$$\frac{y(s)}{x(s)} = \frac{1}{\tau^2 s^2 + 2\lambda\tau s + 1} \tag{5.2.37}$$

We now examine this expression and its inverse for various types of forcing functions or inputs as we did in the case of first order systems. In particular, we shall make use of the roots of the denominator, $s_{1,2}$, which are known as the *poles of the transfer function*.

Unit Step Input — This input leads to the transform:

$$y(s) = \frac{1}{s} \frac{1}{(\tau^2 s^2 + 2\lambda\tau s + 1)} \tag{5.2.38}$$

whose inverse will depend on the magnitude of the characteristic parameter λ. We distinguish three cases:

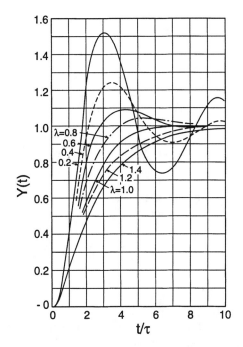

FIGURE 5.5 Response of a second order system to a step change in input. System is underdamped for $\lambda > 1$, overdamped for $\lambda < 1$, and critically damped at $\lambda = 1$. (D.R. Coughanowr, *Process Systems Analysis and Control, 2nd ed.,* McGraw-Hill, New York, 1991. With permission.)

Step Response for $\lambda > 1$ — Here the roots are real and distinct, and the Heaviside expansion yields a sum of exponentials given by:

$$Y(t) = 1 - e^{-\lambda t/\tau}\left[\frac{\lambda}{(\lambda^2-1)^{1/2}}\sinh(\lambda^2-1)^{1/2}t/\tau + \cosh(\lambda^2-1)^{1/2}t/\tau\right] \quad (5.2.39)$$

Plots of this relation for $\lambda > 1$ appear in Figure 5.5. The response in all cases is seen to be a smooth exponential rise to the new steady-state at $Y(t) = 1$. That rise, however, becomes increasingly sluggish as λ is raised, i.e., it takes increasingly longer times to reach the new steady state. One speaks of the system as being overdamped. In a mass and spring system with dashpot, this would correspond to the displaced mass coming to rest in a single half-swing with no oscillations due to the strong damping effect of the dashpot.

Step Response for $\lambda < 1$ — This case is the one most frequently encountered in practice and involves oscillations whose amplitude decay with time, corresponding to a vibrating mass or an oscillating pendulum coming to rest after a few swings. The roots of the quadratic term in Equation 5.2.38 are now complex conjugate with a real negative part, the latter accounting for the exponential decay of the amplitude. Inversion is by partial fractions or by the Heaviside expansion. Using in addition

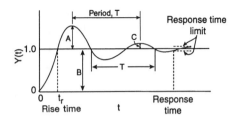

FIGURE 5.6 Characteristic parameters of an underdamped system. (D.R. Coughanowr, *Process Systems Analysis and Control, 2nd ed.,* McGraw-Hill, New York, 1991. With permission.)

the trigonometric transformation expressed by Equation 5.2.32, one obtains, after some manipulation, the inverted form:

$$Y(t) = 1 - \frac{1}{(1-\lambda^2)^{1/2}}\, e^{-\lambda t/\tau} \sin[(1-\lambda^2)^{1/2}\, t/\tau + \phi] \qquad (5.2.40)$$

where $\phi = \tan^{-1}(1-\lambda^2)^{1/2}/\lambda$.

Plots of this oscillatory response also appear in Figure 5.5 for various values of λ. One notes that the amplitudes of the oscillations increase with decreasing values of λ, but all curves ultimately converge to a value of $Y(t) = 1$.

We single out a response curve for a particular value of λ, shown in Figure 5.6, for more detailed scrutiny. One notes a number of characteristic features of the plot, including the rise time, the period of oscillation T, and parameters A, B, and C which are related to the degree of overshoot, and the decay ratio. We define these as follows:

(a) *Overshoot* is the quantity that expresses the degree by which the response exceeds the ultimate steady state. It is defined as the ratio A/B (Figure 5.6) which is related to the characteristic parameter λ by the relation:

$$\text{Overshoot} = A/B = \exp(-\pi\lambda)/(1-\lambda^2)^{1/2} \qquad (5.2.41)$$

(b) *Decay Ratio C/A* is a measure of the relative magnitude of successive peaks and is related to λ by the expression:

$$\text{Decay Ratio} = C/A = \exp[(-2\pi\lambda)/(1-\lambda^2)] = (\text{Overshoot})^2 \qquad (5.2.42)$$

(c) *Rise Time* is the time required for the response to reach its first steady-state value. There is no explicit expression for it in terms of system parameters but it can be shown that it increases with the value of λ.

(d) *Response Time* is the time required for the response to come within a specified interval, usually taken as ± 5%, of the ultimate steady-state (see Figure 5.6).

(e) *Oscillation Period and Frequency* is yet another quantity that can be directly expressed in terms of the system parameters. The pertinent relation is given by:

$$T = \frac{1}{v} = \frac{2\pi}{\omega} = \frac{2\pi\tau}{(1-\lambda^2)^{1/2}} \qquad (5.2.43)$$

where ω = circular frequency in radians, v = frequency in cycles/time, and the period T in time/cycle.

(f) *Natural Frequency* ω_0. We had seen in Illustration 5.2.1 that an undamped system has its own natural frequency w_0. This frequency is obtained by removing the first derivative in Equation 5.2.36, i.e., by setting $\lambda = 0$. We obtain from Equation 5.2.43

$$T_0 = \frac{1}{v_0} = \frac{2\pi}{\omega_0} = (2\pi\tau) \qquad (5.2.44)$$

Note that the phenomenon of resonance which we had seen for the undamped system with sinusoidal forcing does not arise when $\lambda \neq 0$, i.e., when the system is damped.

The noteworthy feature of the above development is that some important parameters of the system response can be directly deduced, and deduced quantitatively, from the coefficients of the underlying ODE. No solution is required, only the evaluation of the characteristic parameter λ, and in the case of Equation 5.2.43, that of the time constant τ as well. This parallels to some extent features we had noted in connection with the D-operator method discussed in Chapter 4. The connection there was between the qualitative shape of the solution — periodic, exponential, or a combination thereof — and the coefficients of the ODE contained in the so-called characteristic roots. We shall return to this in a subsequent section and establish complete equivalence between the characteristic equation that arises in the D-operator method, and a characteristic equation derived from the transfer function of a system.

Step Response for $\lambda = 1$ — For this value of the characteristic parameter, the quadratic term in Equation 5.2.38 yields identical roots. Inversion of the equation which can be accomplished by partial fractions or by convolution (see Illustration 5.1.1, Item 1) yields the expression:

$$Y(t) = 1 - \left(1 + \frac{t}{\tau}\right)e^{-t/\tau} \qquad (5.2.45)$$

Figure 5.5 shows this to be the border line between overdamped and underdamped behavior, and the system is consequently referred to as being *critically damped*. Physically, it represents the condition of *quickest* attainment of the new steady-state, a desirable response but one which is difficult to implement in practice.

Unit Impulse Input — Response of Equation 5.2.36 to a unit dirac pulse, with a transform of 1, yields:

$$y(s) = \frac{1}{\tau^2 s^2 + 2\lambda\tau s + 1} \qquad (5.2.46)$$

We refrain from going into the details of the inversion and merely summarize the resulting responses for the three values of the critical parameter λ. We have

For $\lambda > 1$:

$$Y(t) = \frac{1}{\tau} \frac{1}{(\lambda^2 - 1)^{1/2}} e^{-\lambda t / \tau} \sinh(\lambda^2 - 1)^{1/2} t / \tau \qquad (5.2.47)$$

For $\lambda < 1$:

$$Y(t) = \frac{1}{\tau} \frac{1}{(1 - \lambda^2)^{1/2}} e^{-\lambda t / \tau} \sin(1 - \lambda^2)^{1/2} t / \tau \qquad (5.2.48)$$

For $\lambda = 1$:

$$Y(t) = \frac{1}{\tau^2} t e^{-t / \tau} \qquad (5.2.49)$$

A graphical representation of these curves appears in Figure 5.7. The behavior is very similar to that seen in Figure 5.5 for the response to a unit step input, except that the system now returns to its original state. $\lambda > 1$ again corresponds to an overdamped system, $\lambda < 1$ to an underdamped system, and $\lambda = 1$ is the dividing line between the two, i.e., corresponds to critical damping.

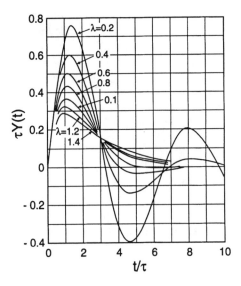

FIGURE 5.7 Response $\tau Y(t)$ to an impulse input. (D.R. Coughanowr, *Process Systems Analysis and Control, 2nd ed.,* McGraw-Hill, New York, 1991. With permission.)

Sinusoidal Input — The input considered here again has the form:

$$X(t) = A \sin \omega t$$

We apply it to the full Equation 5.2.36, i.e., we include damping. The system consequently has no natural frequency of its own and resonance does not raise.

The transform to be inverted is of the form:

$$y(s) = \frac{A\omega}{(s^2 + \omega^2)(\tau^2 s^2 + 2\lambda\tau s + 1)} \tag{5.2.50}$$

which upon application of standard inversion methods yields the response:

$$Y(t) = \frac{A}{\{[1 - (\omega\tau)^2]^2 + (2\lambda\omega\tau)^2\}^{1/2}} \sin(\omega\tau + \phi) \tag{5.2.51}$$

with the phase angle ϕ given by:

$$\phi = -\tan^{-1} \frac{2\lambda\omega\tau}{1 - (\omega\tau)^2} \tag{5.2.52}$$

We note the following features of Equation 5.2.51:

- The frequency of the response ω is identical to that of the forcing function.
- The output lags the input by a phase angle $|\phi|$. It can be seen from Equation 5.2.52 that the argument of the inverse tangent approaches zero as $\omega \rightarrow \infty$, and that $|\phi|$ consequently approaches 180° asymptotically. This is in contrast to the response of first order systems whose phase angle is at most 90°.
- The ratio of output amplitude to input amplitude is given by:

$$\{[1 - (\omega\tau)^2]^2 + (2\lambda\omega\tau)^2\}^{-1/2} \tag{5.2.53}$$

and can be greater or smaller than 1, depending on the magnitude of λ and $\omega\tau$. Both amplification and attenuation, thus, are possible. This is again in contrast to the behavior of first order systems, whose amplitude ratio never exceeds 1.

We conclude, for the time being, our consideration of system responses. It will be resumed in Section 5.5 where we consider Laplace domain analysis. The preceding two illustrations have, however, given us a fairly thorough look at the responses of first and second order systems to a variety of forcing functions. Most of these were seen to be stable, i.e., they attained a finite steady state as $t \rightarrow \infty$. An exception occurred in undamped second order systems which could respond to sinusoidal forcing with the natural frequency ω_0 of the system by producing oscillations of increasing amplitude, leading to "runaway" or unstable behavior. Such instabilities arise with greater frequency in systems of order > 2, and it is these instabilities, and methods for their avoidance, that will be given particular attention.

Illustration 5.2.5   The Horizontal Beam Revisited

In Practice Problem 4.6, the reader was asked to solve, with the methods available in Chapter 4, a fourth order ODE describing the deflection y of a horizontal beam subjected to a force. Although this was not mentioned there, such problems are usually of a boundary value type. Boundary value ODEs are not the natural domain of application of the Laplace transform, but it can be adapted to such problems by retaining the missing initial values as unknowns and evaluating them from boundary values given at the end of the domain.

The equation describing the deflection of a loaded beam is generally of the form:

$$\frac{d^4 Y}{dx^4} = \frac{W(x)}{EI} \qquad (5.2.54)$$

where EI is the product of Young's modulus E and moment of inertia I, also called the *flexural rigidity,* and $W(x)$ is the distributed load. The fourth order derivative comes about as follows:

- The internal bending moment $M(x)$ exerted between adjacent spans is proportional to the local curvature with the flexural rigidity as its proportionality constant. Thus,

$$M(x) = EI\, Y'' \qquad (5.2.55)$$

- The bending moment $M(x)$ in turn gives rise to a vertical internal shear force $F(x)$ with a moment $F(x)dx = dM$ so that:

$$F(x) = \frac{dM}{dx} = EI\, Y''' \qquad (5.2.56)$$

- Finally, an increment of the load in the horizontal direction, $W(x)dx$ (kg) leads to an incremental increase $dF(x)$ of the internal shear force, yielding:

$$W(x) = EI\, Y^{(4)} \qquad (5.2.57)$$

The Boundary Conditions, four of which are required, depend on the way in which the beam is anchored. They are different from the Type I, II, and III BCs we had described in Chapter 4 since they involve higher order derivatives.

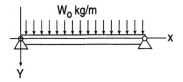

FIGURE 5.8 Diagram of a uniformly loaded beam subject to deflection Y(x).

- For clamped, built-in or otherwise fixed ends, the deflection at those points is zero and the beam is horizontal with zero derivatives. Hence,

$$Y(0) = Y(l) = Y'(0) = Y'(l) = 0 \qquad (5.2.58)$$

These Conditions can still be classified as Type I and II.

- For Hinged or Simply-Supported Ends the deflection is again zero but in addition the beam ends at points of inflection, so that

$$Y(0) = Y(l) = Y''(0) = Y''(l) = 0 \qquad (5.2.59)$$

Here only the first two BC's are of Type I.

- For a Single Free End, the conditions there are

$$Y''(1) = Y'''(1) = 0 \qquad (5.2.60)$$

where the second condition expresses the fact that curvature is at a minimum. Both of these conditions fall outside the Type I to III classification.

We consider as our example the simple case of a beam carrying a uniform load W (kg/m) over the interval $0 \le x \le 1$. The ends are simply-supported (see Figure 5.8). The system is then described by the equation:

$$\frac{d^4Y}{dx^4} = \frac{W_0}{EI} \qquad (5.2.61)$$

with Boundary Conditions

$$Y(0) = 0 \quad Y''(0) = 0 \quad Y'(l) = 0 \quad Y''(l) = 0 \qquad (5.2.62)$$

Laplace transformation of the ODE 5.2.61 yields:

$$s^4 y(s) - s^3 Y(0) - s^2 Y'(0) - s Y''(0) - Y'''(0) = \frac{W_0}{EIs} \qquad (5.2.63)$$

The second and third terms drop out because of the first two items of Equation 5.2.62. The remaining initial conditions $Y''(0)$ and $Y'''(0)$ are carried into the inversion process as unknowns. We obtain in the first instance:

$$y(s) = \frac{Y''(0)}{s^2} + \frac{Y'''(0)}{s^4} + \frac{W_0}{EIs^5} \qquad (5.2.64)$$

Inversion is by Item 4 of Table 5.2 and yields:

$$Y(x) = Y''(0)x + \frac{1}{6}Y'''(0)x^3 + \frac{W_0 x^4}{24\,EI} \qquad (5.2.65)$$

The unknown initial condition $Y''(0)$ and $Y'''(0)$ are obtained by substitution of the two remaining boundary conditions of Equation 5.2.59 into the solution Equation 5.2.62. There results:

$$Y''(0) = \frac{W_0 l^3}{24\,EI} \quad Y'''(0) = -\frac{W_0 l}{2\,EI} \qquad (5.2.66)$$

The final deflection profile is then given by the expression:

$$Y(x) = \frac{W_0}{24\,EI}(l^3 x - 2lx^3 + x^4) \qquad (5.2.67)$$

5.3   BLOCK DIAGRAMS: A SIMPLE CONTROL SYSTEM

Hitherto, the Laplace transform had been applied to simple systems consisting of a *single* ODE. When more than one or two equations are involved, it becomes convenient to represent the system graphically by means of a so-called block diagram in which each physical unit of the process is assigned a block with appropriate input and output leading into and out of the block, and the relevant transfer function $G(s)$, which is the ratio of transforms of input to output inscribed within the block. Thus,

$$\begin{array}{ccccc} \text{Input or} & \rightarrow & \text{Transfer} & \rightarrow & \text{Output} \\ \text{forcing function} & & \text{function } G(s) & & \text{or response} \end{array}$$

$$\begin{array}{c} \text{Single unit} \\ \text{or process} \end{array}$$

When more than one input is involved, the representation is by means of a so-called summing junction, given the following circular symbol:

$$\begin{array}{c} \text{Input} \\ \downarrow + \\ \text{Input} \rightarrow^+ \quad \otimes \quad \rightarrow \text{Output} \end{array}$$

The symbol may have several inputs but only one output.

A. System

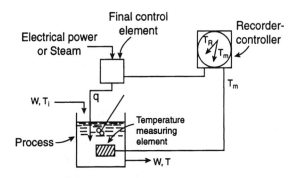

B. Initial Block Diagram

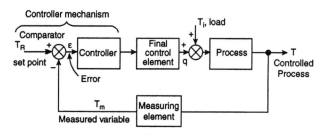

C. Final Block Diagram

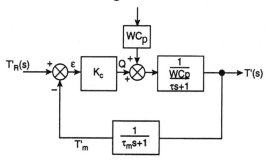

FIGURE 5.9 Control of a hot water tank with inflow of water: (A) schematic diagram, (B) initial construction of the block diagram, (C) final block diagram. (D.R. Coughanowr, *Process Systems Analysis and Control, 2nd ed.,* McGraw-Hill, New York, 1991. With permission.)

To illustrate the genesis and use of block diagrams, we consider a simple physical example consisting of a well-stirred water heater with constant in- and outflow shown in Figure 5.9A. The temperature in the tank is to be maintained at a constant value T_R. This is achieved by means of a controller which is fed a signal representing the measured temperature T_m and translates it into an Error $\varepsilon = T_R - T_m$. To correct this error, the controller in turn causes the electrical heater to provide the necessary heat input to reduce the error ε, i.e., to raise the temperature T_m toward the desired level

T_R. When the controller changes that heat input in proportion to the error read, we speak of *proportional control*.

The actions described and the elements of the system are represented in the block diagram shown in Figure 5.9B. Starting on the left of the diagram, a summing junction receives input T_R (the desired temperature, or set-point) and T_m (the measured temperature) and composes it into the difference given by the error $\varepsilon = T_R - T_m$. The summing junction here is the comparator, an internal device of the controller which compares the received measured temperature signal T_m with the desired set-point T_R. The controller then converts the read error ε into a signal to the final control element. In the system considered here which consists of an *electrical* heat supply, the final control element usually consists of a variable transformer which is used to adjust the current to a resistance heater mounted in or on the tank. When steam is used to heat the tank, the final control element will typically be an adjustable steam valve.

We next reach a second summing junction in which the heat from the electrical heater is added to the incoming water with a load represented by its temperature T_i. The sum of these energy terms is then fed to the process, i.e., the heating tank, which yields an output, or response temperature T' that also is the controlled variable. At this point we compose a return loop which takes the tank temperature T', feeds it to a measuring element, usually consisting of a thermocouple or similar device, which in turn sends its output T_m to the comparator of the control element. We have what is commonly referred to as a closed-loop system, typical of control systems of this type. Note that measured temperature T_m does not equal bath temperature T' because of the attendant heat transfer resistance.

Several additional technical terms arise in connection with this control problem which we address briefly below.

The term *negative feedback* is used to describe the fact that the registered difference $\varepsilon = T_R - T_m$ is used to adjust the control element so as to *reduce* the error. Thus, initially when ε is large, the control element, i.e., the heater, is turned on at a relatively high setting in order to achieve a quick return to T_R. As the registered error diminishes, the heat load is correspondingly reduced until $T_m = T_R$, at which point the heater is completely turned off. Such systems are inherently stable. In *positive feedback*, on the other hand, T_m is *added* to T_R, with the result that the heat input to the tank is continually *increased* leading to unstable or runaway behavior. Such positive feedback would never be used intentionally but could arise inadvertently and naturally in more complex systems. One must then address the means available to correct such behavior.

The terms *set-point* and *load* lead to a further distinction in the use of control loops. In the so-called *servo-problem*, heat load is constant but the set-point T_R is deliberately varied in order to achieve a desired variation in the bath temperature. This is the less common mode of operation. In the so-called *Regulator Problem*, on the other hand, heat load T_i varies, either unintentionally or deliberately, and the aim is to bring the bath temperature to some desired and prescribed value T_R. This type of requirement arises with much greater frequency.

We now proceed to finalize the block diagram for the water heater by deriving the model equations and their corresponding transfer function.

5.3.1 WATER HEATER

By performing an unsteady integral energy balance about the tank, we obtain in the first instance:

$$\text{Rate of energy in} - \text{Rate of energy out} = \frac{\text{Rate of change of}}{\text{energy contents}}$$

$$[q + WC_p(T_i - T_0)] - WC_p(T - T_0) = \rho C_p V \frac{dT}{dt}$$

(5.3.1)

which upon introducing deviations from the steady-state can be written in the following form:

$$Q + WC_p(T_i' - T') = \rho C_p V \frac{dT'}{dt}$$

(5.3.2)

where

$$Q = q - q_s$$

$$T_i' = T_i - T_{is}$$

(5.3.3)

$$T' = T - T_s$$

the subscripts denoting the steady state.

Laplace transformation and subsequent rearrangement into transfer function form leads to the expression:

$$G_t(s) = \frac{\text{Output transform}}{\text{Input transform}} = \frac{1/WC_p}{\tau s + 1}$$

(5.3.4)

where τ = residence time = $\rho V/W$.

These terms appear in the summing junction on the right of the final block diagram, Figure 5.9C; that junction being followed by a block containing the transfer function for the tank $(1/WC_p)/(\tau s + 1)$.

5.3.2 MEASURING ELEMENT

An unsteady integral energy balance here, similar to the one taken over the tank and expressed in terms of the deviation variables yields:

$$hA(T_m' - T') = \rho C_p T \frac{dT_m'}{dt}$$

(5.3.5)

Taking the Laplace transform of this expression and expressing it in terms of the transfer function of the measuring element yields:

$$G_m(s) = \frac{\text{Output transform}}{\text{Input transform}} = \frac{1}{\tau_m s + 1} \qquad (5.3.6)$$

where τ_m = time constant of measuring element = $\rho C_p V/hA$. That transfer function is entered in the block located on the closing loop of the diagram.

5.3.3 Controller and Control Element

For the purpose of describing the controller, we assume that we are dealing with proportional control. In this mode, the controller acts to provide heat q to the tank in proportion to the deviation from the desired state T_R, i.e., in proportion to $\varepsilon = T_R - T_m$. Other types of control are the derivative control (D) in which the controller varies the load in proportion to the *time derivative* of the error, and integral control (I) in which q is varied in proportion to the *time integral* of the error. For the present case of proportional control, we can write:

$$q = K_c \varepsilon + q_s \qquad (5.3.7)$$

or

$$Q = q - q_s = K_c \varepsilon$$

of which the Laplace transform is given by:

$$Q(s) = K_c \varepsilon(s) \qquad (5.3.8)$$

and in transfer function form:

$$G_c(s) = \frac{\text{Output transform}}{\text{Input transform}} = K_c \qquad (5.3.9)$$

That transfer function is entered in the block located between the two summing junctions of Figure 5.9C.

Figure 5.9C is quite typical of control loops. More complex ones evidently arise when there is more than one controller involved or if there are several process units. These are taken up in specialized texts on the topic.

5.4 OVERALL TRANSFER FUNCTION; STABILITY CRITERION; LAPLACE DOMAIN ANALYSIS

We use this section to generalize the results of the previous section and to arrive at a criterion for the stability of a control loop. We will be able to carry out the stability analysis without having to solve the model, i.e., instead of returning to the time domain for full examination of the time-dependent solutions, we will be able to remain in the so-called Laplace domain and carry out the analysis there. In this endeavor we will be much aided by the concept of the transfer function which we now proceed to generalize for a single-loop feedback system. The following rules apply:

1. The transfer function relating any pair of variables X and Y in the system is given by the relation:

$$G(s) = \frac{Y(s)}{X(s)} = \frac{\pi_f}{1 + \pi_1} \qquad (5.4.1)$$

where π_f = product of transfer functions in the path between the locations of the signals X and Y, π_1 = product of *all* transfer functions in the loop. Typically, for a single-loop feedback system, that ratio takes the form:

$$\frac{Y(s)}{X(s)} = \frac{G_1 G_2 G_3 ... G_n}{1 + (G_1 G_2 G_3 ... G_n)H} = \frac{G}{1 + GH} \qquad (5.4.2)$$

where H is the transfer function of the closing branch of the loop. For the block diagram shown in Figure 5.9C, for example, Equation 5.4.2 leads to the expression:

$$\frac{T_R'}{T'(s)} = \frac{K_c[1/(WC_p(\tau s + 1)]}{1 + \dfrac{K_c}{WC_p(\tau s + 1)} \dfrac{1}{\tau_m s + 1}} \qquad (5.4.3)$$

2. The transfer function GH in Equation 5.4.2 is termed the *open-loop transfer function* of the system, i.e., it equals the transfer function that would result if the loop were disconnected by cutting its closing branch. If we set the denominator of Equation 5.3.11 equal to zero, we obtain the so-called characteristic equation:

$$1 + \text{open-loop transfer function} = 0$$

or

$$1 + GH = 0 \qquad (5.4.4)$$

The characteristic equation contains all the transfer functions of the loop and through them the coefficients of the constitutive equations. Its roots, also called *poles* and obtained by solving Equation 5.4.4, determine the *nature of the response of the system*, and, hence, its *stability*.

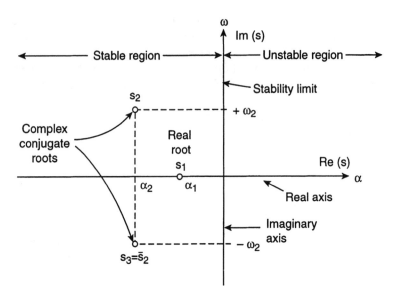

FIGURE 5.10   Representation in the complex plane (Laplace domain) of system stability.

3. The system described by the overall transfer function, Equation 5.4.2, is unstable if *any* one of the roots of the characteristic Equation 5.4.4 lies to the right of the imaginary axis of the complex plane (Figure 5.10). In particular:

   • If there is a root in the right half of the complex plane, the response will contain a term that grows exponentially with time. This will occur both when the root is on the real positive axis as well as when it has conjugate imaginary components.
   • Repeated roots on the real positive axis likewise lead to instability, but those on the real *negative* axis lead to stable behavior.
   • All complex roots appear as conjugates. Those in the left half plane result in a stable system, those in the right half do not.
   • Pure imaginary conjugates on the imaginary axis give rise to limitless pure oscillations, and are in that sense unstable although not unbounded.

What we see here, then, is the emergence of yet another characteristic equation which determines the nature of the solutions of a model. We had encountered such equations earlier in Chapter 4 in the form of the quadratic D-operator equation whose roots led to either periodic or exponential solutions (Table 4.5). Alternatively, the same result could be obtained by solving the characteristic determinant Equation 4.3.22 for the eigenvalues of the coefficient matrix of the model. In nonlinear systems, the nature of the solutions and particularly that of the so-called critical points was again determined by a set of characteristic roots which were identical to the eigenvalues of the Jacobian of the steady-state model equations (cf. Equation 4.5.6). In the present chapter, the behavior of linear second order systems was analyzed via

TABLE 5.4
Summary of Characteristic Equations

Characteristic Equation	Characteristic Roots	Application
$a_0D^2 + a_1D + a_2 = 0$	D_{12}	Second order linear ODEs with constant coefficients in time or distance
$\left\| A - \lambda I \right\| = 0$	Eigenvalues λ_i	Systems of first order linear ODEs with constant coefficients
$\tau^2 s^2 + 2\lambda \tau s + 1 = 0$	Poles $s_{1,2}$	Second order linear ODEs with constant coefficients in time
$1 + GH = 0$	Poles $s_1, \ldots s_n$	Systems of linear ODEs/AEs with constant coefficients in time
$\begin{vmatrix} \dfrac{\partial f_1}{\partial y_1} - \mu & \dfrac{\partial f_2}{dy_1} \\ \dfrac{\partial f_1}{\partial y_2} & \dfrac{\partial f_2}{\partial y_2} - \mu \end{vmatrix} = 0$	Eigenvalues $\mu_{1,2}$	Nonlinear analysis in phase plane

the characteristic parameter λ which was in turn related to the roots of the denominator of the transfer functions, Equation 5.2.37. What we have done in this section is to generalize these methods to systems of n linear ordinary differential and algebraic equations using the concept of transfer functions and the associated block diagrams (Table 5.4). This culminated in the formulation of yet another characteristic equation (Equation 5.4.4) whose roots determine the nature of the solutions and, hence, the stability of the system. These roots are most conveniently located and analyzed in the complex plane. We demonstrate this in the following illustration.

The reader will have noted that these seemingly disparate characteristic equations have one feature in common: positive roots, or complex roots with real positive parts that are "bad," i.e., lead to instability. Conversely, their negative counterparts imply stability of the system.

Illustration 5.4.1 Laplace Domain Stability Analysis

We wish to undertake in this example, a partial analysis in the complex (Laplace) plane of an overall transfer function which leads to a cubic characteristic equation. We have, in the first instance:

$$G(s) = \frac{G_1 G_2}{1 + G_1 G_2 H} \qquad (5.4.5)$$

and specify,

$$G_1 = K_c$$

$$G_2 = \frac{1}{(\tau_1 s + 1)} \frac{1}{(\tau_2 s + 1)} \qquad (5.4.6)$$

$$H = \frac{1}{\tau_3 s + 1}$$

Substitution of Equation 5.4.6 into Equation 5.4.5 leads to the following characteristic equation

$$1 + \frac{K_c / \tau_1 \tau_2 \tau_3}{(s + 1/\tau_1)(s + 1/\tau_2)(s + 1/\tau_3)} = 0 \qquad (5.4.7)$$

We choose time constants $\tau_1 = 1$, $\tau_2 = 1/2$, and $\tau_3 = 1/3$ so that the characteristic equation to be examined becomes the cubic:

$$(s + 1)(s + 2)(s + 3) + K = 0 \qquad (5.4.8)$$

with

$$K = 6 K_c$$

We use K_c, also known as the *controller gain*, as the free parameter to be investigated. In particular we wish to establish for what values of K_c the system becomes unstable. That information can then be used to help us avoid controller designs and settings which would lead to system instability.

Figure 5.11 gives a tabulation of a set of roots of Equation 5.4.8, for various K_c values, together with their graphical representation in the complex Laplace plane. One notes that up to values of $K = 0.39$, i.e., a controller gain of $K_c = 0.39/6 = 0.065$, the roots are all on the real negative axis. This includes the case of $K_c = 0$ (no control) and indicates an exponential decay in the response curves, i.e., the system is overdamped for $0 < K_c < 0.065$. At values of $K > 0.065$, pairs of complex conjugate roots make their appearance, accompanied by one root on the real negative axis. The system is oscillatory with an exponentially decaying amplitude, i.e., it is underdamped. A water shed point is reached at a value of $K_c = 60/6 = 10$ that lies on the imaginary axis. The combination of a pair of complex conjugate roots together with a real one still persists beyond that point, but the former now have a real positive part which gives rise to an exponentially growing amplitude. The value of $K_c = 10$ thus marks the passage from stable to unstable behavior. At the watershed point itself, the response is purely oscillatory with no change in amplitude. Although the response is still bounded, it is nevertheless of an undesirable type since the system is incapable of reaching a stable steady state.

A. Values

$K = 6K_c$	r_1	r_2	r_3
0	-3	-2	-1
0.23	-3.10	-1.75	-1.15
0.39	-3.16	-1.42	-1.42
1.58	-3.45	-1.28 - 0.75i	-1.28 + 0.75i
6.6	-4.11	-0.95 - 1.5i	-0.95 + 1.5i
26.5	-5.10	-0.45 - 2.5i	-0.45 + 2.5i
60.0	-6.00	0.0 - 3.32i	0.0 + 3.32i
100.0	-6.72	0.35 - 4i	0.35 + 4i

B. Graph

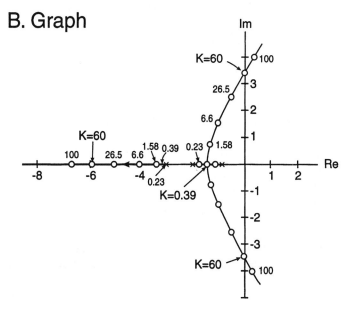

FIGURE 5.11   Roots of a cubic characteristic equation: (A) numerical values, (B) graphical representation. (D.R. Coughanowr, *Process Systems Analysis and Control, 2nd ed.,* McGraw-Hill, New York, 1991. With permission.)

Practice Problems

5.1 Transformation and Inversion of Complex Functions —

(a) Show that:

$$L^{-1}\left\{\ln\left(1+\frac{1}{s^2}\right)\right\} = \frac{2}{t}(1-\cos t)$$

(Hint: Differentiate the transform with respect to s, then apply Item 9 of Table 5.1.)

(b) Find the inverse of $s/(s + 1)^3$.

Answer: $te^{-t}(1 - t/2)$

(c) Use a shifting theorem to evaluate $L^{-1} (s\, e^{-4\pi s/5})/(s^2 + 25)$.

(d) Show that $L\{\delta(t - a)\} = e^{-st}$. Use the fact that $L\{\delta(t)\} = 1$ $\{\delta(t)\} = $ Dirac function.

(e) Find $L^{-1} \dfrac{2s^2 - 4}{(s+1)(s-2)(s-3)}$.

Answer: $-\dfrac{1}{6}e^{-t} - \dfrac{4}{3}e^{2t} + \dfrac{7}{2}e^{3t}$

5.2 Response of Second Order Systems — Derive Equations 5.2.39 and 5.2.40.

5.3 Solution of Simultaneous ODEs — Find the solution to the system of equations:

$$X'(t) - 2Y'(t) = F(t)$$

$$X''(t) - Y''(t) + Y(t) = 0$$

with $X(0) = X'(0) = Y(0) = Y'(0) = 0$.

(Hint: Eliminate one of the transforms, say y(s), algebraically and invert. Repeat the procedure for x(s).)

Answer: $X(t) = \displaystyle\int_0^t F(\tau)d\tau - 2\int_0^t F(\tau)\cos(t - \tau)d\tau$

$$Y(t) = -\int_0^t F(\tau)\cos(t - \tau)d\tau$$

5.4 Radioactive Decay Series — The decay of radioactive elements is the classical example of a reaction which is accurately described by a first order rate law. Consider the series:

$$N_1 \xrightarrow{k_1} N_2 \xrightarrow{k_2} N_3 \xrightarrow{k_3} N_4$$

where $N_i = $ number of atoms of element i and the reaction rates are represented by:

(1) $dN_1/dt = -k_1 N_1$ (2) $dN_2/dt = -k_2 N_2 + k_1 N_1$
(3) $dN_3/dt = -k_3 N_3 + k_2 N_2$ (4) $dN_4/dt = k_3 N_3$

Show that the number of atoms of the last and stable species is given by:

$$\frac{N_4}{N_1^0} = 1 - \frac{k_2 k_3 e^{-k_1 t}}{(k_2 - k_1)(k_3 - k_1)} - \frac{k_1 k_3 e^{-k_2 t}}{(k_1 - k_2)(k_3 - k_2)} - \frac{k_1 k_2 e^{-k_3 t}}{(k_1 - k_3)(k_2 - k_3)}$$

Note that the ODEs are not coupled so that they can in principle be solved in succession. This could be done by using the D-operator method but the repeated appearance of nonhomogeneous terms would require the evaluation of a set of particular integrals. The Laplace transformation avoids this step and is, therefore, easier to apply.

5.5 Oscillation of an Electrical RLC Circuit — A circuit consisting of an induction coil with inductance L, a resistor with resistance R, and a capacitor with capacitance C connected in series and subjected to an alternating voltage $E = E_0 \sin \omega t$. Derive an expression for the current i as a function of time.

5.6 Point Load on a Horizontal Beam — A horizontal beam with its ends clamped is subjected to a concentrated (point) load of F_0 at the position x = L/3. Derive an expression for the resulting deflection.

(Hint: The load can be expressed in terms of a Dirac function $F_0 \delta(x-L/3)$. For the transformation of such a function, see Practice Problem 5.1d.)

Answer: (for O < x < L/3 only) $Y(x) = 2F_0 x^2(3L-5x)/81$ EI

5.7 Design of a Thermocouple for Oscillating Temperature Fluctuation — A thermocouple is to be used to register sinusoidal temperature oscillations given by the expression:

$$T(t) - 50 = 100 \sin [2t(\text{sec})]$$

The dimension of the thermocouple, composed of cylindrical wires, should be such that the maximum temperature is registered within 3% of its actual value. What is the maximum permissible diameter to achieve this?

Data: h = 1000 J/sm²K, ρ = 900 kg/m³, C_p = 0.4 kJ/kg K.

(Hint: Use an equation of the form given by Equation 5.2.34.)

5.8 More on the Response of a Second-Order System — A second order system has a transfer function given by:

$$\frac{y(s)}{x(s)} = \frac{s-10}{5s^2 + 3s + 1}$$

Verify that the system is underdamped and determine, without inverting:

(a) The decay ratio
(b) The overshoot
(c) The period of oscillation

5.9 Calculation of Off-Set — In proportional control of a closed-loop system subjected to a unit step change, the response never attains the new steady-state but shows instead an "off-set," i.e., is displaced from the true value by a relatively small and constant amount.

Given the transform:

$$y(s) = \frac{110}{s(s+5)(s+3)(s+1)}$$

calculate the magnitude of the offset for the system.
(Hint: Use the final value theorem.)

5.10 Use of Laplace Transform to Solve Integral Equations — Show that the solution of the integral equation:

$$Y(t) = at + \int_0^t Y(\tau)\sin(t-\tau)d\tau$$

is given by

$$Y(t) = a\left(t + \frac{1}{6}t^3\right)$$

(Hint: Apply the convolution theorem.)

REFERENCES

Chapters on the Laplace transforms appear in introductory texts on differential equations, as well as books on advanced mathematics for engineers. See References to Chapter 4. Numerous specialized texts exist. Among them, the monograph by Churchill that deals with applications to both ODE and PDEs, as well as other integral transforms, stands out.
R.V. Churchill. *Operational Mathematics*, 3rd ed., McGraw-Hill, New York, 1972.

Laplace and other integral transforms are also treated in the monograph:
C.J. Tranter. *Integral Transforms in Mathematical Physics*, 2nd ed., Methune, London, 1956.

A highly readable compendium of theorems and solved problems, both in ODEs and PDEs, appears in:
M.R. Spiegel. *Theory and Problems of Laplace Transforms*, Schaum, New York, 1965.

The treatment of process control concepts is the preserve of specialized monographs, including:

D.R. Coughanowr. *Process Systems Analysis and Control, 2nd ed.,* McGraw-Hill, New York, 1991.

W.L. Luyben. *Process Modeling, Simulation and Control for Chemical Engineers, 2nd ed.,* McGraw-Hill, New York, 1990.

The latter deals extensively with problems drawn from industry. Tables of Laplace transforms as well as other integral transforms appear in Churchill's and Spiegel's monographs, and in standard mathematical handbooks. More extensive tabulations are found in:

A. Erdelyi, (Ed.) *Tables of Integral Transforms, vols. I and II,* McGraw-Hill, New York, 1954.

6 Special Topics

This isn't right. It's not even wrong.

Wolfgang Pauli
(reference to a proposed new theory)

When I make a mistake, it's a beaut.

Fiorello La Guardia

Hitherto our approach had been to draw on a range of disciplines for illustrations and practice problems. A division into topics, when it occurred, was with respect to the type of balance to be used or the mathematical methodology to be applied. No scientific or engineering subdiscipline was singled out for special scrutiny.

In the present chapter, we invert the procedure. Several subtopics are chosen with each topic drawing on the tools we had provided in the preceding chapters. The mathematics are kept, as before, at the level of algebraic and ordinary differential equations.

Three topics are examined:

1. In *Biomedical Engineering, Biology, and Biotechnology* we study models of living systems (biomedical engineering and biology) as well as technical adaptations of bioprocesses (biotechnology, membrane processes). Stirred tanks, here referred to as *compartmental models,* make frequent appearances, as well as their counterpart, the distributed model, the latter under steady-state conditions. Hence, one can expect both algebraic and ODEs to arise.

2. A *Visit to the Environment* enables us to address a topic of particular interest to a number of disciplines, including Environmental Science and Engineering, Civil Engineering, and Chemical Engineering. The topic permeates our daily lives and thus, is of general interest as well. Here again we make use of both compartmental and distributed models which are usually used in the context of mass balances.

3. *Welcome to the Real World* is a topic dear to our hearts. In it we draw on the collective consulting and industrial experience of the author and his colleagues to address what are best termed real-life or real-world problems. The tools we use are still the same, but they now have to be used with much greater skill and imagination. It becomes much easier to commit a major and costly gaffe, as we tried to indicate with the cited

sayings at the head of the chapter. The deadly sin here is not so much *being wrong* as it is a calculational error, or a misplaced term or wrong unit, though undesirable, that can be rectified during editing. What can have much more serious consequences is the use of a wrong concept or a wrong hypothesis. This is what has to be avoided above all else. If we are to be flawed, we would rather be *wrong* than *not right.*

The general approach is the same as that used in previous chapters. After a brief introduction, we proceed to present the core material by means of a series of illustrative examples. This is followed up with a selection of practice problems which are again worth a second look since they are often used to introduce additional new concepts. References to all three sections appear at the end of the chapter.

6.1 BIOMEDICAL ENGINEERING, BIOLOGY AND BIOTECHNOLOGY

We start the section on biomedical engineering by considering a number of compartmental models used particularly in the context of drug administration and the uptake of toxic substances in various body compartments. These compartments encompass body fluids (plasma, intercellular fluids) as well as body tissues (fat, muscle, bone). Experimental data fitted to these models can be used to derive local flow rates, transport coefficients, tissue permeabilities, partition coefficients, and other parameters of interest. As always, one should look in the model solutions for the unusual, e.g., beneficial or pathological behavior. The compartmental models are followed up by distributed models, also known as local models which are used to predict steady-state distributions of different state variables, principally concentration, and for parameter estimation. We address as well a number of important applications of biomedical engineering, such as membrane processes and the release of drugs into flowing systems.

We next turn to biology, principally in the context of molecular or cell biology and examine the seminal paper by Turing on morphogenesis. We conclude our considerations with selected topics, again given as illustrations, from the contemporary field of biotechnology. In these deliberations we stay mostly at the AE and ODE levels. When PDEs arise, we merely use their solutions, leaving their derivation to later chapters.

Illustration 6.1.1 One-Compartment Pharmacokinetics

In spite of their often severely limited validity, one-compartment models are still the most popular device for analyzing body functions or the reaction to external inputs. Three specific situations arise.

1. *Injection or short-term exposure to a substance:* Blood volume and cardiac output in the adult human are approximately 5 l and 5 l/min respectively. An instantaneous or short-term input, denoted as "load" in Figure 6.1A, is thus "turned over" or distributed within the blood approximately once

A. Injection and Clearance

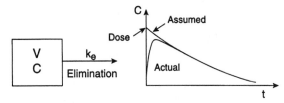

B. Infusion

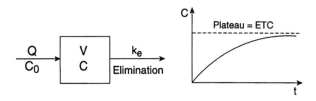

FIGURE 6.1 One-compartment models: time course of drug concentration during (A) clearance and (B) infusion.

every minute. This is the reason for the almost instantaneous effect of many drug injections and allows us to assume that the distribution of drugs within the plasma approaches uniformity, i.e., stirred-tank configuration, shortly after injection. Note, however, that by contrast the total volume of body fluid is approximately 50 l so that turnover there occurs only once every 10 min.

2. *Clearance:* Subsequent to injection, the body slowly metabolizes, excretes, or otherwise disposes of the injected substance. That process is referred to as "clearance" (Figure 6.1A). The assumption made here is that the blood, or the totality of body fluids, has reached a near uniform level, that exposure has ceased and that the concentration starts to decline in accordance with a simple one-compartment model and linear rate law, brought about by various body functions.

3. *Infusion:* In this situation, a continuous influx and elimination of the drug (or toxic substance) takes place, ultimately leading to a constant plateau, referred to as the "effective therapeutic concentration," or ETC (Figure 6.1B). When that plateau is reached, influx and elimination are exactly in balance and the system is at steady-state.

We now consider a specific example. In a well-known classical study, a 392 mg "loading dose" of the stimulant aminophylline was administered to a patient. Blood samples taken over the next 10 h yielded the following data:

t (h)	1	2	5	6	8	10
C (mg/l)	8.53	7.28	4.52	3.85	2.81	2.04

The following questions are to be addressed:

(a) What is the ETC (briefly attained at the outset, i.e., at t = 0)?
(b) What is the apparent rate constant k_e of elimination?
(c) What is the apparent volume of distribution?
(d) What is the apparent rate of elimination k_eC and apparent flow rate Q?
(e) For a required ETC of 10 mg/l, what infusion rate should be used and what is the time necessary to attain 95% of the ETC under these conditions?

We start with a lead-in model describing the clearing process. After cessation of the injection, we have:

$$\text{Rate of drug in} - \text{Rate of drug out} = \frac{\text{Rate of change in}}{\text{drug content}}$$

(6.1.1)

$$0 - Vk_eC = V\frac{dC}{dt}$$

where k_eC = rate of elimination.

One obtains by integration by separation of variables:

$$\ln C/C_0 = -k_et \qquad (6.1.2)$$

or

$$\log C/C_0 = -\frac{k_e}{2.303}t$$

A semilog plot of the given data in accordance with Equation 6.1.2 is shown in Figure 6.2 and yields the following data:

Effective Therapeutic Concentration (ETC): The ETC is obtained by extrapolation of the semilog plot to t = 0 and yields the approximate value ETC ≈ 10 mg/l.

Apparent Elimination Rate Constant k_e: The value of this parameter is obtained from the slope of Figure 6.2. Using the value of C = 2.04 mg/l obtained after 10 h, we have for that slope:

$$-\frac{k_e}{2.303}\Delta t = \log C/C_0$$

(6.1.3)

$$-\frac{k_e}{2.303}10 = \log 2.05/10 = -0.69$$

Hence,

$$k_e = \frac{(0.69)(2.303)}{10} = 0.159\,\text{hr}^{-1} \qquad (6.1.4)$$

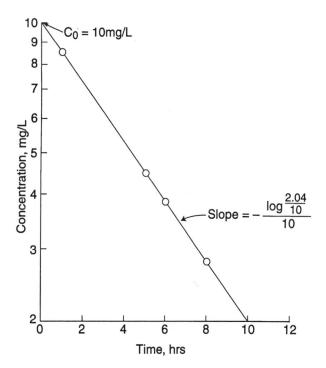

FIGURE 6.2 Experimental data for the clearance of the drug ammophylline from a patient. The slope of the semilog plot yields the elimination constant k_e, the intercept the ETC.

Apparent Distribution Volume V: We obtain this from the relation:

$$V = \frac{\text{Dose D (mg)}}{\text{ETC (mg / l)}} = \frac{392}{10} = 39.2 \ \text{l}$$

Note that this value is not too far from the value of approximately 50 l for the total volume of body fluids (blood and intracellular fluids).

Apparent Rate of Elimination and Apparent Flow Rate Q_a: The "out" term $k_e CV$ in Equation 6.1.1 also can be written in the equivalent form QC, so that $Q = k_e V$. We obtain:

$$Q_a = k_e V = (0.159 \ \text{hr}^{-1})(39.2 \ \text{l}) = 6.23 \ \text{l/hr}$$

This term expresses the rate of passage of the drug to the intracellular fluid, most commonly through cellular membranes. Since the process is diffusive rather than convective in nature, we must regard Q_a as a fictitious although equivalent flow rate.

Required Infusion Rate $Q_l C_0$: This quantity is obtained directly from the steady-state condition:

$$\text{Rate of Infusion} = \text{Rate of Elimination}$$

$$Q_i C_0 = k_e \, C_{ETC} \, V \tag{6.1.5}$$

$$Q_i C_0 = (0.159)(10)(39.2) = 62.3 \text{ mg/h}$$

Time to 95% of ETC: Here we invoke the mass balance applicable to infusion, Figure 6.1B. We obtain:

$$\text{Rate of drug in} - \text{Rate of drug out} = \begin{array}{c} \text{Rate of change of} \\ \text{drug content} \end{array}$$

$$\tag{6.1.6}$$

$$Q_i C_0 - k_e CV = V \frac{dC}{dt}$$

Integrating by separation of variables we obtain:

$$\frac{1}{k_e} \ln \frac{Q_i C_0 / V}{Q_i C_0 / V - k_e \, 0.95 C_{ETC}} = t \tag{6.1.7}$$

or

$$\frac{1}{0.159} \ln \frac{62.3 / 39.2}{62.3 / 39.2 - (0.159)(0.95)(10)} = t$$

$$t = 18.9 \text{ h}$$

Comments:

One notes here the wealth of information obtained from just a single equation and a set of experimental data. Not only were we able to derive a rate constant and physiological volumes and flow rates, but these parameters could then be applied to a different model, that of infusion, to analyze conditions during that process. Single compartment models, though capable of providing much useful information, are often refined into two-compartment models or multicompartment models encompassing several body organs and fluids. Single sets of data are then no longer sufficient and one must resort to more sophisticated experimentation and analysis. Two popular and largely self-explanatory two-compartment models are shown in Figure 6.3. One of these is addressed in Practice Problem 6.1.3.

We note that in biomedical modeling, body processes such as excretion, are expressed either as first order *reactions* (kCV) or as equivalent apparent flow terms $Q_a C$. This duality may lead to some confusion but has become a standard feature and, therefore, must be accommodated.

A. Compartments in Series

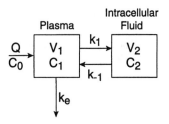

B. Compartments in Parallel

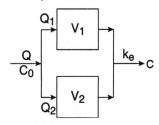

FIGURE 6.3 Examples of two-compartment models: (A) compartments in series, (B) compartments in parallel.

Illustration 6.1.2 Blood–Tissue Interaction as a Pseudo One-Compartment Model

Here we consider the more complex and realistic model in which flowing blood containing a dissolved substance is in contact with surrounding tissue. In principle, there are concentrations variations in both the axial and lateral directions which would ordinarily lead to a set of coupled PDEs. In simple models the lateral variations are usually neglected and if one makes the additional assumption that both phases are well mixed, one reduces what would otherwise have been a distributed system to a more manageable cne-compartment model (well-stirred). The two phases are assumed to be in equilibrium, the two concentrations being related by a partition coefficient K (see Figure 6.4A).

Suppose one wishes to derive a partition coefficient from a set of measurements in which a tracer substance is injected into a blood vessel at one point and its variation with time is monitored at some location downstream (or "distal" in medical parlance) from the point of injection. The model equations that will yield this information are as follows:

Blood phase:

$$\text{Rate of tracer in} - \text{Rate of tracer out} = \frac{\text{Rate of change of}}{\text{tracer content}}$$

(6.1.8)

$$QC_0 - \begin{bmatrix} QC_B \\ +N \end{bmatrix} = V_B \frac{dC_B}{dt}$$

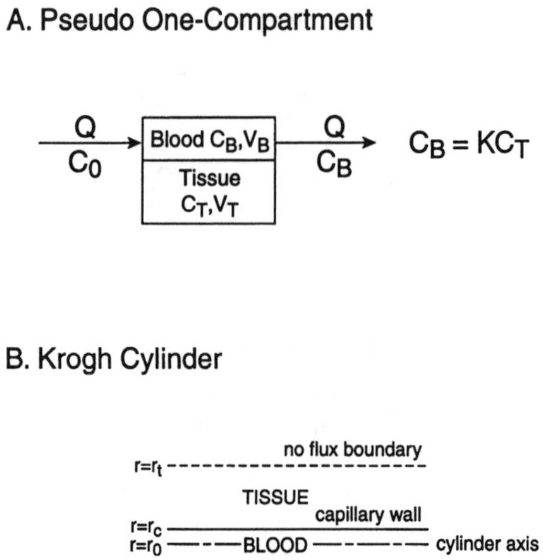

A. Pseudo One-Compartment

B. Krogh Cylinder

FIGURE 6.4   Models of blood–tissue interaction: (A) pseudo one-compartment model with blood and tissue in equilibrium, (B) nonequilibrium distributed model with radial diffusion.

Tissue phase:

$$N - 0 = V_T \frac{dC_T}{dt} \tag{6.1.9}$$

where N = rate of interphase transport.

Since there are three state variables, N, C_B, and C_T, a third relation is required that is given by:

Equilibrium relation:

$$C_B = K\,C_T \tag{6.1.10}$$

We add Equations 6.1.8 and 6.1.9 to eliminate the unknown quantity N, substitute the equilibrium relation into the result, and obtain:

$$Q(C_0 - C_B) = \left(V_B + \frac{V_T}{K}\right)\frac{dC_B}{dt} \tag{6.1.11}$$

Integration by separation of variables yields the result:

$$C_B = C_0\left[1 - \exp\left(-\frac{Q}{V_B + \frac{V_T}{K}}t\right)\right] \tag{6.1.12}$$

or

$$-\ln\frac{C_0 - C_B}{C_0} = \frac{Q}{V_B + \dfrac{V_T}{K}} t$$

With flow rate Q known and estimates of the vessel volume V_B and surrounding tissue volume available, the partition coefficient K can be obtained from the slope of a semilog plot of experimental distal concentrations $(1 - C_B/C_0)$ vs. time t.

Illustration 6.1.3 A Distributed Model: Transport Between Flowing Blood and Muscle Tissue

Simple one-dimensional distributed models also can be used for parameter estimation. We consider here experiments in which radioactive rubidium was injected into muscle tissue and then cleared for brief periods. Rb-concentration in the effluent blood was monitored in a set of runs conducted at different flow rates Q. The following data were obtained:

Q(ml/min)	28.6	17.3	7.4
C_L/C_0	0.27	0.37	0.65

The data are to be used to determine the product of tissue permeability P and the unknown transfer area A. A knowledge of $P \times A$ is of importance in assessing the effect of drugs and other stimuli designed to increase mass transfer through alteration of either P or A, or both. Because of the brief period of clearance, tissue concentration is considered constant (and well-stirred) at a level C*. A steady-state one-dimensional mass balance over a difference element Δz then yields:

$$\text{Rate of tracer in} - \text{Rate of tracer out} = 0$$

$$[QC\,|_x + P\pi d\Delta x(C* - C)] - QC\,|_{x+\Delta x} = 0 \tag{6.1.13}$$

Dividing by Δx and going to the limit, we obtain the ODE:

$$P\pi d(C* - C) = Q\frac{dC}{dx} \tag{6.1.14}$$

which can be integrated by separation of variables to yield:

$$\frac{C_L}{C*} = 1 - \exp\left(-\frac{P\pi dL}{Q}\right)$$

or

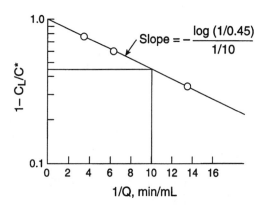

FIGURE 6.5 Experimental data for the clearance of radioactive rubidium from muscle tissue. The slope of the plot yields the tissue permeability as the product PA.

$$\ln(1 - C_L/C^*) = -PA(1/Q) \qquad (6.1.15)$$

Values of PA can then be obtained from the slope of a semilog plot of experimental concentrations $C^*/(C^* - C_L)$ vs. the inverse flow rate $1/Q$. The results are shown in Figure 6.5 and yield a value of PA = 7.95 ml/min.

Illustration 6.1.4   Another Distributed System: The Krogh Cylinder

The assumption of uniform concentration within the tissue made in previous illustrations holds only, and then approximately, for very thin layers of tissue or tissue of generally small dimensions. When this no longer holds, concentration distributions will arise in the lateral direction that must be accounted for in the model. Among the first studies to address this problem was that by Krogh in 1919 who considered radial diffusion into the tissue, accompanied by metabolic consumption with a constant, i.e., zero order, consumption rate. The model may be used to trace the fate, for example, of oxygen or nutrients diffusing into a muscle. Figure 6.4B gives a sketch of the geometry of the system examined. Axial concentration variations are neglected which is a reasonable assumption in view of the high concentration of oxygen and nutrients and the relatively slow rate of uptake. A mass balance taken over a cylindrical difference element then leads to the following expression:

$$\text{Rate of solute in} - \text{Rate of solute out} = 0$$

$$-D_{eff}\,2\pi rL\frac{dC}{dr}\bigg|_r - \left[\begin{array}{c} -D_{eff}\,2\pi rL\dfrac{dC}{dr}\bigg|_{r+\Delta r} \\ +k_0\,2\pi r\Delta rL \end{array}\right] = 0 \qquad (6.1.16)$$

where k_0 is the zero order rate constant. Division by $2\pi\Delta rL$ and going to the limit $\Delta r \to 0$ yields:

$$D_{eff}\left(\frac{d^2C}{dr^2} + \frac{1}{r}\frac{dC}{dr}\right) - k_0 = 0 \qquad (6.1.17)$$

Note that here, as in other diffusional processes through a variable area, the *product* of area and gradient has to be differentiated, leading to the usual two derivatives characteristic of these processes.

Since no terms in C appear in the equation, use of the so-called p-substitution, $p = \dfrac{dC}{dr}$, seems appropriate (see Item 9, Table 4.4). We obtain the expression:

$$\frac{dp}{dr} + \frac{1}{r}p = k_0 / D_{eff} \qquad (6.1.18)$$

This is a linear, nonhomogeneous ODE with variable coefficients which can in principle be solved by the methods given under Item 6 of Table 4.4. We use instead a clever alternative method that consists of multiplying each side by r dr, thus reducing these to total differentials or to "exact form." r dr can be regarded as an integrating factor, not listed in Table 4.9. We obtain:

$$r\,dp + p\,dr = (k_0/D_{eff})\,r\,dr \qquad (6.1.19)$$

or

$$d(pr) = (k_0/2\,D_{eff})\,d(r^2) \qquad (6.1.20)$$

Hence, a first integration yields:

$$pr = (k_0/2\,D_{eff})r^2 + C_1 \qquad (6.1.21)$$

A second integration is arrived at as follows. We have, from Equation 6.1.21:

$$p = \frac{dC}{dr} = (k_0/2\,D_{eff})r + C_1/r \qquad (6.1.22)$$

Integrating this expression by separation of variables yields the general solution:

$$C = (k_0/4\,D_{eff})r^2 + C_1 \ln r + C_2 \qquad (6.1.23)$$

Integration constants are evaluated from the following boundary conditions:

1. At the inner radius $r = r_c$, $C = C_0$ (constant solute concentration in the blood)

2. At the outer radius $r = r_t$, $\dfrac{dC}{dr} = 0$ (no flux at outer surface)

Together, these two equations yield the following relations for the integration constants:

$$C_1 = -(k_0/2\,D_{eff})r_t^2 \tag{6.1.24}$$

and

$$C_2 = C_0 - (k_0/4\,D_{eff})r_c^2 + (k_0/2\,D_{eff})r_t^2 \ln r_c \tag{6.1.25}$$

We obtain, for the final form of the solution:

$$C - C_0 = (k_0/D_{eff})\left[\frac{r^2 - r_c^2}{4} - \frac{r_t^2}{2}\ln r/r_c\right] \tag{6.1.26}$$

Comments:

Equations of the form Equation 6.1.17 arise in a number of other disciplines, among them diffusion with a zero order reaction in a cylindrical catalyst pellet and conduction out of a cylinder with constant heat generation. Although the boundary conditions here are somewhat different than those usually encountered in the above mentioned cases, the *general* solutions seen there have direct applicability. Thus, Equation 4.3.76, which is the general solution for diffusion and first order reaction in a cylindrical catalyst pellet, can be used directly to extend the case of zero order metabolic consumption in a Krogh cylinder to the more complex case of a first order reaction. The boundary conditions, of course, are different since the catalyst pellet is usually solid not hollow and its surface permeable to reactant. These differences, notwithstanding, it is still useful to look to other disciplines for partial or complete solutions. It takes a good nose and some persistence to do this, but may help avoid unnecessary work as well as the stigma of "having reinvented the wheel."

Illustration 6.1.5   Membrane Processes: Blood Dialysis

Mass transport across natural or artificial membranes arises in a biomedical and biological context in a number of important ways. In living organisms, passage through all membranes and through the cellular walls of various conduits such as blood vessels, the branches of the lung, and the tubular structures of the kidney, plays an important role in the functioning of those organs. Artificial devices such as hemodialyzers and heart–lung machines that employ synthetic membranes to duplicate some of the body functions, are now commonplace. We note that membrane processes also are well established in industry where they are used in the separation, enrichment, and purification of liquid and gaseous mixtures.

Hemodialyzers, also popularly known as artificial kidneys, are devices in which the blood of patients with diseased kidneys is contacted with a so-called *dialysate solution* across a semipermeable artificial membrane, or "hollow fiber." Metabolic wastes, such as urea and kreatinin, excess electrolytes, and water pass from the blood and across the membrane to the dialysate that consists of a saline solution similar in osmotic concentration to that of normal body fluids. The devices resemble, in construction and configuration, the classical shell-and-tube heat exchangers, the hollow fibers carrying the blood corresponding to heat exchanger tubes, while the shell side carries the dialysate solution. Operation may be cocurrent or countercurrent. Devices also exist in which the dialysate side is "well-stirred," with no in- or outflow. These are less frequently encountered.

An additional distinction needs to be made. In the first case (Membrane Resistance Predominant), taken up below, the principal mass transfer resistance resides in the membrane wall which may be regarded as equivalent to a film resistance. The model and the analysis of the system may then be expected to resemble those of a shell-and-tube heat exchanger with no radial temperature variations other than those across the films at the wall. In the second case (Fluid Resistance on the Blood Side Predominant), the fluid side resistance predominates. Since flow in the hollow fibers is usually laminar, concentrations can be expected to vary in both radial and axial directions. This leads to a PDE on the tube side, while the shell-side, which is usually in turbulent flow or well stirred, remains at the ODE level. Its contribution to the overall resistance is generally neglected.

The PDE for the tube side which also is referred to as a "Graetz Problem," will be discussed in more detail in Chapter 8 (Illustrations 8.2.3 and 8.3.1). The treatment here is confined to the use of mass transfer coefficients that are extracted from the solution of the Graetz problem and will be presented in graphical form for immediate use in simple model calculations. The actual solution of the PDE is not addressed.

Membrane Resistance Predominant — The model equations, similar in form to those of the heat exchanger and applied to cocurrent flow, are as follows:

Tube-side mass balance:

$$\text{Rate of solute in} - \text{Rate of solute out} = 0$$

$$Q_B C_B \mid_z - \left[\begin{array}{c} Q_B C_B \mid_{z+\Delta z} \\ + K\pi d(C_B - C_D)_{avg} \Delta z \end{array} \right] = 0 \tag{6.1.27}$$

Shell-side mass balance:

$$\left[\begin{array}{c} Q_D C_D \mid_z \\ + K\pi D(C_B - C_D)_{avg} \Delta z \end{array} \right] - Q_D C_C \mid_{z+\Delta z} = 0 \tag{6.1.28}$$

Upon dividing by Δz and going to the limit, we obtain the two ODEs:

$$Q_B \frac{dC_B}{dz} + K\pi d(C_B - C_D) = 0 \tag{6.1.29}$$

$$Q_D \frac{dC_D}{dz} + K\pi d(C_B - C_D) = 0 \tag{6.1.30}$$

where the subscripts $_B$ and $_D$ refer to blood and dialysate respectively, and K = permeability of the membrane (m/s).

We now reach back and introduce the "trick" we had used there in arriving at a *design* equation for the heat exchanger. Each equation is divided by its flow rate Q and the equations subtracted. This yields an ODE in the state variable $(C_B - C_D)$ which can be integrated immediately by separation of variables to obtain:

$$\ln \frac{C_{Bi} - C_{Di}}{C_{Bo} - C_{Do}} = KA\left(\frac{1}{Q_B} + \frac{1}{Q_D}\right)$$

(6.1.31)

where subscripts $_i$ and $_o$ denote inlet and outlet conditions respectively.

This expression is then cast into the "log mean" form, as was done in the case of the heat exchanger, by invoking the *integral* mass balances:

$$W = -Q_B(C_{Bo} - C_{Bi}) = Q_D(C_{Do} - C_{Di})$$

(6.1.32)

Combination of Equations 6.1.31 and 6.1.32 leads, after some rearrangement, to the final compact design equation:

$$W = KA(LMCD)$$

(6.1.33)

where W = total amount of solute removed from the blood, and LMCD is the log-mean concentration difference, given by:

$$LMCD = \frac{(C_{Bi} - C_{Di}) - (C_{Bo} - C_{Do})}{\ln(C_{Bi} - C_{Di})/(C_{Bo} - C_{Do})}$$

(6.1.34)

The design Equation 6.1.33 corresponds to its heat exchanger counterpart, Equation 3.3.17. To use it, W is first established for a desired outlet concentration in the blood, C_{Bo}, using the integral balance Equation 6.1.32. Next, C_{Do} is calculated using the same integral balances and the result substituted into the LMCD expression. The final step consists of solving Equation 6.1.33 for A, that is the total internal membrane area required to achieve the desired purification level.

Equations of more general applicability can be derived by solving the ODEs 6.1.29 and 6.1.30. Similar general solutions were seen to arise for the heat exchanger by solving the corresponding ODE *energy* balances. We do not give the details here but present instead the final expressions obtained:

For the cocurrent case:

$$E = \frac{1 - \exp[-N_T(1 + Z)]}{1 + Z}$$

(6.1.35)

For the counter-current case:

$$E = \frac{1 - \exp[N_T(1 - Z)]}{Z - \exp[N_T(1 - Z)]}$$

(6.1.36)

TABLE 6.1
Heat Exchanger and Dialyzer Parameters

Heat Exchanger	Dialyzer
1. Capacity ratio $(FC_p)_{min}/(FC_p)_{max}$	Flow rate ratio $Z = Q_B/Q_D$
2. Number of transfer units $N_T = UA/(FC_p)_{Min}$	Number of transfer units $N_T = KA/Q_B$
3. Effectiveness $\varepsilon = \dfrac{C_c(T_{t\,out} - T_{t\,in})}{C_{Min}(T_{h\,in} - T_{c\,in})}$	Extraction ratio $E = (C_{Bi} - C_{Bo})/(C_{Bi} - C_{Di})$

---

where the parameters Z, N_T, and E are defined as follows:

$$Z = Q_B/Q_D = \text{Flow rate ratio}$$

$$N_T = K_A/Q_B - \text{Number of mass transfer units}$$

$$E = (C_{Bi} - C_{Bo})/(C_{Bi} - C_{Do}) = \text{Extraction ratio}$$

Since inlet dialysate concentration C_{Di} is usually $= 0$, the extraction ratio can be viewed as the fraction of solute removed by the dialyzer $(C_{Bi} - C_{Bo})/C_{Bi}$.

These expressions are general purpose equations that can be used not only for design (A in N_T), but also for parameter estimation (K in N_T) and the calculation of effluent concentration C_{Bo} for different flow ratios. The reader will note that Z, N_T, and E have their counterparts in the case of the shell-and-tube heat exchanger with identical respective meanings. We summarize these for convenience in Table 6.1.

Fluid Resistance on the Blood Side Predominant — As previously mentioned, this is a PDE problem whose solution is represented graphically in Figure 6.6. That solution is initially obtained in terms of concentration distributions C(r,z) which can be used to extract an equivalent fluid phase mass transfer coefficient k_f by means of the relation:

$$k_f(C_{avg} - C_{wall}) = -D\left(\frac{\partial C}{\partial r}\right)_{wall} \tag{6.1.37}$$

The coefficient k_f has been averaged over the tube length as a log-mean value $\overline{k}_f$ and is shown in terms of the dimensionless Sherwood number Sh_f of the ordinate of the graph. The abscissa values of zD/vd^2 represent dimensionless distance. The parameter $Sh_w = k_w d/D$ is the so-called wall Sherwood number and contains the wall mass transfer coefficient or membrane permeability in units of length/time. K is frequently given in units of (length)^2/time, in which case it has to be divided by

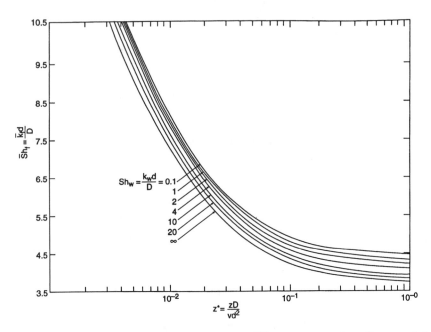

FIGURE 6.6 Plot of log-mean Sherwood number $\overline{Sh}_f$ vs. dimensionless distance z^* in tubular flow with radial diffusion. The parameter Sh_w (wall Sherwood number) is proportional to the permeability of the tubular wall. (From C.K. Colton, K.A. Smith, P. Stroeve, and E.W. Merrin. *AIChE J.*, 17:4, 372, 1971. With permission.)

wall thickness for use in the wall Sherwood number. $\overline{k}_f$ values extracted from the fluid Sherwood number can then be used directly in ODE models of the dialyzer or their solutions. We demonstrate this with the following numerical example.

The effluent urea concentration is to be calculated for a dialyzer made up of a bundle of 100 tubes 17 cm long, with a total area of 1000 cm^2 and a permeability K of 5×10^{-3} cm/s. Total blood flow rate is 1 cm^3/s with an inlet urea concentration of 1000 ppm. The value of urea diffusivity in blood is taken as 2×10^{-5} cm^2/s. We assume in addition that the dialysate flow rate is much larger than that of blood $Q_D \gg Q_B$, so that urea concentration there is vanishingly small. Flow pattern need not be specified under these conditions since the model is reduced to a single tubular mass balance:

$$Q_B \frac{dC_B}{dz} + K\pi D\, C_B = 0 \qquad (6.1.38)$$

This expression comes from Equation 6.1.29 for the special case $C_D = 0$ and integrates by separation of variables to yield:

$$C_{Bo}/C_{Bi} = \exp(-KA/Q_B) \qquad (6.1.39)$$

We use the expression to evaluate blood outlet concentration C_{Bo} assuming that either the membrane or the fluid side provides the controlling resistance.

Membrane resistance predominant: Here we obtain from Equation 6.1.39:

$$C_{Bo} = 1000 \exp[(-5 \times 10^{-3})(1000/1)] = 6.74 \text{ ppm}$$

Fluid resistance predominant: Figure 6.6 is used to obtain a value for the mean mass transfer coefficient $\overline{k}_f$. We have:

$$\frac{zD}{vd^2} = \frac{zD\pi/4}{vd^2\pi/4} = \frac{zD\pi/4}{Q_{tube}} = \frac{(17)(2\times10^{-5})\pi/4}{10^{-2}} = 2.67\times10^{-2}$$

The corresponding fluid Sherwood number is read from Figure 6.6 at a wall Sherwood number $Sh_w = \infty$, i.e., for conditions of no membrane resistance. The value obtained from the ordinate is $Sh_f = 5.6$, so that:

$$\overline{k}_f = 5.6 \ D/d$$

Diameter d is obtained from the area of a single tube:

$$d = \frac{A}{\pi z} = \frac{10}{\pi 17} = 0.187 \, \text{cm}$$

It follows that:

$$\overline{k}_f = (5.6)(2 \times 10^{-5})/0.187 = 6.0 \times 10^{-4} \text{ cm/s}$$

One notes immediately that the fluid-side mass transfer coefficient $\overline{k}_f$ is an order of magnitude smaller than the membrane permeability K (= 5×10^{-3} cm/s). Urea extraction, thus, is expected to be considerably less than what was obtained by neglecting fluid-side resistance. The result for the blood outlet concentration given by Equation 6.1.39 is

$$C_{Bo} = 1000 \exp [(- 6.1 \times 10^{-4})(1000/1)] = 543 \text{ ppm}$$

Thus, with the fluid side resistance now accounted for, urea extraction is barely 50%, compared to over 99% when the membrane resistance was assumed to predominate.

We note that Figure 6.6 allows calculations to be made for the case when *both* resistances are significant. Fluid phase coefficients are then read at the appropriate value of the wall Sherwood number Sh_w, and the inverse of the two coefficients added to obtain the overall mass transfer coefficient K_0:

$$\frac{1}{K_0} = \frac{1}{\overline{k}_f} + \frac{1}{K} \tag{6.1.40}$$

where K = membrane permeability in units of length/time.

Illustration 6.1.6   Release or Consumption of Substances at the Blood Vessel Wall

It is frequently required to calculate the concentrations which arise when a substance is released at a vessel wall into blood in laminar flow or, conversely, undergoes a reaction at the wall and is consumed there. A simple example of substance release into *turbulent* flow was given in Illustration 3.2.9.

One notes that this situation is not unlike dialysis in which the fluid resistance predominates, since in both cases one is confronted with concentration changes in both the radial and axial directions. In fact, the two cases represent Graetz problems and solutions of the type shown in Figure 6.6 apply to both dialysis, as well as reactive events of some type at the blood vessel wall. This makes intuitive sense since dialysis may be regarded as a "reactive event" in which the permeating solute is the reactant being "consumed" by diffusional outflow through the membrane wall.

Consumption as well as production or release of substances at the blood vessel wall occur in a number of important contexts. Anticoagulants may be applied to the surface of artificial implants or imbedded within their porous structure from which they are slowly released over time to prevent blood clotting. Blood coagulation itself, whether it results from an injury or from a pathological condition (thrombosis), consists of a complex series of reactive events at the wall of the blood vessel which can be natural or an artificial implant. In analyzing these cases, it becomes important to have a sense of the magnitude of the anticoagulant concentrations involved, particularly those prevailing at the wall. Solutions of the Graetz problem provide that information.

In the case of blood vessels and their associated flow rates, certain simplifications arise. When these vessels have a diameter greater than about 0.1 mm, i.e., are of the usual size of practical interest, radial concentration changes resulting from a reactive event are confined to a very thin boundary layer near the wall. Wall concentrations vary with axial distance as more substance is produced or consumed, but concentrations in the fluid *core* undergo only negligible changes in both the radial and axial direction. We show this in Figure 6.7 where the domain in which

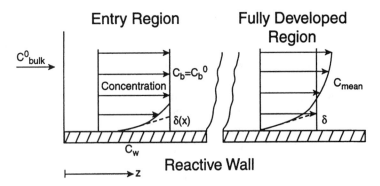

FIGURE 6.7   Mass transport in flow through a tube with a reactive wall. The left side shows the concentration profile in the entry region; the right side, the profile for the fully developed region.

this occurs is identified as the *entry region*. Concentrations begin to penetrate the fluid core only when d < 0.1 mm, i.e, in the smaller blood vessels or in capillaries. This ultimately leads to what is termed the *fully developed region* in which the concentration profile is a parabola extending across the entire vessel diameter.

In the entry region, which is the one of interest here, transport across the boundary layer can be expressed in terms of the usual mass transfer coefficient:

$$k_f = D/\delta \tag{6.1.41}$$

where δ = effective film thickness and D = diffusivity of the species. The associated profiles are known as the Lévêque solution of the Graetz problem, from which an equivalent mass transfer coefficient may be extracted.

For our purposes here, we dispense with the $\overline{k}_f$ values of Figure 6.6, which are log-mean values averaged over entire tube length and present instead an expression, derived from the Lévêque solution, for the *local* mass transfer coefficient k_f:

$$k_f = 0.6\left(\frac{\dot{\gamma}D^2}{z}\right)^{1/3} \tag{6.1.42}$$

where $\dot{\gamma}$ = shear rate in reciprocal time, z = axial distance from the inlet. Physiological shear rates typically span the range 50 to 1000 s^{-1}. A detailed derivation of this expression is given in Chapter 8, Illustration 8.2.3.

We now apply these concepts to two simple cases.

Constant Release Rate — Suppose that an anticoagulant, in order to be effective, has to have a concentration in the blood of 0.5 µg/ml. A graft coated with the agent has a measured release rate $N = 5 \times 10^{-5}$ µg/cm²s. We wish to ascertain whether, with this release rate, the required protective concentration can be attained at the wall and at a distance of (a) 10 cm and (b) 0.1 cm from the inlet. The applicable shear rate is $\dot{\gamma} = 1000$ s^{-1} and diffusivity of the agent is estimated at $D = 10^{-6}$ cm²/s. Vessel diameter is 1 cm.

Since the entry region which applies here (d > 0.1 mm) shows negligible variations in bulk concentration, we can set $C_{bulk} = 0$ and obtain for the local flux N:

$$N = k_f (C_{wall} - C_{bulk}) = k_f C_w \tag{6.1.43}$$

Solving for C_w and using k_f given by Equation 6.1.42, this becomes:

$$C_w = \frac{N}{k_f} = \frac{N}{0.6(\dot{\gamma}D^2/z)^{1/3}} \tag{6.1.44}$$

We obtain, at $z = 10$ cm:

$$C_w = \frac{5\times10^{-5}}{0.6(10^3\,10^{-12}/10)^{1/2}} = 1.8\,\mu g/ml$$

and at $z = 0.1$ cm

$$C_w = \frac{5 \times 10^{-4}}{0.6(10^3\ 10^{-12}\ /\ 0.1)} = 0.39\,\mu g\,/\,ml$$

Thus, the required wall concentration C_w of 0.5 µg/ml is exceeded in both cases.

First Order Reactions at the Wall — In this second case we consider the situation where a particular species is either consumed or produced by a first order reaction as may happen in the process of blood coagulation. The model equations for the two cases at steady state are given by:

$$k_f(C_b - C_w)\ =\ k_w\,C_w$$

$$\text{Rate of arrival}\qquad \text{Rate of consumption}$$

(6.1.45)

$$k_f(C_w - C_b)\ =\ k_w\,C_w$$

$$\text{Rate of departure}\qquad \text{Rate of production}$$

(6.1.46)

where the subscripts $_b$ and $_w$ again refer to bulk and wall conditions, and k_w is the first order rate constant. Solving for C_w we obtain the combined relation:

$$C_w = \frac{k_w C_b}{1 \pm k_w\,/\,k_f}$$

(6.1.47)

where the positive sign refers to consumption, the negative sign to production.

Let us now consider the results predicted by that equation. For first order consumption (positive sign), the behavior is rather unexceptional. Since k_f varies inversely with distance (Equation 6.1.42), C_w will gradually diminish as the flow moves farther into the tube. A high rate of consumption (large k_w) also will promote a decrease in wall concentration. This is as expected.

The case of first order *production* (negative sign) is more interesting. We remind the reader at the outset that one should always be on the alert when dealing with *fractions containing differences*, since either the numerator or the denominator (or both) may go to zero for certain parameter values, leading to zero or unbounded values of the state variable. In Equation 6.1.47 one expects this kind of behavior to arise when the ratio of reaction constant to mass transfer coefficient k_w/k_f approaches unity. Let us consider a specific numerical example.

Suppose the production rate constant k_w of a coagulant on a particular synthetic material has been determined at 10^{-3} cm/s. We set $\dot\gamma$ at 1000 s^{-1} and use diffusivity $D = 10^{-6}$ cm²/s for the coagulation. Then, in order to have parity of k_w and k_f, we must have:

$$z^{1/3} = \frac{0.6(\dot\gamma D^2)^{1/3}}{k_w} = \frac{0.6(10^3 \times 10^{-12})^{1/3}}{10^{-3}}$$

or

$$z = 0.216 \text{ cm}$$

Thus, coagulant concentration at the wall, C_w, would become unbounded at about 2 mm from the inlet and coagulation would ensue. If, on the other hand, the production could be inhibited by a suitable anticoagulant, dropping the rate constant to, say $k_w = 10^{-4}$ cm/s, we would obtain:

$$z^{1/3} = \frac{0.6(10^3 \times 10^{-12})^{1/3}}{10^{-4}}$$

or

$$z = 216 \text{ cm}$$

Thus, unbounded concentrations would not arise in implants of physiologically relevant lengths under these conditions.

It must be noted that unbounded coagulant levels would evidently not arise in practice since natural inhibitors present in the blood would prevent this from happening. The simple model presented does not take this into account. It does indicate, however, that *abnormally high* levels may arise as the rate of coagulant production approaches that of removal by mass transport. The model also serves the useful purpose of providing rough numerical values for the "design" of appropriate coagulation inhibitors.

Illustration 6.1.7   A Simple Cellular Process

Cellular processes can assume a variety of forms. In one version, substances within the cell undergo a reaction, accompanied by diffusional inflow and outflow of reactants and products through the cell wall. This type of process is considered in the next example dealing with Turing's model of morphogenesis (Illustration 6.1.8). The present example considers events that take place within the membrane of the cell rather than its interior, and are triggered by so-called receptors embedded within the cell wall itself. These receptors are large protein molecules capable of "communicating" with the external, extracellular fluid, as well as the internal cytoplasmic domain (Figure 6.8). They are involved in four distinct processes:

1. *Binding of ligand* molecules from the extracellular fluid. This process enables the receptors to "sense" the environment and to transmit this fact to the interior of the cell.
2. *Signaling* involves passing the information inherent in the binding process on to the cell interior where it may give rise to a variety of secondary processes such as growth, secretion, contraction, or adhesion. The latter occurs, for example, during the deposition and subsequent adhesion of blood platelet to an injured vessel wall or an artificial surface.

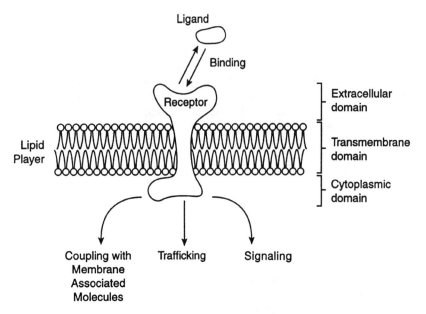

FIGURE 6.8   Diagram of the reactions of a receptor embedded in a cellular wall. (D.A. Lauffenburger and J.J. Linderman, *Receptors: Models for Binding, Trafficking, and Signaling,* Oxford University Press, U.K., 1993. With permission.)

3. In *Trafficking*, the receptors themselves may undergo changes which include a physical displacement into the cytoplasm (termed internalization), as well as degradation and synthesis.
4. Finally, in *Coupling with Membrane Associated Molecules*, the receptors interact with neighboring molecules in the membrane.

We consider the first item of ligand binding only and examine it in some detail. The simple kinetic model usually applied to ligand-receptor interactions is of a reversible form described by:

$$R + L \underset{k_r}{\overset{k_f}{\rightleftarrows}} C \qquad (6.1.48)$$

with the rate given by:

$$\frac{dC}{dt} = k_f RL - k_r C$$

where R = number of receptors/cell, C = number of ligand-receptor complexes per cell, and L = ligand concentration in the extracellular fluid in moles/L. Thus, we have the somewhat unusual combination of a second order reaction in the forward direction in the reverse direction. k_f (M^{-1} $Time^{-1}$) and k_r ($Time^{-1}$) are the associated rate constants. Since both R and L as well as C vary with time, two additional equations are required. These are most conveniently established from the cumulative receptor and ligand balances. Thus,

$$R_T = R + C \tag{6.1.49}$$

and

$$L_0 = L + \frac{n}{N_{Av}} C \tag{6.1.50}$$

where the subscripts $_T$ and $_0$ denote total and initial concentrations, respectively, n = number of cells and N_{Av} = Avogadro's number. The ratio n/N_{Av} is used to convert the units of C to the molar concentration of L. Substitution of these relations into Equation 6.1.49 yields the following expression in the density C of the ligand-receptor complex:

$$\frac{dC}{dt} = k_f [R_T - C]\left[L_0 - \left(\frac{n}{N_{Av}}\right)C\right] - k_r C \tag{6.1.51}$$

This is a first order nonlinear ODE in C, and it is of some comfort to note that it can be integrated by separation of variables.

We consider two cases: (1) constant ligand concentration $L = L_0$. This is tantamount to the assumption that the density C of the complex formed is small compared to the ligand concentration available, and is equivalent to the limiting case $(n/N_{Av})C \ll L_0$. For this condition, the ODE 6.1.51 reduces to the form:

$$\frac{dC}{dt} = k_f [R_T - C]L_0 - k_r C \tag{6.1.52}$$

It is customary to nondimensionalize the variables, setting $u = C/R_T$ = fractional coverage, and $\tau = k_r t$. Introducing, in addition, the equilibrium dissociation constant $K_D = k_r/k_f$, we obtain the compact form:

$$\frac{du}{d\tau} = (1-u)\frac{L_0}{K_D} - u \tag{6.1.53}$$

Solution is by separation of variables that leads, after some rearrangement, to the expression:

$$u(t) = u_0 \exp\left\{-\left(1+\frac{L_0}{K_D}\right)\tau\right\} + \frac{L_0/K_D}{1+L_0/K_D}\left[1-\exp\left\{-\left(1+\frac{L_0}{K_D}\right)\tau\right\}\right] \quad (6.1.54)$$

where $u_0 = C_0/R_T$ and C_0 = initial concentration of complex.

An expression for the equilibrium concentration C_{eq} can be obtained by letting $\tau \to \infty$ or by setting the derivative in Equation 6.1.54 equal to zero. In either case the result is given by:

$$u_{eq}R_T = C_{eq} = \frac{R_T}{1+K_D/L_0} \quad (6.1.55)$$

We note in this expression that for large values of the dissociation constant K_D, C_{eq} tends to zero, as expected. Small values of K_D (very little dissociation) lead, in the limit, to the value $C_{eq} = R_T$, i.e., all receptors are bound to ligands and we have saturation.

(2) Variable ligand concentration. Here the full Equation 6.1.51 has to be solved. We rewrite it for this purpose in expanded and nondimensionalized form and obtain:

$$\frac{du}{d\tau} = \frac{R_T(n/N_{Av})}{K_D}u^2 - \left(\frac{L_0}{K_D} + \frac{R_T(n/N_{Av})}{K_D} + 1\right)u + \frac{L_0}{K_D} \quad (6.1.56)$$

or

$$\frac{du}{d\tau} = au^2 - bu + c$$

Integration can again be accomplished by separation of variables, noting that this requires the roots $u_{1,2}$ of the quadratic expression on the right of Equation 6.1.56. We can then make use of the following integration formula available in mathematical tables:

$$\int \frac{dx}{(a+bx)(a'+b'x)} = \frac{1}{ab'-a'b}\ln\frac{a'+b'x}{a+bx} \quad (6.1.57)$$

where, for our case, $b = b' = 1$, $a = -u_1$ and $a' = -u_2$ the two roots of Equation 6.1.56. This leads to the integrated expression:

$$t = \frac{1}{u_2-u_1}\ln\frac{u_2-u}{u_1-u}\frac{u_1-u_0}{u_2-u_0} \quad (6.1.58)$$

Solving for the dimensionless complex concentration u, we obtain the final result:

$$u(t) = \frac{u_2 - u_1 \dfrac{u_2 - u_0}{u_1 - u_0} \exp[-(u_1 - u_2)\tau]}{1 - \dfrac{u_2 - u_0}{u_1 - u_0} \exp[-(u_1 - u_2)\tau]} \qquad (6.1.59)$$

where u_2 is the *smaller* of the two roots of the quadratic expression in Equation 6.1.56.

The equilibrium concentration of the ligand-receptor complex, $u_{eq} = C_{eq}/R_T$, can again be obtained in two ways. We can set the derivative in Equation 6.1.56 equal to zero, in which case *two* values are obtained, both of them positive. To resolve this ambiguity, we turn to the transient Equation 6.1.59 and let $\tau \to \infty$. We obtain:

$$u_{eq} = u_2 = C_{eq}/R_T \qquad (6.1.60)$$

i.e., the equilibrium value is equal to the *smaller* root of the quadratic. Let us examine that root more closely. We obtain, after cancelling K_D in numerator and denominator of u_2 and factoring b out of the square root:

$u_2 =$

$$\frac{(L_0 + R_T n/N_{Av} + K_D) - (L_0 + R_T n/N_{Avg} + K_D)\left(1 - \dfrac{4R_T/L_0}{(L_0 + R_T n/N_{Av} + K_D)^2}\right)^{1/2}}{2R_T(n/N_{Av})}$$

$$(6.1.61)$$

which, upon letting $K_D \to \infty$, yield $u_2 = 0$ as required.

Equation 6.1.61 is an unwieldy expression but yields useful *limiting* information. For the case $K_D \to 0$, we write the root in its original form:

$$u_2 = \frac{b - b\left(1 - \dfrac{4ac}{b^2}\right)^{1/2}}{2a} \qquad (6.1.62)$$

Since $\dfrac{4ac}{b^2} \to 0$ as $K_D \to 0$, we can use a Taylor series expansion of the square root term to obtain:

$$u_2 = \frac{b - b\left(1 - \dfrac{1}{2}\dfrac{4ac}{b^2}\right)}{2a} = \frac{c}{b} \qquad (6.1.63)$$

Hence,

$$u_2 = \frac{c}{b} = \frac{L_0/K_D}{L_0/K_D + (n/N_{Av})R_T/K_D + 1}$$

and

$$K_D \to 0 \quad \frac{C_{eq}}{} = \frac{R_T}{1 + \dfrac{(n/N_{Av})R_T}{L_0}} \qquad (6.1.64)$$

Thus, in contrast to the case of constant ligand concentration, Equation 6.1.55, $K_D \to 0$ does not lead to the full saturation value $C_{eq} = R_T$. Rather that value is diminished by a factor of $1/\left(1 + \dfrac{n/N_{Av}R_T}{L_0}\right)$. As L_0 becomes very large, that correction factor tends to unity, i.e., we can still approach, if not fully attain, receptor saturation, provided the initial ligand concentration is large enough.

Comments:

This is a case where the transient solutions, while useful in themselves, also can be fruitfully employed in obtaining the limiting steady-state solutions. The result obtained by the alternative method of setting the derivative of the original ODE equal to zero led, as we have seen, to two solutions. The ambiguity was quickly resolved by resorting to the full transient solution and allowing τ to go to infinity. Thus, the transient solution was useful in establishing the important steady-state solution.

A second point of note is the asymptotic analysis that was applied to the solution. This is an important part of modeling and serves to verify boundary conditions and in general to explore the limiting behavior of the solution. Unexpected features are often discovered in this fashion. Finally, we have here yet another example of a complex physical process which by shrewd modeling leads to a manageable equation and its solution.

Illustration 6.1.8   Turing's Paper on Morphogenesis

In a 1952 paper entitled "The Chemical Basis of Morphogenesis," Turing laid what would become the definitive basis for modeling biological growth. The preamble to the paper states, "In this section a mathematical model of the growing embryo will be described. This model will be a simplification and idealization, and consequently a falsification." This speaks to the honesty and modesty of the author.

The simplification referred to is the initial use of *linear* equations to describe the simultaneous diffusion and reaction of migrating cellular species termed morphogens in the paper. These morphogens which could for example be hormones or other mobile cellular substances undergo changes in concentration as they diffuse and react. An increase in concentration is deemed tantamount to potential growth, and it is these concentration changes in time and space that the model is designed to identify.

Turing examined two cases. In the first, the concentrations arising in a circular array of N cells in contact with one another are considered. The cell interior is assumed to be a well-mixed small tank and the migrating species permeate through the cellular walls into neighboring cells at lower concentration where they undergo one or more first order reactions. For a pair of morphogens of concentration X and Y, this leads to a set of 2N first-order linear ODEs which in Turing's nomenclature have the form:

$$\frac{dX_r}{dt} = f(X_r, Y_r) + \mu(X_{r+1} - 2X_r + X_r)$$

$$\frac{dY_r}{dt} = g(X_r, Y_r) + \nu(Y_{r+1} - 2Y_r + Y_r) \qquad (6.1.65)$$

$$(r = 1, \ldots, N)$$

where μ and ν are the product of area $\times$ transport coefficient, the driving force is given by the concentration differences $X_{r+1} - X_r$, $X_r - X_{r-1}$, etc., and f, g are the reaction terms. Closed form solutions of this model are presented in the paper.

In the second case, diffusion and reaction is assumed to take place in a circular but homogeneous and continuous medium, i.e., the tissue of the organism under consideration. Here the relevant equations are the PDEs of unsteady Fickian diffusion which are coupled but only two in number:

$$\frac{\partial X}{\partial t} = a(X - h) + b(Y - k) + \frac{\mu^1}{\rho^2} \frac{\partial^2 X}{\partial \theta^2}$$

$$\frac{\partial Y}{\partial t} = c(X - h) + d(Y - k) + \frac{\nu^1}{\rho^2} \frac{\partial^2 Y}{\partial \theta^2} \qquad (6.1.66)$$

where ρ = radius, θ = angular distance, μ^1 and ν^1 = diffusivities, and h, k = equilibrium concentrations. Closed form solutions of these equations also are given and their noteworthy feature is that they can be either sinusoidally oscillating and underdamped, overdamped, purely oscillatory, or oscillatory with an ever-increasing amplitude. This is the same type of behavior we had encountered before in second order ODEs with constant coefficients (see Chapters 4 and 5). The consequence is that when oscillatory solutions arise, a circular pattern along the angular variable θ will develop in which morphogen concentrations show maxima at some locations indicating potential for embryonic growth, and minima or zero values at other locations implying very little or no growth.

Turing also presented a numerical example involving several morphogens of which two, X and Y, were tracked. The rates of the reaction, some of which are nonlinear, are as follows:

Reaction	Rate
$Y + K \rightarrow W$	$\dfrac{25}{16} YX$
$2X \rightarrow W$	$\dfrac{7}{64} X^2$
$A \rightarrow X$	$\dfrac{1}{16} 10^{-3} A$
$C^1 \rightarrow X + C$	$\dfrac{55}{32} 10^3 C^1$
$Y \rightarrow B$	$\dfrac{1}{16} Y$

A (a fuel such as glucose) and C^1 (a catalyst or enzyme) are set at 10^3 and 10^{-3} $(1 + \gamma)$, respectively, where γ was allowed at first to rise at the rate 2^{-7} from $-\dfrac{1}{4}$ to $\dfrac{1}{16}$ and then to decrease at the same rate to zero. Diffusivities were set at 5×10^{-8} cm²/s and 2.5×10^{-8} for X and Y, respectively, and cell diameter was assumed to be 0.01 cm, with N = 20 cells arranged in a circular pattern. Evidently this scheme is an artifact, although not an unreasonable one, and it leads to some interesting results.

Solutions for Y, as a function of cell numbers, are shown in Figure 6.9. Turing was at that time associated with the University of Manchester which had just acquired its first computer and although no mention of it appears in the paper, the solution was presumably carried out numerically on that machine. The system, it will be noted, consisted of 2 N = 40 *coupled and nonlinear ODEs*.

The interesting feature of the solution is that in certain cells, the morphogen concentrations rise considerably above their initial values, while in other cells that

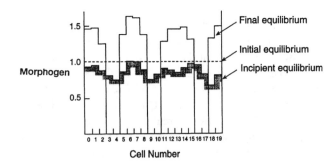

FIGURE 6.9 The Turing model of morphogenesis. Morphogen distribution in a circular array of 20 cells as a function of time. (A.M. Turing, *Phil. Trans. Roy. Soc., London*, 237: 37–72, 1952. With permission.)

TABLE 6.2
Enzyme Classification

Name	Function
1. Oxido reductases	Oxidation-reduction
2. Transferases	Transfer of functional groups
3. Hydrolases	Hydrolysis
4. Lyases	Addition to double bond
5. Isomerases	Isomerization
6. Ligases	Formation of bonds
	(1) C-O
	(2) C-S
	(3) C-N
	(4) C-C

appear in pairs, concentration drops to zero. Something of this sort was anticipated from the solution of the continuous model Equation 6.1.66, although the transition there was smoothly sinusoidal.

The Turing paper concludes by citing growth pattern observed in nature which appear to follow the circular patterns of maxima and minima predicted by his models. One such example is the sea anemone, Hydra. When that organism is deliberately mutilated, the part cut off from the rest has the shape of an open-ended tube with essentially circular tissue symmetry. At some stage, that symmetry at the open end will be disrupted by the appearance of a number of patches. These patches arise at points where the new tentacles are subsequently to appear. One will note the similarity to the discrete concentration peaks shown in Figure 6.9. Another example is provided by young root fibers just breaking out from the parent root. Initially these are almost homogeneous in appearance, but eventually a ring of fairly evenly spaced spots appear, and these later develop into vascular strands. The genius of Turing lies not only in tracking down these seemingly disparate phenomena but providing an elegant and basically simple model for their explanation.

Illustration 6.1.9   Biotechnology: Enzyme Kinetics

Enzymatic reactions are biological processes in which the enzyme E, usually a protein, acts as a catalyst to convert the so-called substrate S, which is the reacting species, to a product P. There are close to 2000 known enzymes. They are very specific in the type of reaction they catalyze, which is seen in the official classification in common use today (Table 6.2).

A rate expression for enzymatic reactions was proposed as early as 1902 by Henri, who based it on the following observations:

- The rate of reaction is first order in the substrate concentration (S) at relatively low concentration levels.
- As the substrate concentration is increased, the reaction order in (S) diminishes continuously from one to zero.

- The rate of reaction is proportional to the total amount of enzyme present E_0. This includes both the bound and unbound forms.

The proposed rate equation was consequently of the form:

$$r = \frac{k_2(E_0)(S)}{K_m + (S)} \tag{6.1.67}$$

where K_m was identified as the dissociation constant of the enzyme–substrate complex.

A more thorough analysis was subsequently undertaken by the team of Michaelis-Menten, which was based on the following reaction mechanism:

$$S + E \overset{k_1}{\underset{k_{-1}}{\rightleftarrows}} ES \tag{6.1.68}$$

$$ES \overset{k_2}{\to} P + E$$

In this scheme, it is assumed that the enzyme E and the substrate reversibly combine to form a complex ES which then dissociates into product P and uncombined enzyme. If the rate is assumed to follow the molecularity of these reactions, one obtains:

$$\frac{d(S)}{dt} = k_{-1}(ES) - k_1(S)(E) \tag{6.1.69}$$

$$\frac{d(ES)}{dt} = k_1(S)(E) - (k_{-1} + k_2)(ES) \tag{6.1.70}$$

Since there are three state variables in these equations, i.e., (E), (S), and (ES), a third expression is required which is given by the following cumulative balance on the enzyme:

$$(E) + (ES) = (E)_0 \tag{6.1.71}$$

This is a set of one linear algebraic equation and two nonlinear ODEs in (S), (E), and (ES) which does not yield an analytical solution and has to be solved numerically. However, the equations reduce to the Equation 6.1.67, subsequently called the Michaelis-Menten equation, provided the following relation holds:

$$\frac{d(ES)}{dt} \tag{6.1.72}$$

This is tantamount to a *quasi steady-state assumption* and implies that the rate of complex formation is rapid compared to its decomposition or its conversion to product P, and that the enzyme-substrate complex, after a brief initial transient period, quickly reaches a constant concentration. Introducing this relation into Equations 6.1.69 and 6.1.70 leads, after some rearrangement, to the expression:

$$\frac{d(S)}{dt} = -\frac{k_2(E)_0(S)}{[(k_{-1}+k_2)/k_1]+(S)} \tag{6.1.73}$$

The term K_m of the original Expression 6.1.67, which the early workers identified with the equilibrium constant $K_m = k_{-1}/k_2$, is now clearly seen to have a somewhat more complex dependence on all three rate constants. It is customary to retain the symbol K_m, however, and one obtains as the final expression:

$$r = -\frac{d(S)}{dt} = \frac{r_{Max}(S)}{K_m+(S)} \tag{6.1.74}$$

where $r_{Max} = k_2(E_0)$ is the maximum rate attainable. A plot of this equation, showing the significance of the parameters appears in Figure 6.10A.

The equation is easily integrated by separation of variables and one obtains the implicit relation in (S):

$$r_{Max}\, t = (S_0) - (S) + K_m \ln (S)_0/(S) \tag{6.1.75}$$

A. Michaelis Menten Rate

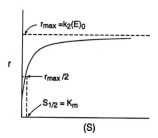

B. Lineweaver - Burk Plot

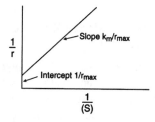

FIGURE 6.10   Plots for the analysis of enzyme kinetics.

To evaluate the coefficients r_{Max} and K_m, from experimental rate data, Equation 6.1.74 can be plotted in various ways so as to yield linear plots. Parameter evaluation results from the respective slopes and intercepts. Two such ways of plotting, given below, have become famous and are named after the originators:

Lineweaver-Burk:

$$\frac{1}{r} = \frac{1}{r_{Max}} + \frac{K_m}{r_{Max}} \frac{1}{(S)} \tag{6.1.76}$$

Eadie-Hofstee:

$$r = r_{Max} - K_m \frac{r}{(S)} \tag{6.1.77}$$

An example of the Lineweaver-Burk plot is shown in Figure 6.10B.

Comments:

It is worth noting similarities of the Michaelis-Menten Equation 6.1.74 to other well-known physical laws. The equation has the same form as the well-known Langmuir adsorption isotherm:

$$q = \frac{q_m C}{b + C} \tag{6.1.78}$$

where q = amount adsorbed/mass sorbent and C = concentration of solute in the fluid (gas or liquid) in contact with the sorbent. q_m represents monolayer loading, i.e., full saturation of the solid and corresponds to r_{Max} of the Michaelis-Menten equation. b is made up of the kinetic parameters of the adsorption and desorption steps and resembles in that respect the Michaelis-Menten constant K_m.

The enzymatic rate expression is also identical in form to two rate laws developed by chemists and chemical engineers to describe *chemically* catalyzed reactions. These are the Langmuir-Hinshelwood, and the Hougen-Watson rate laws. There are other similarities as well as differences between the biochemical and chemical or chemical engineering approaches.

The rate expression for cell growth proposed by Monod and taken up in the next illustration also is of Michaelis-Menten form with some differences in units of rate and kinetic parameters.

Illustration 6.1.10   Cell Growth, Monod Kinetics, Steady-State Analysis of Bioreactors

When a small quantity of living cells is placed in a liquid solution of an essential nutrient at an appropriate temperature and pH, the cells will undergo growth. In the process of consuming nutrients (or substrate S) from the environment, the cells produce metabolic "wastes" which often constitute a desirable product P. Thus, in fermentation processes such as the production of alcoholic beverages, the cells convert carbohydrate substrates into alcohol, while they themselves undergo a growth in numbers. This is referred to as *biomass formation*. We examine here, in the first instance, the pertinent growth kinetics and follow this up by a steady-state analysis of both cell growth and production in a continuous flow stirred bioreactor.

Growth Kinetics — The most commonly used rate expression is that proposed by Monod in 1942. It is basically an empiricism and has, as mentioned, the same form as the Michaelis-Menten equation:

$$\mu = \frac{\mu_{Max}(S)}{K_s + (S)} \tag{6.1.79}$$

μ does not have the conventional units of mass/volume time, but is rather defined as the specific growth rate, i.e., the rate of growth per unit cell mass, with dimensions of reciprocal time. Thus,

$$r_M = \frac{1}{m}\frac{dm}{dt} = \mu\,[t^{-1}] \tag{6.1.80}$$

where m = mass of cells.

Although on occasion the Monod equation may have an underlying physical model which explains its genesis, it is more generally regarded as an empirical law of engineering usefulness. The tools available for extracting parameters from the Michaelis-Menten equation such as Lineweaver-Burk plots, apply here as well.

We note that in order to use these rate expressions in conventional mass balances, μ has to be redimensionalized by multiplication with the cell concentration C (mass/volume). Thus, for Monod kinetics we write:

$$r\,(\text{mass of cells/volume time}) = \frac{\mu_{Max}(S)C}{K_S + (S)} \tag{6.1.81}$$

Steady-State Analysis — A conventional steady-state cell balance around a CSTR, leads to the expression:

$$\text{Rate of cells in} - \text{Rate of cells out} = 0$$

$$\begin{bmatrix} QC_f \\ +(\mu C)V \end{bmatrix} - [QC] = 0 \tag{6.1.82}$$

which is expanded using Equation 6.1.80 and rewritten in the form:

$$DC_f + \left[\frac{\mu_{Max}(S)}{K_S + (S)} - D\right]C = 0 \tag{6.1.83}$$

where the subscript $_f$ refers to feed. Here $D = Q/V$ is the reciprocal of the residence time τ we had encountered before in connection with the conventional CSTR. It is the preferred quantity used in biochemical engineering work and is termed the *dilution rate*. One notes that it equals the number of tank volumes which pass through the vessel per unit time.

A similar steady-state balance for the substrate leads to the expression:

$$D[(S)_f - (S)] - \frac{1}{Y_{CS}} \frac{\mu_{Max}(S)}{K_S + (S)} C = 0 \qquad (6.1.84)$$

where Y_{CS} = mass of cells produced/mass of substrate consumed. This latter quantity is a constant for a particular system under consideration. Equations 6.1.83 and 6.1.84 are two coupled algebraic equations in the substrate and cell concentrations (S) and C. They are collectively known as the *Monod chemostat model*.

A common case is that of a reactor which initially contains a certain mass of cells and is then fed continuously with nutrient substrate S free of cells ($C_f = 0$). We do not address the initial transient period and solve instead for the steady-state substrate and cell concentrations. We obtain from the chemostat equations:

$$S = \frac{DK_S}{\mu_{Max} - D} \qquad (6.1.85)$$

and

$$C = Y_{Cg}[(S)_F - (S)] \qquad (6.1.86)$$

or

$$C = Y_{Cg}\left[(S)_F - \frac{DK_S}{\mu_{Max} - D} \right]$$

One notes from these expressions that the cell concentration C at first declines slowly, and then more rapidly as the dilution rate D increases and approaches μ_{Max}. Simultaneously, the effluent substrate concentration (S) experiences a rise until it reaches the value of the substrate inlet concentration $(S)_F$ (Figure 6.11). At that point, as seen from Equation 6.1.86, C will have dropped to zero. That condition, termed *washout*, is attained at a dilution rate given by:

$$D_{crit} = \frac{\mu_{Max}(S)_F}{K_S + (S)_F} \qquad (6.1.87)$$

In other words at flow rates corresponding to D_{crit}, the cells do not have sufficient time to grow, and those which existed in the vessel are washed away in the effluent.

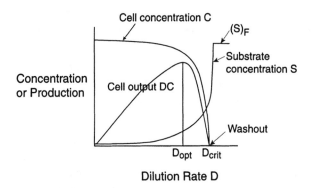

FIGURE 6.11 Concentration and production of cells as a function of dilution rate in a continuous flow stirred-tank bioreactor at steady-state.

A second quantity of interest is the rate of cell output, given by the product DC in units of mass of cells per unit volume and time. Since C declines with increasing D, the product DC will pass through a maximum. Using the product derivative d(DC)/dD obtained from Equations 6.1.85 and 6.1.86, and setting it equal to zero one obtains, for maximum cell output, the optimum dilution rate:

$$D_{opt} = \mu_{Max}\left(1 - \sqrt{\frac{K_S}{K_S + (S)_F}}\right)$$
(6.1.88)

That maximum turns out to be a sharp one and is located in close proximity to D_{crit} (Figure 6.11). Thus, a small increase in D of a few percent above D_{opt} will cause a sudden drop in both C and DC to zero, i.e., washout will ensue. Therefore, it is advisable to operate at dilution rates well below D_{opt} to avoid the region of high sensitivity in its vicinity. This entails some loss in potential cell production but leads to greater stability and robustness of the system. Identification of such regions is one of the benefits to be derived from modeling.

The obtain the product concentration (P) in the effluent, we use an appropriate steady-state mass balance for P and obtain:

$$\text{Rate of product in} - \text{Rate of product out} = 0$$

$$\left[\begin{array}{c} Q(P)_f \\ +Y_{PC}\mu CV \end{array}\right] - [Q(P)] = 0$$
(6.1.89)

or alternatively,

$$D[(P)_f - (P)] + Y_{PC}\,\mu C = 0$$
(6.1.90)

where Y_{PC} = mass of product formed per mass of cells, which is a characteristic quantity for a particular biochemical reaction. We combine this expression with the

Monod Equation 6.1.79 and those resulting from the Monod chemostat model, Equations 6.1.83 and 6.1.84 and obtain, after elimination of μ, C and (S):

$$(P) - (P)_f = \frac{Y_{PC}Y_{CS}}{D} \frac{\mu_{Max}\left[(S)_f - \dfrac{DK_S}{\mu_{Max} - D}\right]}{1 + \dfrac{\mu_{Max} - D}{D}} \qquad (6.1.91)$$

One notes that production shutdown (i.e., $(P) - (P)_f = 0$) occurs at the same critical dilution rate as that given by Equation 6.1.87 since the numerator in Equation 6.1.92 then becomes zero. D_{opt}, representing the best flow rate for product formation, again lies close to D_{crit} which is the worst condition forcing us, reluctantly, to operate somewhat below optimum dilution rates.

Comments:

The analysis we have presented has been almost entirely algebraic, the exception being the determination of D_{opt}. It was nevertheless possible to establish important features of the operation of biochemical stirred tank reactors and to provide simple guidelines for their successful and near optimal operation.

The terminology used by biotechnologists requires an adjustment in our thinking. We had been accustomed to analyzing reactor behavior in terms of residence time $\tau = V/Q$. Large values of τ were good, giving high yields, small values of τ were bad. The effect of the inverse quantity, the dilution rate $D = 1/\tau$ in a biochemical context is more complex. High values of D, i.e., small residence times, can be very good, in fact lead to optimum conversion, but a relatively small increase in D beyond that point leads to complete shutdown of the reaction, i.e., washout occurs. Thus, small residence times can be both very good and very bad and these conditions are in close proximity to each other. This is a novel feature not encountered in conventional reactor engineering and deserves the attention of the analyst.

Practice Problems

6.1.1 Blood Flow Rate to the Heart Muscle — A viable method for measuring blood uptake by the heart muscle (myocardium) from blood flowing through the heart chamber (ventricle) is to perfuse the heart with a hdyrogen-saturated solution of saline and blood. Because of its high mobility, hydrogen is quickly distributed throughout the heart muscle. Subsequent clearance of the muscle with clear blood, during which the hydrogen remains almost uniformly distributed in the muscle at any given instant, yielded the following results:

H_2-Concentration	100	50	25	10	2.5
Time, min	0	1	1.8	2.9	4.65

Assuming a myocardium volume of 100 cc, which is that of the average medium-sized dog, calculate the rate of blood flow through the myocardium.

Answer: 79.5 cc/min

6.1.2 Flow Rate by Dye Dilution — Flow rates Q to and through an organ may be determined by adding a dye or other tracer to the ingoing blood stream and monitoring the concentrations in the outflow. Type and size of the chosen tracer substance are such that one can assume it stays strictly in the blood phase and does not permeate surrounding tissue. Derive an expression for Q in terms of measurable quantities.

6.1.3 Two-Compartment Model — Consider the two-compartment model shown in Figure 6.2B. Show that the average concentration C of the two mixed effluent streams is given by:

$$C = f_1 C_1(0)e^{-k_1 t} + f_2 C_2(0)e^{-k_2 t}$$

and identify the parameters.

6.1.4 Analogy Between Dialysis and Heat Exchange — Use Table 6.1 listing analogous terms for dialysis and heat exchange plus Equation 6.1.36 for countercurrent dialysis to derive the corresponding expression for the countercurrent heat exchanger (cf. Equation 3.3.19).

6.1.5 Ultrafiltration — Ultrafiltration is a membrane process in which a solution, containing for example a protein, is concentrated by applying pressure to it and forcing the solvent across a semipermeable membrane, i.e., a membrane more permeable to the solvent than it is to the solute. Some of the latter will usually leak through as well, i.e., the process is not 100% efficient.

In a test run of a batch ultrafiltration unit involving a particular membrane and protein dissolved in water, it was found that at any given instant the concentration C_p in the product stream — the so-called permeate — is always one tenth of that in the solution left behind on the high pressure side, termed the *retentate* (C_R). Thus, $C_p = 0.1\ C_R$.

(a) Calculate the fraction of Retentate that remains, if the process is to double the concentration C_p.
(b) What is the actual separation achieved, i.e., what is the value of $C_p/(C_R)_{avg}$ at the end of the process? How does this compare with the inherent separation factor?

(Hint: The model of the process is similar to that of Rayleigh distillation where the separation factor α takes the place of the inherent separation factor sought here.)
Answers: (a) 0.463; (b) 14.5, 10

6.1.6 Protein Reaction in Large Blood Vessels — A protein contained in blood flowing in a cylindrical tube with diameter > 0.1 mm undergoes a reaction at the wall with Michaelis-Menten kinetics. We had seen that for such systems concentration changes are confined to a thin boundary layer near the wall and $C_b = C_b^0 =$ constant. Show that the local wall concentration is given by the expression:

$$C_w = \frac{1}{2}(r_{Max}/k_f + K_m - C_b^0)\left[\left(1 + \frac{4K_m C_b^0}{r_{Max}/k_f + K_m - C_b^0}\right)^{1/2} - 1\right]$$

where k_f is given by Equation 6.1.42.
(Hint: Adapt Equation 6.1.45 to Michaelis Menten Kinetics.)

6.1.7 Solute Release in a Small Blood Vessel — In blood vessels with $d < 0.1$ mm, concentration changes occasioned by a reaction or other event at the tubular wall, both wall concentration and in the fluid bulk vary with distance. Consider the case of a solute released at the tubular wall at the constant rate N (mol/cm²s). Derive expressions for (a) the wall concentration and (b) the mean bulk concentration as a function of distance z at steady state.

Answer: (b) $(C_b)_{avg} = 4 \, Nz/vd$

6.1.8 Deposition of Cells from a Flowing Medium — Consider the case of cells or some similar entities in a flowing medium arriving at the vessel wall and adhering to it. An example would be the deposition of platelets from flowing blood on the site of an injury or onto an artificial implant.

Show that the fractional surface coverage S as a function of time t and axial distance from the inlet z is given by:

$$\ln(1-S) - [k_w/k_f(z)]S + \frac{k_w C_b^0}{\rho_p}t = 0$$

where C_b^0 = concentration in the bulk fluid, taken to be constant. The rate of deposition r_d is assumed to follow the relation:

$$r_d = k_w C_w (1 - S)$$

where $(1 - S)$ = fraction of uncovered surface.

(Hint: Express S as the time integral of the arrival rate of the cells and eliminate C_w using an additional algebraic mass balance.)

6.1.9 Ligand Binding to a Solution Receptor — In Illustration 6.1.7, the case was examined in which a ligand became bound to a receptor embedded in a cell membrane. We now wish to consider the situation in which both the ligand and the receptor of radius R move freely and interact, in the extracellular fluid. Show that at steady-state the ligand concentration L(r) around a receptor placed at the origin of a spherical domain is given by:

$$L(r) = L(\infty) - \frac{k_r R L_\infty}{4\pi DR + k_r}\left(\frac{1}{r}\right)$$

where k_r = intrinsic first-order association rate constant, D = diffusivity.

6.1.10 Critical and Optimum Dilution Rate — Derive the Expressions 6.1.87 and 6.1.88.

6.1.11 Tubular Bioreactor — Consider the case of a tubular reactor taking a feed of concentration C_0 in cells, and $(S)_0$ in substrate. Derive the following implicit substrate profile for the reactor:

$$[C_0 + Y_{CS}(C_0 + K_S)] \ln \frac{C_0 + Y_{CS}[(S) - (S)_0]}{C_0} - K_S Y_{CS} \ln \frac{(S)}{(S)_0} = \mu_{Max} \tau [C_0 + Y_{CS}(S)_0]$$

where τ = residence time = z/v.

(Hint: Make a differential balance for the substrate and an integral balance for both cells and substrate.)

6.2 A VISIT TO THE ENVIRONMENT

We turn here to an examination of models that arise in connection with environmental problems. Although Environmental Science and Engineering has, like any discipline, its own definitions, language, and nomenclature, much of what we see there has a familiar look to it. Thus, we will be, as before, making use of the following tools:

- *Phase Equilibria.* Because the solutes of environmental concern are frequently encountered at relatively low concentrations, phase equilibrium relations often fall in the linear range, i.e., one deals with partition or distribution coefficients or Henry's constants. We will address these shortly in some detail.
- *Mass Transfer Coefficients.* These arise in a natural way when considering transport between the three principal environmental media, i.e., air, soil, and water, as well as transport from these media to living organisms. Extensive use is made of the two-film theory.
- *Reaction Rates.* Solutes may undergo reaction principally by reactive interaction with soil or sediment, or by metabolic degradation through bacterial action or enzymatic processes in general.
- *Compartments.* Extensive use is made of the stirred tank concepts. A body of water such as a lake, the local atmosphere, or a living organism are examples of entities that are, at least as a first approximation, represented by compartmental models. Much of what one sees here has its counterpart in biomedical models or more conventional engineering applications.
- *Distributed Models.* These are brought in primarily when dealing with flow as in rivers, estuaries, oceans and air currents, and in groundwater movement.

All of the above are treated in ways similar to those encountered before. Some special features when dealing with phase equilibria, need to be noted, however.

TABLE 6.3
Partition Coefficients

Solute	Log K_{OW}	K_{OW} (m³/m³)	K_{OC} (m³/m³)	$H \left(\dfrac{kg\,Water}{kg\,Soil} \right)$
Butadiene	1.99	98	39	0.39
n-Pentane	3.45	2800	1100	11
n-Hexane	4.11	13,000	5200	52
Cyclohexane	3.44	2800	1100	11
Benzene	2.13	135	54	0.54
Toluene	2.69	490	200	2.0
Styrene	2.88	760	300	3.0
Range of alkanes	2.8–6.25	630–1.8×10^6	250–7.1×10^5	2.5–7100
Range of aromatics	2.13–5.52	140–3.3×10^5	54–1.3×10^5	5.4–1300
Methyl chloride	0.91	8.1	3.3	0.033
Methylene chloride	1.25	18	7.1	0.071
Chloroform	1.97	93	37	0.37
Carbon tetrachloride	2.64	440	180	1.8
Chlorobenzene	2.80	630	250	2.5
Range of chloroalkanes	0.91–3.93	8.1–8500	3.3–3400	0.033–34
Range of chlorobenzenes	2.80–5.50	630–3.2×10^5	250–1.3×10^5	2.5–1300
Range of PCBs	3.90–8.26	7.9×10^3–1.8×10^8	3.2×10^3–7.3×10^7	32–7.3×10^5

It has become the convention in environmental work to make extensive use of the so-called octanol-water partition coefficient K_{OW} which describes the distribution of a solute between octanol and water. Thus,

$$(C)_O = K_{OW}(C)_W \qquad (6.2.1)$$

where $(C)_O$ = solute concentration in octanol, $(C)_W$ = solute concentration in the water phase and K_{OW} is in units of m³ water/m³ octanol.

Octanol, or more properly 1-octanol, was chosen as a correlating substance because it has a similar carbon to oxygen ratio as lipids, and in general mimics sorption and dissolution of solutes on and in organic matter. It is sparingly soluble in water and readily available in pure form. K_{OW} should be viewed as a measure of hydrophobicity, i.e., the tendency of a chemical to partition out of water, and is consequently an inverse measure of the solubility of a solute in water.

Table 6.3 lists K_{OW} values for a range of organic chemicals. Also tabulated are values of K_{OC} which is the partition coefficient of a solute between organic carbon (OC) and water. They are obtained from the empirically established relation:

$$K_{OC} = 0.4 \, K_{OW} \qquad (6.2.2)$$

The last column lists values of H, the Henry constants for solutes distributed between water and soil. The values were obtained by assuming a carbon content in soil of 2% and a soil density of 2000 kg/m$_3$. Hence,

$$H = 0.1 \, K_{OC} \tag{6.2.3}$$

A special equilibrium relation is worth noting, that of describing solute distribution between fish and water. Here the relevant partition coefficient K_{FW} can again be expressed in terms of the octanol-water partition coefficient, and is given by the simple linear relation:

$$K_{FW} = 0.048 \, K_{OW} \tag{6.2.3a}$$

This can be viewed as expressing the assumption that a fish is about 5% lipid or that a fish behaves as if it is about 5% octanol by volume.

In what follows we shall proceed as was done in the case of the biomedical illustrations by first considering systems described by compartmental models, followed by an examination of distributed models. Various media interactions, such as soil–water, fish–water, and air–water, are taken up. Finally, we delve in some detail into the topic of wastewater treatment involving several different processes. The models here are kept as usual at the AE and ODE level. Occasional use is made of the *results* of PDE models. Actual *solutions* are deferred to Chapter 9.

Illustration 6.2.1 Mercury Volatilization from Water

Substances with low solubility in water, such as various hydrocarbons, chlorinated organics such as DDT, and mercury, can still have high partial pressures p or fugacities because of their exceptionally high activity coefficients γ. The relevant relation is given by:

$$p_i = \gamma_i \, x_i \, P_i^0 \tag{6.2.4}$$

where P_i^0 = pure component vapor pressure. The equation can be recast in the form:

$$y_i = \gamma_i \, \frac{P_i^0}{P_T} x_i \tag{6.2.5}$$

where the group $\gamma_i \dfrac{P_i^0}{P_T}$ can be viewed as an air–water partition coefficient which is generally high. The loss of even a small amount of solution by evaporation could, thus, be expected to result in a marked drop of pollutant concentration. This is small comfort for the environment as a whole, since the toxic substances are merely being transferred from one medium to another. It is, nevertheless, a quite dramatic effect exemplified by a 1986 study that an estimated 60 tonnes of PCBs, chloroform, and chlorobenzenes are released into the atmosphere from the mist over Niagara Falls per year. Note in this connection that each tiny droplet acts as a highly efficient evaporating stirred tank.

We consider here a body of water containing dissolved mercury at or near the saturation level and wish to calculate the reduction of mercury content that occurs when a mere 0.01% of the solution is evaporated. We shall view this as a Rayleigh distillation type of problem, with the evaporated liquid assumed to be in equilibrium with the "well-stirred" liquid of uniform concentration. The equilibrium relation, Equation 6.2.5, that will be needed in the model, contains the activity coefficient γ which is not usually known or easily measured. We circumvent the difficulty by relating γ to solubility, which is a well-established known quantity. This is done by considering a system consisting of pure mercury in equilibrium with its saturated aqueous solution. Equating chemical potentials for the two phases, we obtain:

$$\mu^0(T,p) = \mu^0(T,p) + RT \ln \gamma x_{sat} \qquad (6.2.6)$$

from which it follows that:

$$\gamma \, x_{sat} = 1 \qquad (6.2.7)$$

or

$$\gamma = 1/x_{sat}$$

This result agrees with the intuitive notion that the smaller the solubility x_{sat}, the higher its "escaping tendency" in terms of partial pressure or fugacity.

We now proceed to derive the usual mass balances:

Total mass balance:

$$\text{Total moles in} - \text{Total moles out} = \frac{\text{Rate of change in}}{\text{total content}}$$

$$0 - D = \frac{d}{dt} W \qquad (6.2.8)$$

Component mass balance:

$$\text{Moles mercury in} - \text{Moles mercury out} = \frac{\text{Rate of change in}}{\text{mercury content}}$$

$$0 - y_{Hg} D = \frac{d}{dt} x_{Hg} W \qquad (6.2.9)$$

where y and x are the vapor and liquid phase mole fractions. These two relations are supplemented by a statement of phase equilibrium:

Equilibrium relation:

$$y_{Hg} = \frac{P_{Hg}}{P_{Hg} + P_{H_2O}^o} \cong \frac{\gamma_{Hg} x_{Hg} P_{Hg}^o}{P_{H_2O}^o} = \frac{x_{Hg} P_{Hg}^o}{x_{sat} P_{H_2O}^o} \qquad (6.2.10)$$

Note that the partial pressure of air is excluded from this expression, since we are concerned with equilibrium compositions of the binary mercury–water system.

Equations 6.2.8 and 6.2.9 are divided to eliminate D, and dt and Equation 6.2.10 introduced into the result. We obtain:

$$\frac{x_{Hg} P_{Hg}^o}{(x_{Hg})_{sat} P_{H_2O}^o} = x_{Hg} + W \frac{dx_{Hg}}{dW} \qquad (6.2.11)$$

Integration by separation of variables yields the expression:

$$\left[\frac{P_{Hg}^o}{(x_{Hg})_{sat} P_{H_2O}^o} - 1 \right] \ln \frac{W}{W_0} = \ln \frac{x}{x_0} \qquad (6.2.12)$$

The data to be introduced at this stage are as follows:

Mercury solubility: 3×10^{-2} mg/L $\cong 2.7 \times 10^{-9}$ mol/fraction (25°C)
Mercury vapor pressure: 0.173 Pa (25°C)
Water vapor pressure: 3.17×10^3 Pa (25°C)

Substitution of these values into Equation 6.2.12 yields:

$$\left[\frac{0.173}{2.7 \times 10^{-9}(3170)} - 1 \right] \ln(1 - 10^{-4}) = \ln \frac{x}{x_0}$$

where we have substituted 0.01% = 10^{-4} for the fraction evaporated.

Taylor series expansion of the logarithmic term on the left yields:

$$\ln(1 - 10^{-4}) \cong -10^{-4}$$

so that

$$\ln\left(\frac{x}{x_0} \right)_{Hg} = -2.02$$

and

$$(x/x_0)_{Hg} = 0.133$$

Thus, the fraction of mercury volatilized, $1 - x/x_0$, equals ≈ 0.87, a phenomenal amount considering that only 0.01% of the solution has been evaporated.

Comments:

A number of pitfalls were astutely avoided by drawing on background knowledge from appropriate subdisciplines. The fact that γ_{Hg} was unknown and could not be located in the literature on vapor–liquid equilibria could have brought the proceedings to a halt. Instead we drew on intuitive reasoning that γ should be related to solubility, and knowing that the latter was tabulated, established the relation by means of elementary thermodynamics.

It would have been tempting to calculate y_{Hg} from the conventional relation $p_i = y_i P_{Tot}$, with $P_{Tot} = 1$ atm. This would have led to a wrong result since the partial pressure of air would have been included. It required some thought to realize that y_{Hg} refers to the mole fraction in the system H_2O-Hg, not H_2O-Hg-air.

Finally, even though the logarithm of $1 - 10^{-4} = 0.9999$ could have been easily evaluated by pocket calculator, we prefer drawing on first year calculus to obtain the same result in a more elegant way.

Illustration 6.2.2   Rates of Volatilization of Solutes from Aqueous Solutions

In the previous illustration we had established the degree of depletion which occurs when a hydrophobic substance such as mercury evaporates from an aqueous solution. No mention was made of the *time frame* in which this happens. Indeed we had eliminated time by division of the two constitutive mass balances. To obtain the full transient solutions, additional information is required on the evaporation rates and the associated transport coefficients. Table 6.4 gives a compilation of the relevant parameters for a number of hydrophobic solutes of environmental interest. These calculated values show that, with few exceptions, the transport resistance resides almost entirely in the liquid. The half-life τ, i.e., the time required to reduce the original concentration by half, listed in the last column for $L = V/A = 1$ m, ranges in values from several hours to several months in the case of large molecules of low diffusivity such as pesticides. This attests to the dangerously long retention times that may be exhibited by these substances.

The model equation for the evaporation process takes the following form:

$$\text{Rate of solute in} - \text{Rate of solute out} = \frac{\text{Rate of change of}}{\text{solute content}}$$

$$0 - k_L A(C - C_S) = V \frac{dC}{dt} \tag{6.2.13}$$

where we have assumed that the mass transfer resistance resides entirely in the liquid phase. If one further sets the surface concentration $C_S = 0$ (negligible solute in the air), Equation 6.2.13 immediately integrates to the expression:

$$C = C_0 \exp \left(-k_L t/(V/A)\right) \tag{6.2.14}$$

TABLE 6.4
Calculated Evaporation Parameters and Rates at 25°C

Compound	Solubility, mg/L	Vapor Pressure, mmHg	k_L, m/h	Resistance in Liquid Phase, %	τ for L = 1 m, h
n-Octane	0.66	14.1	0.124	>99.9	5.55
2,2,4-Trimethylpentane	2.44	49.3	0.124	>99.9	5.55
Benzene	1780	95.2	0.144	95.6	4.81
Benzene at 10°C	1750	45.5	0.137	91.3	5.03
Toluene	515	28.4	0.133	96.3	5.18
o-Xylene	175	6.6	0.123	95.4	5.61
Cumene	50	4.6	0.119	98.3	5.79
Naphthalene	33	0.23	0.096	82.2	7.15
Biphenyl	7.48	0.057	0.092	85.5	7.52
DDT	1.2×10^{-3}	1×10^{-7}	9.34×10^{-3}	13.2	73.9
Lindane	7.3	9.4×10^{-6}	1.5×10^{-4}	0.19	4590
Dieldrin	0.25	1×10^{-7}	5.33×10^{-5}	0.078	12,940
Aldrin	0.2	6×10^{-6}	3.72×10^{-3}	5.4	185
Mercury	3×10^{-2}	1.3×10^{-3}	0.092	97.8	7.53

Source: From D. Mackay and P.J. Leinonen, *Environmental Science and Technology, vol. 9,* American Chemical Society, Washington, D.C., 1975.

where the half-life τ is given by:

$$\tau = 0.69 \ (V/A)/k_L \qquad (6.2.15)$$

Let us consider the case of the mist over Niagara Falls and track the evaporation of mercury from a droplet of 1 mm diameter (V/A = 1/6 mm). Converting the half life of 7.53 h listed in Table 6.4 for V/A = 1 m to 1/6 mm we obtain:

$$\tau = (7.53)(3600)10^{-3}/6$$

$$\tau = 4.5 \ s$$

i.e., the loss of mercury to the atmosphere is nearly instantaneous. For DDT, the value is about 10 times higher, still fast enough to ensure almost complete DDT loss to the atmosphere during the life-time of the droplet over the Falls.

Illustration 6.2.3   Bioconcentration in Fish

In Figure 6.12 we display the various mechanisms by which toxic solutes can enter and leave fish. They are largely self-explanatory and are all expressed in terms of first order rate laws. The first of these to be quantified in 1979 and used in measurements for parameter estimation was the uptake and return of the solute through the gills:

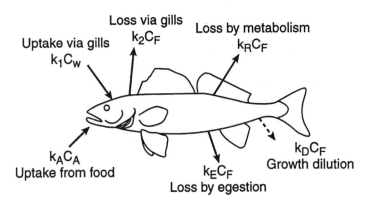

FIGURE 6.12 Uptake and loss of a toxic substance in fish. (D. Mackay, *Multimedia Environmental Models, The Fugacity Approach,* Lewis Publishers, Chelsea, MI, 1991. With permission.)

$$\frac{dC_F}{dt} = k_1 C_W - k_2 C_F \tag{6.2.16}$$

where the subscript $_F$ denotes the fish.

If the concentration C_W in the water is assumed constant, integration by separation of variables yields the expressions:

For uptake:

$$C_F/C_W = k_1/k_2[1 - \exp(-k_2 t)] \tag{6.2.17}$$

For clearance ($k_1 = 0$):

$$C_F/C_{Fo} = \exp(-k_2 t) \tag{6.2.18}$$

We note that as $t \to \infty$, the uptake concentration ratio C_F/C_W approaches k_1/k_2, which may be regarded as a partition coefficient of this particular mechanism. Parameter estimation is usually done by running the uptake to saturation so that $C_F/C_W = k_1/k_2$, and follow this up by clearance to establish the value of k_2.

When all mechanisms are considered with the exception of growth dilution, a long-term effect, the rate expression becomes:

$$\frac{dC_F}{dt} = (k_1 + k_A)C_W - (k_2 + k_R + k_E)C_F \tag{6.2.19}$$

where it has been assumed that $C_A \approx C_W$, which is often the case.

Integration by separation of variables then leads to the expression:

$$C_F/C_W = \frac{k_1 + k_A}{k_2 + k_R = k_E}\{1 - \exp[-(k_2 + k_R + k_E)t]\} \tag{6.2.20}$$

The entire process of solute accumulation is referred to as bioconcentration, and that due to food intake in particular as biomagnification. The effect can be staggering, particularly in the case of chlorinated aromatics and PCB's (see Table 6.3). Choosing the pesticide DDT with an octanol–water partition coefficient $K_{ow} = 1.6 \times 10^6$, and applying the simple correlation Equation 6.2.3 we obtain the following magnification:

$$K_{FW} = \frac{C_F}{C_W} = 0.048 \, K_{ow} = (0.048)1.6 \times 10^6 = 7.7 \times 10^4$$

i.e., an almost *100,000-fold increase* in concentration. Since DDT solubility in water is 1.2×10^{-3} mg/l (see Table 6.4), the concentration in the fish rises to $7.7 \times 10^4 \times 1.2 \times 10^{-3} = 92$ mg/l, or approximately 1/10 of a gram in a fish of 1 l volume.

Illustration 6.2.4   Cleansing of a Lake Bottom Sediment

When contaminated water flows into a lake, the contaminant undergoes various changes, including metabolization, volatilization, and partitioning onto the sediment, the latter being particularly prevalent. After emissions have ceased, the solute slowly desorbs into the water and it is this cleansing process we wish to address here.

We start the analysis by considering a full model of concentration changes both in the lake water and the sediment. We have:

Component balance on lake water:

$$\text{Rate of solute in} - \text{Rate of solute out} = \frac{\text{Rate of change of}}{\text{solute content}}$$

$$\left[\begin{matrix} Q_1 C_1 \\ +K_0 A_s (C*-C) \end{matrix} \right] - Q_2 C = \frac{d}{dt}(VC) \qquad (6.2.21)$$

Component balance on sediment:

$$\text{Rate of solute in} - \text{Rate of solute out} = \frac{\text{Rate of change of}}{\text{solute content}}$$

$$0 - K_0 A_s (C*-C) = \rho_s V_s \frac{dq}{dt} \qquad (6.2.22)$$

Total volumetric balance:

$$\text{Rate of volume in} - \text{Rate of volume out} = \frac{\text{Rate of change}}{\text{of volume}}$$

$$Q_1 - Q_2 = \frac{d}{dt}(V) \qquad (6.2.23)$$

Equilibrium relation:

$$q = HC^* \qquad (6.2.24)$$

These four equations in the four state variables C (kg/m^3), C* (kg/m^3), q (kg/kg sediment), and lake volume V constitute a full compartmental model. A solution by Laplace transforms is feasible but somewhat cumbersome. Fortunately, the model can be reduced to a single equation by making the reasonable assumption that solute concentration in the lake is, because of its large volume, negligibly small. We then obtain, from Equations 6.2.22 and 6.2.24:

$$-\frac{K_0 A_s}{H} q = \rho_s V_s \frac{dq}{dt} \qquad (6.2.25)$$

which integrates to the expression:

$$t = \frac{\rho_s V_s H}{K_0 A_s} \ln \frac{q_o}{q} \qquad (6.2.26)$$

where the subscript $_s$ refers to sediment and $V_s/A_s = h_s$ = depth of active sediment layer. The challenge here, as has been the case elsewhere, lies not so much in setting up and solving the model but rather in the proper estimate of the parameter, in particular the overall mass transfer coefficient K_0, which is composed of the sediment and fluid phase mass transfer coefficients in accordance with Equation 3.2.15. Some suggestions for its estimation have become available, which we summarize below.

Sediment Phase Mass Transfer Coefficient k_s — Reasonable predictions can be made by setting the effective diffusivity in the sediment $D_{eff} = D_L \varepsilon^2$, where D_L is the solute diffusivity in free water and ε the sediment pore fraction. We then have for the sediment mass transfer coefficient:

$$k_s = \frac{D_L \varepsilon^2}{h_s} \qquad (6.2.27)$$

Fluid Phase Mass Transfer Coefficient — Here the predictions are more uncertain since varying degrees of turbulence may prevail at the sediment-lake water interface. A suggested correlation is given by the expression:

$$k_L = 0.29 \, [D_L \, (m^2/day)]^{1/2} \, (m/day) \qquad (6.2.28)$$

with a suggested range for D_L values of 0.0086 – 8.6 m^2/day. We, thus, have to accept a possible ~30-fold variation in mass transfer coefficient.

No correlation for the active layer depth h_s appear to be available. A value of h_s = 1 cm can be used as a first estimate.

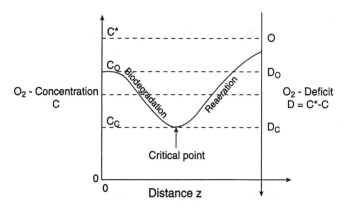

FIGURE 6.13   The Streeter-Phelps model. Dissolved oxygen profiles in a river with a steady influx of a pollutant.

Illustration 6.2.5   The Streeter-Phelps River Pollution Model: The Oxygen Sag Curve

In this classical 1925 study, probably the first attempt to model the fate of a chemical in the environment, Streeter and Phelps derived an equation that described the oxygen profile in a river which undergoes a steady influx of pollutant at some point upstream. Initially, biodegradation of the pollutant causes a decline in dissolved oxygen C or, viewed slightly differently, an increase in the oxygen deficit $D = C^* - C$ where C^* is the equilibrium solubility of oxygen in water. As the pollutant concentration L decreases through biodegradation, the decline in oxygen concentration slows and ultimately passes through a minimum, the so-called critical point, as oxygen supply from the atmosphere replenishes the river. Further "reaeration" ultimately restores the oxygen concentration to full saturation levels (Figure 6.13).

In their model, Streeter and Phelps did not consider pollutant adsorption on river sediment, an important removal mechanism which will be addressed in the following illustration. Also neglected were the effects of runoff and respiration by algae. Thus, only biodegradation and reaeration rates needed to be considered, both of which were assumed to be first order in concentration. The model equations are then as follows:

Oxygen mass balance:

$$\text{Rate of oxygen in} - \text{Rate of oxygen out} = 0$$

$$\left[+k_L a(C^* - C)_{avg}^{QC|_z} A_C \Delta z \right] - \left[+k_r L A_C \Delta z^{QC|_{z+\Delta z}} \right] = 0 \tag{6.2.29}$$

which becomes, in the limit $\Delta z \to 0$:

$$v\frac{dC}{dz} + k_r L - k_L a(C^* - C) = 0 \tag{6.2.30}$$

where $v = Q/A_C$ = superficial river velocity, $k_L a$ = volumetric mass transfer coefficient m^2/m^3 river, k_r = reaction rate constant, and L = pollutant concentration.

Alternatively we can write in terms of the oxygen deficit $D = C^* - C$,

$$v \frac{dD}{dz} \quad - \quad k_r L \quad + \quad k_L aD = 0$$

$$\text{Flow} \qquad \text{Reaction} \quad \text{Mass transfer}$$

$$(6.2.31)$$

Pollutant mass balance:

Rate of pollutant in − Rate of pollutant out = 0

$$QL|_z - \begin{bmatrix} QL|_{z+\Delta a} \\ + k_r L A_C \Delta z \end{bmatrix} = 0$$

which yields the ODE:

$$v \frac{dL}{dz} + k_r L = 0 \qquad (6.2.32)$$

The latter equation can be immediately integrated by separation of variables and we obtain:

$$L = L_0 \exp\left(-\frac{k_r}{v} z \right) \qquad (6.2.33)$$

This intermediate result gives the pollutant concentration profile in the river. Substitution of L into Equation 6.2.31 then leads to the ODE in the oxygen deficit:

$$v \frac{dD}{dz} + k_L aD = k_r L_0 \exp\left(-\frac{k}{v} z \right) \qquad (6.2.34)$$

This equation is of the form:

$$y' + f(x)y = g(x) \qquad (6.2.35)$$

which has the solution (see Item 6, Table 4.4):

$$y = \exp \int -f(x)dx \left[\int g(x) \exp \int f(x)dx + K \right] \qquad (6.2.36)$$

Upon evaluation of the integrals we obtain:

$$D = \exp\left(-\frac{k_L a}{v} z\right)\left[\frac{k_r L_0}{k_L a - k_r} \exp\left(\frac{k_L a - k_r}{v} z\right) + K\right] \qquad (6.2.37)$$

Using the boundary condition $D = D_0$ at $z = 0$ to evaluate the integration constant K finally yields:

$$D = \left(D_0 - \frac{k_r L_0}{k_L a - k_r}\right)\exp\left(-\frac{k_L a}{v} z\right) + \frac{k_r L_0}{k_L a - k_r}\exp\left(-\frac{k_r}{v} z\right) \qquad (6.2.38)$$

This is the Oxygen Deficit Profile in the river, shown in Figure 6.13.

Comments:

Equation 6.2.38 is often cast into the more convenient form:

$$D = \left(D_0 - \frac{L_0}{f-1}\right)\exp\left(-\frac{fk_r}{v} z\right) + \frac{L_0}{f-1}\exp\left(-\frac{k_r}{v} z\right) \qquad (6.2.39)$$

where $f = k_L a/k_r$ is the so-called self-purification rate (dimensionless). When $f = 1$, D is indeterminate ($\infty - \infty$) and has to be evaluated by L'Hopital's rule.

The critical point, or minimum shown in Figure 6.13, is evaluated by setting $dD/dz = 0$. There results:

Critical distance:

$$z_c = \frac{v}{k_r(f-1)} \ln\left\{f\left[1 - (f-1)\frac{D_0}{L_0}\right]\right\} \qquad (6.2.40)$$

and

Critical oxygen deficit:

$$D_c = (L_0/f)\{f[1 - (f-1)(D_0/L_0)]\}^{1/1-f} \qquad (6.2.41)$$

Two alternative terms used in environmental work are worth noting.

1. Pollutant concentrations are often expressed in terms of the so-called biochemical oxygen demand (BOD) which is the oxygen consumed by the pollutant in mg/L, established in a standard test. Thus, BOD is seen to be proportional to pollutant concentration L.
2. Distance z from the pollution source is frequently replaced by the quantity $t = z/v$, appropriately called *flow time*. Since z always occurs in the combination z/v, all previously cited solutions can be expressed in terms of flow time t.

Illustration 6.2.6   Contamination of a River Bed (Equilibrium)

Contamination of river sediments by a chemical dissolved in the water involves a complex series of steps. We note at the outset that even in the most complex models, complete mixing in the vertical direction is usually assumed, thus reducing the dimensionality of the model. This removes only one difficulty. The following factors still have to be considered:

1. Mass transport on the water-side of the interface.
2. Mass transport within the sediment.
3. Biochemical degradation within the sediment phase.
4. Sorption onto suspended sediments.

Items 1 and 2 were addressed in Illustration 6.2.4 in the context of lake bottom sediment clearance, and similar parameter values can be expected to apply to river sediments although the water-side mass transfer coefficient will usually be higher because of increased turbulence. Of note is the new fact that concentrations are distributed in both time and distance so that a PDE results. Even if linear first order rate laws are assumed, this is still a fairly complex problem. We will address it, at least in part, in Chapter 9.

In this illustration we address the sorption step onto the river bed only, omitting consideration of biodegradation and the effect of suspended solids. To avoid the PDE, we assume phase equilibrium to prevail at any point in time or distance. This implies that the solute propagates as a rectangular front, rather than the S-shaped profile which materializes in practice (Figure 6.14A). The equilibrium front bisects the actual profile at the midpoint so that the predicted arrival times will over estimate the time of first appearance and underestimate the onset of full saturation. Since the actual fronts are often quite sharp, particularly for solutes with high Henry constants, the range separating the two points in time can be quite short. At any rate, the results obtained from the equilibrium model are a highly useful *first step* in analyzing this complex problem, particularly in the absence of transport rate data.

To arrive at an appropriate relation for these calculations, we perform a cumulative solute balance on the river bed. It takes the form:

$$Y_F v \rho_f A_c t \quad = \quad q_F \rho_b A_c z \quad + \quad Y_F \rho_f A_c z$$

Amount introduced to time	Amount retained by sediment	Amount in river water

(6.2.42)

where Y_F = kg solute/kg water in the feed, q_F = kg solute/kg sediment in equilibrium with Y_f.

In most practical applications, the product vt is much higher than the length of the contamination zone z, so that the second term on the right can be neglected. Cancelling cross-sectional area A_c and rearranging we obtain:

A. Loading

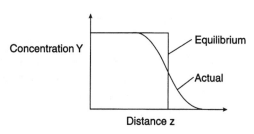

B. Clearance

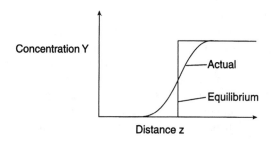

FIGURE 6.14 Pollutant profiles in river sediment during: (A) the contamination period, (B) the recovery period.

$$z/t = \frac{\rho_f v}{\rho_b (q/Y)_F} = \frac{\rho_f v}{\rho_b H} \qquad (6.2.43)$$

where $(q/Y)_F$ is the loading ratio at the inlet conditions and equals the Henry constant H at low concentrations. Note that the river bed density ρ_b has to be based on unit volume of the river plus the sediment. We, therefore, must use the expression $\rho_b = \rho_s[h_s/(h_s + h_r)]$, where ρ_s is now the sediment density, h_s and h_r the effective sediment and river depth, respectively.

The equation can be used to calculate time of arrival t at a certain position z or, conversely, the position z of the front after a lapsed time t. We reiterate that the values thus obtained lie between the points of first arrival and onset of full saturation, but often are not too far removed from them.

Let us illustrate the use of Equation 6.2.43 with a numerical example. We assume a river velocity v = 1m/s, sediment specific gravity of $h_s/(h_s + h_r) = 10^{-2}$, and a Henry constant $H = 10^3$ kg water/kg sediment. We wish to calculate the location of the rectangular front after 10 days of inflow. One obtains:

$$z = \frac{\rho_f v}{\rho_b H} t = \frac{1}{2 \times 10^{-2}} \frac{1}{10^3} (3600)(24)(10)$$

$$z = 43.3 \text{ km}$$

Thus, a *minimum* of over 40 km have been contaminated after 10 days.

Illustration 6.2.7   Clearance of a Contaminated River Bed (Equilibrium)

Here the surprising fact which emerges is that under linear equilibrium conditions, clearance produces the *same* rectangular front seen during loading (Figure 6.14B). Elongation of that front is solely due to transport resistance. The clearance time will be 10 days, the same as the contamination time.

Comments:

The fact that the same expression, Equation 6.2.43, applies to both adsorption and desorption, implies that for linear sorption equilibria clearance time always equals loading time or time of exposure to the contaminant. This may come as a surprise to environmentalists who are accustomed to dealing with long recovery times. Such long times do arise, but only as a consequence of long exposure times. This assumes, of course, that the process is one of *linear* sorption only, and that there is no *chemical interaction* of the contaminant with the river bed.

When the sorption equilibrium is no longer linear, i.e., when it departs from Henry's law, marked differences in exposure and recovery times arise. The same form of expression, Equation 6.2.43 is still retained, but with the subtle difference that to calculate time or distance of contamination or clearance, Henry's constant is replaced by the loading ratio $(q/Y)_F$. Thus,

For exposure/contamination:

$$z/t = \frac{\rho_f v}{\rho_b (q/Y)_F}$$

(6.2.44)

For clearance/recovery:

$$z/t = \frac{\rho_f v}{\rho_b H}$$

Since $(q/Y)_F \ll H$, the time required to contaminate a given length of river sediment will be considerably less than that required for clearance, even under equilibrium conditions. Such departures from linearity do not occur with highly hydrophobic solutes but do arise with increasing solubility of the chemical. Aliphatic and aromatic alcohols, sulfonated compounds and similar, more hydrophilic solutes fall into this category.

Suppose that the river is quite shallow and its depth of the same order as that of the sediment so that $h_s/(h_s + h_r) \approx 1$. It would then take 1000 days, instead of 10, to contaminate a 43.3 km stretch of river sediment and an equal period of time for recovery.

Illustration 6.2.8   Minimum Bed Requirements for Adsorptive
Water Purification (Equilibrium)

Although water purification is not generally taken up within the context of environmental modeling, the discharge of contaminated water has a direct impact on the environment. Removal of aqueous pollutants is of considerable importance to the environmental scientist or engineer.

We wish to consider the purification of an aqueous effluent saturated with n-hexane, benzene, and toluene using an activated carbon bed. Because of the low solubility of the hydrocarbons involved, one can assume that operation will be in the linear, Henry's law region. Estimates of Henry constants can be obtained from the corresponding water–soil Henry constants (Table 6.3) by assuming carbon content in the soil to be 1%. If, in addition, we set the carbon bed specific gravity at 0.5, Henry constants for the adsorbent can be obtained by multiplying the values for water–soil by a factor of 200. Thus, using Table 6.3, we obtain:

	$H\left(\dfrac{\text{kg water}}{\text{kg soil}}\right)$	$H\left(\dfrac{\text{kg water}}{\text{kg carbon}}\right)$
n-Hexane	52	10,400
Benzene	0.54	108
Toluene	2.0	400

These are clearly only approximate values, since the adsorptive capacity of commercial carbon will, at least to some extent, differ from that of the organic matter found in soil. Actual values, however, are usually unavailable, even from the suppliers who tend to measure capacities at higher loadings outside the Henry law region. Table 6.3 and similar compilations found in the environmental literature can serve as useful estimates of these otherwise unavailable parameters. To obtain an expression for minimum bed weight, we return to Equation 6.2.43 and rearrange it into the form:

$$\frac{z\rho_b}{t\rho_b v} = \frac{1}{H} \tag{6.2.45}$$

Multiplying numerator and denominator of the left side by bed cross-section, we obtain:

$$\frac{A_c z\rho_b}{A\, t\rho_f v} = \frac{\text{Bed weight}}{\text{Weight of fluid treated}} = \frac{1}{H}$$

or

$$W_m = 1/H \qquad (6.2.46)$$

Thus, we arrive at the simple and illuminating result that the minimum bed weight required per unit weight of feed W_m is given by the *inverse* of the Henry constant. This agrees with the physical notion that a high value of H will give high carbon loadings and result in a lower bed requirement.

To apply this expression to the system under consideration, we first note that in multicomponent adsorption, the solutes propagate through the bed in the sequence of their affinity for the sorbent, the least strongly held one, i.e., the component with the lowest Henry constant, moving ahead of the solutes with higher H values. In the case in hand, benzene with the lowest H will break through first, followed by toluene, with *n*-hexane bringing up the rear. The bed requirement thus will have to be based on the *lightest* component, i.e., the solute with the lowest Henry constant. We obtain:

$$W_m = 1/108 = 9.3 \times 10^{-3} \frac{kg\,bed}{kg\,feed}$$

i.e., a minimum of approximately 10 grams of carbon will be required for every kilogram of feed treated. This would seem to be an acceptable value.

Illustration 6.2.9   Actual Bed Requirements for Adsorptive Water Purification (Nonequilibrium)

The model for this case, to be described in Chapter 7 under the heading "Chromatographic Equations," requires the solution of two PDEs consisting of unsteady and distributed solute balances on the fluid and solid phases, respectively. Though somewhat complex and lengthly, it is within the reach of conventional PDE solution methods (Laplace transformation) and is briefly taken up under the Practice Problems of Chapter 9. Fortunately, the results can be cast into a simple form expressed in terms of two dimensionless parameters.

Dimensionless distance:

$$N = K_0 a \frac{z}{v} \qquad (6.2.47)$$

Dimensionless time:

$$T = K_0 a \frac{\rho_f}{\rho_b} \frac{t}{H} \qquad (6.2.48)$$

Solutions of the PDEs as function of these parameters are given in Table 6.5 at effluent concentration levels 1% and 10% of the inlet feed. The following features are of note.

TABLE 6.5
Parameters for Nonequilibrium Adsorption

$$T = K_0 a \frac{\rho_f}{\rho_b} \frac{t}{H}$$

$N = K_0 a \dfrac{z}{v}$	1% Breakthrough	10% Breakthrough
1000	900	950
800	700	740
600	520	550
400	330	360
200	150	170
100	70	85
80	52	65
60	37	48
40	22	30
20	7.8	13
10	2.5	5.0
8	1.2	3.5
6	0.38	2.2
5	0.1	1.6
4.75	0.035	0.85
3	—	0.32
	$T \leq 0$ for $N \leq 4.50$	$T \leq 0$ for $N \leq 2.30$

The overall mass transfer coefficient is given in the form $K_0 a$ (time^{-1}) where a is the exterior surface area of the adsorbent per unit volume of bed. For industrial adsorbents, $K_0 a$ typically vary over the interval $10^{-2} - 10^{-4}$ s^{-1}. Values within this range can be used in estimating *actual* bed requirements or breakthrough times for a given size of bed, using the information provided in Table 6.5.

The aforementioned table also reveals two interesting limiting cases. For $N > 1000$, the difference in breakthrough times at the 1% and 10% levels is less than 5%. This implies that the adsorption front is quite sharp and breakthrough times and bed lengths approach the values calculated from Equation 6.2.43. Put another way, at these high values of N, which carry with them high transport rates and long residence times, the system is close to local equilibrium behavior. At low values of N, on the other hand, a point is reached where dimensionless time T obtained from the model solution first drops to zero and then turns negative. The latter values are invalid, but the value $T = 0$ has a physical meaning. It implies that no complete purification of the fluid is possible below the threshold value of N, and that solute at some fraction of the feed value will break through the instant fluid reaches the bed outlet. Thus, for $N \leq 4.50$, solute at 1% of the feed concentration reaches the bed exit untreated, for $N \leq 2.30$ the breakthrough concentration is 10% of the feed level. Evidently when this happens, one must increase N by increasing bed height z or lowering fluid velocity v in order to utilize the bed at all.

We illustrate the use of Table 6.5 with some calculation for the system n-hexane, benzene, toluene previously treated under equilibrium conditions in the preceding illustration. We set the following parameter values:

$K_0a = 10^{-2}$ s^{-1}
z $= 2$ m
v $= 10^{-3}$ m/s
H $= 108$ (see Illustration 6.2.8)
ρ_b $= 500$ kg/m^3

and obtain

$$N = K_0 a \frac{z}{v} = 10^{-2} \frac{2}{10^{-3}} = 20$$

which gives, from Table 6.5, a value of dimensionless time $T = 7.8$ at the 1% level. Hence, the breakthrough time t of this level is given by:

$$t = T \frac{\rho_b}{\rho_f} \frac{H}{K_0 a} = \frac{(7.8)(500)(108)}{(1000)(10^{-2})}$$

$$t = 4.2 \times 10^4 \text{ s} = 11.7 \text{ hrs}$$

Actual bed requirement W_a is given by the expression:

$$W_a = \frac{N}{T} \frac{1}{H} = \frac{N}{T} W_m$$

as can be verified by examining the units of N/T. We obtain, for our case:

$$W_a = \frac{N}{T} W_m = \frac{20}{7.8} W_m = 2.6 W_m$$

$$W_a = (2.6)(9.3 \times 10^{-3}) = 2.4 \times 10^{-2} \frac{\text{kg bed}}{\text{kg feed}}$$

Thus, the actual bed requirement is 2.6 times the minimum calculated in the previous illustration under equilibrium conditions. In industrial applications, it is common practice to size a bed at 2 to 4 times the minimum requirement to account for mass transfer resistance. The value we obtained here falls within that range. We note in closing that better bed utilization and longer breakthrough times can be achieved by increasing bed height or reducing fluid velocity. Table 6.5 gives us a quick scan of what can be achieved in this fashion. Thus, if we were to raise N, by appropriate manipulation of z and v five-fold to a value of $N = 100$, we would obtain:

$$W_a = \frac{N}{T} W_m = \frac{100}{70} W_m = 1.43 W_m$$

i.e., approximately one half of the previous bed requirement.

Practice Problems

6.2.1 Simultaneous Evaporation of Several Solutes — Show that when two chemicals evaporate simultaneously under equilibrium conditions, the fraction x/x_0 of each remaining after a fraction f of the solution has been evaporated is in the ratio:

$$\frac{(x/x_0)_1}{(x/x_0)_2} \cong \frac{(1-f)^{P_1^0/x_1 * P_{H_2O}^0}}{(1-f)^{P_2^0/x_2 * P_{H_2O}}}$$

where $x^* =$ solubility in mol fraction.

6.2.2 Evaporation of a Chemical from a River Carrying Suspended Solids — Rivers have the ability to carry considerable amounts of suspended matter. The Yellow River in China and the Rio Grande in the U.S. may contain as much as 10 g solids/l while a clear mountain stream may contain as little as 1 mg/l. The world average is about 200 mg/l.

Consider a stream carrying a volatile chemical both dissolved in the water as well as adsorbed on the suspended solids. Show that under steady-state conditions, the fraction f of chemical desorbed by release to the atmosphere is given by the expression:

$$f = 1 - \exp\left[-\frac{K a \tau}{1 + H C_s}\right]$$

Identify the various terms.

6.2.3 Evaporation from Water with Suspended Solids — The water supply to a well-mixed basin is contaminated with a chemical, concentration C_f, and contains, suspended solids as well carrying a contaminant concentration of the same chemical. The suspended solids are present at a uniform concentration C_s, and volume of the basin may be assumed constant. While in the basin, the water releases the chemical to the atmosphere by evaporation, simultaneously receiving additional chemical from the suspended solids. Both processes are transport controlled.

Derive an expression for the steady-state concentration of the chemical in the effluent.

6.2.4 Evaporation in Mixed Flow — Consider release of a chemical to the atmosphere from a river in plug flow which flows into two well-mixed basins in series. Show that the fraction released F after passage through all three units is given by:

$$F = 1 - \frac{\exp[-(K a \tau)_1]}{[1+(K a \tau)_2][1+(K a \tau)_3]}$$

and identify the terms.

6.2.5 The Streeter-Phelps Model —

(a) Derive Equations 6.2.40 and 6.2.41.

(b) Consider a stream taking a constant inflow of a chemical with a BOD of L_0 = 15 mg/l. The dissolved oxygen deficit at that point is D_0 = 3 mg/l. The biodegradation rate constant is estimated at k_r = 0.23 day^{-1}, and the self-purification rate f at 2.0. Calculate the dissolved oxygen deficit one day distant from the point of pollutant discharge.

(Hint: Use Equation 6.2.39.)

Answer: (b) 4.3 mg/L

6.2.6 Henry's Constant for Activated Carbon — Estimate the Henry's constant for adsorption of carbon tetrachloride from water onto activated carbon.

(Hint: Use Table 6.3.)

6.2.7 Velocity of Propagation of a Sorption Front —

(a) Calculate the velocity of the midpoint of an adsorption front propagating through soil in contact with contaminated groundwater, using the following data:

Henry constant $H = 10^3$ kg water/kg soil
Flow velocity $v = 1$ mm/s
Specific gravity of soil $s = 2.5$

(b) What is the position of the midpoint after 100 days?
Answer: (b) 3.5 m

6.2.8 Transport in Stratified Layers — Lakes and similar water basins often exhibit departures from well-mixed behavior because of stratification. In one simple model of this phenomenon, it is assumed that an unmixed layer of thickness Δh is sandwiched between two well-stirred compartments of height h_1 and h_2, respectively. Compartment 1 adjoining the bottom has an initial concentration C_1^0, while that of compartment 2 is C_2^0. The concentration gradient across the unmixed layer, termed a *pycnocline*, can be assumed to be linear.

Derive the following solution for the unsteady behavior of compartment 1 and identify the parameters K_1 and K_2.

$$C_1 = \frac{K_1}{h_1 + h_2 + \Delta h}\left\{1 - \exp\frac{Dt}{\Delta h}\left(\frac{1+K_2}{h_1}\right)\right\} + C_1^0 \exp\left[-\frac{Dt}{\Delta h}\left(\frac{1+K_2}{h_1}\right)\right]$$

(Hint: Combine an unsteady balance with a cumulative balance.)

6.3   WELCOME TO THE REAL WORLD

The illustrations and practice problems considered in this section all arose in an industrial, commercial, or otherwise "real world" context. Such problems are usually beset by a lack of pertinent information, or seeming lack thereof, baffling complexities and a tendency to invite the question: Where do I start?

Models are often not required at all. Their place is then taken by the application of some seemingly unrelated physical principle and the need for good physical insight. On other occasions the required models are simple or have to be kept simple in order to arrive at an answer within a reasonable time. In yet another category of problem, the need to model is craftily hidden and one is led to it only after a long search for alternative solutions. All of these features place the real world problems in a special class by themselves. One is no longer confronted with the obvious application of a particular principle which is the hallmark of textbook problems. The present monograph has had its share of them. Instead, one has to draw on a wide range of skills and knowledge and apply them astutely and with a steady eye. The exercise can be frustrating, but also exhilarating when a solution is finally found.

A deflationary word of caution. Having successfully solved the problem, it is not uncommon to find that the solution is rejected or the advice not heeded. This may be due to reluctance to undertake changes, skepticism about the solution offered, or the intervention of external factors such as market forces. That, too, has to be accepted as part of the real world.

In the illustrations and practice problems which follow we shall encounter all of these features, and it will be shown how the various difficulties were ultimately overcome. We hope that from these examples, a philosophy of approach or even a methodology unstructured though it may be, will emerge to guide the reader in this difficult task. At any rate, the attempt will have been made.

Illustration 6.3.1   Production of Heavy Water by Methane Distillation

Although nuclear power generation is nowadays regarded with suspicion if not downright hostility, this was not the case in the early 1960s when the author became involved in a project aimed at developing new methods of heavy water production.

Reactors based on uranium as a fuel fall into two broad categories: those that use the costlier enriched uranium and those that employ natural uranium at its natural level of abundance of the fissionable isotope U^{235}. The latter has to be used in conjunction with a so-called moderator, usually highly purified graphite or heavy water D_2O. These moderators slow down emitted neutrons to the "thermal" speeds required for an efficient chain reaction to occur. The notorious Chernobyl rector was based on a graphite — natural uranium combination. Heavy water is used as moderator in the Canadian designed CANDU reactors. Most U.S. installations use enriched uranium as a fuel; hence, they do not require a moderator.

In the early 1960s almost all the heavy water in use was produced by the so-called GS Process, in which deuterated water HDO is enriched from its natural abundance of about 600 ppm to 1 to 5% by chemical exchange between the source water and hydrogen sulfide. Final purification is by conventional distillation using high efficiency packing.

With the cost of D_2O at \$50/kg and several hundred tonnes of the material being required per reactor, there was a considerable incentive to search for cheaper production methods. One alternative being considered in the early 1960s was that of methane distillation. This was prompted by the new development of shipping large tonnages of natural gas in liquefied form (LNG). It was envisaged that facilities could be erected at ports of trans-shipment that would separate the deuterated component CH_3D by distillation prior to vaporizing and piping the fuel.

To make distillation attractive, a high value of the separation factor $\alpha = y_{CH_3D} / x_{CH_3D}$ is crucial. These values are, for isotope mixtures, very close to 1, requiring a disproportionately large number of stages, or *theoretical plates* N_p, for a successful enrichment process. It is known that at total reflux, the number of theoretical stages is inversely proportional to $\alpha - 1$:

$$N_p \propto \frac{1}{\alpha - 1} \qquad (6.3.1)$$

A consequence of this relation is that small increases of α above unity can dramatically reduce the required size of the distillation unit. Thus, an increase of α 1.001 to 1.002, a seemingly puny increment, reduces the number of theoretical plates by half.

Low pressure measurements of α for the system CH_3D-CH_4 had shown a steady increase until, at 1 atm, it attains a value of $\alpha = 1.0035$. Theoretical considerations indicated that this trend would continue as temperature was increased above the normal boiling point. Economic evaluations had, for their part, shown that distillation would become competitive with the GS process at $\alpha = 1.025$. Thus, the door was opened to the potential use of high pressure distillation for the enrichment of CH_3D. The cryogenic technology for such a process was well established and posed no undue difficulty.

A research program, sponsored by a major oil company with large interests in natural gas, was initiated to determine values of α up to the critical point, $P_C \cong 46$ atm. Rayleigh distillation was chosen over single stage equilibration since the former provides a greater degree of enrichment and, hence, lessens the requirement for high precision in the determination of isotopic content of the phases. α was then determined from the expression (Chapter 2, Practice Problem 2.3):

$$\alpha - 1 = \frac{\ln x_f / x_i}{\ln V_f / V_i} \qquad (6.3.2)$$

Here we have replaced moles n in the still by volume V, since the molar density of the mixture remains essentially unchanged during the course of distillation. A special high pressure, transparent, and calibrated cell was used to allow determination of the initial and final volumes V_i and V_f.

The initial results were disappointing. A separation factor of only 1.007 was obtained at a pressure P/P_{crit} of approximately 0.7, even though theoretical considerations indicated α values as high as 1.05 should be attainable. Considerable time was spent verifying the validity of the analytical results. To ensure proper equilibration of the phases during distillation, the vapor withdrawal rate was reduced to a minimum and a magnetic stirrer provided for both phases. Sample withdrawal was carried out with extreme care to avoid disturbing the equilibrium. Some 6 months were spent in revision and verification without any improvement in the results.

It was at some unspecified point that it became apparent that the model itself, i.e., Equation 6.3.2, may be at fault. Precisely how this came about cannot be recalled, but it was suspected that the high pressure used, abnormal for a Rayleigh distillation, might be at the root of the problem. The model equations, when examined in this light, led to the conclusion that the vapor phase which is routinely neglected in low pressure mass balances would now have to be included because of its high density. Below we sketch the revised model equations and the results obtained:

Total mol balance:

$$\text{Rate in} - \text{Rate out} = \text{Rate of change of contents}$$

$$0 - D = \frac{d}{dt}(\rho_v V_v + \rho_\ell V_\ell) \tag{6.3.3}$$

Component balance:

$$\text{Rate of } CH_3D \text{ in} - \text{Rate of } CH_3D \text{ out} = \frac{\text{Rate of change in}}{CH_3D \text{ content}}$$

$$0 - yD = \frac{d}{dt}(x\rho_\ell V_\ell + y\rho_v V_v) \tag{6.3.4}$$

Equilibrium relation:

$$y = \alpha\, x \tag{6.3.5}$$

Since we have one more variable, the vapor volume V_v, than was previously the case, an additional relation is required. We use the fact that vapor and liquid volumes must add up to the known still volume V_s, and obtain:

$$V_v + V_\ell = V_s \tag{6.3.6}$$

Using this relation to eliminate V_v, the material balances become:

$$-D = \frac{d}{dt}(\rho_\ell - \rho_v)V_\ell \tag{6.3.7}$$

$$-\alpha xD = \frac{d}{dt}[x\rho_\ell V_\ell + \alpha x\rho_v(V_s - V_\ell)] \qquad (6.3.8)$$

We now divide the two equations as usual to eliminate D and dt, separate variables, and obtain:

$$\frac{1}{\alpha-1}\frac{dx}{x} = \frac{dV_L}{V_\ell + \alpha\dfrac{\rho_v}{\rho_L}(V_s - V_\ell)}$$

or equivalently,

$$\frac{1}{\alpha-1}\frac{dx}{x} = \frac{d\phi}{\phi + \alpha R(1-\phi)} \qquad (6.3.9)$$

where we have nondimensionalized the variables by introducing:

$R = \rho_v/\rho_\ell$ = Phase density ratio
$\phi = V_\ell/V_s$ = Liquid-to-still volume ratio

Integration yields:

$$\alpha - 1 = \frac{(1-\alpha R)\ln(x_f/x_i)}{\ln\dfrac{\alpha R + (1-\alpha R)\phi_f}{\alpha R + (1-\alpha R)\phi_i}} \qquad (6.3.10)$$

which converts to a good approximation to the explicit form:

$$\alpha - 1 \cong \frac{(1-R)\ln(x_f/x_i)}{\ln\dfrac{R + (1-R)\phi_f}{R + (1-R)\phi_i}} \qquad (6.3.11)$$

where the subscripts $_i$ and $_f$ refer to the initial and final states, respectively.

In the limit $R \to 0$, the expression reduces, as it should, to the classical Rayleigh Equation 6.3.2.

A numerical example will serve to illustrate the difference in the results obtained by the two expressions. We set, for this purpose, density ratio $R = 0.5$, initial liquid-to-still volume $\phi_i = 0.5$, final liquid-to-still volume $\phi_f = 0.025$, measured liquid phase depletion in CH_3D, $x_f/x_i = 0.98$. We are considering conditions where the operation is carried out a few atmospheres below the critical pressure, 95% of the initial liquid is boiled off, and a 2% decline in CH_3D content is recorded. We obtain, from Equations 6.3.2 and 6.3.10 respectively,

Classical Rayleigh:

$$\alpha - 1 = \frac{\ln x_f / x_i}{\ln \phi_f / \phi_i} = \frac{\ln 0.98}{\ln 0.05}$$

$$\alpha = 1.0067$$

Revised Rayleigh:

$$\alpha - 1 = \frac{(1-R)\ln(x_f / x_i)}{\ln \dfrac{R + (1-R)\phi_f}{R + (1-R)\phi_i}} = \frac{(1-0.5)\ln(0.98)}{\ln \dfrac{0.5 + (1-0.5)0.025}{0.5 + (1-0.5)0.5}}$$

$$\alpha = 1.026$$

Thus, the crucial factor $\alpha - 1$ is about four times that calculated by the Classical Rayleigh Equation. This translates into *a four-fold reduction* in the size of distillation unit required.

Postscript:

A methane distillation plant for the production of heavy water was never built. Market forces intervened to negate the promising results. The sponsors acquired a company specializing in the design of nuclear reactors based on enriched uranium and their interest in heavy water waned. The CANDU reactor, which had a special appeal to countries without uranium enrichment facilities, ran into tough competition when the U.S. design was put on the market. France developed plutonium-based reactors that also became available for export. Environmental concerns focused primarily on the safe disposal of spent fuel began to make themselves felt. By the end of the 1980s this factor and the outcry over the Three-Mile Island and Chernobyl accidents had brought nuclear reactor construction to a near stand-still in many countries and led to an outright ban in others. This is the situation at the time of writing. Thus, the best-laid plans of mice and men ... .

Illustration 6.3.2   Clumping of Coal Transported in Freight Cars

This seemingly mundane problem which developed into a major headache for coal companies involved the clumping together of coal lumps transported in open freight cars due to the suspected freezing of surface moisture. The resulting conglomerate of coal had to be broken up at considerable expense and inconvenience at the point of destination.

Although ambient temperatures below zero were occasionally encountered during transport, the clumping also occurred when, according to the sources, the temperatures were above freezing. As usual, a fast and cheap remedy was desired.

One often starts such problems by questioning the validity of the supporting information. Were the temperatures really above zero when the problem arose? How then could freezing occur? Or was it some organic surface component which gelled or reacted to cause adhesion?

The freight cars were open at the top and unsealed along the sides with gaps between members of the enclosing structure. This would cause exposure of the load to air flowing above and through the contents and possibly result in evaporative cooling. An examination of the low temperature humidity chart (Chapter 3, Figure 3.18) shows that wet-bulb temperatures at or below zero occur when the dry-bulb temperature is still above zero. Thus, a T_{db} of ~ 9°C yields a wet-bulb value of 0°C, 5°C drops it to –3, etc. Thus, the potential exists for freezing of moisture or other surface components.

The suggestions conveyed to the company was to cover the top of the load with canvas and if possible seal the sides of the freight cars. This would stop the air flow which causes evaporative cooling. Stagnant air does not show this effect.

Comments:

Clearly no modeling was used and physical insight was invoked instead. The temptation to model nevertheless existed. One could, for example, derive unsteady temperatures profiles for a moist lump of coal exposed to a change in ambient temperature. Heat transfer would be by conduction from the interior of the lump to the surface and from there by convection to the flowing air. Provision could be made for a latent heat term once freezing commenced. The model would consist of a linear PDE with a Type III surface boundary condition if a single lump of coal of uniform surface conditions is considered. A somewhat complex but manageable model. Inclusion of surface variations, or variations in air temperature, would escalate the complexity as would a change from a single lump of coal to an array. Numerical solutions would almost certainly have to be resorted to. This would earn applause in academic circles but not necessarily from the coal companies.

- Humidity charts are usually available only in the high temperature range (Chapter 3, Figure 3.18), hence, the conclusions given here may not have been drawn for lack of information.
- The fate of the recommendations is not known. They may have been implemented or cast aside for an alternative more palatable to management. This is a frequent occurrence but should not deter the practicing scientist or engineer.

Illustration 6.3.3   Pop Goes the Vessel

Many industrial problems are diagnosed correctly by plant personnel and appropriate steps taken to remedy them. They then become part of plant lore and often the subject of much hilarity. "Boy, how could we have let this one happen?," etc.

For example, a process vessel (unspecified size, material, or process) was to be purged of residual liquid solvent left in the vessel from the previous operation. This was to be accomplished by passing steam into the vessel for a brief period, condensing the effluent vapor mixture, and separating the solvent for recycling. Shortly after the start of the steaming procedure and with the exit valve open, the flange connecting the vessel to the valve popped off with what appeared to be the force of an explosion.

Initial suspicions centered on the possibility of an air leak having caused the formation of an explosive air–solvent vapor mixture. When this was ruled out, attention turned to the possibility of a pressure buildup due to the evaporating solvent which was deemed to have been given "insufficient time" to flow out. Steam pressure alone could not have caused the accident since that pressure was, with the valve open, well within vessel and piping specifications. However, since steam has sufficient latent heat to vaporize two to four moles or more of solvent per mole steam, it became evident that the situation may have developed into one of "choking flow." In other words, the exit pipe and valve diameters were not large enough to accommodate the combined flow of uncondensed steam and evaporated solvent, and a "standing pressure wave" of considerable magnitude developed within the vessel (see Chapter 3, Illustration 3.6.3 and Figure 3.27). A larger valve and exit pipe diameter was called for and these changes were implemented. No further mishap occurred.

Comment:

Choking flow or limiting flow conditions are one of the most frequently encountered causes of system or process malfunction and failure. These conditions, as we had seen, arise only in the flow of compressible fluids, a topic which is inadequately covered in many undergraduate curricula. Most fluid mechanics texts make some mention of limiting compressible flow without, however, outlining all the consequences of this behavior. The standing wave formation is only given passing notice, and the attendant effect of possible pressure buildup none at all. It is well worth making awareness of this phenomenon part of the arsenal of the practicing scientist or engineer.

Illustration 6.3.4   Debugging of a Vinyl Chloride Recovery Unit

Vinyl chloride monomer (VCM) is a volatile substance (boiling point: 14°C) used as a starting material for the production of polyvinyl chloride (PVC). It has been identified as a potential carcinogen and occupational health regulations call for an upper limit of 1 to 5 ppm VCM in factory air.

A preferred method of air purification is to pass VCM-laden air through beds of activated carbon. These beds operate on a four-step cycle: (1) saturation with VCM to 1 ppm breakthrough, (2) stripping of the adsorbed VCM with steam which is subsequently condensed leaving essentially pure gaseous VCM for drying and recycling, (3) drying of the carbon bed with hot air, and (4) cooling of the regenerated bed with cold purified air (Figure 6.15). A dual-bed system is commonly employed so that while one bed is "on stream" the second bed can be regenerated and prepared for the adsorption step. The time period allowed for each step is typically as follows:

1. Saturation — 4 h
2. Steaming — 2 h
3. Drying — 1½ h
4. Cooling — ½ h

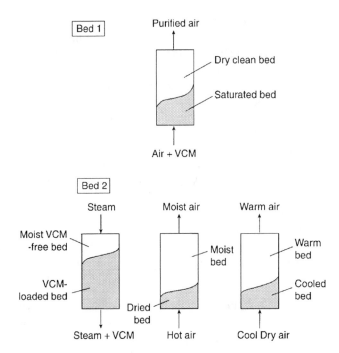

FIGURE 6.15 Removal of vinyl chloride monomer from air. Operation of the adsorption purifier.

A major producer of PVC experienced difficulties with a newly installed adsorption system. The unit performed satisfactorily for single test runs, but during cycling the VCM level in the effluent air rose to unacceptable levels. Inspection of the beds revealed considerable residual moisture. Inadequate drying during Step 3 was therefore considered to be a possible reason for the malfunctioning of the bed.

Additional data provided were as follows:

Bed dimensions:	1.2 m × 1.4 packed height
Bed charge:	775 kg
Carbon pellet diameter:	1/4 in. = 6.3×10^{-3} m
Bed density:	480 kg/m³
Pellet density:	800 kg/m³
Drying air temperature:	120°F = 48.9°C
Drying air humidity:	Negligible
Air flow rate:	~ 0.1 kg/s

Condensed moisture on the bed is commonly calculated by adding: latent heat of desorption $\cong 2 \times$ heat of vaporization + sensible heat required to heat carbon bed and vessel from 20°C to 100°C.

The latent heat of desorption calculation required equilibrium loading data that were obtained from the adsorbent manufacturer. A value of q = 0.2 kg VCM/kg carbon was calculated. Specific heats and latent heat of vaporization were obtained from standard sources. These calculations were carried out in-house and yielded an estimated weight of condensate of 100 kg.

A precise modeling of the drying step is a fairly formidable task. Solute balances over the gas and solid phases as well an energy balance are required to describe the system. Three coupled PDEs will result which are nonlinear because of the nonlinearity of the equilibrium relation. Estimation of the transport parameters poses an additional problem. Although a numerical solution is possible in principle, this method of attack is far too elaborate for an initial appraisal. An asymptotic approach which avoids the PDEs suggests itself, at least as a starting point.

The situation here is pleasantly different in that the primary source of malfunction had been identified, and a considerable amount of background information and data was available. The suspicion had already arisen that the air supply and/or its temperature may have been inadequate to evaporate the 100 kg of water in the specified time interval ($1^1/_2$ h). Thus, a good deal of groundwork had been done.

When queried about their choice of air blower and its delivery rate (0.1 kg/s) plant personnel responded that it was based on the assumption that the condensate was at or near 100°C. This was a major conceptual error. A basic knowledge of the Psychometric Chart or of humidification operations should have led to the realization that evaporative cooling would reduce the temperature of the condensate well below 100°C. This in turn would dramatically reduce the evaporation rate since the vapor pressure driving force is an exponential function of temperature.

If one assumes that the entire bed attains the wet-bulb temperature after an initial start-up period, the model reduces to a single ODE of the type encountered in Chapter 2, Illustration 2.7 (Drying of a Nonporous Plastic Sheet), i.e., for this case:

$$G_s \frac{dY}{dz} - k_Y a(Y^* - Y) = 0 \qquad (2.50)$$

Drying time then can be obtained, as was the case there, by a cumulative moisture balance over the bed.

In Illustration 2.7 a further simplification was proposed which assumed the effluent air to be fully saturated at the wet-bulb or adiabatic saturation humidity Y_{wb} ($= Y_{as}$). This approach avoided the necessity to estimate the mass transfer coefficient $k_Y a$, and provided a lower limit to the required drying t, or if t is specified, the required air flow rate G_s.

Let us proceed along these lines. We first perform a cumulative mass balance which yields the relations:

$$Y_{wb}\left(\frac{kg\,water}{kg\,air}\right) G_s\left(\frac{kg\,dry\,air}{S}\right) t = 100\,kg \qquad (6.3.12)$$

and with $t = 1^1/_2$ h $= 5400$ s,

$$(G_s)_{Min} = \frac{100}{Y_{wb}\,5400} = \frac{1}{54\,Y_{wb}} \qquad (6.3.13)$$

TABLE 6.6
Minimum Drying Air Flow Rates

T_{db} °C	25	50	75	100	125
$Y_{db}\left(\dfrac{kg\,H_2O}{kg\,air}\right)$	0.00 6	0.01 3	0.02 1	0.02 8	0.03 8
$(G_s)_{Min}$ (kg/s)	3.1	1.4	0.88	0.66	0.49

The Psychometric Chart (Chapter 3, Figure 3.19) is now used to establish values of $(G_s)_{Min}$ for various levels of incoming air temperatures T_{db}. This is done in the usual fashion by first fixing the point $(T = T_{db}, Y_{db} = 0)$ and then moving from that point upward and to the left along the adiabatic saturation line to a point of intersection with the 100% relative humidity curve. The ordinate of that latter point yields the value of Y_{wb} to be used in Equation 6.3.13. The results obtained are summarized below.

Examination of Table 6.6 shows that the drying air provided in the plant at $T_{db} \cong 50°C$ and $G_s = 0.1$ kg/s *underestimated* the *minimum* requirement $(G_s)_{Min}$ by a factor of 14. Even at an air temperature of $T_{db} = 125°C$, the minimum flow required was still *five* times that actually provided. Clearly a combination of both higher air temperatures and larger blower capacities would be required to meet the drying specifications. The final recommendation made was for a blower with a capacity of 1 kg/s and an air temperature of 125°C. This provides a safety factor of 2 over the corresponding $(G_s)_{Min}$ of 0.49 kg/s.

Comments:

One will note that a series of engineering approximations were made to arrive at an initial recommendation. The amount of condensate accumulated in the bed was calculated by adding approximate sensible and latent heat requirements. A more precise model again leads to three coupled nonlinear PDEs with the added complication that heat losses to the vessel wall now have to be taken into account. The approximate method of estimation has proved itself fairly reliable in practice and, therefore, is widely used.

In providing minimum flow rate values, the tacit assumption was made that the condensate was present as *free* moisture. Although carbon is generally hydrophobic and not prone to adsorb much water at 100°C, some penetration of condensate into the porous structure is highly likely and a falling rate drying period will have to be added to the evaporation of free moisture, thus raising the air flow requirement. We have tried to allow for this by providing a safety factor of two in the recommended value for G_s. Whether this is in fact sufficient, will have to be borne out by tests.

Mass transfer resistance was neglected in this first appraisal, but one can easily return to Equation 2.50 and carry out a more refined analysis along the lines given in Illustration 2.7.

One will note that for the second time in four illustrations, the Humidity Chart has come to the fore. That chart, along with the Compressible Flow Chart (Chapter

3, Figure 3.17), are among the dozen or so most frequently used tools in engineering practice. We shall have occasion to encounter them again in other applications.

Illustration 6.3.5   Pop Goes the Vessel (Again)

We consider here a lawsuit in which the relevant facts were as follows. The plaintiff, a scrap metal dealer, filed suit for damages against an oil company which supplied him with hydraulic oil. The oil is used in hydraulic presses to crush and compact scrap metal. The necessity arose to repair the storage tank holding the oil, and the suppliers offered to store the oil for the duration of the repairs. The oil was hauled away and returned in a tank truck after the repairs were completed. It was then pumped back into the storage tank. Subsequently the need for additional welding repairs arose. Since the location was at the top of the tank separated from the air by ~ 1 m³ head space, and the oil itself is nonvolatile and nonexplosive, no need was felt to remove the oil prior to welding. Shortly after welding started, an explosion occurred that caused considerable material damages, but fortunately no serious injuries.

Plaintiff claimed that the tank-truck had been contaminated with gasoline from previous deliveries which had caused an explosive gasoline–air mixture to form in the head space. Defendants responded that the truck had been thoroughly cleaned and that no more than traces of gasoline could have been left behind in the truck and the connecting lines. The case then hinged on determining the minimum amount of gasoline which would cause an explosion. If found small or even minuscule, a ruling against the defendant might be expected.

Consultants to the scrap dealer and his insurance company located the following data:

Gasoline:
> Explosive limits in air: 2.3 to 7.5 mol %
> Average molar mass: 86
> Specific gravity: 0.73
> Vapor pressure (25°C): 400 mm Hg

Hydraulic oil:
> Nonexplosive, essentially nonvolatile
> Volume: 1165 Imperial gallons
> Average molar mass: 425
> Specific gravity: 0.88

Two cases were considered.

1. The gasoline did not, or did not have time, to dissolve completely in the hydraulic oil. A part of it at least floated to the top of the oil because of its lower specific gravity. This would give a lower bound to the amount of gasoline required to produce an explosive mixture.
2. The gasoline dissolves completely in the oil where it forms an ideal solution and exerts a vapor pressure in accordance with Raoult's law. This yields an upper bound.

Case 1 is the more likely scenario. Applying the ideal Gas law and Daltons' law, one obtains:

$$p_{gasoline}V = n_{gasoline}RT = \left(\frac{m}{M}\right)_{gasoline} RT \qquad (6.3.14)$$

and

$$p_{gasoline} = y_{gasoline}\, P_T \qquad (6.3.15)$$

where $p_{gasoline}$ = partial pressure of gasoline; P_T = total pressure, m, M = mass and molar mass of gasoline respectively, y = mol fraction of gasoline in air, V = volume of head space, and n = moles of gasoline in air.

Using the lower explosive limit for $y_{gasoline}$ = 0.013, and solving for m, one obtains:

$$m_{gasoline} = \frac{y_{gasoline}P_{Tot}VM_{gasoline}}{RT}$$

$$m_{gasoline} = \frac{(0.013)(1.01 \times 10^5)(1)(86)}{(8.31)(298)} \qquad (6.3.16)$$

$$m_{gasoline} = 45.6\,gms \quad or \quad 62.5\,ml$$

Thus, a very thin layer of gasoline floating on top of the hydraulic oil would have been sufficient to cause the explosion.

Comments:

The small amount of gasoline required placed the defendants in a weak position. They argued that if gasoline was indeed present, sufficient amounts could have evaporated to exceed the upper explosive limit (7.5 mol %). The mixture would then have been too "rich" to produce an explosion. This was countered with the argument that the gasoline concentration at the top of the tank would be quite uneven and, if too rich, could be easily diluted by air movement to produce a mixture within the explosive range.

The reader will note that "modeling" here was at a very low and elementary level. Nevertheless, an important principle of modeling found its way into the solution, that of providing upper and lower bounds to the answer, i.e., "bracketing the solution." The upper bound yielded a value of approximately 30 l gasoline, a substantial amount which was unlikely to have been left in the truck after flushing. Thus, Case 2 was considered too unlikely to have occurred and was not a serious contender in the deliberations.

Postscript:

The case did not come to trial. It was settled out of court for a considerable sum in favor of the plaintiff.

Illustration 6.3.6   Potential Freezing of a Water Pipeline

In this example, again from an industrial source, it was proposed to pump water from a plant to a supply of exhaust steam 500 m away where the water is heated and subsequently returned to the plant. A "double jeopardy" situation was to be considered in which flow is interrupted due to pump failure and the stationary water simultaneously exposed to an ambient temperature of –5°C for as long as 10 hours. The question posed was whether this would result in freezing of the water and ultimate failure of the pipe. The following data were assembled:

Pipe:

> 6 in. schedule 40
> Internal diameter $d_i = 15.7$ cm
> Wall thickness w = 0.71 cm
> Density $\rho_s = 7800$ kg/m^3
> Heat capacity $C_{ps} = 0.473$ kJ/kg K

Water–Ice:

> Heat capacity of water Cpw = 4.2 kJ/kg K
> Compressibility of water $\beta = -\dfrac{1}{V}\dfrac{dV}{dp} \cong 4.4 \times 10^{-6}$ atm^{-1}
> Density of ice $\rho_i = 920$ kg/m^3
> Latent heat of freezing $\Delta H_f = -335$ kJ/kg

Heat transfer coefficients:

> External h_0 = average for still air (see Chapter 3, Table 3.11) = 10 W/m^{2}K
> Internal: assume natural convection
> $h_i = 1.32\,(\Delta T/d_i t)^{1/4} = 1.32\,(25/0.157)^{1/4} = 4.69$ W/m^{2}K
> $U = [(1/h_i + 1/h_0]^{-1} = 3.20$ W/m^{2}K

To obtain some limiting values for this complex problem it was assumed that the cooling process takes place in three steps.

1. Relatively fast cooling of the pipe wall to 0°C. The time required to achieve this is assumed to be much less than that taken up by the water.
2. Cooling of the water to 0°C. The water is taken to be of uniform temperature, not an unreasonable assumption in view of the natural convection process assumed.
3. Formation of ice. This is a moving-boundary problem with an attendant removal of latent heat of freezing. The freeze-drying problem, Illustration 3.3.12, may be invoked for guidance.

The model equation for step 2 takes the form:

$$\text{Rate of energy in} - \text{Rate of energy out} = \frac{\text{Rate of change of}}{\text{energy content}} \tag{6.3.17}$$

$$0 - UA(T_w - T_a) = (V\rho Cp)_w (dT/dt)$$

The equation is integrated by separation of variables and we obtain:

$$t = \frac{(\rho C_p V / A)_w}{U} \ln \frac{T_i - T_a}{T_f - T_a} \tag{6.3.18}$$

where the subscripts $_{i, f}$ refer to initial and final states respectively. T_a is the ambient temperature $= -5°C$. We obtain

$$t = \frac{(1000)(4.2 \times 10^3)(0.157/4)}{3.22} \ln \frac{20 - (-5)}{0 - (-5)}$$

$$t = 8.3 \times 10^4 \text{ s} = 23 \text{ h}$$

Thus, the danger of freezing appears unlikely to arise.

Comments:

The model assumption of a well-stirred liquid phase and heat transfer by natural convection is generally considered to be a valid one. Supporting experimental evidence has come from cooling studies of stagnant oil in a pipe and other similar systems.

The full model for *both pipe and water* which would yield even longer cooling times takes the form:

Pipe wall:

$$h_i A(T_w - T_s) - h_0 A(T_s - T_a) = (\rho V_s C_p)_s \frac{dT_s}{dt} \tag{6.3.19}$$

Water:

$$-UA(T_w - T_a) = (\rho V C_p)_w \frac{dT_w}{dt} \tag{6.3.20}$$

The freezing process, though unlikely to occur here, is worth some scrutiny. We had previously considered the freezing of water exposed to cold air in Chapter 3, Practice Problem 3.3.5, but the body of water there was unconfined and open to the atmosphere. Water enclosed in a vessel filled to capacity will, as is well known, cause a pressure rise due to the higher specific volume of the ice. This may ultimately cause the pipe to rupture. The pressure rise is a function of temperature and can be calculated from the thermodynamic equilibrium relation:

$$\frac{dp}{dT} = \frac{\Delta H_f}{T \Delta V} \tag{6.3.21}$$

(Recall that for vapor-liquid equilibrium, one sets $\Delta V \sim RT/p$ and obtains the Clausius-Clapeyron Equation d ln $p/dT = \Delta H_v/RT^2$.)

Let us calculate the equilibrium freezing pressure predicted by this equation. We have:

$$\Delta V = V_{ice} - V_{water} = \frac{1}{0.92} - \frac{1}{1} = 8.7 \times 10^{-4} \ m^3/g$$

and with $\Delta H_f = -335$ J/g obtain:

$$\Delta p \cong \frac{(\Delta T)(\Delta H_f)}{T \Delta V} = \frac{(-5)(-335)}{273.16(8.7 \times 10^{-8})}$$

$$\Delta p = 55.4 \ Mpa = 547 \ atm$$

"Safe" tensile strengths τ for steel are often set at 500 Mpa, so that one obtains for the bursting pressure, using the hoop stress formula, Equation 3.4.21:

$$p = \frac{\tau \Delta d}{d} = \frac{(5 \times 10^8)(1.42 \times 10^{-4})}{(0.157)}$$

$$p = 45.2 \ Mpa = 446 \ atm$$

Thus, with these values, the pipe would burst at a pressure approximately 25% below the equilibrium pressure of ice–water at −5°C. The solution that suggests itself is to use higher quality steel (see Chapter 3, Table 3.15) or to increase wall thickness by ~ 30%. The higher cost involved makes this unpalatable. The need to do so, however, does not arise since the cooling time is high enough to prevent the onset of freezing.

The case in question came to the author's attention several years after its occurrence. At the time some deliberations took place in-house which did not lead to any conclusions. The problem was left in abeyance, and no further action taken. This is quite commonplace with baffling problems. A quick calculation along the lines indicated would have provided some assurance that no action was required.

Illustration 6.3.7 Failure of Heat Pipes

The problem considered here involved a cement plant where so-called heat pipes, to be described below, had been installed on the circumference of an inclined rotary kiln at the lower (and hotter) end near the entry point of the combustion gases. Some 50 such devices, each made of nominal 2 in. diameter, high-schedule steel pipe, and some 3 m length had been welded approximately 40 cm apart onto the kiln wall.

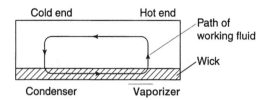

FIGURE 6.16   Schematic diagram of a heat pipe.

The purpose of these pipes was to cool the kiln shell at the hot end by releasing heat to the atmosphere and, thus, prevent damage to the kiln shell.

Heat pipes have been defined as "closed structure(s) containing some working fluid which transfers thermal energy from one part of the structure to another part by means of vaporization of a liquid, transport, and condensation of the vapor, and the subsequent return of the condensate from the condenser by capillary action to the evaporator." (See references at end of this chapter). The fact that no gravity is required for the return flow of condensate make this particular configuration an attractive cooling device in space applications (cooling of electronic devices and of the spacecraft surface facing the sun). Working fluids range from freons (low temperature application) to water and alcohols for intermediate temperatures and liquid metals for high temperatures. A sketch of the device is shown in Figure 6.16.

In the particular application considered here, water was used as working fluid and the wick dispensed with in favor of gravity return flow of the condensate. The pipes were inclined by some 15°, the upper and colder end acting as condenser. Heat from the kiln shell would pass to the heat pipes where it would cause evaporation of water. The water vapor would flow to the cold end, condense there, and return to the hot end by gravity flow. The process would then repeat itself. The pipes performed satisfactorily for several days to weeks, but their performance declined thereafter until they became inoperative.

Some preliminary heat transfer calculations were made to verify that the pipe dimensions were sufficient to provide the necessary flux and this was confirmed. Some thought was given to the possibility that the critical temperature of water had been exceeded but this turned out to be unfounded. Since ordinary tap water had been used, fouling of the surface was a possibility. This line of thought, i.e., the reduction of the heat transfer coefficient by some internal process, quickly led to the consideration of a possible reaction of the steel with the water, producing hydrogen gas and iron oxides. Heat transfer would then become gas–film controlled, and this together with the formation of low conductivity oxides would bring about a considerable lowering of the heat transfer rate to the atmosphere.

Sample heat pipes were detached from the kiln (temporarily out of operation) and holes drilled into them. Even though the pipes were cold, an escape of gas was noticed which could be ignited, causing a mild explosion. This seemed to confirm the presence of hydrogen gas.

The solution then rested upon the proper choice of material. A specialized steel, the type still confidential, was recommended, together with the suggestion that thoroughly degassed, distilled water be used. Alternative working fluids without the corrosive properties of water were considered, but rejected principally because of their lower latent heat and limited temperature range.

Comments:

The pipes were filled with distilled water as suggested, repeatedly evacuated, sealed, and installed. They performed satisfactorily over a long period of time and aided in the protection of the kiln nose from overheating and consequent damage to the kiln shell.

The need to model arose only briefly here, and was quickly abandoned in favor of what might be termed physical reasoning. Evidently some knowledge of the heat transfer coefficients of gases and of evaporating and condensing liquids is needed. Table 3.11 in Chapter 3 served as a handy guide, indicating that still air would have a coefficient at least three orders of magnitude lower than that of condensing steam or boiling water. Hydrogen gas would have somewhat higher values because of its higher thermal conductivity, but would still have h values vastly lower than that of the working fluid. Thus, a satisfactory solution was found based on a knowledge of chemistry, metallurgy, and heat transfer. The necessity to draw on several fields of expertise is a frequent occurrence in troubleshooting problems.

Illustration 6.3.8   Coating of a Pipe

It often comes about that an informal opinion is sought on a particular industrial problem without going through the formalities of a secrecy agreement. This happens when the problem is not a particularly serious one and it is merely desired to obtain a second opinion to confirm the validity of solutions arrived at in-house. In such cases it is customary not to reveal details of the process involved, and the problem is outlined only in general terms and often circumlocutory language. We reproduce the language used in this particular situation verbatim:

"A length of pipe L with possible ID ranging from d_1 to d_2 and possible thickness from t_{p1} to t_{p2} is to be coated with two layers of dissimilar material A and B (see Figure 6.17 which is the original drawing provided). The thickness of the two layers is the same (t_c), while the thermal conductivities may be expressed as k_1 and k_2. The original temperature of the pipe is T_1, and it needs to be cooled down to T_2 with water spray. Now the complications are as follows: material A is applied first, followed by material B in a continuous process (see diagram). Due to the temperature of the pipe, the coatings will be molten and need to be solidified by the spray of water before the pipe can be handled. The question is what line speed (v) can be

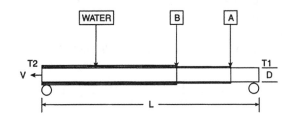

FIGURE 6.17   Coating of a steel pipe with a double layer of molten plastics A and B.

used if this process is to be carried out on a continuous (basis), i.e., the pipe enters one end at T_1 (and) must be at T_2 before it can be handled again."

The physical situation here is one frequently encountered in industry but rarely treated in textbooks, i.e., the movement of solids or solid entities akin to an assembly line. We had encountered a similar process in Chapter 2, Illustration 2.5 (Thermal Treatment of Steel Strapping) and an additional example will appear in Illustration 6.3.9. Indeed, Illustration 2.5 provides some immediate guidelines for the possible modeling of the process under consideration here. We had indicated that the annealing of the strapping by heat transfer to an isothermal medium (the lead bath) could be modeled much like the case of a steam-heated pipe, or shell-and-tube heat exchanger, with solid flow replacing that of conventional fluids. This is the approach we shall adopt here. In doing so we avoid the more precise but cumbersome model made up of three coupled PDEs which describe the axial and radial temperature variations under steady-state conditions.

To apply the simpler model, we make the following assumptions:

Heat transfer to the water spray is controlled by the resistances of the two coatings, i.e., the steel pipe is taken to have a uniform temperature at any particular position, and the surface temperature of the coatings approaches that of the water impinging on the pipe and evaporating. These are reasonable assumptions considering the high values of boiling heat transfer coefficients (see Chapter 3, Table 3.11) and the high conductivity of steel compared to that of the coatings.

Latent heats of solidification are either not involved or are small compared to the sensible heat changes of the steel pipe. Axial conduction in the steel wall and heat given off to the interior of the pipe are negligible.

With these simplifications in hand, the model reduced to the following energy balance:

$$\text{Rate of heat in} - \text{Rate of heat out} = 0$$

$$H\,|_z - \begin{bmatrix} H\,|_{z+\Delta z} \\ +q_{avg} \end{bmatrix} = 0 \qquad (6.3.22)$$

$$\rho_s v_s \,\pi dt_s C_{ps}(T_s - T_{ref})\,|_z - \begin{bmatrix} \rho_s v_s \,\pi dt_s\, Cp\,(T_s - T_{ref})\,|_{z+\Delta z} \\ + \dfrac{(T_s - T_w)_{avg}\,\pi d\Delta z}{t_c(1/k_1 + 1/k_2)} \end{bmatrix} = 0$$

where t = thickness and the subscripts $_s$ and $_c$ refer to steel and coating, respectively. Note that $\rho_s v_s \,\pi dt_s$ is the pipe "flow rate" in kg steel/s and the heat transfer coefficient $U = [t_c(1/k_1 + 1/k_2)]^{-1}$.

Dividing by $\pi d\Delta z$ and going to the limit yields the ODE:

$$(\rho vtC_p)_s \frac{dT_s}{dz} + \frac{T_s - T_w}{t_c(1/k_1 + 1/k_2)} = 0 \qquad (6.3.23)$$

which can be immediately integrated by separation of variables to yield:

$$z = (\rho v t C_p)_s [t_c (1/k_1 + 1/k_2)] \ln \frac{T_{s1} - T_w}{T_{s2} - T_w} \qquad (6.3.24)$$

where z = length of cooling section.

Comments:

The line velocity v can be calculated for a specified length of cooling section z, or conversely, z determined for a prescribed value of v. z is seen to be proportional to both the line velocity and wall thickness t. This is as expected. Somewhat less expected is the fact that z does not depend on pipe diameter d which cancels out in Equation 6.3.22. This is at variance with the results obtained in-house.

The value to be used for T_w is somewhat of a question mark. The principal heat transfer mechanism will be one of evaporation of water, since latent heat effects outweigh sensible heating of the water by a factor of at least seven. A first approximation would be to set T_w equal to the water temperature at the source. This will provide a *minimum* value of the length of cooling section required, or the *maximum* permissible line velocity for a given z.

A first estimate of the required water flow rate F_w can be obtained from an *integral* energy balance by setting the sensible heat change of the steel wall equal to the cumulative latent heat of evaporation. Thus,

$$\rho_s \, v\pi dt_s z C_{ps}(T_{s1} - T_{s2}) = F_w \Delta H_w \qquad (6.3.25)$$

where ΔH_w = latent heat of evaporation per unit mass of water. F_w does not include that portion of water which fails to make contact with the pipe or evaporative losses in transit, and is thus to be considered a *minimum* value.

Taking latent heat of solidification into account brings about a considerable escalation in the complexity of the problem. In the radial direction, one would be dealing with a moving-boundary problem, akin to that considered in Chapter 3, Illustration 3.3.12 (Freeze-Drying). In the axial direction one has to track both liquid and solid phases of the coating which calls for an approach similar to that used in Illustration 3.6.7 (Forced Convection Boiling). Consideration of both these factors would require a PDE model. Let us see whether we were justified in neglecting these latent heat effects by examining the ratio of sensible heat changes in the pipe wall q_s to possible latent heat effects in the coating q_c. We have:

$$\frac{q_s}{q_c} = \frac{\rho_s \, v\pi dt_s z C_{ps}(T_{s1} - T_{s2})}{\rho_c \, v\pi dt_c z \Delta H_c}$$

$$\frac{q_s}{q_c} = \frac{\rho_s t_s}{\rho_c t_c} \frac{C_{ps}(T_{s1} - T_{s2})}{\Delta H_c} \qquad (6.3.26)$$

Conservative estimates of the density and thickness ratios of steel and coating leads to the value:

$$\frac{\rho_s \; t_s}{\rho_c \; t_c} \cong (10)(5) = 50$$

For the thermal ratio $C_{ps}\Delta T/\Delta H_c$, we assume $\Delta T = 100°C$ and $\Delta H_c = 100$ J/g (approximately one third that of the corresponding value for water). We obtain:

$$\frac{C_{ps}\Delta T}{\Delta H_c} = \frac{(0.473)(100)}{100} = 0.473$$

with a total value for the ratio of q_s/q_c of:

$$\frac{\text{Sensible heat of steel}}{\text{Latent heat of coating}} \frac{q_s}{q_c} = (50)(0.4730) = 24$$

Thus, according to these conservative estimates, latent heat effects account for about 4% of the total heat load. We feel justified, therefore, in focusing our attention on the sensible heat changes undergone by the pipe.

It will have been noted that our model only yields *minimum* values for the length of cooling section z and water flow rate F_w and an upper limit for the line velocity v. These are nevertheless useful boundaries to have and can be easily moved by imposing more severe (though, in our opinion, artificial) conditions. Thus, an external heat transfer resistance equivalent to a transfer coefficient of 500 or even 100 W/m²K could be added to the conductive resistance. This is left to the discretion of the reader.

Illustration 6.3.9 Release of Potentially Harmful Chemicals to the Atmosphere

In this example, also from an industrial source, a fairly precise description of the proposed process equipment was made available (see Figure 6.18). The nature of the chemical involved, however, was disguised as a phantom substance, "benzoic acid." The problem was posed as follows:

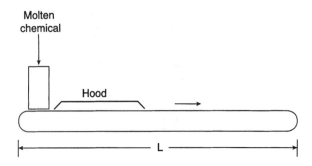

FIGURE 6.18 Emissions into a fume hood during the cooling of a molten chemical.

A chemical company is making solid benzoic acid from (its) molten state. This chemical is heated up to 140°C and then is poured onto a metal belt moving at 4 ft/s to make solid benzoic acid. The thickness of the flake (~1/20 in.) can be changed by changing the belt velocity. The production rate of the chemical is 10,000 lbs/h. A hood is placed above the belt in the first 20 ft to remove the chemical vapor released from the benzoic acid in the course of cooling. The hood flow rate is 1000 SCF/min. The cross-sectional area of the hood is 20 × 5 ft (the width of the belt). The chemical freezes at 120°C. Since the chemical vapor may cause health or fire hazard, the upper limit of the vapor concentration is set at 2%. Is the design sufficient to cool the chemical so that the vapor concentration in the hood is below the upper limit to prevent the fire or health hazard? The advice solicited was, "What is the appropriate mass transfer and heat transfer coefficient for this problem?"

We will attempt here to arrive at some numerical results using the phantom benzoic acid as a test substance. Since the major concern was to keep the concentration in the vented air below a prescribed tolerance level, our focus will be on mass transfer aspects of the problem.

The flow pattern in the fume hood is evidently a complex one, with air being drawn in horizontally through the hood clearance (dimension unknown), and then changing direction by 90° before passing into the vent duct. Mass transfer coefficients for this particular geometry and flow pattern probably exist but cannot be easily located. Numerical simulation is another option and would require the simultaneous solution of the relevant mass and momentum balances in those dimensions. We choose instead to examine two simple but meaningful asymptotic cases which provide upper and lower limits to benzoic acid concentration in the vented air. In the first and worst case scenario, we assume the air to leave saturated with benzoic acid at either the inlet temperature of 140°C or the freezing point of 120°C. The calculation here is straightforward, involving only the vapor pressures of the acid at those temperatures and provides an upper limit to the expected concentration. In the second case we include the mass transfer resistance by assuming conditions in the immediate vicinity of the moving belt to be represented by flow over a flat plate of length one half that of the fume hood. This is deemed to provide a lower bound to the benzoic acid concentration in the air.

The data assembled for both these calculations are as follows:

Vapor pressure of benzoic acid:	T°C	120	140
	p (mm Hg)	7	18

Kinematic viscosity of air:	$v = 1.5 \times 10^{-5}$ m²/s
Schmidt number of air:	$Sc \cong 1$
Assumed length of flat plate:	$l = 3$ m
Assumed clearance of hood:	$w = 0.1$ m
Air flow rate:	$Q = 1000$ SCF/min $= 0.47$ m³/s
Flow area through clearance:	$A_f = 1.57$ m²
Mass transfer area:	$A_m = 9.3$ m²
Horizontal velocity:	$v = Q/A_f = 0.30$ m/s

The following results are obtained for the two cases in question:

(1) No Mass Transfer Resistance (Saturation)
Mole fraction y = vapor pressure/total pressure
At $120°C$ $y = 7/760 = 0.0092$
At $140°C$ $y = 18/760 = 0.024$

Thus, even in this limiting and adverse case, the mole fraction of benzoic acid is well below the prescribed value of 0.02 at $120°C$, and only marginally higher at the inlet temperature of $140°C$. One suspects, however, that the specified limits were set artificially high to disguise the actual process.

(2) With Mass Transfer Resistance
We use the correlation for mass transfer given in Chapter 3, Table 3.5 which takes the form

$$St = k_c/v = 0.66 \ Re^{-1/2} \ Sc^{-2/3} \quad Re < 10^5$$

and

$$St = k_c/v = 0.036 \ Re^{-0.2} \ Sc^{-2/3} \quad Re > 10^6$$

For the Reynolds number we have:

$$Re = \frac{lv}{v} = \frac{(3.0)(0.30)}{1.5 \times 10^{-5}} = 6 \times 10^4$$

and hence,

$$k_c = 0.66 \ v \ Re^{-1/2} \ Sc^{-2/3} = (0.66)(0.30)(6 \times 10^4)^{-1/2}(1)$$

$$k_c = 8.1 \times 10^{-4} \ m/s$$

For the saturation concentration C^* at the moving belt surface assumed here at $120°C$, we have from the Ideal Gas law:

$$C^* = \frac{n}{V} = \frac{p}{RT}$$

$$C^* = \frac{(7/760)(1.013 \times 10^5)}{(8.314)(393)}$$

$$C^* = 0.286 \, mol/m^3$$

The rate of transfer of benzoic acid to the air is then given by:

$$N_A \cong k_c \, A_m \, (C^* - 0)$$

$$N_A \cong 8.1 \times 10^{-4} \, (9.3)(0.286)$$

$$N_A = 2.15 \times 10^{-3} \text{ mol/s}$$

One notes that the concentration in the bulk of the air C has been set = 0. Once that value is known and seen to be significant, the calculations can be further refined (see below).

To obtain the mol fraction of benzoic acid in the air, we require the total molar flow rate of air N_T, since $y = N_A/N_T$. We have:

$$N_T = \frac{P_T Q}{RT} = \frac{(1.013 \times 10^5)(0.471)}{(8.31)(298)}$$

$$N_T = 19.2 \text{ mol/s}$$

Hence, we obtain:

$$y = N_A / N_T = \frac{(6.65 \times 10^{-4})}{19.2}$$

$$y = 1.11 \times 10^{-4} \text{ mol fraction}$$

or approximately 100 ppm by volume.

In molar concentration units, the corresponding value is given by:

$$C = y \frac{P_T}{RT}$$

$$C = 1.11 \times 10^{-4} \, (1.013 \times 10^5) / (8.314)(298)$$

$$C = 4.54 \times 10^{-3} \text{ mol/m}^3$$

Thus, the concentration C in the bulk of the air is seen to be less than 2% that of the saturation value C^*, justifying our omission of the term in calculating the evaporation rate N_A.

Comments:

It is felt that, if anything, the mass transfer coefficient was considerably overestimated resulting in an overestimation of the effluent concentration. No account was taken of the stagnant zone which must perforce exist around the central area under the hood where the flows from different inlet segments converge. This factor alone could result in a considerable lowering of the average benzoic acid concentration in the effluent.

It may be counter argued that the average temperature chosen, 120°C, was too low, resulting in an underestimation of the exiting concentration. Certainly at the inlet to the fume hood, the temperature would be closer to that of the feed, 140°C. Let us consider the extreme case where the entire charge under the hood is at 140°C. C* would then increase in proportion to the rise in vapor pressure and, consequently, so would the effluent concentration. We obtain:

$$\frac{y_{140}}{y_{120}} = \frac{P_{140}}{P_{120}} = \frac{18}{7} = 2.57$$

Thus, benzoic acid content in the air would rise to 2.9×10^{-4} mol fraction, still comfortably below the prescribed maximum of 0.02.

It is of some interest to consider the effect of air flow rate Q on y. An increase in Q should, on the one hand, have a proportional diluting effect through N_T, the molar flow rate of air, but at the same time increase k_c in proportion to $v/Re^{1/2}$, i.e., $Q^{1/2}$. The net effect is an overall dilution with $\dfrac{Q^{1/2}}{Q} = Q^{-1/2}$. Thus, doubling flow rate would decrease effluent concentration by a factor of $2^{1/2} = 1.41$.

Illustration 6.3.10   Design of a Marker Particle (Revisited)

A small entrepreneur with an interest in scuba diving had the idea of marketing marker particles that upon release under water would rise at a velocity of 60 ft/min = 0.305 m/s, the maximum value recommended for the safe ascent of divers. Too fast an ascent causes air dissolved in the blood to be released too rapidly leading to disabling symptoms, such as vomiting, loss of consciousness, etc. It can in severe instances be fatal.

The particles were to be carried by the diver in a small pouch and be clearly visible upon release. An optimum size range of 2 to 4 cm was suggested. To facilitate manufacture, regular shapes such as spheres, disks, and cylinders were preferred, as were cheap materials. A further stipulation was that the particles had to be effective in waters of different temperatures, salinity, and viscosity, i.e., in lakes as well as oceans of different regions. Water density variations of ± 10% have to be allowed for.

The topic of particle movement in fluids had been addressed in considerable detail in Chapter 3, Section 3.4. Three relevant facts emerge from that discussion:

- Steady-state values are attained very quickly, within seconds or fractions of a second, so that transient behavior need not be considered.
- Movement of particles with d = 2 to 4 cm and a velocity of 0.305 m/s fall entirely in the turbulent region (see Chapter 3, Table 3.14). The drag coefficient C_D will consequently be constant, with values of 0.44 and 1.2 for spheres and disks or short cylinders respectively.
- The steady-state force balance for rising particles takes the form:

$$\rho_p V_p g + C_D A \frac{v^2}{2} \rho_f - \rho_f V_p g = 0$$

$$\text{Gravity} \quad\quad \text{Drag} \quad\quad \text{Buoyancy}$$

(3.4.35)

where the subscripts $_f$ and $_p$ denote the fluid and particle respectively.

Equation 3.4.35 can be rearranged to yield:

For spheres:

$$\rho_p / \rho_f = 1 - \frac{3}{4}(C_D v^2) / dg$$

(6.3.27)

For disks/cylinders:

$$\rho_p/\rho_f = 1 - 1/2(C_D v^2)/Lg$$

where L = length of disk or cylinder.

A value of ρ_p/ρ_f too close to unity is undesirable, since small water density variations in that range cause inordinately large changes in the velocity of rise. As can be seen from Equation 6.3.27 a particle with the correct design velocity at ρ_s/ρ_f = 0.8 would, on encountering a density ratio of 0.9, see its velocity drop by a factor $\left(\dfrac{1-0.9}{1-0.8}\right)^{1/2} = 0.71$. For this reason, it is wise to design for density ratios $\rho_p/\rho_f <$ 0.8. However, since smaller values of ρ_p/ρ_f require small particles to meet the specified velocity of rise, a point will be quickly reached where the size falls below the desired range of 2 to 4 cm. The dilemma is illustrated in the following table of particle dimensions calculated from Equation 6.3.27.

One notes that at $\rho_p/\rho_f = 0.8$, which we consider to be the upper allowable limit, the sphere has fallen below the acceptable range of 2 to 4 cm, while the cylinder remains above it. A disk 2.5 cm × 2.5 cm is a possible recommendation. Materials with a specific gravity in the desired range 0.4 to 0.8 include readily available high density polyethylene and polypropylene and, hence, pose no problem. The particles, however, would have to be sealed to exclude water.

TABLE 6.7
Size of Particles with a Velocity of Rise of 0.305 m/s

Density Ratio ρ_s/ρ_f	0.9	0.8	0.5	0.1
Diameter of sphere, cm	3.1	1.6	0.63	0.34
Length of cylinder, cm	5.7	2.9	1.1	0.63

Comments:

Although only one simple model Equation 6.3.27 was required, it took some skill to use it in the analysis of the system. The density ratio not only had to be identified as the crucial parameter determining particle size, but its sensitive impact on velocity of rise at values near unity recognized and an upper limit to its value set. We were helped by the groundwork done in Chapter 3, Section 3.4 which led to a quick identification of the flow regime and, hence, the values of C_D.

Postscript:

The initial recommendation of a disk 2.5 × 2.5 cm was not adopted. Trial runs showed that cylindrical shapes wobbled too much on rising through water and difficulties were experienced in sealing them effectively. The final design consisted of *hollow* plastic spheres of approximately 2.0 cm diameter containing calibrated amounts of *solid ballast* to yield the correct velocity of rise. They were brightly colored for good visibility and easy recovery. A design of this type also had been under consideration but had been rejected in favor of cheaper shapes. The afore-mentioned factors, however, made the hollow sphere the final design of choice in spite of its higher manufacturing cost.

Practice Problems

6.3.1 Explosion of a Refrigerator — Thirty percent by weight of an organic substance of molar mass 225 dissolved in diethyl ether were stored in loosely corked flasks in the refrigerator of a chemical laboratory. The refrigerator had not been provided with an explosion-proof motor and, subsequently, an explosion occurred. Could it have been caused by ether vapors?

Data: Vapor pressure of ether (3°C): 24.3 kPa
         Explosive limits of ether: 1.85 – 36.5 mol %

6.3.2 Another Moving Boundary Problem–Melting of Glycerol — Partially solid-ified glycerol with an approximate melting point of ~ 18°C contained in a tank is to be rendered fluid by external steam heating. The time required to achieve this is to be calculated. Plant engineers had suggested the formula:

$$t = \frac{mC_p\Delta T}{q}$$

(a) Critically analyze this expression.

(b) Show that the moving boundary approach leads to the equation:

$$t = \frac{0.25}{\pi} \frac{m\Delta H}{kL\Delta T}$$

(c) Provide your own recommendation for the proper calculation of the time required.

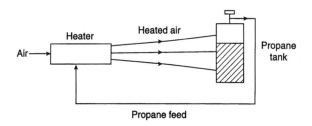

FIGURE 6.19   Air-heater/propane cylinder configuration leading to a propane fire.

6.3.3 Propane Cylinder Fire — In a fire insurance claim, the cause of a propane fire in an underground tunnel construction site had to be determined. The relevant events were as follows.

Just prior to their afternoon departure, workers on the site connected a fresh propane tank to an air heater of a type frequently used on construction sites to speed up the drying of the concrete and provide warm surroundings. The heater was turned on and left running. Approximately 3½ hours later a fire was detected during a check of the site. The propane cylinder feeding the heater, standing about 1.2 m from the heater outlet and fully exposed to the air jet, was leaking propane which had ignited into a substantial fire (Figure 6.19). Extensive damage had been done to various installations in the tunnel.

Investigators focused on three possible causes:

1. A leaky cylinder valve had caused propane gas to escape from the tank which subsequently ignited on contact with the heater. The cylinder manufacturers would in this case be liable.
2. A defect in the heater had caused a primary fire that in turn heated the propane tank to vent temperature. The relief disk on the cylinder was set to rupture at ~ 25 atm, corresponding to a propane equilibrium temperature of 66°C. This scenario would make the heater manufacturers liable.
3. The tank, which was inadvertently (or deliberately?) placed in the path of the air, had been heated to the point where the relief disk ruptured and the escaping propane vapors subsequently caught fire on contact with the heater. The insurers of the construction company would in this case have to pay for the damage caused.

The technical consultants were asked to determine whether 3½ hours were sufficient time to heat the tank to venting conditions. Evidently the insurers of the heater and gas cylinder manufacturers had an interest in proving this to be right, while insurers of the construction company did not. The following data were assembled.

Heater:
Outlet diameter: 0.203 m
Outlet temperature: 191°C
Outlet velocity: 9.65 m/s

A properly functioning unit provides air at 49°C above ambient temperatures at a distance of 3.1 m.

Propane tank:
    Diameter: 0.382 m
    Height: 1.17 m
    Total volume: 0.189 m³
    Liquid propane content: 45.4 kg
    Weight of empty container: 45.4 kg
    Initial pressure (10°C): 7 atm
    Venting pressure: 25.1 atm (66°C)
    Steel density: 7800 kg/m³
    Steel heat capacity: 0.473 kJ/kg K

Propane:
    Liquid density: 577 kg/m³
    Liquid heat capacity: 2.42 kJ/kg K
    Heat of vaporization: –353 kJ/kg

Air (150°C):
    Density: 0.826 kg/m³
    Viscosity: 2.14×10^{-5} Pa s
    Thermal conductivity: 0.0351 W/mK
    Heat capacity: 1 kJ/kg K

Comments:
To simplify this complex heat transfer problem, one could start by setting a lower limit to the time required to raise the temperature of the tank from 10°C to 66°C (25.1 atm). This can be done by considering sensible heat requirements only, neglecting for the time being the heat of vaporization and the pressure loss due to propane withdrawn as feed to the heater. If this t_{min} exceeds the specified time period of 3½ h, scenario 3 can be safely dismissed. If it falls below it, the calculations will have to be refined.

Determination of the heat transfer rate from air to tank requires a knowledge of the overall heat transfer coefficient as well as the air temperature in the vicinity of the tank. Heat transfer resistance is likely to be entirely on the air side, since the process inside the tank is one of free convection combined with nucleate boiling with an attendant high heat transfer coefficient (see Chapter 3, Table 3.11). At any rate, neglecting the internal resistance tends to further reduce the value of t, which is a desirable trend, since we wish to establish a lower bound to the time requirement. To estimate the temperature of the arriving air, one craftily makes use of the manufacturer's performance guarantee given above. It is left to the reader to apply it to an appropriate model.

To further minimize time, one can assume the temperature along the entire circumference to be uniform and identical to that of the arriving air. The jet will expand during its passage from the heater and it is suggested that the expansion ratio be set at 1.5. This conservative value will further reduce the value of t.

Determination of the appropriate heat transfer area poses an additional problem. One can set its width equal to that of the arriving jet, or to the cylinder area in contact with the liquid propane, the latter tending to give lower t values.

It should be kept in mind that the sensible heat requirements of both the tank itself, as well as its contents must be taken into account. The two are of equal weight, but steel has approximately two and one half times the volumetric heat capacity of liquid propane. It will, therefore, represent a preponderant portion of the load.

The reader should not be discouraged if no clear-cut answers are obtained. This is often the case, making it necessary to provide a *range* of answers. This should, however, always be accompanied with an indication of one's own personal preference.

6.3.4 Malfunction of a Dryer — A through-flow dryer consisting of a cylindrical vessel filled with granular material requires an air flow rate estimated at 5×10^{-2} kg/s for proper drying of the charge. After passage through the bed of granular material it is vented to the atmosphere through a piping system consisting of 30.5 m of straight 5 cm ID steel pipe, one flow contraction and expansion each, 2 tees, 5 elbows, and 3 globe valves fully open. Frictional losses in the dryer are negligible and the air is delivered at a pressure of 122 kPa. It was found that drying times exceeded the specifications.

Identify the reason for malfunction and propose remedies.

6.3.5 More on Freezing Pipes — An inert gas with physical properties similar to those of air is to be piped through a 1 m diameter pipe 1000 m long at the rate of 25,000 kg/h. The gas enters at 30°C, 100 kPa gauge, and is saturated with water.

The pipe runs above ground and may be exposed to winter temperatures of –30°C and wind velocities of 30 km/h for as long as 2 weeks. This can cause undesirable ice formation both in the flowing gas and at the pipe wall.

One is asked whether the installation of an outside insulation which may cost up to $200,000 is warranted. Illustration 6.3.6 may be of some use as a guide.

6.3.6 Potential Thermal Stress Cracking of a Weld — During erection of a catalytic cracking unit in an oil refinery, concern arose that thermal gradients in the steel supports might cause stress cracking of the connecting welds (see Figure 6.20). The reactor, itself insulated, was known to reach temperatures of about 500°C, and ambient temperatures as low as –30°C could be anticipated in the winter months.

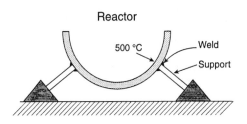

FIGURE 6.20   Welded support of a catalytic cracking reactor.

Structural engineers specified a maximum permissible temperature gradient at the weld of 15°C/cm. A suggested remedy was to cover the supports with insulation, but it was not known how thick the insulation should be or indeed whether this would solve the problem.

Data:

      Thermal conductivity of steel: 43 W/mK
      Thermal conductivity of insulation: 0.12 W/mK
      Heat transfer coefficient to air: see Table 3.11
      Diameter of support: 0.1 m
      Length of support: 0.5 m

(Hint: Attempt an "asymptotic" solution, with the support bare, a temperature at ground level of –30°C and a gradient at the reactor end of 15°C/cm. Extract a heat transfer coefficient from the solution. Its value is proportional to the maximum permissible rate of heat transfer. Calculate the equivalent thickness of insulation which will match this value.)

6.3.7 Solution Mining of Potash — Underground deposits of potash (KCl or sylvite) are frequently harvested by a technique called *solution mining*. The procedure consists of cracking the deposit open by pumping high pressure water through an "injection well" drilled to one end of the deposit ("hydrofracturing"). A second well, the so-called production well, is drilled at the far end of the fracture. Water is then continuously pumped into the deposit through the injection well, dissolving potash as it passes through the open fracture and returning to the surface through the production well as a KCl solution.

It is desirable in these operations to have an *a priori* estimate of the KCl solution in the effluent since this will determine the production rate of the mine. Calculations are complicated by the fact that the dissolution of KCl is a highly endothermic process, with solubility C^* decreasing as the temperature drops. Water entering the fracture thus will dissolve KCl at a rate proportional to $(C^* - C)$, but the driving force will diminish rapidly as C^* drops due to endothermicity and C rises due to dissolution of KCl. One may expect production concentrations to be considerable below isothermal values.

It has been argued that the endothermic effects are at least in part counterbalanced by heat flow from the surrounding deposit. An assessment of this contribution is not straightforward, since temperature variations in both horizontal and vertical directions make themselves felt. The reader is nevertheless urged to attempt an analysis of the problem. The required information is, as stated, the KCl concentration at the production end.

The following data may be of use:

Average geothermal temperature gradient: 30°C/km
Average heat flux in the Earth: 5.0×10^{-2} J/m²s
Average thermal conductivity of the Earth: 1.7×10^{-3} J/msK
Average heat of solution of KCl: 1.8×10^4 kJ/mol
Solubility of KCl in water: 20°C 4.66 mol/L; 100°C 7.61 mol/L

Comments:

Fracture depth and dimensions vary but typical values which can be used in the analysis are

Depth: 1 km
Fracture height: 50 cm
Fracture width: 50 m
Fracture length: 500 m
Water velocity: 0.1 m/s

It is probably best to start by considering the asymptotic cases of isothermal and adiabatic operation. These will provide upper and lower bounds to the solution sought. Contributions of heat flux from the surroundings may then be grafted onto these results.

Widening of the fracture with time is a complication, but it is not far-fetched to assume that this can be countered by increasing flow rate to maintain a constant velocity and transport coefficients. Thus, except for an initial start-up period, the operation may be assumed to be at a near steady-state.

Flow rate itself is an important parameter which needs to be considered. A reduction in flow has the effect of raising the effluent concentration (unless saturation had already been attained), but at the same time reduces the volumetric production rate. Thus, there exists an *optimum* flow rate at which the total mass of potash extracted is at a *maximum*. It is suggested that this flow rate rather than an arbitrary fixed value be used as a basis of comparison of the results obtained from various models.

6.3.8 Heat Transfer from a Falling Solder Bead — A consultant in a court case was required to determine the temperature attained by liquid solder beads which formed during the soldering of copper pipe and inadvertently dropped a distance of 10 m through still air onto potentially combustible material (straw and paper). It is considered that a temperature of 180 to 200°C would be sufficient to cause ignition.

The following data for solder are provided:

Diameter: 5 mm
Density: 8460 kg/m^3
Melting point: 183°C
Initial temperature: 240°C
Latent heat: 22.9 kJ/kg
Heat capacity: 0.19 kJ/kg K

Comments:

The first item to determine is the time of fall which one would expect to be very short [0(1 s)]. The terminal velocity, therefore, may not have been attained, and this should be taken into account.

Since transient conditions may prevail, the heat transfer coefficient could vary during the fall. Velocity as a function of time would have to be incorporated into the energy equation for a rigorous treatment. Alternatively, one could "bracket the solution" by considering heat transfer at $v = 0$ and v_{Max}. This would provide upper and lower bounds for the bead temperature upon arrival on the ground. One notes the extremely low values of both heat capacity and latent heat. This augurs well for a rapid cooling of the bead and hence for the construction company. It is particularly important in this case to obtain quick results, since an actual test could be run with little inconvenience and provide concrete proof one way or the other. This is more acceptable to the court than "theoretical calculations."

REFERENCES

From among the multitude of textbooks and other reference sources, we cite only the handful which we leaned on in writing this chapter. They are, for the most part, standards in their field and are recommended for a first reading of their respective topics.

Biomedicine, Biology, and Biotechnology
Physiological models, both of the compartmental and distributed type, are well presented in an easily understood style in:
S. Middleman. *Transport Phenomena in the Cardiovascular System,* Wiley-Interscience, New York, 1972.
D.O. Cooney. *Biomedical Engineering Principles,* Marcel Dekker, New York, 1976.
The latter also contains a lucid exposition of membrane processes in both living systems and artificial devices (dialyzers).

Pharmocokinetics, and their related models, are treated in the monograph:
M. Gibaldi and D. Perrier. *Pharmocokinetics, 2nd ed.,* Marcel Dekker, New York, 1982.

The physiology of blood flow as well as models related to it appear in:
W.R. Milnor. *Hemodynamics,* Williams and Wilkins, Baltimore, 1982.
D.A. McDonald. *Blood Flow in Arteries, 3rd ed.,* Lea & Farber, Philadelphia, 1990.

Those interested in the more advanced mathematics which give rise to exotic physiological behavior are referred to:
A.L. Goldberger and B.J. West. *Chaos in Biological Systems,* Plenum Press, New York, 1987.
B.F. Gray and S.K. Scott. *Chemical Oscillations and Instabilities: Nonlinear Chemical Kinetics,* Oxford University Press, New York, 1990.

The intricacies of cell behavior and the associated models are described in:
D.A. Lauffenburger and J.J. Linderman. *Receptors: Models for Binding, Trafficking and Signaling,* Oxford University Press, New York, 1993.

The landmark paper by Turing appeared in:
A.M. Turing. The chemical basis of morphogenesis, *Phil. Trans. Roy. Soc. London,* 237: 37–72, 1952.

Reaction and release of substances at a tubular wall are treated in papers by the author:
D. Basmadjian and M.V. Sefton. Relationship between release rate and surface concentration for heparinized materials, *J. Biomed. Mat. Res.,* 17: 509–518, 1983.

D. Basmadjian. The effect of flow and mass transport in thrombogenesis, *Ann. Biomed. Eng.*, 18: 685–709, 1990.

The pre-eminent text on biotechnology is by:
J.E. Bailey and D.F. Ollis. *Biochemical Engineering Fundamentals, 2nd ed.*, McGraw-Hill, New York, 1986.

A Visit to the Environment
Good introductions to environmental engineering in general can be found in:
H.S. Peavy, D.R. Rowe, and G. Tchobanoglous. *Environmental Engineering*, McGraw-Hill, New York, 1985.
M.L. Davis and D. Cornwell. *Introduction to Environmental Engineering, 2nd ed.*, McGraw-Hill, New York, 1991.

A wealth of models related to environmental systems are given in:
L.J. Thibodeaux. *Environmental Chemodynamics. Movement of Chemicals in Air, Water and Soil, 2nd ed.*, McGraw-Hill, New York, 1996.

A highly readable introduction to modeling using the fugacity concept is given in the treatise:
D. Mackay. *Multimedia Environmental Models. The Fugacity Approach,* Lewis Publishers, Chelsea, MI, 1991.

Adsorption and desorption processes in an environmental as well as industrial context are described in:
D. Basmadjian. *The Little Adsorption Book,* CRC Press, Boca Raton, FL, 1996.

Welcome to the Real World
Here one had to draw on a broad range of topics, mostly covered and referenced in previous chapters of this book. An exception is the heat pipe (Illustration 6.3.7), a relatively new and unusual device which is well reviewed in:
E.R.F. Winter and W.O. Barsch. *The Heat Pipe, Adv. Heat Transfer, vol. 7,* Academic Press, New York, 1971.
D. Mackay and P.J. Leinonen, *Environmental Sciences and Technology, vol. 9,* American Chemical Society, Washington, D.C., 1975.

7 Partial Differential Equations: Classification, Types, and Properties; Some Simple Transformations and Solutions

Give me a (partial) derivative and I will invert the world.

Isaac Newton

Science is a differential equation. Religion is a boundary condition.

Arthur Eddington
(reference to Cosmology and Big-Bang Theory)

The reader will have noted our avoidance, up to this point, of any use of Partial Differential Equations (PDEs). We limited ourselves to ODEs which arose from unsteady-state "stirred tank" and from steady-state "one-dimensional pipe" models, and from algebraic integral or cumulative balances. These equations served us well in a good many cases, yielding close approximations of the exact solutions or, at the very least, upper or lower bounds to them. Cases do arise, however, where PDEs can no longer be avoided or circumvented by valid simplifications and assumptions. In particular, PDEs will have to be addressed in the following situations:

- All "one-dimensional pipe" processes which operate under unsteady or transient conditions. These include heat exchangers, packed columns, or tubular reactors with time-varying feed temperatures, concentrations, or flow rates, and turbulent duct flow with time varying inlet pressures or velocities. Note that in some instances one can use a quasi-steady-state assumption, in which case the model reverts to the ODE or AE level.
- Thermal conduction or diffusive processes in which temperature or concentration vary with time and distance or, if at steady-state, vary in more than one dimension. Exceptions occur when transport coefficients are large or system dimensions small, so that the system may be approximated

as a stirred tank. This was done in the case of the thermocouple response given in Illustration 3.3.3, and was valid there by virtue of the high thermal conductivity and small dimension of the device. When size is more substantial, as in the quenched steel billet shown in Figure 1.1, internal temperature gradients can no longer be ignored, and the full PDE model has to be applied.

- Transport of mass, energy, or momentum in external viscous flow around submerged objects or in internal duct flow under steady or transient conditions. In duct flow, this leads to the so-called Graetz Problem for heat and mass transfer, briefly introduced in Chapter 6, Illustration 6.1.5 (Membrane Processes), or to the Navier-Stokes equation for momentum transfer. The classical example of the use of PDEs in external flows is the derivation of the drag coefficient for flow around a sphere (Stokes' law). The reader will note that we specified viscous or laminar flow for these systems. For turbulent flow, steady state PDE models are usually replaced by ODEs or algebraic equations containing lumped transport parameters such as heat and mass transfer or drag coefficients which are determined experimentally. Numerous examples of this treatment appear in the preceding chapters.

- Viscous compressible flow in which velocity and pressure vary with distance and time or, if at steady-state, vary in more than one dimension. Both internal and external flows, as well as sonic and supersonic conditions, are included. This is a vast and complex field usually treated under the heading Aerodynamics. We note again that under steady turbulent flow conditions, one reverts to ODE or algebraic models with empirical friction factors or drag coefficients. Examples of these cases appeared in Chapter 3, Section 3.5.

- Inviscid, i.e., frictionless flow, in more than one dimension. The slightly more restrictive case of so-called *irrotational* or *potential flow* is included here. The one-dimensional case of inviscid flow was taken up at the ODE level and led to the formulation of Bernoulli's equation (Chapter 3, Illustration 3.4.7).

- Unsteady, transverse displacements of fluids and solids. This includes wave propagation and the vibrations of strings or membranes and leads to the so-called wave equation.

The above summary includes some of the more important sources of partial differential equations. PDEs evidently arise in many other contexts as well which were not touched upon. Some of these will become apparent as this chapter and those that follow evolve.

We now turn to the task of describing various properties, classes, and boundary conditions of PDEs, and follow this up with some simple transformations and with a first glimpse of certain elementary solutions and solution methods. Properties and classes are largely those we had seen in an ODE context but some new subcategories make their appearance which we present and justify. The solution methods are at this stage kept at a simple level and make no heavy demands in terms of prior knowledge or the use of exotic techniques.

7.1 PROPERTIES AND CLASSES OF PDEs

7.1.1 ORDER OF A PDE

The order of a PDE is defined by the order of its highest derivative. This is the same definition as that used for ODEs. Thus,

Fourier's equation:

$$\alpha \frac{\partial^2 T}{\partial x^2} = \frac{\partial T}{\partial t} \tag{7.1.1}$$

is a second order PDE,

Biharmonic equation:

$$\frac{\partial^4 u}{\partial x^4} + 2 \frac{\partial^2}{\partial x^2} \left(\frac{\partial^2 u}{\partial y^2} \right) + \frac{\partial^4 u}{\partial y^4} = 0 \tag{7.1.2}$$

is a fourth order PDE, and

Continuity equation:

$$\frac{\partial v_x}{\partial x} + \frac{\partial v_y}{\partial y} + \frac{\partial v_z}{\partial z} = 0 \tag{7.1.3}$$

is a first order PDE.

We describe briefly the occurrence of PDEs of various orders, which again parallels that seen in ODEs.

7.1.1.1 First Order PDEs

First order PDEs are found in the description of convective transport, i.e., in the absence of diffusive (second order) transport terms. The continuity Equation 7.1.3, which represents a convective flow mass balance in three-dimensional Cartesian space, is an example of a first order PDE. Such equations also arise in a host of convective "one-dimensional pipe" processes operating under *unsteady* conditions. A heat exchanger with fluctuating inlet temperature or flow rate is the classical example in this category. First order PDEs are seen as well in the description of convective mass and heat transfer between a fluid and a *stationary* solid medium. Examples of such processes were given, without reference to the underlying equations, in Chapter 6, Illustration 6.2.6, dealing with riverbed contamination, and in Illustration 6.2.10 of an adsorptive water purification process.

7.1.1.2   Second Order PDEs

The classical examples of this type are Fourier's and Fick's equations. In one-dimensional rectangular coordinates they take the form:

Fourier:

$$\alpha \frac{\partial^2 T}{\partial x^2} = \frac{\partial T}{\partial t} \tag{7.1.1}$$

Fick:

$$D \frac{\partial^2 C}{\partial x^2} = \frac{\partial C}{\partial t} \tag{7.1.4}$$

The celebrated Navier-Stokes equation, to be described in more detail later, consist of three second order PDE Momentum Balances.

7.1.1.3   Higher Order PDEs

PDEs of order greater than two occur with much lesser frequency. They are seen in solid mechanics and elasticity theory (cf. the biharmonic Equation 7.1.2). They also make their appearance in the course of introducing the so-called stream function ψ which is defined in terms of fluid velocities in the x and y directions, v_x and v_y.

$$v_x = -\frac{\partial \psi}{\partial y} \quad v_y = \frac{\partial \psi}{\partial x} \tag{7.1.5}$$

Introduction of ψ serves the purpose of coalescing velocity components in a mass or momentum balance into a *single* term involving ψ, thus simplifying the underlying PDE. The penalty to be paid is an increase in the *order* of the equation by one.

7.1.2   HOMOGENEOUS PDEs AND BCs

This definition again parallels that given for ODEs, i.e., it refers to equations which do not contain *separate* terms in the independent variable or constant. Thus, Fourier's Equation 7.1.1 is homogeneous, but if one adds to it a heat source S which is constant or dependent on time and distance the equation becomes nonhomogeneous. Hence,

$$\alpha \frac{\partial^2 T}{\partial x^2} + S(x,t) = \frac{\partial T}{\partial t} \tag{7.1.6}$$

is a nonhomogeneous PDE. Similarly the following boundary conditions are both nonhomogeneous:

$$T(x,0) = f(x) \qquad\qquad (7.1.7)$$

$$T(0,t) = g(t)$$

7.1.3 PDEs with Variable Coefficients

As in the case of ODEs, the term *variable* implies changes in the coefficients of the derivative as a function of the independent, not the dependent variable. Such models arose as we had seen whenever diffusive transport took place through an area which varied with distance. Thus, for radial diffusion in a long cylinder, the unsteady Fick's diffusion Equation 7.1.4 becomes:

$$D\left[\frac{\partial^2 C}{\partial r^2} + \frac{1}{r}\frac{\partial C}{\partial r}\right] = \frac{\partial C}{\partial t} \qquad\qquad (7.1.8)$$

where the quotient $1/r$ is the variable coefficient. It is not unreasonable to expect that the solutions of this equation will contain the same "exotic" Bessel functions we had encountered in the steady-state version of this equation.

7.1.4 Linear and Nonlinear PDEs: A New Category — Quasilinear PDEs

The classification here is again very much akin to that we had seen with ODEs — a PDE is linear if the dependent variable and its derivatives appear in *linear* combination. Thus, the most general version of a second order linear PDE in two independent variables has the form:

$$A(x,y)u_{xx} + B(x,y)u_{xy} + C(x,y)u_{yy} + D(x,y)u_x$$
$$+ E(x,y)u_y + F(x,y)u + G(x,y) = 0 \qquad\qquad (7.1.9)$$

where the subscripts on the dependent variable u denote differentiation with respect to x and y. Note that here again the variable coefficients A through G can be arbitrarily nonlinear without violating the linearity of the PDE itself. According to this definition, Fourier's Equation 7.1.1, the biharmonic Equation 7.1.2, the continuity Equation 7.1.3, and Fick's Equation 7.1.4 are all *linear*.

When the PDE is not linear, a distinction is made between so-called quasilinear PDEs and Fully Nonlinear PDEs. The former is defined as an equation in which the *highest derivative* is still linear, but not necessarily the lower derivatives or the dependent variable itself. For example:

Linear: $\qquad\qquad\qquad x^2 u_{xx} + \exp(y)u_{yy} = 0$

Quasilinear: $\qquad\qquad\qquad u_{xx} = u_{yy} + u_t^2 \qquad\qquad (7.1.10)$

Fully nonlinear: $\qquad\qquad\qquad u_{tt} = u_{xx} + u_{yy}^2$

The motivation for introducing this new category of quasilinear PDEs lies in their behavior which differs from that of fully nonlinear PDEs, and in the fact that a fairly complete theory for them has been developed (see Chapter 9: Method of Characteristics). No such comprehensive treatment exists as yet for fully nonlinear PDEs.

What sets linear PDEs apart is that here one can again apply the Superposition Principle, i.e., if a set of independent solutions is known, their *sum* will also be a solution. The famous (and much-dreaded) Fourier Series solutions of the linear Fourier and Fick's equations are the result of precisely such a superposition procedure. Details will appear in Chapter 9 under the Separation of Variables Method. Superposition cannot in general be applied to either quasilinear or fully nonlinear PDEs.

7.1.5 ANOTHER NEW CATEGORY: ELLIPTIC, PARABOLIC, AND HYPERBOLIC PDEs

These categories draw their nomenclature from a similar classification for algebraic equations in two variables x and y. The reader may recall that for the general equation:

$$ax^2 + 2bxy + cy^2 + d = 0 \qquad (7.1.11)$$

one obtains:

An ellipse if: $b^2 - ac < 0$

A parabola if: $b^2 - ac = 0$

A hyperbola if: $b^2 - ac > 0$

To conform to this classification, the PDE, which is here a second order one with variable coefficients, is arranged in the form:

$$A(x,y)u_{xx} + 2B(x,y)u_{xy} + C(x,y)u_{yy} = F(x,y,u_x,u_y) \qquad (7.1.12)$$

The resulting categories, with properties and examples, are presented in Table 7.1. We note that the classification is not a trivial one since it reflects the nature of the problem (boundary value BVP or initial value IVP, singly or in combination) and through it the solution methods to be used. The Laplace transformation, for example, is usually reserved for IVPs only. A similar motivation for classifying equations arose at the ODE level where a distinction was made between second order equations with constant and variable coefficients. The former were solved by the D-operator method, while the latter required the use of series solutions.

Quasilinear first order PDEs, or rather sets of them, have the same three categories, but they are arrived at in a slightly different fashion. We write the set in vector-matrix form:

$$A(u,x,y)u_x + B(u,x,y)u_y + C(u,x,y) = 0 \qquad (7.1.13)$$

TABLE 7.1
Elliptic, Parabolic, and Hyperbolic Second Order PDEs

Criterion	Type of PDE	Example	Properties
$B^2 - AC < 0$	Elliptic	Laplace's equation $$\frac{\partial^2 u}{\partial x^2} + \frac{\partial^2 u}{\partial y^2} = 0$$	Boundary value problem
$B^2 - AC = 0$	Parabolic	Fourier's equation $$\alpha \frac{\partial^2 u}{\partial x^2} = \frac{\partial u}{\partial t}$$	Mixed BV and IV problem
$B^2 - AC > 0$	Hyperbolic	Wave equation $$c^2 \frac{\partial^2 u}{\partial x^2} = \frac{\partial^2 u}{\partial t^2}$$	Mixed BV and IV problem or IV problem

---

and set the criteria as follows:

The set is   if the eigenvalues of $\det\left|\underset{\sim}{A} - \lambda \underset{\sim}{B}\right| = 0$ are

Elliptic	Imaginary
Parabolic	Real and identical
Hyperbolic	Real and distinct

Application of this criterion is best studied in the context of the example given in Illustration 7.1.1.

7.1.6 BOUNDARY AND INITIAL CONDITIONS

Classification of BCs and ICs follows that established for ODEs but now has the names of mathematicians attached to them. Dimensionality is also increased so that a more general formulation is called for. We summarize the main features for convenience.

There are three major types of boundary and initial conditions.

1. *Type I (Dirichlet) BCs* contains the dependent variable only. The initial conditions usually fall into this category and in rectangular coordinates have the form:

$$u(0,S) = u_0$$

or more generally,

$$u(0,S) = f(x,y,z) \qquad (7.1.14)$$

where S denotes a bounding surface of the system.

The novelty here, compared to the ODE case is that the initial condition need not be a constant but can have an initial distribution in space $f(x,y,z)$. Thus, the quenched steel billet shown in Chapter 1, Figure 1.1 could have, at the start of the operation, a temperature distribution $f(0,x)$ rather than a constant and uniform value T_0.

2. *Type II (Neumann) BCs* contain the derivative only, usually taken normal to a surface S and denoted by $\partial u/\partial n$. The general condition is of the form:

$$\frac{\partial u}{\partial n}(t,S) = f(t) \tag{7.1.14}$$

and includes the special case:

$$\frac{\partial u}{\partial n}(t,S) = 0 \tag{7.1.15}$$

The latter condition applies when u is a maximum or minimum in a particular location, e.g., the center of symmetry, or when the boundary is impermeable to mass, energy, or momentum flux.

3. *Type III (Robin) or Mixed BC.* This condition contains both the derivative $\partial u/\partial n$ and the dependent variable u and has the general form:

$$\frac{\partial u}{\partial n}(t,S) = f[u(S),t] \tag{7.1.16}$$

It frequently arises at phase boundaries where the rate of convective transport in one phase (moving fluid) must equal diffusive transport in the other phase (stationary fluid or solid). For this particular case, Equation 7.1.16 becomes:

$$-K_1 \frac{\partial u}{\partial n}(t,S) = K_2[u(t,S) - u_o(t)] \tag{7.1.17}$$

(Specific forms of Equation 7.1.17 will be presented in Illustration 7.1.2.)

Two additional points need to be noted. The number of BCs required usually equals the sum of the highest order of the derivatives with respect to a particular independent variable. Thus, for the one-dimensional Fourier's Equation 7.1.1, we require two BCs for the second order derivative and one BC (or rather IC) for the first order time derivative. A total of three boundary conditions, therefore, are required to solve this equation. It often happens that additional BCs can be specified but are not used. They must nevertheless be satisfied by the solution.

Most analytical and numerical methods can easily handle complex initial conditions but have difficulty with complex boundary conditions, particularly those occasioned by unusual geometries. There is an incentive to simplify or transform difficult boundary conditions even if this results in a more complicated initial condition. An example of this type of transformation is taken up in Illustration 7.3.3.

Illustration 7.1.1   Classification of PDEs

Properties and classifications of the following PDEs is to be established.

$$(\text{I}) \qquad \frac{\partial^2 u}{\partial x^2} + \frac{\partial^2 u}{\partial y^2} + S(x,y) = 0 \qquad (7.1.18)$$

This PDE, known as Poisson's equation, is a second order, nonhomogeneous equation in the two independent variables x and y. It is linear since the derivatives appear in linear combination. The nonhomogeneous term $S(x,y)$, although arbitrary in form, is a function of the independent variables only and, therefore, does not affect linearity.

Comparison with Equation 7.1.12 yields the criterion:

$$B^2 - AC = 0 - (1)(1) = -1 < 0$$

Hence, according to Table 7.1.1, Poisson's equation is elliptic.

$$(\text{II}) \qquad -G_s \frac{\partial Y}{\partial z} = [\varepsilon \rho_g + \rho_b f'(Y)] \frac{\partial Y}{\partial t} \qquad (7.1.19)$$

This PDE is a special case of the so-called Chromatographic Equation which expresses variations in solute concentration Y of a fluid flowing through a stationary sorptive medium under equilibrium conditions (see Section 7.2). The term $f'(Y)$ is the derivative of the equilibrium relation:

$$q = f(Y) \qquad (7.1.20)$$

and is generally nonlinear in form.

The equation is a first order, homogeneous PDE in the two independent variables, distance z and time t. It is not linear because of the product $f'(Y)(\partial Y/\partial t)$, but neither is it fully nonlinear. Since the highest derivatives, $\partial Y/\partial z$ and $\partial Y/\partial t$, appear in linear form, it is a quasilinear PDE.

(III) Two-dimensional compressible irrotational (i.e., frictionless) flow is described by:

$$(v_x^2 - c^2)\frac{\partial v_x}{\partial x} + (v_x v_y)\frac{\partial v_y}{\partial x} + v_x v_y \frac{\partial v_x}{\partial y} + (v_y^2 - c^2)\frac{\partial v_y}{\partial y} = 0$$

$$-\frac{\partial v_x}{\partial y} + \frac{\partial v_y}{\partial x} = 0 \qquad (7.1.21)$$

These are two first order homogeneous PDEs in the two velocity components v_x and v_y, with c = velocity of sound. The second equation is linear and the first one quasilinear by virtue of the fact that its highest derivatives appear in linear form.

To determine whether the set is elliptic, parabolic or hyperbolic, we identify the coefficient matrices of the partial derivatives as:

$$\underset{\sim}{A} = \begin{pmatrix} v_x^2 - c^2 & v_x v_y \\ 0 & 1 \end{pmatrix} \tag{7.1.22}$$

and

$$\underset{\sim}{B} = \begin{pmatrix} v_x v_y & v_y^2 - c^2 \\ -1 & 0 \end{pmatrix}$$

Hence,

$$\det \left| \underset{\sim}{A} - \lambda \underset{\sim}{B} \right| = \begin{vmatrix} v_x^2 - c^2 - \lambda v_x v_y & v_x v_y - \lambda(v_y^2 - c^2) \\ \lambda & 1 \end{vmatrix} = 0 \tag{7.1.23}$$

or

$$\lambda_{1,2} = \frac{v_x v_y \pm c[v_x^2 + v_y^2 - c^2]^{1/2}}{(v_y^2 - c^2)} \tag{7.1.24}$$

This results in the following classification:

Eigenvalues $\lambda_{1,2}$	Velocities	Flow	PDE
Imaginary	$v_x^2 + v_y^2 < c^2$	Subsonic	Elliptic
Identical and real	$v_x^2 + v_y^2 = c^2$	Sonic	Parabolic
Distinct and real	$v_x^2 + v_y^2 > c^2$	Supersonic	Hyperbolic

Thus, the PDEs can fall into any one of the three categories (elliptic, parabolic, hyperbolic) depending on whether the flow regime is subsonic, sonic, or supersonic. Consequently, one can expect changes in both solution methods and solution behavior as the flow regimes change.

Illustration 7.1.2   Derivation of Boundary and Initial Condition

Leaching of a Slurry in a Stirred Tank — A slurry of porous solid particles assumed to be thin flakes and containing a soluble component is to be leached in a stirred tank of solvent (Figure 7.1A). We wish to derive BCs and ICs for the full PDE model in terms of solid and external fluid concentrations C_s and C_f.

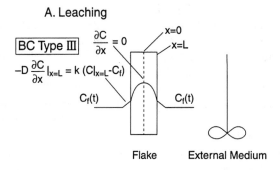

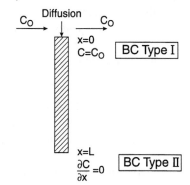

FIGURE 7.1 Examples of physical systems with BCs of Type I, II, and III (Dirichlet, Neumann, Robin).

The internal mass transfer is assumed to be Fickian. Equation 7.1.4 applies and requires three BCs/ICs, two for the second order derivative and one for the first order time derivative. We obtain:

IC $\qquad\qquad C_s(x,0) = C_s^0$ (assumed uniform)

BC I $\qquad\qquad \dfrac{\partial C_s}{dx}\bigg|_{x=0} = 0 \,(\text{symmetry})$

or

$$C_s(0,t) = \text{bounded} \qquad\qquad (7.1.25)$$

BC II $\qquad\qquad -D\dfrac{\partial C_s}{\partial x}\bigg|_{x=L} = k[C_s(L) - C_f(t)]$

where k is a mass transfer coefficient.

BC I is of type II, BC II of Type III or Mixed Type. The latter expresses equality of diffusive flux at the surface and convective removal through a film resistance. Fick's equation is coupled to an external integral unsteady mass balance, which leads to a first order ODE in the fluid concentration C_f requiring an initial condition: IC — $C_f(0) = 0$, assuming clean solvent at the start of the operation.

Systems of PDEs coupled to ODEs arise frequently in diffusive processes taking place in a confined, well-stirred medium. In these cases, four boundary and initial conditions are required for each of the participating species. Solutions of such systems are taken up in Chapter 8, Illustration 8.2.5.

Diffusion into a Narrow Capillary — A liquid containing a solute at a concentration C^0 flows over the opening of a capillary containing pure solvent (Figure 7.1B). The solute diffuses into the capillary which is sealed at the bottom. This type of arrangement has been used to determine diffusivities from average solute concentrations in the capillary measured at various time intervals. Substitution of the values into the solution of Fick's Equation 7.1.4 allows the relevant diffusion coefficient D to be extracted (see Practice Problem 9.2.7).

The required boundary and initial conditions that are three in number are as follows:

IC $\qquad\qquad\qquad C(0,x) = 0$ (Pure Solvent at t = 0) $\qquad\qquad$ (7.1.26)

BC I $\qquad\qquad C(t,0) = C^0$ (Concentration at open end)

Here it is assumed that flow of the liquid is fast enough that there are no significant changes in external solute concentration. The same effect may be obtained by contacting the capillary with a large volume of a well-stirred fluid.

BC II $\qquad\qquad \left.\dfrac{\partial C}{\partial x}\right|_{x=L} = 0$ (No flux at sealed end) $\qquad\qquad$ (7.1.27)

Alternatively, we have:

$$C(t,L) - \text{Bounded}$$

7.2 PDEs OF MAJOR IMPORTANCE

The previous section gave the reader a first glimpse of PDEs and their properties. The reassuring fact emerged that except for one or two new features, these properties were very much like those we had seen at the ODE level. We now open the door slightly wider and expose the reader to a listing of PDEs of major importance. These are presented in *scalar* Cartesian form to make them easier to decipher. The more general *vectorial* representation is deferred to the next chapter.

Although still somewhat intimidating in appearance, the reader will take comfort from the fact that these equations share some familiar features with ordinary differential equations. Thus, convective transport is still described by first order derivatives, diffusive transport by second order derivatives, and interphase transport, is, as before, proportional to a linear driving force. These PDEs are for the most part similar in appearance to ODEs we had seen in previous chapters and may be viewed as multidimensional extensions of the balances we had encountered at the ODE level. In fact, we shall see that if we reverse the process by *reducing* dimensionality we can, in many instances, recover an ODE balance seen before.

7.2.1 FIRST ORDER PARTIAL DIFFERENTIAL EQUATIONS

7.2.1.1 Unsteady Tubular Operations (Turbulent Flow)

We noted in the introduction to the chapter that all systems of the one-dimensional pipe category, which led to first order ODEs under steady-state conditions, become PDEs when time-dependent inlet conditions are imposed. They will be *first order* PDEs since the rate of change term will be a first order derivative. Thus, for the steam heated pipe described in Illustration 2.2 the relevant energy balance now reads:

$$F(t)C_p \frac{\partial T}{\partial z} - U(t)\pi d(T_s - T) = \rho C_p \frac{\partial T}{\partial t} \qquad (7.2.1)$$

with inlet temperature in general given by:

$$T(t,0) = f(t)$$

Flow rate $f(t)$ and inlet temperature can vary individually or in combination with time t and affect the heat transfer coefficient $U(t)$ as well.

Similar first order PDEs arise in tubular reactors and in co-current and counter-current continuous mass and heat transfer operations. Turbulent flow conditions had been specified since laminar flow leads to radial diffusive processes and results in second order PDEs. These are described in Section 7.2.2, the Graetz Problem.

One notes that for the steady state, Equation 7.2.1 reduces to the ODE (2.15) for the steam-heated pipe and we are on familiar ground again. Thus, the two equations differ only by the single unsteady term $\rho C_p \frac{\partial T}{\partial t}$. If, on the other hand, we drop the convective term $F(t)C_p(\partial T/\partial z)$, we recover an unsteady stirred tank balance which leads again to familiar territory.

7.2.1.2 The Chromatographic Equations

These equations describe concentration changes that occur when a fluid containing a solute, or devoid of it, flows through or over a stationary matrix of solid sorptive material. The latter may be "clean" or loaded with solute. We had considered problems of this type as an environmental context in Chapter 6, Illustration 6.2.8 without going into the details of the underlying partial differential equations. We now consider these both under equilibrium and nonequilibrium conditions where the fluid phase is a gas.

Equilibrium (No Mass Transfer Resistance) — We had already seen this case in Illustration 7.1.1 where the PDE was of the form:

$$-G_s \frac{\partial Y}{\partial z} = [\varepsilon \rho_g + \rho_b f'(Y)] \qquad (7.1.19)$$

where $f'(Y)$ is the derivative of the equilibrium relation:

$$q = f(Y) \qquad (7.1.20)$$

and $\varepsilon \rho_g$ can usually be neglected.

A more general formulation for several solutes is given by the two-phase mass balance:

$$-G_s \frac{\partial Y_i}{\partial z} = \rho_b \frac{\partial q_i}{\partial t} + \varepsilon \rho_g \frac{\partial Y_i}{\partial t} \qquad (7.2.2)$$

with the equilibrium relation:

$$q_i = f(Y_1, Y_2 \dots Y_n) \qquad (7.2.3)$$

and $I = 1, 2, \dots n$. Here q = solid phase concentration (kg solute/kg solid) and Y = gas phase concentration (kg solute/kg carrier). G_s is the carrier mass velocity (kg/s · m²), ρ_b and ρ_g the bed and carrier density (kg/m³), ε the bed void fraction.

We, thus, obtain, after substitution of Equation 7.2.3 into Equation 7.2.2, n coupled first order PDEs in the fluid concentrations $Y_1, Y_2 \dots Y_n$.

Nonequilibrium (With Mass Transfer Resistance) — Here the relevant equations are given by:

Gas-phase mass balance:

$$-G_s \frac{\partial Y}{\partial z} - K_{0Y}a(Y - Y^*) = \varepsilon \rho_g \frac{\partial Y}{\partial t}$$

$$\text{Flow} \qquad \text{Mass transfer} \qquad \text{Unsteady term} \qquad (7.2.4)$$

Solid phase mass balance:

$$K_{0Y}a(Y - Y^*) = \rho_b \frac{\partial q}{\partial t} \qquad (7.2.5)$$

Equilibrium (inverted):

$$Y^* = f(q) \qquad (7.2.6)$$

Here again it is of some comfort to see that omission of the unsteady term in Equation 7.2.4 yields the familiar steady-state gas phase mass balance, Equation (2.20), which we had encountered while modeling a countercurrent gas absorber. The reader should attempt to overcome the initial mistrust of PDEs by reducing them, whenever possible, to ODEs which are familiar from more conventional steady-state and one-dimensional situations.

7.2.1.3   Stochastic Processes

Stochastic processes that deal with the probability of an event occurring are frequently described by the Fokker-Planck equation:

$$\beta \frac{\partial}{\partial x}(xP) + D \frac{\partial^2 P}{dx^2} = \frac{\partial P}{\partial t} \tag{7.2.7}$$

and its reduced form (D = 0):

$$\beta x \frac{\partial P}{\partial x} + \beta P = \frac{\partial P}{\partial t} \tag{7.2.8}$$

The latter is a linear, homogeneous first order PDE with variable coefficients. Physically, the equation expresses the probability that a random variable has the value x at time t. Thus, in so-called *random walk* processes, P will be the probability distribution of the position x of a particle at a given time t. Other stochastic processes can be described by the same equation.

7.2.1.4   Movement of Traffic

It seems at first sight surprising that movement of traffic which consists of discrete vehicular entities can be described by a differential equation. This is achieved by defining a vehicle density C (# per unit distance x) and a vehicle flux q (# crossing x per unit time), corresponding to concentration C and flux N_A in ordinary mass transport. A simple "mass balance" then yields the expression:

$$-\frac{\partial q'}{\partial x} = \frac{\partial C}{\partial t} \tag{7.2.9}$$

where flux q' is given by the product of density C and velocity v:

$$q' = Cv \tag{7.2.10}$$

v in turn depends on density, since high densities, for example, lead to low velocities. A simple relation which is often used to express this fact has the form:

$$v = v_{Max}\left(1 - \frac{C}{C_{Max}}\right) \qquad (7.2.11)$$

Thus, when $C \cong 0$, traffic moves at its maximum speed. Conversely, when $C = C_{Max}$, traffic comes to a halt, i.e., we have a bumper-to-bumper traffic jam.

Substitution of Equations 7.2.10 and 7.2.11 into the mass balance Equation 7.2.9 yields a single PDE in the vehicle density C, as a function of time and position:

$$v_{Max}\left(\frac{C}{C_{Max}} - 1\right)\frac{\partial C}{\partial x} = \frac{\partial C}{\partial t} \qquad (7.2.12)$$

The equation is first order, quasilinear, and homogeneous. We shall encounter it again in Chapter 9, Section 9.3 (Method of Characteristics).

7.2.1.5 Sedimentation of Particles

The treatment of this case is analogous to that of traffic problems, i.e., one performs in the first instance a mass balance which leads to Equation 7.2.9, where C is now the number of particles per unit volume and flux q is in terms of number of particles settling per unit area and time. An auxiliary relation is then introduced, much like that given by Equations 7.2.10 and 7.2.11 to relate flux to concentration:

$$v = v_{Max}\left(1 - \frac{C}{C_{Max}}\right) \qquad (7.2.11)$$

The final PDE is then identical to that given by Equation 7.2.12.

The auxiliary Relation 7.2.11 holds in simple situation but more complex relations, both for traffic and sedimentation problems are needed in other cases. These are described in specialized monographs (see references at end of Chapter 9).

7.2.2 Second Order Partial Differential Equations

7.2.2.1 Laplace's Equation

This equation, which is among the most important relations of mathematical physics, is given in Cartesian coordinates by the expression:

$$\frac{\partial^2 u}{\partial x^2} + \frac{\partial^2 u}{\partial y^2} + \frac{\partial^2 u}{\partial z^2} = 0 \qquad (7.2.13)$$

The solution of this equation yields the steady-state distribution of the state variable u. That variable is often referred to as a *potential* or *potential function,* and the study of its behavior as *potential theory.* The reason for this designation is that

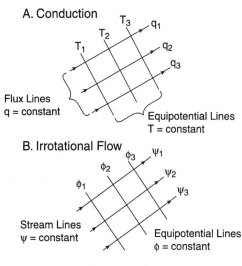

A. Conduction

Flux Lines
q = constant

Equipotential Lines
T = constant

B. Irrotational Flow

Stream Lines
ψ = constant

Equipotential Lines
φ = constant

C. Electrostatics and Gravitation

Force Lines

Equipotential Lines
V = constant

FIGURE 7.2   Physical systems described by Laplace's equation.

in many applications of Laplace's equation, u represents a driving potential for a particular physical process leading to the movement of mass and heat. In other cases it serves to generalize force fields which are related to the movement of mass or electrical charges. We summarize these applications below.

Conduction — Here Laplace's equation has the specific form in rectangular coordinates:

$$\frac{\partial^2 T}{\partial x^2} + \frac{\partial^2 T}{\partial y^2} + \frac{\partial^2 T}{\partial z^2} = 0 \tag{7.2.14}$$

The solution represents the steady-state temperature distribution in three-dimensional Cartesian space. It can be displayed as a "flow net" (Figure 7.2A) in which the lines T = constant are the equipotential lines or isotherms which carry no heat, and the orthogonal set of flux lines q = constant are the pathways along which conduction takes place with the components of q given by Fourier's law, i.e.,

$$q_x = -k_x \frac{\partial T}{\partial x}, \quad q_y = -k_y \frac{\partial T}{\partial y}, \quad q_z = -k_z \frac{\partial T}{\partial z} \tag{7.2.15}$$

It is comforting to note that for the one-dimensional case, Equation 7.2.14 reduces to

$$\frac{d^2T}{dx^2} = 0 \qquad (7.2.16)$$

with the solution:

$$T = Ax + B \qquad (7.2.17)$$

This is the well-known linear temperature profile which arises in unidirectional heat conduction between two isothermal plates.

Diffusion — The counterpart of Equation 7.2.14 for mass diffusion is given by:

$$\frac{\partial^2 C}{\partial x^2} + \frac{\partial^2 C}{\partial y^2} + \frac{\partial^2 C}{\partial z^2} = 0 \qquad (7.2.18)$$

where concentration C is the potential corresponding to temperature T, and the mass flux $N_{x,y,z} = -D \dfrac{\partial C}{\partial(x,y,z)}$ takes the place of conductive flux q.

Flow Through Porous Media — Here the driving potential is the hydrostatic pressure p, and Laplace's equation takes the form:

$$\frac{\partial^2 p}{\partial x^2} + \frac{\partial^2 p}{\partial y^2} + \frac{\partial^2 p}{\partial z^2} = 0 \qquad (7.2.19)$$

p is related to the velocity components v_x, v_y, v_z via the auxiliary D'Arcy's law which is the counterpart to Fourier's and Fick's law:

$$v_x = -\frac{K_x}{\mu}\frac{\partial p}{\partial x}, \quad v_y = -\frac{K_y}{\mu}\frac{\partial p}{\partial y}, \quad v_z = -\frac{K_z}{\mu}\frac{\partial p}{\partial z} \qquad (7.2.20)$$

The Ks in this expression represent permeabilities of the porous medium in the three directions.

The solution of Equation 7.2.19 represents the pressure distribution in the porous medium that can in turn be used to derive the velocity distribution by back-substitution into Equation 7.2.20, giving us a complete description of the flow field in a porous medium. Note that no flow takes place along the equipotential lines p = constant.

Irrotational or Potential Flow — Although a precise definition of irrotational flow requires the use of vector calculus (see Chapter 8), it suffices for our present purposes to identify it with frictionless flow. Some exceptions to this definition do occur but they are quite rare.

The flow in question has a potential function associated with it, the so-called velocity potential ϕ which is related to the two-dimensional velocity components v_x and v_y via the expressions:

$$v_x = \frac{\partial \phi}{\partial x} \quad v_y = \frac{\partial \phi}{\partial y} \tag{7.2.21}$$

Alternative formulations using negative gradients also may be used.

The best way to obtain a physical sense of this quantity is to note that for $\phi =$ constant, the velocity components vanish, i.e., there is no flow along equipotential lines $\phi =$ constant. In this respect, ϕ has the same properties as the potential functions for conduction (T), diffusion (C), and flow in porous media (p). Orthogonal to this network of lines is the network of flow that is the streamlines of the flow field. These lines have the properties that a second function, the so-called stream function ψ, is invariant along them, $\psi =$ constant (see Figure 7.2B). That function also can be related to the two-dimensional velocity components, as follows:

$$v_x = -\frac{\partial \psi}{\partial y} \quad v_y = \frac{\partial \psi}{\partial x} \tag{7.2.22}$$

Both ψ and ϕ satisfy Laplace's equation as can be seen by differentiating Equations 7.2.21 and 7.2.22. Thus,

$$\frac{\partial^2 \phi}{\partial x^2} + \frac{\partial^2 \phi}{\partial y^2} = 0$$
$$\frac{\partial^2 \psi}{\partial x^2} + \frac{\partial^2 \psi}{\partial y^2} = 0 \tag{7.2.23}$$

One can solve for either ϕ or ψ and obtain, by direct substitution into Equations 7.2.21 and 7.2.22, the velocity distribution in the flow field. To obtain a complete description of the flow, we require in addition the pressure distribution $p(x,y)$. This is arrived at from Bernoulli's equation which for the present purposes takes the form (incompressible flow):

$$\frac{p_1}{\rho} + \frac{v_x^2 + v_y^2}{2} = \frac{p_2}{\rho} + \frac{v_x^2 + v_y^2}{2} \tag{7.2.24}$$

Gravitational and Electrostatic Fields — The potential function for gravitational and electrostatic fields derives from the empirical laws due to Newton (gravity) and Coulomb (electrostatics) that the attractive forces between two masses or two charges of opposite sign varies directly with the product of the mass m or charges q, and inversely with the square of the distance between them:

TABLE 7.2
Potential Functions of Laplace's Equation

Process	Potential Function	Relation to Process Variables		
Conduction	Temperature T	$q_x = -k_x \dfrac{\partial T}{\partial x}$	$q_y = -k_y \dfrac{\partial T}{\partial y}$	$q_z = -k_z \dfrac{\partial T}{\partial z}$
Diffusion	Concentration C	$N_x = -D_x \dfrac{\partial C}{\partial x}$	$N_y = -D_y \dfrac{\partial C}{\partial y}$	$N_z = -D_z \dfrac{\partial C}{\partial z}$
Flow through porous media	Pressure p	$v_x = -\dfrac{K_x}{\mu}\dfrac{\partial p}{\partial x}$	$v_y = -\dfrac{K_y}{\mu}\dfrac{\partial p}{\partial y}$	$v_z = -\dfrac{K_z}{\mu}\dfrac{\partial p}{\partial z}$
Irrotational flow	Velocity potential ϕ		$v_x = \dfrac{\partial \phi}{\partial x} \quad v_y = \dfrac{\partial \phi}{\partial y}$	
Gravitation electrostatics	Potential V	$F_x = C\dfrac{\partial V}{\partial x}$	$F_y = C\dfrac{\partial V}{\partial y}$	$F_z = C\dfrac{\partial V}{\partial z}$

$$F_G = C_1 \frac{m_1 m_2}{r^2} \quad F_e = C_2 \frac{q^+ q^-}{r^2} \qquad (7.2.25)$$

It can be shown that these empiricism lead to the definition of a potential function V, which is related to the Cartesian force components as follows:

$$F_x = C\frac{\partial V}{\partial x} \quad F_y = C\frac{\partial V}{\partial y} \quad F_z = C\frac{\partial V}{\partial z} \qquad (7.2.26)$$

where we have generalized both the potential function and the proportionality constant into single entities (Figure 7.2C). One notes that these "auxiliary relations" are nearly identical in form to the relations applicable to conduction, diffusion, and flow through porous media with the exception that the derivatives of the potential function V take a positive sign, as did the velocity potential. Differentiation along constant force lines converts Equation 7.2.26 to Laplace's equation:

$$\frac{\partial^2 V}{\partial x^2} + \frac{\partial^2 V}{\partial y^2} + \frac{\partial^2 V}{\partial z^2} = 0 \qquad (7.2.22)$$

We have summarized for convenience the relevant potential functions for the various cases discussed in Table 7.2.

7.2.2.2 Poisson's Equation

Poisson's equation is obtained by adding what may be called a Source Term A to Laplace's Equation. This yields the general form:

TABLE 7.3
Source Terms in Poisson's Equation

Process	$A(x,y,z)$	Source Term
Conduction	$S(x,y,z)/k$	$S(J/sm^3)$
Gravitation	$4\pi\rho(x,y,z)$	$\rho(kg/m^3)$
Electrostatics	$4\pi\rho(x,y,z)$	$\rho(C/m^3)$

$$\frac{\partial^2 u}{\partial x^2} + \frac{\partial^2 u}{\partial y^2} + \frac{\partial^2 u}{\partial z^2} + A(x,y,z) = 0 \qquad (7.2.28)$$

Such nonhomogeneous terms $A(x,y,z)$ arise in the steady-conduction of heat through a medium with distributed or uniform heat sources, in gravitational fields with distributed masses and in electrostatic fields with distributed charges. The exact form of $A(x,y,z)$ is summarized for the convenience of the reader in Table 7.3.

7.2.2.3 Helmholtz Equation

Here a linear term in the state variable u is added to Laplace's equation to yield:

$$\frac{\partial^2 u}{\partial x^2} + \frac{\partial^2 u}{\partial y^2} + \frac{\partial^2 u}{\partial z^2} + Au = 0 \qquad (7.2.29)$$

Occurrence of this equation is more limited. It arises principally in diffusional processes accompanied by a first order reaction. For example, diffusion in three dimensions in a solid matrix, in which the reactants undergo a first order irreversible reaction is given by the expression:

$$\frac{\partial^2 C}{\partial x^2} + \frac{\partial^2 C}{\partial y^2} + \frac{\partial^2 C}{\partial z^2} + \frac{k_r}{D}C = 0 \qquad (7.2.30)$$

An identical form arises in nuclear processes in which neutron density ϕ takes the place of concentration C, and the rate term is given by the expression:

$$\frac{v\Sigma_f - \Sigma_a}{D}\phi$$

where $\Sigma_{f,a}$ are the so-called fission and absorption cross-sections, and v = number of neutrons produced per fission event. The reader will note that upon dropping the derivatives in y and z, we recover the ODE for diffusion and reaction in a catalyst slab.

7.2.2.4 Biharmonic Equation

This equation, used as an example of a higher order PDE, has the two-dimensional rectangular form:

$$\frac{\partial^4 u}{\partial x^4} + 2\frac{\partial^2}{\partial x^2}\left(\frac{\partial^2 u}{\partial y^2}\right) + \frac{\partial^4 u}{\partial y^4} = 0 \tag{7.1.2}$$

It arises in certain areas of solid mechanics, such as elasticity theory where u describes the displacement in the solid body. In fluid mechanics, the equation is encountered in the description of *creeping flow,* i.e., slow viscous flow, in which u becomes the stream function ψ (see Chapter 8, Equation 8.4.15).

7.2.2.5   Fourier's Equation

We use the term Fourier's equation to denote the unsteady version of the expression for steady-state conduction, Equation 7.2.14. For constant physical properties, it takes the rectangular form:

$$\alpha\left[\frac{\partial^2 T}{\partial x^2} + \frac{\partial^2 T}{\partial y^2} + \frac{\partial^2 T}{\partial z^2}\right] = \frac{\partial T}{\partial t} \tag{7.2.31}$$

where $\alpha = k/\rho Cp$ = thermal diffusivity. A derivation of the one-dimensional version of this equation is given in Illustration 7.2.1.

7.2.2.6   Fick's Equation

Fick's equation is the diffusional counterpart to Fourier's equation and is identical to it in form, with concentration C replacing temperature, and mass diffusivity D taking the place of thermal diffusivity α. We have in Cartesian coordinates:

$$D\left[\frac{\partial^2 C}{\partial x^2} + \frac{\partial^2 C}{\partial y^2} + \frac{\partial^2 C}{\partial z^2}\right] = \frac{\partial C}{\partial t} \tag{7.2.32}$$

Although many solutions to this equation are identical in form to those of the conduction equation, there are sufficient differences in the two processes that a separate treatment of the topic becomes desirable. This is reflected in the existence of separate monographs devoted to the subject (see References).

7.2.2.7   The Wave Equation

The Wave equation describes not only, as the name implies, wave propagation phenomena, but applies quite generally to physical processes which result in the *disturbance* or *displacement* of fluid or solid elements. It has the Cartesian form:

$$\frac{\partial^2 u}{\partial x^2} + \frac{\partial^2 u}{\partial y^2} + \frac{\partial^2 u}{\partial z^2} = \frac{1}{c^2}\frac{\partial^2 u}{\partial t^2} \tag{7.2.33}$$

where c is a constant and a function of the physical process under consideration. We summarize specific applications below.

Transverse Vibrations in a String — The one-dimensional form of Equation 7.2.33 applies here, with u(x,t) describing the displacement of an element of the string in the transverse direction. The constant c^2 equals H/ρ where H is the horizontal component of the tension along the string. The derivation of the PDE appears in Illustration 7.2.1.

One-Dimensional Sound Propagation — Here the constant c represents the velocity of sound:

$$c = \left(\frac{\partial p}{\partial \rho}\right)^{1/2}$$

and the displacement is related to the local pressure p by the relation:

$$p - p_0 = -c^2 \rho_0 \frac{\partial u}{\partial x} \qquad (7.2.34)$$

where the subscript o denotes the undisturbed state.

Transverse Vibrations in a Membrane — Vibrations of a thin membrane of width L are represented by the two-dimensional wave equation, with $c^2 = TL$ and u(x,y,t) the displacement in the transverse direction. T is the uniform tension of the membrane. Other applications include the propagation of tidal and electromagnetic waves, as well as elastic waves in a solid.

7.2.2.8 The Navier-Stokes Equations

The Navier-Stokes equation is a vectorial force or momentum balance for viscous fluid flow. It has three component balances, of which we reproduce one in the Cartesian z direction:

$$-\rho\left[v_x \frac{\partial v_z}{\partial x} + v_y \frac{\partial v_z}{\partial y} + v_z \frac{\partial v_z}{\partial z}\right] + \mu\left[\frac{\partial^2 v_z}{\partial x^2} + \frac{\partial^2 v_z}{\partial y^2} + \frac{\partial^2 v_z}{\partial z^2}\right]$$

Momentum due to flow   Viscous Forces

$$-\frac{\partial p}{\partial z} \qquad -\rho g_z \quad = \quad \rho \frac{\partial v_z}{\partial t}$$

Pressure force   Gravity   Unsteady term

$$(7.2.35)$$

Together with the continuity equation, the Navier-Stokes equations comprise four PDEs in the state variables v_x, v_y, v_z, and p. Their solution represents a complete description of the flow field.

As usual, one can gain a better physical understanding of these formidable equations by reducing them to simpler and more familiar cases. Thus, for steady inviscid ($\mu = 0$), one-dimensional steady flow, Equation 7.2.35 becomes:

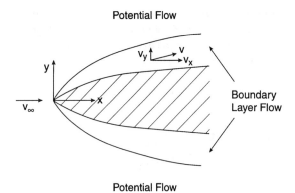

Potential Flow

FIGURE 7.3   Flow about a submerged body. Division of the flow field into boundary layer flow and potential flow.

$$v \frac{dv}{dz} + \frac{1}{\rho} \frac{dp}{dz} + g = 0 \qquad (7.2.35a)$$

which is the differential form of the Bernoulli equation.

We shall return to the Navier-Stokes equations in Chapter 8, Section 8.4 where they will be discussed in greater detail and refinement.

7.2.2.9 The Prandtl Boundary Layer Equations

In boundary layer theory it is assumed that viscous or frictional effects in exterior flows are confined to a thin layer adjacent to the surface of the submerged body. Outside this region flow is essentially frictionless or, to be more precise, we are dealing with potential or irrotational flow (Figure 7.3). An analysis due to Prandtl established that viscous forces and those due to bulk flow in the y-direction are negligible compared to those operating in the x-direction. Under these conditions, the three Navier-Stokes momentum balances will reduce to a single two-dimensional balance which is supplemented by the corresponding continuity equation. We obtain:

Momentum balance:

$$-\rho \left[v_x \frac{\partial v_x}{\partial x} + v_y \frac{\partial v_x}{\partial y} \right] + \mu \frac{\partial^2 v_x}{\partial x^2} - \frac{dp}{dx} = 0 \qquad (7.2.36)$$

Continuity equation:

$$\frac{\partial v_x}{\partial x} + \frac{\partial v_y}{\partial y} = 0 \qquad (7.2.37)$$

The pressure gradient which is significant only in the x-direction is established from the solution of the potential flow equations in conjunction with Bernoulli's

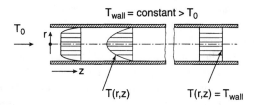

FIGURE 7.4 The Graetz problem in heat transfer. Development of steady axial and radial temperature distributions.

Equation 7.2.35a. Here again we shall retrace the various steps in greater detail in Chapter 8, Section 8.4 where we also shall provide a detailed derivation of these important equations.

7.2.2.10 The Graetz Problem

The nature of this problem may be deduced from Figure 7.4. It consists essentially of the derivation of the axial and radial temperature profiles which result when a fluid in viscous flow and with inlet temperature T_0 flows through a duct whose wall temperature is kept constant at some value T_w. T_w is assumed to be higher than T_0 in the figure, but it can equally well be set lower. A steady-state energy balance in cylindrical coordinates leads to the PDE (see Illustration 7.2.1):

$$v(r)\frac{\partial T}{\partial z} = \alpha\left[\frac{\partial^2 T}{\partial r^2} + \frac{1}{r}\frac{\partial T}{\partial r}\right] \qquad (7.2.38)$$

whose solution provides the desired profile $T(r,z)$.

This classical problem has been extended to encompass a variety of wall boundary conditions, duct geometries, axial conduction, as well as non-Newtonian fluids. It will be evident to the reader that an expression identical in form to Equation 7.2.38 applies to *mass* transport which may arise in membrane processes or when a substance is either released or reacted at the tubular wall.

Because of the scope and importance of the topic, entire monographs listing solutions and solution methods have been devoted to the subject (see References at the end of the Chapter 8). Further details and illustrations dealing with this problem will appear in Chapter 8, Sections 8.2 and 8.3.

Illustration 7.2.1 Derivation of Some Simple PDEs

The derivation of PDEs can be accomplished in several ways.

- At the simplest level, one uses an extension of the methodology established for algebraic and ordinary differential equations. This consists of invoking various conservation laws and applying the scheme: Rate in – Rate out = Rate of change of contents.

For force balances use is also made of Newton's law. This method can be applied easily to simple PDEs but becomes increasingly cumbersome as the geometry and the balances grow in complexity.

- One can use the above approach to derive the PDE for a simple geometry and generalize the results by means of vector calculus. This is the approach used in most texts on transport phenomena, but will not be taken up here.
- One can start immediately with a vector/tensor representation of the basic conservation laws and apply these to various geometries of interest. This requires considerable background in the basic laws and manipulations of vector and tensor calculus. Some examples of this approach will be given in Chapter 8.

For the present, we limit ourselves to the simplest methodology and use it to derive some elementary PDEs.

Fourier's Equation in One Dimension — We apply an energy balance to the differential element shown in Figure 7.5A and obtain

$$\text{Rate of energy in} - \text{Rate of energy out} = \frac{\text{Rate of change of}}{\text{energy contents}}$$

(7.2.39)

$$q\,|_x - q\,|_{x+\Delta x} = \left(\frac{\partial H}{\partial t}\right)_{avg}$$

and in expanded form:

$$-kA\frac{\partial T}{\partial x}\bigg|_x - \left(-kA\frac{\partial T}{\partial x}\bigg|_{x+\Delta x}\right) = \rho C_p A\Delta x\left(\frac{\partial T}{\partial t}\right)_{avg}$$

where it is to be noted that the time derivative is an *average* over the difference element.

Dividing by $A\Delta x$ and letting $\Delta x \to 0$, there results:

$$\frac{\partial}{\partial x}k\frac{\partial T}{\partial x} = \rho Cp\frac{\partial T}{\partial t}$$

(7.2.40)

where $(\partial T/\partial t)_{avg}$ has now become a *point* quantity.

For constant thermal conductivity k, this reduces to the form given previously:

$$\alpha\frac{\partial^2 T}{\partial x^2} = \frac{\partial T}{\partial t}$$

(7.1.1)

where $\alpha = k/\rho Cp$ = thermal diffusivity.

The Graetz Problem — In this instance the energy balance is taken over the annular cylindrical element shown in Figure 7.5B. Energy in convective flow enters

A. Fourier's Equation

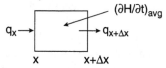

B. Graetz Problem

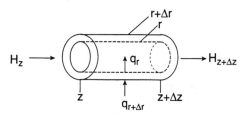

C. Vibrating String

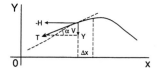

FIGURE 7.5 Difference elements for the derivation of PDEs.

and leaves the element axially at z and $z+\Delta z$ and conductive flux enters and leaves radially at positions $r+\Delta r$ and r. The process is at steady-state and we obtain:

$$\text{Rate of energy in} - \text{Rate of energy out} = 0$$

$$\begin{bmatrix} H\mid_{z} \\ +q\mid_{r+\Delta r} \end{bmatrix} - \begin{bmatrix} H\mid_{z+\Delta z} \\ +q\mid_{r+\Delta r} \end{bmatrix} = 0 \qquad (7.2.41)$$

or in expanded form:

$$\begin{bmatrix} v_{avg}(r)\rho Cp2\pi r\Delta r(T-T_{o})_{z} \\ +k\Delta z\left(2\pi r\dfrac{\partial T}{\partial r}\right)_{r+\Delta r} \end{bmatrix} - \begin{bmatrix} v_{avg}(r)\rho Cp2\pi r\Delta r(T-T_{o})_{z+\Delta z} \\ +k\Delta z\left(2\pi r\dfrac{\partial T}{\partial r}\right)_{r} \end{bmatrix} \qquad (7.2.42)$$

Several features are of note here:

- Velocity v varies in general with radial distance r and an average value $v_{avg}(r)$ has to be specified over the radial increment Δr. That term becomes a point quantity v(r) upon going to the limit $\Delta r \to 0$.

- Fourier's law of heat conduction takes a positive sign since the process takes place in the negative radial direction.
- The radial perimeter $2\pi r$, as well as the temperature gradient $\partial T/\partial r$, have to be differentiated upon going to the limit $\Delta r \to 0$. Note that the perimeter in the conduction term has been left as $2\pi r$, not $[2\pi(r + \Delta r), 2\pi r)$. The latter formulation, often used by novices, leads to messy and sometimes incorrect results. Similarly, the area of the radial increment is given as $2\pi r \, \Delta r$ rather than $\pi(r + \Delta r)^2 - \pi r^2$, to avoid unnecessary complications.
- The axial enthalpy flow F (kg/s) H (J/kg) becomes in expanded form $v\rho A C_p(T - T_0)$.

We now proceed to divide Equation 7.2.42 by $2\pi r \Delta r \Delta x$ and obtain:

$$-\left[\frac{v_{avg}(r)\rho Cp(T - T_0)_{z+\Delta z} - v_{avg}(r)\rho Cp(T - T_0)_z}{\Delta z}\right]$$

$$+\left[\frac{1}{r}\frac{k\left(r\dfrac{\partial T}{\partial r}\right)_{r+\Delta r} - k\left(r\dfrac{\partial T}{\partial r}\right)_r}{\Delta r}\right] = 0 \quad (7.2.43)$$

Letting Δz and Δr go to zero and taking care to differentiate the entire product $(r \, \partial T/\partial r)$, we obtain after rearrangement:

$$v(r)\frac{\partial T}{\partial z} = \alpha\left(\frac{\partial^2 T}{\partial r^2} + \frac{1}{r}\frac{\partial T}{\partial r}\right) \quad (7.2.44)$$

where $\alpha = k/\rho \, Cp$ = thermal diffusivity and $v(r)$ has now become a point quantity. Graetz originally solved the problem for v = constant, and it was not until 1956 that a solution to the variable case $v(r)$ became available.

The Vibrating String — This system requires a force balance of which the principal components and the attendant deflection of the string are depicted in Figure 7.5C. $V(x,t)$ is the restoring vertical force which varies with time and distance x while the horizontal component H of the tension T is constant over the length of the string and time invariant. It is further assumed that the angle α remains small so that the incremental length of string is given by its projection Δx. In other words, we are limiting ourselves to vibrations of *small amplitude* such as those experienced by the strings of musical instruments.

With these considerations in place, we obtain the following relation between horizontal and vertical force components H and $V(x,t)$:

$$V(x,t) = -H \tan \alpha = -H\frac{\partial Y}{\partial x} \quad (7.2.45)$$

where Y is the vertical displacement of the string. Applying this relation to a difference element Δx of the string and invoking Newton's law to describe its motion, we obtain:

$$\rho \Delta x \frac{\partial^2 Y}{\partial t^2} = -H\left(\left.\frac{\partial Y}{\partial x}\right|_x - \left.\frac{\partial Y}{\partial x}\right|_{x+\Delta x} \right) \qquad (7.2.46)$$

where ρ = mass per unit length of string and $\partial^2 Y / \partial t^2$ is the acceleration of the element. Dividing by $\rho \, \Delta x$ and letting $\Delta x \rightarrow 0$ we finally obtain:

$$\frac{\partial^2 Y}{\partial x^2} = \frac{1}{c^2} \frac{\partial^2 Y}{\partial t^2} \qquad (7.2.47)$$

where $c^2 = H/\rho$. Equation 7.2.47 is seen to be the one-dimensional version of the general wave Equation 7.2.33.

7.3 USEFUL SIMPLIFICATIONS AND TRANSFORMATIONS

Since the task of solving PDEs is, in many cases, a considerable undertaking, it is worthwhile and indeed often mandatory to simplify the PDEs prior to embarking on a solution. These simplifications may take various forms, which we summarize below.

- Elimination of independent variables or reduction to an ODE
- Elimination of dependent variables or reduction in number of PDEs
- Reduction to homogeneous form
- Change of independent variables and reduction to canonical form
- Simplification of geometry
- Nondimensionalization

Some of these simplifications had already been practiced at the ODE level. Thus, our favorite track of dividing simultaneous first order ODEs had led to the elimination of the independent variable, and sometimes of a dependent variable as well (see Chapter 3, Illustration 3.2.7 and Chapter 6, Illustration 6.3.1). Dependent variables also could on occasion be eliminated algebraically to reduce the number of ODEs in a set at the cost of raising the order of the equations (Illustration 3.3.2). Both the D-operator method and the Laplace transform were, in a sense, simplifying devices which reduced the ODEs to algebraic forms. These techniques have their counterparts at the PDE level. Let us consider these methods in some detail.

7.3.1 ELIMINATION OF INDEPENDENT VARIABLES: REDUCTION TO ODEs

The device of eliminating independent variables or reducing the PDE to lower dimensionality is used in virtually all major analytical solution methods. This includes the method of separation of variables, integral transforms of various types, similarity transformation, and the method of characteristics. We sketch the principal steps of some of these procedures below. More detailed coverage is provided in Chapter 9.

7.3.1.1 Separation of Variables

The basic line of attack here is to assume that the solution is made up of the *product* of functions of the independent variables:

$$u(x,y,z,t) = f(x)g(y)h(z)k(t) \tag{7.3.1}$$

This assumption has the effect of reducing the PDE to an equivalent set of ODEs. We demonstrate this for the simple case of the one-dimensional Fourier's equation. Introducing the assumed solution form $T = f(x)g(t)$ into the PDE $\alpha\, \partial^2 T/\partial x^2 = \partial T/\partial t$, we obtain the result:

$$\frac{\partial T}{\partial t} = f(x)g'(t), \frac{\partial^2 T}{\partial x^2} = f''(x)g(t) \tag{7.3.2}$$

Substitution into Fourier's equation and some rearrangement leads to the relation:

$$\frac{f''(x)}{f(x)} = \frac{1}{\alpha}\frac{g'(t)}{g(t)} \tag{7.3.3}$$

where we have cleverly grouped functions of the same variable together.

Now functions of two different independent variables cannot be equal unless they are constant. We therefore obtain:

$$\frac{f''(x)}{f(x)} = \frac{1}{\alpha}\frac{g'(t)}{g(t)} = -\lambda^2 \text{ (a constant)} \tag{7.3.4}$$

and, hence, the equivalent set of ODEs:

$$\frac{d^2f}{dx^2} + \lambda^2 f = 0$$

$$\frac{dg}{dt} + \alpha\lambda^2 g = 0 \tag{7.3.5}$$

These equations can be solved independently and subsequently developed into a general solution of the PDE. This will be demonstrated in Chapter 9.

7.3.1.2 Laplace Transform

We retain the example of the one-dimensional Fourier's equation and formally apply the transformation. One obtains:

$$\int_0^\infty \frac{\partial T}{\partial t} e^{-st} dt = \alpha \int_0^\infty \frac{\partial^2 T}{\partial x^2} e^{-st} dt \qquad (7.3.6)$$

The left side yields the customary expression for the Laplace transform of a first order derivative. Thus,

$$\int_0^\infty \frac{\partial T}{\partial t} e^{-st} dt = s\overline{T}(s) - T(0) \qquad (7.3.7)$$

where $\overline{T}(s)$ is the transformed temperature, and $T(0)$ the initial condition.

The right side is evaluated by reversing the order of differentiation and integration. This procedure is justified under some mild conditions of continuity and existence. We obtain:

$$\int_0^\infty \frac{\partial^2 T}{\partial x^2} e^{-st} dt = \alpha \int_0^\infty \frac{d^2}{dx^2} T e^{-st} dt = \frac{d^2}{dx^2} \int_0^\infty T e^{-st} dt = \alpha \frac{d^2 \overline{T}}{dx^2} \qquad (7.3.8)$$

Thus, the transform of the derivative has become the derivative of the transform. Combining the results of Equations 7.3.7 and 7.3.8 we obtain the following ODE in the transformed variable $\overline{T}$:

$$\alpha \frac{d^2 \overline{T}}{dx^2} = s\overline{T} - T(0) \qquad (7.3.9)$$

This is a linear second order nonhomogeneous ODE in $\overline{T}(s)$, which can be solved by standard techniques. Subsequent inversion of the result $\overline{T} = f(x,s)$ then yields the solution of the PDE $T(x,t)$. A more detailed exposition of the method will be given in Chapter 9.

7.3.1.3 Similarity or Boltzmann Transformation: Combination of Variables

In this method, two independent variables of the PDE, for example, x and y or x and t, are combined into a single new independent variable η, termed the *similarity variable*. This is achieved by means of the following transformation:

$$\eta = y/x^n \quad \text{or} \quad \eta = x/t^n \qquad (7.3.10)$$

Although other functional form functions exist and can be applied, the Form 7.3.10 is by far the most extensively used. The first such transformation, proposed by Boltzmann in 1894 to solve a nonlinear conduction problem had the form:

$$\eta = xt^{-1/2} \qquad (7.3.11)$$

It has been used in a number of other contexts since.

The reason for choosing the particular Form 7.3.10 resides in the requirement that in combining the two independent variables one must, at the same time, bring about a coalescence of two boundary conditions into a single BC. Such coalescence is difficult to achieve in finite geometries, but if one limits oneself to a semi-infinite or infinite medium, the Transformation 7.3.10 will give us the desired result. Thus, in the conduction problem considered by Boltzmann, an initial condition at $t = 0$ would be available, as well as a boundary condition at $x \to \infty$ and the temperatures for both conditions would be the same. If the Form 7.3.11 is chosen, these conditions will lead to the same value of the similarity variable, i.e., $\eta = \infty$, thus bringing about the desired merger of initial and boundary conditions.

The view we have presented above is a very limited one, designed to give the reader a first introduction to the technique of similarity transformation. The underlying theory is much broader and more profound, and is aimed at deducing general transformations which will lead to a simplification and contraction of partial differential equations. It is based on concepts of group transformation and invariant groups, and is the subject of specialized monographs (see References at the end of the chapter).

In the course of performing a similarity transformation, one is required to express partial derivatives in the old independent variables x and y (x and t) in terms of the new similarity variable η. This is done by what is known as the *chain rule of partial differentiation* which is described in standard calculus texts. The derivation of the pertinent formulas is somewhat cumbersome, and we therefore have summarized the more important results for convenience in the accompanying Table 7.4. These can be used directly to transform "old" derivatives into "new" ones.

Illustration 7.3.1   Heat Transfer in Boundary Layer Flow over a Flat Plate: Similarity Transformation

To illustrate the use of the similarity transformation and the attendant simplifications that result, we consider the situation depicted in Figure 7.6. A flat plate maintained at a constant temperature T_p is exposed to a flow of colder air with an approach temperature of T_0. Heat transfer takes place through the so-called thermal boundary layer and into the semi-infinite medium of flowing air. That thin layer adjacent to the surface of the exposed plate contains the temperature variations which result from the heat transfer process and which range from T_p at the plate to T_0 at the outer edge of the layer. The thermal boundary layer has a counterpart, the so-called momentum boundary layer that expresses momentum transfer from the air to the stationary plate and contains the velocity variations in the flowing air. They range from a value of $v = 0$ at the surface of the plate to the free stream velocity $v = v_0$ at the edge of the layer and beyond.

TABLE 7.4
Transformation of Partial Derivatives

Change $u = f(x,y)$ to $u = g(X,Y)$

A. First Derivatives

$$\frac{\partial u}{\partial x} = \frac{\partial u}{\partial X}\frac{\partial X}{\partial x} + \frac{\partial u}{\partial Y}\frac{\partial Y}{\partial x}$$

$$\frac{\partial u}{\partial y} = \frac{\partial u}{\partial X}\frac{\partial X}{\partial y} + \frac{\partial u}{\partial Y}\frac{\partial Y}{\partial y}$$

or in general

$$\begin{array}{c}\text{Old derivative of u with}\\\text{respect to old independent}\\\text{variable i}\end{array} = \sum_{j} \left\{ \begin{array}{c}\text{Partial derivative of u}\\\text{with respect to new}\\\text{independent variable j}\end{array} \times \frac{\partial j}{\partial i} \right\}$$

B. Second Derivatives

$$\frac{\partial^2 u}{\partial x^2} = \frac{\partial u}{\partial X}\frac{\partial^2 X}{\partial x^2} + \frac{\partial^2 u}{\partial X^2}\left(\frac{\partial X}{\partial x}\right)^2 + 2\frac{\partial^2 u}{\partial X\partial Y}\frac{\partial X}{\partial x}\frac{\partial Y}{\partial x} + \frac{\partial u}{\partial Y}\frac{\partial^2 Y}{\partial x^2} + \frac{\partial^2 u}{\partial Y^2}\left(\frac{\partial Y}{\partial x}\right)^2$$

$$\frac{\partial^2 u}{\partial y^2} = \frac{\partial u}{\partial X}\frac{\partial^2 X}{\partial y^2} + \frac{\partial^2 u}{\partial X^2}\left(\frac{\partial X}{\partial y}\right)^2 + 2\frac{\partial^2 u}{\partial X\partial Y}\frac{\partial X}{\partial y}\frac{\partial Y}{\partial y} + \frac{\partial u}{\partial Y}\frac{\partial^2 Y}{\partial y^2} + \frac{\partial^2 u}{\partial Y^2}\left(\frac{\partial Y}{\partial y}\right)^2$$

$$\frac{\partial^2 u}{\partial x\partial y} = \frac{\partial u}{\partial X}\frac{\partial^2 X}{\partial x\partial y} + \frac{\partial^2 u}{\partial X^2}\frac{\partial X}{\partial x}\frac{\partial X}{\partial y} + \frac{\partial^2 u}{\partial X\partial Y}\frac{\partial Y}{\partial x}\frac{\partial X}{\partial x} + \frac{\partial u}{\partial Y}\frac{\partial^2 Y}{\partial x\partial y}$$

$$+ \frac{\partial^2 u}{\partial X\partial Y}\frac{\partial Y}{\partial y}\frac{\partial X}{\partial x} + \frac{\partial^2 u}{\partial Y^2}\frac{\partial Y}{\partial x}\frac{\partial Y}{\partial y}$$

Theoretical analysis of these two boundary layers has revealed that the thermal layer is much thinner than the momentum boundary layer and lies essentially within the linear portion of the velocity profile. This brings about a considerable simplifications of the energy balance required to derive the temperature profile in the boundary layer. The balance is taken over the element shown in Figure 7.6B, leading in the first instance to the following expression

$$\text{Rate of energy in} - \text{Rate of energy out} = 0$$

$$[H_x + q_y] - [H_{x+\Delta x} + q_{y+\Delta y}] = 0 \tag{7.3.12}$$

In expanded form we obtain:

$$\left[\begin{array}{c} v\rho CpW\Delta y(T - T_o) \\ -kW\Delta x\frac{\partial T}{\partial y}\Big|_y \end{array}\right] - \left[\begin{array}{c} v\rho CpW\Delta y(T - T_o)_{x+\Delta x} \\ -kW\Delta x\frac{\partial T}{\partial y}\Big|_{y+\Delta y} \end{array}\right] = 0 \tag{7.3.13}$$

A. The Boundary Layer

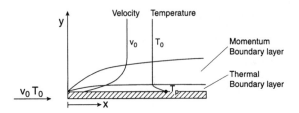

B. Difference Element

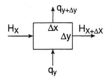

FIGURE 7.6   Heat transfer in boundary layer flow around a flat plate.

where W = width of the plate and $v = \dot{\gamma}y$. $\dot{\gamma}$ is the shear rate of the air at the plate and equals the slope v/y of the linear portion of the velocity profile.

Upon dividing by $W\Delta x \Delta y$ and letting Δx, $\Delta y \rightarrow 0$, there results:

$$-\dot{\gamma}y\rho Cp\frac{\partial T}{\partial x} + k\frac{\partial^2 T^2}{\partial y} = 0 \qquad (7.3.14)$$

We now introduce the dimensionless temperature $\theta = (T_p - T)/(T_p - T_0)$ and obtain, after slight rearrangement, the compact form:

$$\frac{\partial \theta}{\partial x} = \frac{A}{y}\frac{\partial^2 \theta}{\partial y^2} \qquad (7.3.15)$$

with $A = \alpha/\dot{\gamma}$ and $\alpha = k/\rho Cp =$ thermal diffusivity.

The associated boundary conditions are as follows:

At the plate edge: $\theta(0,y) = 1$ (7.3.15a)

At the plate surface: $\theta(x,0) = 0$ (7.3.15b)

In the free stream: $\theta(x,\infty) = 1$ (7.3.15c)

This represents the system to be solved.

The Conditions 7.3.15a and 7.3.15c, given as they are at values of $x = 0$ and $y = \infty$ indicate that a similarity transformation may be possible. We, therefore, specify a similarity variable of the form:

$$\eta = y/x^n \tag{7.3.16}$$

and proceed to evaluate n. That parameter has to be such that the transformed PDE 7.3.15 becomes an ODE in η only and is free of any terms containing the old independent variables x and y. We use Table 7.4 to transform old derivatives in x and y to new derivatives with respect to η. This yields:

$$\frac{\partial\theta}{\partial x} = \frac{\partial\theta}{\partial\eta}\frac{\partial\eta}{\partial x} = -n\frac{\partial\theta}{\partial\eta}yx^{-(n+1)} = -n\frac{\partial\theta}{\partial\eta}\eta x^{-1}$$

$$\frac{\partial^2\theta}{\partial y^2} = \frac{\partial\theta}{\partial\eta}\frac{\partial^2\eta}{\partial y^2} + \frac{\partial^2\theta}{\partial\eta^2}\left(\frac{\partial\eta}{\partial y}\right)^2 = \frac{\partial^2\theta}{\partial\eta^2}x^{-2n} \tag{7.3.17}$$

Substitution of these expressions into the PDE 7.3.14 gives the result:

$$-n\frac{\partial\theta}{\partial\eta}\eta x^{-1} = \frac{Ax^{-2n}}{\eta x^n}\frac{\partial^2\theta}{\partial\eta^2} \tag{7.3.18}$$

One notes that the terms in the old independent variable x will cancel if we impose the condition $n = 1/3$. The resulting ODE is then given by:

$$\frac{d^2\theta}{d^2\eta} + \frac{\eta^2}{3A}\frac{d\theta}{d\eta} = 0 \tag{7.3.19}$$

with the similarity variable η given by:

$$\eta = y/x^{1/3} \tag{7.3.20}$$

The boundary conditions are now only two in number with the first one resulting from the merger of Equations 7.3.15a and 7.3.15c and having the value:

$$\theta = 1 \quad \text{at} \quad \eta = \infty \tag{7.3.20a}$$

Added to this is the old BC Equation 7.3.15b which now becomes:

$$\theta = 0 \quad \text{at} \quad \eta = 0 \tag{7.3.20b}$$

The Equation 7.3.19 is seen to be a second order *linear* ODE with variable coefficients and devoid of terms in θ other than the derivatives. This suggests a p-substitution (Item 9 of Table 4.4) and results in the reduced ODE:

$$\frac{dp}{d\eta} + \frac{\eta^2}{3A} p = 0 \qquad (7.3.21)$$

This equation is immediately integrable by separation of variables to yield:

$$p = \frac{d\theta}{d\eta} = C_1 \exp(-\eta^3 / 9A) \qquad (7.3.22)$$

A second integration, also by separation of variables, leads to the result:

$$\theta = C_1 \int_0^\eta \exp(-z^3 / 9A) dz + C_2 \qquad (7.3.23)$$

where z is the integration variable.

From the boundary conditions 7.3.20, we obtain:

$$C_2 = 0 \qquad (7.3.24)$$

and

$$C_1 = \left(\int_0^\infty \exp(-z^3 / 9A) dz \right)^{-1}$$

giving as the final result:

$$\theta(\eta) = \frac{\int_0^\eta \exp(-z^3 / 9A / dz)}{\int_0^\infty \exp(-z^3 / 9A / dz)} \qquad (7.3.25)$$

The integrals in this expression are both convergent. The result can be expressed in terms of the old coordinates x and y by making use of Equation 7.3.20. An identical solution arises in the so-called Lévêque solution of the Graetz problem, which is taken up in Chapter 8, Illustration 8.2.3.

Comments:

The reader may have noted that the first integration constant was formulated in terms of a pre-exponential coefficient in Equation 7.3.22 rather than as an additive constant. Both procedures are valid, as long as the boundary conditions are ultimately satisfied. The additive constant, however, fails to do this and has to be replaced by the method adopted here. This seemingly trivial change in procedure is indispensable for the successful solution of the problem.

The temperature profiles in the boundary layer change in the direction of flow (x), but only in scale, not in shape. They are for this reason termed *self-similar* and the associated solution method is, as we have seen, referred to as a similarity transformation. Boundary layer profiles of velocity and concentration are likewise self-similar as are certain profiles which arise in unsteady conduction and diffusion. One consequence of this behavior is that the wall shear rate $\dot{\gamma} = (\partial v_x / \partial y)_{y=0}$ which is needed in the result of Equation 7.3.25, is a constant which can be extracted from the drag coeffiicent C_D of the relevant drag force. Thus,

$$F_D = C_D A_C \rho \frac{v_0^2}{2} \tag{7.3.26}$$

and

$$\tau_w = \mu \dot{\gamma} = F_D / A_C = C_D \rho \frac{v_0^2}{2} \tag{7.3.27}$$

where τ_w = shear stress at the plate.
    Hence,

$$\dot{\gamma} = C_D (\rho / \mu) \frac{v_0^2}{2} \tag{7.3.28}$$

Values of C_D can be found in Table 3.14.

7.3.2   Elimination of Dependent Variables: Reduction of Number of Equations

Dependent variables can on occasion be reduced in number, particularly when they represent the components of a vector quantity. The classical example is that of the stream function ψ which serves to combine the velocity components v_x and v_y of two-dimensional fluid flow into a single entity via the previously given relation

$$v_x = -\frac{\partial \psi}{\partial y} \quad v_y = \frac{\partial \psi}{\partial x} \tag{7.1.5}$$

    Evidently some skill and imagination is required to formulate a new dependent variable which will bring about the desired reduction in both number of equations and dependent variables. We illustrate an example of its application below.

Illustration 7.3.2   Use of the Stream Function in Boundary Layer Theory: Velocity Profiles Along a Flat Plate

External Boundary Layer Flow in two dimensions had previously been described by the Prandtl Boundary Layer Equations 7.2.36 and 7.2.37. For flow over a flat plate, the pressure term dp/dx vanishes and we obtain

Momentum balance:

$$-\left[v_x\frac{\partial v_x}{\partial x}+v_y\frac{\partial v_x}{\partial y}\right]+v\frac{\partial^2 v_x}{\partial x^2}=0 \qquad (7.3.29)$$

Continuity equation:

$$\frac{\partial v_x}{\partial x}+\frac{\partial v_y}{\partial y}=0 \qquad (7.2.37)$$

where $v = \mu/\rho$ = kinematic viscosity.

Introduction of the stream function into the momentum balance leads to the relation

$$-\left[\frac{\partial\psi}{\partial y}\frac{\partial^2\psi}{\partial x\partial y}-\frac{\partial\psi}{\partial x}\frac{\partial^2\psi}{\partial y^2}\right]+v\frac{\partial^3\psi}{\partial y^3}=0 \qquad (7.3.30)$$

A similar substitution into the continuity equation brings about the following interesting result:

$$\frac{\partial^2\psi}{\partial x\partial y}-\frac{\partial^2\psi}{\partial y\partial x}\equiv 0 \qquad (7.3.31)$$

i.e., the difference in the derivatives is identically zero. The continuity equation is eliminated and the desired reduction in the number of equations thus is accomplished. The price to be paid is that the new Equation 7.3.30 is one order higher than the previous momentum balance. Such equations, however, are easier to handle than the previous coupled pair of PDEs.

We note that Equation 7.3.30 is homogeneous and quasilinear since the highest derivative appears in the linear form. We further note that the geometry and the boundary conditions are similar to those we had seen in Illustration 7.3.1. Similarity transformation therefore suggests itself as a possible solution route and this does in fact turn out to be the case. It leads to a third order ODE, known as the Blasius equation, which is of the form:

$$f'''(\eta)+\frac{1}{2}f(\eta)f''(\eta)=0 \qquad (7.3.32)$$

where f is a modified nondimensionalized stream function.

The original system of two PDEs, Equations 7.3.26 and 7.2.37, one of which was quasilinear, thus has been reduced to a single nonlinear ODE of boundary value type. This represents a considerable simplification even though the order has increased by one.

7.3.3 ELIMINATION OF NONHOMOGENEOUS TERMS

Nonhomogeneous terms can complicate the solution of differential equations and in some instances render a solution method inapplicable. At the ODE level, the presence of such terms required the evaluation of a particular integral for use in the D-operator method. The Laplace transform, on the other hand, did not encounter such difficulties and was capable of handling both homogeneous and nonhomogeneous ODEs with equal ease although the solution became more complex in form. At the PDE level, integral transforms again are well suited for handling nonhomogeneous equations, but the powerful method of separation of variables, previously sketched in Section 7.3.1, requires both the PDE and the boundary conditions to be homogeneous for its successful application. The presence of nonhomogeneous terms in the PDE usually renders the assumption of separable variables, expressed by Equation 7.3.1, invalid, while nonhomogeneous boundary conditions complicate the evaluation of undefined constants which arise in the course of the solution. Thus, there is considerable incentive to eliminate nonhomogeneous terms. Another prominent example of the benefits of this procedure is the reduction of the nonhomogeneous Poisson Equation 7.2.20 to Laplace's Equation 7.2.13. The latter has been studied more extensively and has a host of known solutions.

A promising line of attack when dealing with such equations is to introduce a *new* dependent variable v of the form:

$$v = u + g(x,y,z,t) \qquad (7.3.33)$$

where u is the original dependent variable and g(x,y,z,t) is of the *same functional form* as the nonhomogeneous term in the original PDE or the boundary condition. This function g should contain a sufficient number of unknown constants to satisfy the condition of homogeneity for both the PDE and the BCs. There is no requirement for the initial condition to be homogeneous which can serve as a convenient repository for functional forms that take the place of the eliminated nonhomogeneous terms.

The method suggested here is particularly well suited for nonhomogeneous terms of *polynomial form*. We illustrate its use in the following example.

Illustration 7.3.3   Conversion of a PDE to Homogeneous Form

We consider the system:

$$\frac{\partial^2 u}{\partial t^2} = c^2 \frac{\partial^2 u}{\partial x^2} + Ax \qquad (7.3.34)$$

with BCs and ICs

$$u(0,t) = 0 \qquad (7.3.35a)$$

$$u(1,t) = 0 \qquad (7.3.35b)$$

$$\frac{\partial u}{\partial t}(x,0) = 0 \qquad (7.3.35c)$$

$$u(x,0) = 0 \qquad (7.3.35d)$$

where x has been normalized to the interval (0,1).

Physically, this set of equations can be seen as representing a string which is clamped at both ends and is initially horizontal, with zero deflection. A force which is linear in the horizontal distance x is applied to it and results in time dependent deflections u(x,t). The task is to eliminate the nonhomogeneous term Ax while maintaining the boundary conditions Equations 7.3.35a to c in homogeneous form. Since four homogeneity conditions are to be satisfied, a third order polynomial with four arbitrary constants suggests itself as a trial function g(x). We, therefore, specify:

$$v = u + a' + b'x + c'x^2 + d'x^3 \qquad (7.3.36)$$

Trials with this function, which we omit for brevity, indicate that the quadratic term has to be dropped for the constants to be independent of x. We consequently make the new specification:

$$v = u + a + bx + dx^3 \qquad (7.3.37)$$

and obtain the following results:

For the PDE:

$$\frac{\partial^2 v}{\partial t^2} = c^2 \frac{\partial^2 v}{\partial x^2} - 6dx + Ax \rightarrow d = \frac{A}{6} \qquad (7.3.38)$$

For BC 7.3.35a:

$$u(0,t) = v(0,t) - a = 0 \rightarrow a = 0 \qquad (7.3.39)$$

For BC 7.3.35b:

$$u(1,t) = v(1,t) - (a + b + d) = 0 \rightarrow b = -\frac{A}{6} \qquad (7.3.40)$$

For BC 7.3.35c:

$$\frac{\partial u}{\partial t}(x,0) = \frac{\partial v}{\partial t}(x,0) = 0 \qquad (7.3.41)$$

i.e., the boundary condition remains homogeneous without the appearance of any of the coefficients. Three such coefficients therefore will suffice to render the system homogeneous, with the exception of the IC 7.3.35d. The final transformed model is then as follows:

$$\frac{\partial^2 v}{\partial t^2} = c^2 \frac{\partial^2 v}{\partial x^2} \qquad (7.3.42)$$

with BCs and ICs:

$$v(0,t) = 0 \qquad (7.3.43a)$$

$$v(1,t) = 0 \qquad (7.3.43b)$$

$$\frac{\partial v}{\partial t}(x,0) = 0 \qquad (7.3.43c)$$

$$v(x,0) = -\frac{A}{6}(x - x^3) \qquad (7.3.43d)$$

and the relation between old and new dependent variable given by:

$$v = u - \frac{A}{6}(x - x^3) \qquad (7.3.44)$$

Comments:

The nonhomogeneous term in Equation 7.3.43d is more complex than the term which was eliminated, Ax. This is nevertheless no disadvantage since a high degree of nonhomogeneity can be tolerated in the initial condition without seriously affecting the ease of solution.

Application of the method was not totally automatic. Some trial-and-error was required which is not unusual for the successful application of transformations involving unknown functions.

7.3.4 CHANGE IN INDEPENDENT VARIABLES: REDUCTION TO CANONICAL FORM

A change in independent variables can, on occasion, result in a simplification of the PDE through a reduction in the number of terms that appear in it or by bringing it into a form more suitable for analysis. A systematic way of achieving possible simplifications is by the procedure known as *reduction to canonical,* or "regular" form. The original purpose of this method was to cast PDEs into the same form as the classical Laplace, Fourier, and Wave equations and to extend the results obtained from the study of these relatively simple equations to more complex forms. In the process of this change in variables one encounters the so-called characteristic equations which also find a place in the method of characteristics, a solution technique to be discussed in greater detail in Chapter 9.

Justification for the steps used in the reduction of PDEs to canonical form can be found in various sources referenced at the end of the chapter. For our present purposes we limit ourselves to an outline of these steps without providing either justification or proof and address only two classes of equations: (1) single second order PDEs in two independent variables and (2) sets of two quasilinear first order PDEs.

The general form for the first class considered here is

$$A(x,y)u_{xx} + 2B(x,y)u_{xy} + C(x,y)u_{yy} = F(x,y,u_x,u_y) \qquad (7.3.45)$$

We note that the equation is identical to that used to arrive at the categories of elliptic, parabolic, and hyperbolic PDEs. There is, as we shall see, a direct link between these categories and the number of characteristics which arise in the course of reduction to canonical form.

The steps in the application of the procedure are as follows:

Step one — Formulate an ODE in the independent variables x and y which has a quadratic form with coefficients identical to those in the PDE 7.3.45. Thus, we form:

$$A\left(\frac{dy}{dx}\right)^2 + 2B\left(\frac{dy}{dx}\right) + C = 0 \qquad (7.3.46)$$

Step two — Solve the quadratic equation to obtain the two roots in dy/dx:

$$\left(\frac{dy}{dx}\right)_{1,2} = \frac{-B \pm (B^2 - AC)^{1/2}}{A} \qquad (7.3.47)$$

These two ODEs are the so-called *characteristic equations* or *characteristic directions*.

Step three — Integrate the two Equations 7.3.47 to obtain:

$$f_1(x,y) = C_1 \quad \text{and} \quad f_2(x,y) = C_2 \qquad (7.3.48)$$

where C_1 and C_2 are the integration constants. These two algebraic equations form two families of curves which are referred to as *characteristics* of the PDE 7.3.45. Physically they may be regarded as propagation pathways in (y,x) or (x,t) space of a particular physical entity such as the deflection u of a certain magnitude in a vibrating string, or of a certain wave height v in wave propagation problems. The reader will note that for hyperbolic PDEs with $(B^2 - AC) > 0$, there are two real and distinct characteristics equations and characteristics; for parabolic PDEs $(B^2 = AC)$, there is only one of each; and for elliptic PDEs $(B^2 - AC < 0)$, none. We summarize these features for convenience in Table 7.5.

Step four — Set the new independent variables $\bar{x}$ and $\bar{y}$ equal to the characteristic function $f_{1,2}$. Thus,

$$\bar{x} = f_1(x,y) \quad \bar{y} = f_2(x,y) \qquad (7.3.49)$$

TABLE 7.5
Characteristics of Second Order PDEs

Type of PDE	$B^2 - AC$	Roots of Equation 7.3.46	Number of Characteristics
Elliptic	< 0	Complex conjugate	0
Parabolic	= 0	Real and equal	1
Hyperbolic	> 0	Real and distinct	2

When the roots of the quadratic are real and equal, there is only one characteristic function and, hence, only one new independent variable. The second one is then established by making it as close as possible in form to but independent from the first variable. An example of this procedure appears in Illustration 7.3.4.

Difficulties also arise when the roots are complex conjugates. A second change in variables is then performed which takes the form:

$$\alpha = \frac{1}{2}(\overline{x} + \overline{y}) \text{ and } \beta = \frac{1}{2}i(\overline{x} - \overline{y}) \qquad (7.3.50)$$

This procedure serves to eliminate the imaginary part of $\overline{x}$ and $\overline{y}$, and is taken up in Practice Problem 7.7.

Step five — Reformulate the old PDE in terms of the new independent variables $\overline{x}$ and $\overline{y}$, or α and β, so that u(x,y) now becomes $v(\overline{x},\overline{y})$ or $v(\alpha,\beta)$. This completes the reduction to canonical form.

Step six — As a final step, the new PDE is solved and the old independent variables x,y reintroduced into the solution to obtain the solution in the form u = F(x,y).

The second reduction to canonical form we consider is that of a set of two first order quasilinear PDEs. We had encountered this system in a general form as Equation 7.1.13 which is repeated here for convenience:

$$A(u,x,y)\,u_x + B(u,x,y)\,u_y + C(u,x,y) = 0 \qquad (7.1.13)$$

where u_x and u_y were first order partial derivatives. A characteristic equation,

$\det|A - \lambda B| = 0$ was then introduced whose eigenvalues λ determined whether the set was elliptic, parabolic, or hyperbolic. It turns out that the same eigenvalues also represent solutions of a quadratic equation in dy/dx which is completely analogous to Equation 7.3.46 used for second order PDEs. We therefore can obtain the characteristic equation by writing:

$$\left(\frac{dy}{dx}\right)_{1,2} = \lambda_{1,2} \qquad (7.3.51)$$

and these equations can in turn be integrated to obtain the characteristics:

$$F_1(x,y) = C_1 \quad F_2(x,y) = C_2 \tag{7.3.52}$$

The new independent variables $\bar{x}$ and $\bar{y}$ are then established, again in completely analogous fashion to the case of second order PDEs, by writing:

$$\bar{x} = F_1(x,y) \quad \text{and} \quad \bar{y} = F_2(x,y) \tag{7.3.53}$$

We note that the characteristic Equation 7.3.51 can only be integrated if the coefficients of the PDE, $\underset{\sim}{A}$ and $\underset{\sim}{B}$ and hence $\underset{\sim}{\lambda_{1,2}}$ are independent of $\underset{\sim}{u}$. When this is not the case, other techniques have to be applied.

Illustration 7.3.4   Reduction of PDEs to Canonical Form

As a first example, we consider the reduction to canonical form of the following second order PDE:

$$\frac{\partial^2 u}{\partial x^2} + 2\frac{\partial^2 u}{\partial x \partial y} + \frac{\partial^2 u}{\partial y^2} = 0 \tag{7.3.54}$$

Step one — We form the quadratic equation in the characteristic direction dy/dx and obtain:

$$\frac{d^2 y}{dx^2} + 2\left(\frac{dy}{dx}\right) + 1 = 0 \tag{7.3.55}$$

Step two — Equation 7.3.54 is solved to yield the characteristic directions:

$$\left(\frac{dy}{dx}\right)_{1,2} = -1 \tag{7.3.56}$$

These roots are real and identical, and the PDE is therefore parabolic.

Step three — The Equation 7.3.55 is next integrated, resulting in a single characteristic:

$$f_1(x,y) = y + x = C_1 \tag{7.3.57}$$

Step four — The new independent variable $\bar{x}$ is set equal to $f_1(x,y)$. Thus,

$$\bar{x} = y + x \tag{7.3.58}$$

A second new variable $\bar{y}$, distinct and independent from $\bar{x}$, and close to it in form is established by writing:

$$\bar{y} = y - x \qquad (7.3.59)$$

Step five — The old PDE is reformulated in terms of the new independent variables $\bar{x}$ and $\bar{y}$. To aid in this procedure, use is made of the conversion formulas, given in Table 7.4. This is fairly routine work which is omitted here for brevity. The final result is given by:

$$\frac{\partial^2 v}{\partial \bar{x}^2} = 0 \qquad (7.3.60)$$

Step six — Equation 7.3.60 can be immediately integrated to yield the result:

$$v = \bar{x} f_1(\bar{y}) + f_2(\bar{y}) \qquad (7.3.61)$$

Note that since $v = F(\bar{x},\bar{y})$, the integration "constants" f_1 and f_2 must in fact be functions of the second new independent variable $\bar{y}$. Reintroduction of the old variables then leads to the solution:

$$u = (x + y)f_1(y - x) + f_2(y - x) \qquad (7.3.62)$$

This expression, referred to as the fundamental solution of the PDE is, of course, not a final result since $f_{1,2}$ still needs to be evaluated from the boundary conditions, which may not be a simple task. Knowing the functional form of the solution, however, is in itself a very useful result which provides a starting point for analyzing the physical process underlying the original PDEs. Note that Equation 7.3.62 was arrived at by a simple transformation of independent variables, carried out in a rather mechanical fashion. This is no reason to disdain it.

As a second example, we consider the reduction to canonical form of the chromatographic equations consisting of fluid and solid phase mass balances (Equations 7.2.4 and 7.2.5), and the equilibrium relation (Equation 7.2.6). For our present purposes we assume the latter to be linear, so that:

$$Y^* = m\,q \qquad (7.3.63)$$

We introduce this relation into the two mass balances and rewrite them to conform to the general formulation of (7.3.13). There results:

$$\frac{G_s}{\varepsilon \rho_g} \frac{\partial Y}{\partial z} + 0 + \frac{\partial Y}{\partial t} + 0 + (K_{0Y}a / \varepsilon \rho_g)(Y - Y^*) = \qquad (7.3.64)$$

$$0 + 0 + 0 + \frac{\partial Y^*}{\partial t} - \frac{mK_{0Y}a}{\rho_b}(Y - Y^*) = 0 \qquad (7.3.65)$$

These are two linear PDEs in the two dependent variables Y and Y* which we now proceed to reduce to canonical form using the procedure outlined in the previous section.

Step one — We start by establishing the coefficient matrices A and B which appear in the general formulation of the PDEs given in Equation 7.1.13. They are relatively simple since the coefficients here are constant, and take the form:

$$\underset{\sim}{A} = \begin{pmatrix} G_s / \varepsilon\rho_g & 0 \\ 0 & 0 \end{pmatrix}$$

$$\underset{\sim}{B} = \begin{pmatrix} 1 & 0 \\ 0 & 1 \end{pmatrix}$$

(7.3.66)

so that

$$\det\left|\underset{\sim}{A} - \lambda\,\underset{\sim}{B}\right| = \begin{vmatrix} G_s / \varepsilon\rho_g - \lambda & 0 \\ 0 & 0 - \lambda \end{vmatrix} = 0$$

(7.3.67)

Solution of the quadratic in λ resulting from this expression leads to the two distinct and real roots:

$$\lambda_1 = 0 \quad \lambda_2 = G_s/\varepsilon\rho_g$$

(7.3.68)

The set of PDEs therefore is hyperbolic.

Step two — We now establish the characteristic equations by setting the characteristic directions dy/dx equal to the eigenvalues λ. Thus,

$$\left(\frac{dz}{dt}\right)_1 = 0 \quad \left(\frac{dz}{dt}\right)_2 = G_s / \varepsilon\rho_g$$

(7.3.69)

Step three — This step involves the integration of the ODEs 7.3.47 and yields the following characteristics:

$$f_1(z,t) = z = C_1$$

(7.3.70)

or

$$f_1(z,t) = t = C_1$$

and

$$f_2(z,t) = z - \frac{G_s}{\varepsilon\rho_g}t = C_2$$

(7.3.71)

or

$$f_2(x,t) = t - \frac{\varepsilon \rho_g}{G_s} z = C_2$$

Step four — We can now proceed to the formulation of the new independent variables $\bar{x}$ and $\bar{y}$, which are equal to the characteristic function $f_{1,2}$. Thus,

$$\bar{x} \text{ and } z \quad \text{or} \quad \bar{x} = t \qquad (7.3.72)$$

and

$$\bar{y} = z - \frac{G_s}{\varepsilon \rho_B} t \quad \text{or} \quad \bar{y} = t - \frac{\varepsilon \rho_g}{G_s} z \qquad (7.3.73)$$

Step five — The new independent variables are introduced into the PDE, and the new derivatives evaluated by means of the formula of Table 7.4. We chose the combination:

$$\bar{x} = z \quad \bar{y} = t - \frac{\varepsilon \rho_g}{G_s} z$$

and obtain:

$$G_s \frac{\partial Y}{\partial \bar{x}} + K_{0Y} a(Y - Y^*) = 0 \qquad (7.3.74)$$

and

$$\frac{\partial Y}{\partial \bar{y}} - \frac{K_{0Y}}{\rho_b} a(Y - Y^*) = 0$$

Step six — The constant coefficients of this set can be taken into the independent variables, leading to the following compact form:

$$\frac{\partial Y}{\partial \alpha} + (Y - Y^*) = 0$$

$$\frac{\partial Y^*}{\partial \beta} - (Y - Y^*) = 0 \qquad (7.3.75)$$

where

$$\alpha = \frac{K_{0Y}a}{G_s} z$$

$$\beta = \frac{m\,K_{0Y}a}{\rho_b}\left(t - \frac{\varepsilon\rho_g}{G_s} z\right)$$

In most practical applications, the second term in β can be neglected. This simplification leads to the dimensionless parameters N and T given by Equations 6.2.47 and 6.2.48.

We thus have achieved a considerable simplification of the original set of PDEs 7.3.72 and 7.3.73 with relatively little effort. The solution of these equations is addressed in Chapter 9, Practice Problem 9.2.8.

One notes from Equations 7.3.72 and 7.3.73 that, while one of the old independent variables is retained unchanged, the linear combination (Equation 7.3.72) of z and t is merged into a single new variable $\bar{y}$. This type of merger can in principle be applied to any model PDEs which contain the following combination of first order derivatives:

$$A\,\partial u/\partial x + B\,\partial u/\partial y \qquad\qquad (7.3.76)$$

This quantity is sometimes referred to as a *convective derivative* and arises naturally in all unsteady convective processes. We shall encounter it again in the context of atmospheric dispersion in Illustration 7.4.5.

7.3.5 SIMPLIFICATION OF GEOMETRY

The geometry of a system and the boundary conditions associated with it have a major impact on both the ease of solution and its form. Simplifications often appear to be trivial or self-evident, while on other occasions the changes effected are clearly of major importance.

Suppose, for example, that one wishes to monitor the penetration into the ground of the daily temperature variations that occur at the surface of a particular location of the Earth. Since the depth of penetration is, at most, of the order of meters, it is evident that the geometry can be considered planar and semi-infinite. The curvature of the Earth or its spherical shape do not enter into the picture. The effect of these obvious simplifications, which may at first sight appear to be minor, is in fact quite considerable. The solution procedure itself is simplified and the result can be expressed in the compact form of a single function rather than an infinite series of functions.

Consider next the case of a buried steam line, assumed to be isothermal, which loses heat to the near-by surface of the ground. Here there is an immediate difficulty which resides in the mixed nature of the geometry, planar for the surface, and circular or cylindrical for the pipe. The underlying model itself is simple and adequately described by Laplace's equation, but the boundary conditions have to be specified at z = 0 and r = R and, hence, belong to different coordinate systems. There are ways of interrelating the two which leads to rather messy solutions. A more elegant and powerful method is that of *conformal mapping* in which functions of a complex variable are used to introduce new independent variables that transform the system into a simpler geometry. Laplace's equation remains invariant under the transformation and is solved by standard techniques once the geometry has been sufficiently simplified. The method requires some background in complex variable theory and will not be taken up in detail here. We, however, do present a short list of solutions, shown in Figure 7.7, which may be deemed of interest to the reader. Additional solutions in the form of "shape factors" for more complex geometries will be given in Chapter 8 (Table 8.10). Note that in Figure 7.7, the dependent variable has been

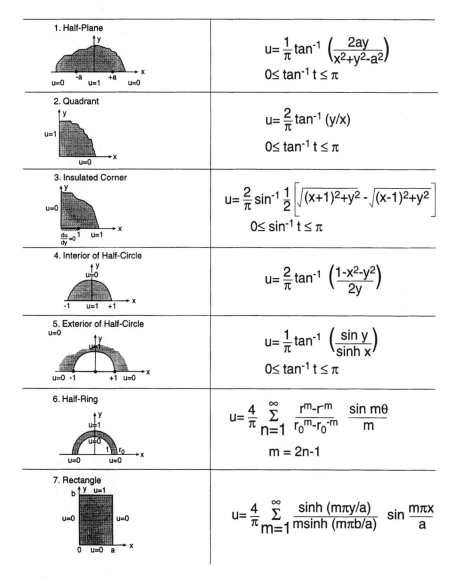

FIGURE 7.7   Solutions of Laplace's equation for various geometries and boundary conditions.

nondimensionalized and represents, for example, dimensionless temperature or electrostatic potential. Thus, any one solution can be applied to several different physical situations described by Laplace's equation.

For the remainder of this section we confine ourselves to the description of some simple transformations applicable to second order PDEs. Most of these are of an obvious type but are often overlooked in the quest for an easier life.

We start by noting that the difficulties caused by geometrical complexity usually increase, for various domains of interest, in the following sequence: [doubly infinite] < semi-infinite< one-dimensional planar < circular or radial cylindrical < radial spherical < two- and three-dimensional cartesian < angular cylindrical and spherical < other. The doubly infinite domain sometimes give rise to difficult boundary conditions and therefore is placed in brackets. We present below a number of transformations designed to move the system toward lesser complexity.

7.3.5.1   Reduction of a Radial Spherical Configuration into a Planar One

This simplification can be accomplished by introducing a new dependent variable v which is related to the old variable by the product ur, where r = radial variable:

$$v = ur \qquad (7.3.77)$$

The substitution has the effect of bringing about the following transformation:

$$\frac{\partial^2 u}{\partial r^2} + \frac{2}{r}\frac{\partial u}{\partial r} \Rightarrow \frac{\partial^2 v}{\partial r^2} \qquad (7.3.78)$$

A double simplification is thereby effected. The number of terms is reduced and the variable coefficient 2/r is eliminated. Note that boundary conditions have to be altered accordingly. Thus, u(R) becomes v(R) = u(R)R, etc.

7.3.5.2   Reduction of a Radial Circular or Cylindrical Configuration into a Planar One

When a process is confined to a narrow region near the circumference of a circle or cylinder, and boundary conditions are specified on both sides of the strip, the geometry can be reduced to a planar one by cutting it open and unfolding it. An example of the application of this simplification occurs in connection with the freezing of water in a pipe which we considered in Chapter 6, Illustration 6.3.6 without actually addressing the formation of the ice front. Since the thickness of ice required to cause rupture is small compared to the diameter of the pipe, we can unravel it into a planar configuration with boundary conditions set externally by the subzero ambient temperature and internally by the freezing point of water. Although we still have to deal with the complexities of a moving boundary, that task is considerably eased by the fact that the geometry is now planar rather than cylindrical.

7.3.5.3 Reduction of a Radial Circular or Cylindrical Configuration to a Semi-Infinite One

The same confinement of the principal events to a narrow surface strip seen in the previous case occurs here, and is exploited in the same way, by cutting open and unfolding the surface region. It differs, however, in its internal boundary condition which is specified at infinity. This results in the reduction of the cylindrical geometry to a semi-infinite configuration. An example of its application appears in Illustration 8.2.3 dealing with the Lévêque solution of the Graetz Problem. In that example, concentration changes in the flowing fluid are confined to a thin boundary layer at the duct wall, while far away at $r \to \infty$, its value remains constant. The solution is consequently the same as that given for boundary layer flow over a flat plate (Illustration 7.3.1).

7.3.5.4 Reduction of a Planar Configuration to a Semi-Infinite One

This simplification finds its principal application in time-dependent diffusional processes in which the planar surface is exposed to a brief change of the state variable and the resulting variation of near-surface values are to be monitored only for a brief interval. The changes will not have had the time to penetrate into the interior of the planar geometry which can be treated as a semi-infinite domain. An example of this type of behavior is seen in Illustration 7.4.6 which deals with the response of a coated sheet of paper to a brief burst of heat and the simultaneous changes in surface temperature in response to that burst. The surprising fact is that the sheet, which is only fractions of a millimeter thick, can be treated as a semi-infinite medium for the interval in question. This results in a considerable reduction in complexity of both the method of solution and the form of the result.

7.3.6 NONDIMENSIONALIZATION

Nondimensionalization can be applied to both independent and dependent variables and results in a considerable simplification of the model. It is generally achieved by combining the variables with their boundary or initial values in the form of dimensionless ratios. Let us illustrate the procedure and the resulting benefits by means of the following example.

Illustration 7.3.5 Nondimensionalization of Fourier's Equation

Suppose we wish to non-dimensionalize the one-dimensional Fourier's equation:

$$\frac{\partial T}{\partial t} = \alpha \frac{\partial^2 T}{\partial x^2} \tag{7.3.79}$$

with associated boundary and initial conditions:

$$T(0,t) = T_s \qquad \qquad (7.3.80a)$$

$$T(L,t) = T_s \qquad \qquad (7.3.80b)$$

$$T(x,0) = T_0 \qquad \qquad (7.3.80c)$$

The model describes the response of a slab of thickness L and initial temperature T_0 to a step change in surface temperature T_s. The reader may recall it as the quenched steel billet of Chapter 1, Figure 1.1.

We start by nondimensionalizing the distance variable x by dividing it by thickness L, forming the new dimensionless variable $X = x/L$. X is said to be normalized, i.e., it has values ranging from zero to one $0 \le X \le 1$. Fourier's equation now reads:

$$\frac{\partial T}{\partial t} = \frac{\alpha}{L^2} \frac{\partial^2 T}{\partial X^2} \qquad \qquad (7.3.81)$$

Next we proceed to nondimensionalize time t by dividing it by L^2/α, which also has the dimension of time. The resulting dimensionless group is known as the Fourier number $Fo = \alpha t/L^2$. Note that Fo is *not* normalized since it ranges from zero to infinity.

Finally we turn to the nondimensionalization of the dependent variable T. After some thought, we choose $\theta = \dfrac{T - T_s}{T_0 - T_s}$ since this combination normalizes, as well as nondimensionalizes the temperature variable. The model now takes the following form:

$$\frac{\partial \theta}{\partial (Fo)} = \frac{\partial^2 \theta}{\partial X^2} \qquad \qquad (7.3.82)$$

with boundary conditions:

$$\theta(0,Fo) = 0 \qquad \qquad (7.3.83a)$$

$$\theta(1,Fo) = 0 \qquad \qquad (7.3.83b)$$

$$\theta(X,0) = 1 \qquad \qquad (7.3.83c)$$

The benefits of this procedure, which may not be immediately obvious, are as follows:

- Both temperature T and distance x have been normalized, as well as being nondimensionalized. This makes for much greater convenience in presenting the solution in both graphical and numerical form (see in this connection Figure 8.10).

- Time t has been nondimensionalized and merged with the parameters α and L, making for a more compact solution.
- The boundary conditions (a) and (b) have been rendered homogeneous, which now makes it possible to solve the problem by the separation of variables technique. We demonstrate this in Illustration 9.1.3 of Chapter 9.

We note in closing that the various transformations we have presented can all be applied with relative ease. The benefits to be derived by far exceed the effort required to implement them. Two among them, the similarity transformation and the reduction to canonical form have more profound roots since they are linked to the broad topics of group transformations and of characteristics. We do not enter into a discussion of the former, but will take up the topic of characteristics again in Chapter 9 where they are used to arrive at solutions of first order quasi-linear PDEs.

7.4 PDEs PDQ: LOCATING SOLUTIONS IN RELATED DISCIPLINES; SOLUTION BY SIMPLE SUPERPOSITION METHODS

The purpose of the present section is to remove the aura of overwhelming complexity which surrounds the solution of partial differential equations. Part of the fear of PDEs comes from the forbidding appearance of many solutions one glimpses in advanced textbooks. Bessel functions, which may have been accepted grudgingly at the ODE level, now make their appearance in the form of *infinite series.* We are asked not only to accept but more importantly, to use infinite series of infinite series! New functional forms, such as *error functions,* appear on the scene and have to be dealt with. The solution methods themselves, analytical or numerical, can be tedious, lengthy, and fraught with new challenges. Small wonder that we studiously avoided the use of PDEs in the preceding six chapters. They have, however, got to be faced sooner or later.

There are a number of steps we can take to ease the pain. The first is to use existing solutions in the literature which often lurk in unsuspected places. This is not the demeaning or trivial task it appears to be. It requires a good nose, persistence, and a broad knowledge of the underlying sciences and the related literature. It is also a perfectly legitimate way of arriving at solutions and avoids the stigma of "reinventing the wheel." A number of illustrations will be devoted to this topic.

A second technique is to "patch together," or superpose known solutions to *simple* problems to solve *more complex* problems or problems with more complex boundary conditions. Such methods are generally limited to linear PDEs, but once this limitation is accepted, a host of important problems become amenable to this technique. Superposition can be implemented by addition, multiplication, or integration over space or time. We shall demonstrate the use of these methods with several illustrations. The aim throughout this section will be to solve PDEs PDQ (pretty damn quick) without sacrificing rigor.

7.4.1 In Search of a Literature Solution

We already had on a number of occasions pointed out that identical models or identical differential equations may be used to describe processes which, on the surface at least, are quite dissimilar. At the ODE level, a host of quite different physical processes based on the same "stirred tank" concept led to identical forms of first order ODEs. The performance of dialyzers and heat exchangers, with obvious differences in the underlying physics of the process, nevertheless led to a pair of similar ordinary differential equations which differed only in the nature of the coefficients and the state variables. This striking result was highlighted in the comparisons made in Table 6.1.

At the PDE level, we had seen that Laplace's equation and other classical partial differential equations could be used to describe a host of different physical processes drawn from the fields of solid and fluid mechanics, transport phenomena, electrostatics, and gravitation. Here again one can expect that we shall be able to "borrow" from other subdisciplines to solve problems of direct concern to us. Given the necessary skills and some patience, the desired result may be obtained PDQ.

Illustration 7.4.1 Pressure Transients in a Semi-Infinite Porous Medium

In the field of Gas Reservoir Engineering, an important question to be answered is the life-time of a gas field. To estimate this quantity, one has to derive the variations with time and distance within the porous medium of the gas pressure $p(x,y,z,t)$. We consider in this example, the simple case of a semi-infinite medium, initially at a pressure p_0. The well pressure is to be maintained at a constant value of p_w during the life-time of the reservoir. We start by composing a mass balance for compressible, one-dimensional flow. Taken over a difference element Δz, this becomes:

Mass balance:

$$\text{Rate of gas in} - \text{Rate of gas out} = \frac{\text{Rate of change}}{\text{of contents}}$$

$$(\rho v A)_x - (\rho v A)_{x+\Delta x} = \varepsilon A \Delta x \left(\frac{\partial \rho}{\partial t} \right)_{avg} \tag{7.4.1}$$

where $\rho v A = F$ = mass flow rate and ε = porosity of the medium.

Upon dividing by $A \Delta z$ and going to the limit we obtain the continuity equation for flow through a porous medium:

$$-\frac{\partial(\rho v)}{\partial x} = \varepsilon \frac{\partial \rho}{\partial t} \tag{7.4.2}$$

Velocity of flow is related to pressure via the empirical D'Arcy's law:

D'Arcy's law:

$$v = -\frac{K}{\mu}\frac{dp}{dx} \qquad (7.4.3)$$

To complete the model, which contains the three dependent variables ρ, v, and p, the density–pressure relation has to be expressed in terms of an appropriate gas law. We assume isothermal flow and write:

Ideal gas law:

$$\rho = \frac{pM}{RT} \qquad (7.4.4)$$

Upon substituting Equations 7.4.3 and 7.4.4 into Equation 7.4.2, the following quasilinear PDE is obtained:

$$\frac{\partial p}{\partial t} = B\frac{\partial}{\partial x}\left(p\frac{\partial p}{\partial x}\right) = B\left[\left(\frac{\partial p}{\partial x}\right)^2 + p\frac{\partial^2 p}{\partial x^2}\right] \qquad (7.4.5)$$

where $B = K/\varepsilon\mu$.

The boundary conditions to this PDE are as follows:

$$p(0,t) = p_w$$

$$p(\infty,t) = p_0 \text{ (bounded)} \qquad (7.4.6)$$

$$p(x,0) = p_0$$

Success in locating a literature solution hinges on recognizing the equivalence of the term $p(\partial p/\partial x)$ and the diffusional flux $D(C)(\partial C/\partial x)$, where $D(C)$ is a variable, concentration dependent diffusivity. It further requires the knowledge that the latter systems exist and have been successfully solved. At any rate, there is no harm in quickly consulting the pertinent literature and, if need be, locate solutions to the corresponding conduction problem containing the term $k(T)(\partial T/(x)$.

The case of a temperature dependent thermal conductivity $k(T)$, although rare, has been addressed but no convenient solutions are immediately available in standard reference texts (see References at the end of the chapter). Concentration dependent diffusivities $D(C)$ arise with much greater frequency, for example, in the diffusion through polymers, and a number of solutions to Fick's equation with variable diffusivity are available. One which comes closest to our requirements has the form:

$$\frac{\partial(C/C_0)}{\partial t} = \frac{\partial}{\partial x}[D_0 + \alpha D_0(C/C_0)]\frac{\partial C/C_0}{\partial x} \qquad (7.4.7)$$

with BCs for desorption:

$$C/C_0(0,t) = 0$$

$$C/C_0(x,0) = 1 \tag{7.4.8}$$

$$C/C_0(\infty,t) \text{ bounded}$$

To bring Equation 7.4.5 in line with this formulation, we introduce the dimensionless variable $\bar{p} = (p - p_w)/(p_0 - p_w)$ and obtain the revised model:

$$\frac{\partial \bar{p}}{\partial t} = \frac{\partial}{\partial x}[Bp_w + B(p_0 - p_w)\bar{p}]\frac{\partial \bar{p}}{\partial t} \tag{7.4.9}$$

with BCs:

$$\bar{p}(0,t) = 0$$

$$\bar{p}(x,0) = 1 \tag{7.4.10}$$

$$\bar{p}(\infty,t) \text{ bounded}$$

Correspondence between the two cases is established via the expressions:

$$D_0 = Bp_w \quad \alpha p_0 = B(p_0 - p_w) \quad C/C_0 = \bar{p} \tag{7.4.11}$$

The literature solutions were obtained numerically and are given as plots of C/C_0 vs. $x/(4D_0t)^{1/2}$, with α as a parameter (see References).

Comments:

The reader will have noted the skills which were required to arrive at a solution. They included an awareness of the equivalence of $\frac{\partial}{\partial x}\left(p\frac{\partial p}{\partial x}\right)$ and $\frac{\partial}{\partial x}\left(D(C)\frac{\partial C}{\partial x}\right)$, the knowledge (or at least an intuitive feeling) that such solutions existed and the patience to look for them.

The solutions can be used to calculate the time it takes for the reservoir pressure to drop to a prescribed value. This is often taken to be 25% of the initial pressure p_0 since a further drop makes the recompression costs required at the surface unattractive. Secondary methods are often used to recover the residue.

One notes the appearance of the group $x/t^{1/2}$ in the parameters of the solution which suggests that similarity transformation was used to arrive at a solution. It is left to the exercises to show that this results in the ODE:

$$B\left[\bar{p}\frac{d^2\bar{p}}{dy^2} + \left(\frac{d\bar{p}}{d\eta}\right)^2\right] + \frac{1}{2}\eta\frac{d\bar{p}}{d\eta} = 0 \tag{7.4.12}$$

with BCs:

$$\bar{p}(0) = 1$$
$$\bar{p}(\infty) = 0$$
$$(7.4.13)$$

Solutions for other, more realistic reservoir geometries are available in the literature (see References). Among these is the important case of a reservoir of finite thickness and radius, with *radial* flow into the production well. The solutions are similar in form to that given here.

Illustration 7.4.2 Use of Electrostatic Potentials in the Solution of Conduction Problems

It had been noted in Section 7.2.2 that solutions to Poisson's equation can be used to represent both temperature distributions in a region with distributed heat sources, as well as distributions of electrostatic potential in a domain carrying a distribution of charges. The following electrostatic problem has been solved in the literature (see References). The result is fairly complex and is not reproduced here.

$$\frac{\partial^2 V}{\partial x^2} + \frac{\partial^2 V}{\partial y^2} = -h \, (0 < x < \pi, y > 0) \qquad (7.4.14)$$

with BCs:

$$V(0,y) = 0 \quad V(\pi,y) = A \quad (y > 0) \qquad (7.4.15)$$

$$V(x,0) = 0 \quad (\alpha < x < \pi)$$

The domain in question is thus a semi-infinite strip of width $\Delta x = \pi$. We pose the following question. What, if any, conduction problem is represented by the solution of the electrostatic problem?

We start by noting that the source term h equals $4\pi\rho$, where ρ is the charge density in the domain and is assumed to be constant here. Using Table 7.3 as a dictionary, one can transform h into a corresponding heat source term. We obtain:

$$h = S/k \qquad (7.4.16)$$

The electrostatic problem then translates into the following conduction problem:

$$k\left[\frac{\partial^2 T}{\partial x^2} + \frac{\partial^2 T}{\partial y^2}\right] + S = 0 \qquad (7.4.17)$$

with BCs:

$$T(0,y) = 0 \quad T(\pi,y) = A \quad T(x,0) = 0 \qquad (7.4.18)$$

and S = heat source in units of J/m³s.

The solution of this problem represents the steady-state temperature distribution in a semi-infinite strip of width π, with the base and left side at T = 0, the right side at T = A, and uniformly distributed steady heat sources of strength S = hk in the interior of the domain. Note that the width π of the strip can be transformed into an arbitrary length 1 by defining a new length variable $x' = \dfrac{x}{\pi} 1$.

7.4.2 SIMPLE SOLUTIONS BY SUPERPOSITION

7.4.2.1 Superposition of Simple Flows: Solutions in Search of a Problem

The technique we apply here starts by defining some simple stream functions ψ which can be shown to satisfy Laplace's equation in two Cartesian coordinates (x,y) or in polar coordinates (r,θ). These stream functions represent certain simple albeit somewhat artificial flow patterns and are summarized in Figure 7.8.

The stream function $\psi = v_\infty y$ = constant represents rectilinear flow parallel to the x-axis, with an orthogonal network of potential functions $\phi = v_\infty x$ = constant (Figure 7.8A). Both ϕ and ψ satisfy Laplace's equation.

The stream function $\psi = \dfrac{Q}{2\pi}\theta$ = constant represents flow emanating from the origin and proceeding radially outward (Figure 7.8B). The corresponding potential functions are represented by a set of orthogonal concentric circles. Q is the so-called *strength of the source* and physically equals the flow rate per unit depth into the paper. For a sink, the flow is taken to be radially inward, and both the stream function and the velocity component change sign. In both cases ψ satisfies Laplace's equation in polar coordinates (Table 7.6).

The stream function $\psi = \dfrac{Q}{2\pi}\ln r$ = constant represents a clockwise circular flow pattern around the origin, with ϕ = constant making up the radial rays which emanate from the origin and are orthogonal to the circles ψ = constant (Figure 7.8C). This pattern is merely a reversal of that shown by the source, with the roles of ϕ and ψ having been interchanged, and is appropriately termed a *vortex*. Q represents the strength of the vortex and is again given in units of flow rate per unit depth into the paper. For counterclockwise vortices, the signs of both the stream function and the velocities is reversed.

The doublet, shown in Figure 7.8D, is more of an artifact and is not meant to represent any real flow pattern. The streamlines are made up of a set of concentric circles tangent to the x-axis which satisfy Laplace's equation as required.

Other simple flows, such as *point sources* and *point doublets* have been used in the literature but are not taken up here.

System	Stream Function	Velocities
A. Uniform Flow 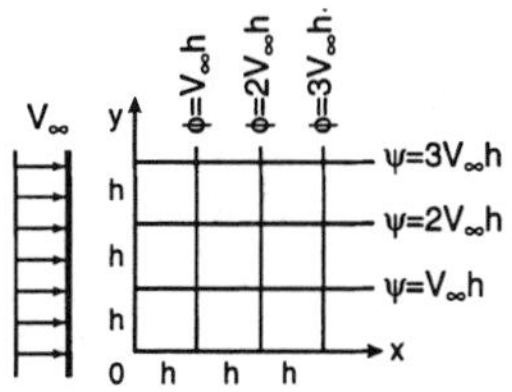 	$\psi = V_\infty y$ $\psi = V_\infty r.\sin\theta$	$v_x = $ constant $v_y = 0$
B. Line Source 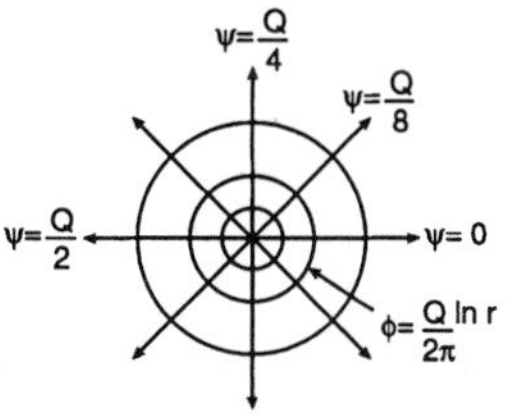 	Source: $\psi = \dfrac{Q\theta}{2\pi}$ Sink: $\psi = -\dfrac{Q\theta}{2\pi}$	Source: $v_\theta = 0 \quad v_r = Q/2\pi r$ Sink: $v_\theta = 0 \quad v_r = -Q/2\pi r$
C. Line Vortex 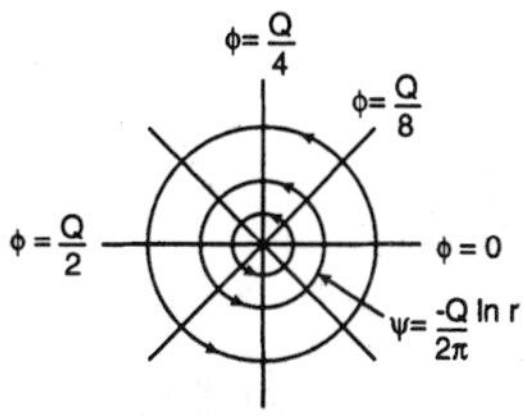 	Clockwise $\psi = \dfrac{Q \ln r}{2\pi}$ Counterclockwise $\psi = -\dfrac{Q \ln r}{2\pi}$	Clockwise $v_\theta = -Q/2\pi r \quad v_r = 0$ Counterclockwise $v_\theta = Q/2\pi r \quad v_r = 0$
D. Doublet 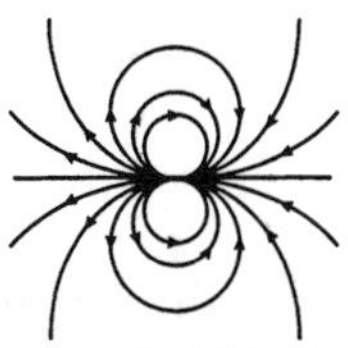 	$\psi = -K\dfrac{\sin\theta}{r}$	$v_\theta = \dfrac{K}{r^2}\sin\theta$ $v_r = -\dfrac{K}{r^2}\cos\theta$

FIGURE 7.8 Compilation of some simple flows used in the solution of Laplace's equation for irrotational flow by superposition.

Proceeding, we superpose various simple flows by adding the corresponding stream functions. The linearity of Laplace's equation guarantees that it is satisfied for any arbitrary sum of such stream functions. However, what, if any real potential flow problem has been solved by superposing the simple flows? If no real flow pattern emerges from a particular superposition, new combinations are tried. Note that both addition and subtraction can be used resulting in a host of possible combinations.

TABLE 7.6
Stream Functions, Velocity Potentials
Velocities, and Laplace's Equation

Cartesian Coordinates	Polar Coordinates

(1) ψ and ϕ

$$\frac{\partial \psi}{\partial x} = -\frac{\partial \phi}{\partial y} \qquad\qquad \frac{\partial \psi}{\partial \theta} = r\frac{\partial \phi}{\partial r}$$

$$\frac{\partial \psi}{\partial y} = \frac{\partial \phi}{\partial x} \qquad\qquad \frac{\partial \psi}{\partial r} = -\frac{1}{r}\frac{\partial \phi}{\partial \theta}$$

(2) Velocity components

$$v_x = \frac{\partial \psi}{\partial y} = \frac{\partial \phi}{\partial x} \qquad\qquad v_\theta = -\frac{\partial \psi}{\partial r} = \frac{1}{r}\frac{\partial \phi}{\partial \theta}$$

$$v_y = -\frac{\partial \psi}{\partial x} = \frac{\partial \phi}{\partial y} \qquad\qquad v_r = \frac{1}{r}\frac{\partial \psi}{\partial \theta} = \frac{\partial \phi}{\partial r}$$

(3) Laplace's equation

$$\frac{\partial^2 \psi}{\partial x^2} + \frac{\partial^2 \psi}{\partial y^2} = 0 \qquad\qquad \frac{\partial^2 \psi}{\partial \theta^2} + r\frac{\partial}{\partial r}\left(r\frac{\partial \psi}{\partial r}\right) = 0$$

$$\frac{\partial^2 \phi}{\partial y^2} + \frac{\partial^2 \phi}{\partial y^2} = 0 \qquad\qquad \frac{\partial^2 \phi}{\partial \theta^2} + r\frac{\partial}{\partial r}\left(r\frac{\partial \phi}{\partial r}\right) = 0$$

We term this procedure *"a solution in search of a problem."* This is evidently a reversal of the conventional process of first specifying a problem and then seeking its solution, but the procedure has a legitimate place in mathematical analysis and has led to many fruitful results. A summary of several classical superpositions appears in Figure 7.9.

The results of the superpositions displayed in this figure show several recognizable flow patterns.

In Figure 7.8A, a sink and a clockwise vortex have been superposed resulting in spiral flow into the origin. This resembles the flow pattern in a draining tank or in a tornado and agrees with the intuitive notion that the combination of circular and radial flow should result in streamlines of a spiral form converging to the origin.

In Figure 7.9B, uniform flow has been superposed onto a doublet. Here it is difficult to anticipate the resulting flow pattern and a detailed analysis of the stream functions has to be undertaken. This is done in Illustration 7.4.1. The result indicates that the pattern represents potential flow around a circle or cylinder, or around "humps" which diminish in height as one moves outward. The relations given in Table 7.6 enable us to calculate velocity distributions around the cylinder which can then be substituted into the Bernoulli equation to arrive at a pressure distribution. These are highly useful results to have been obtained by simple manipulations of the stream function and Bernoulli's equation.

System	Stream Function	Velocities
A. Tornado 	Superposition of Counterclockwise Vortex and Sink $$\psi = -\frac{Q\theta}{2\pi} - \frac{Q}{2\pi}\ln r$$	$$v_\theta = \frac{Q}{2\pi r}$$ $$v_r = -\frac{Q}{2\pi r}$$
B. Flow Around Cylinder 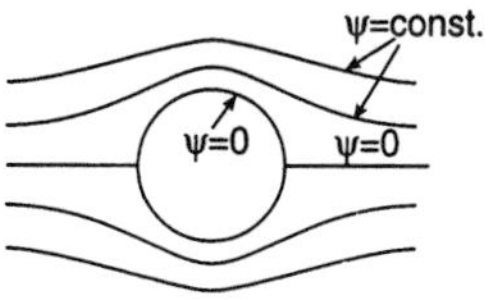 ψ=const. ψ=0 ψ=0	Superposition of Uniform Flow and Doublet $$\psi = v_\infty r\sin\theta - \frac{K\sin\theta}{r}$$	$$v_\theta = -v_\infty\sin\theta - \frac{K\sin\theta}{r^2}$$ $$v_r = v_\infty\cos\theta - \frac{K\cos\theta}{r^2}$$
C. Rankine Half-Body 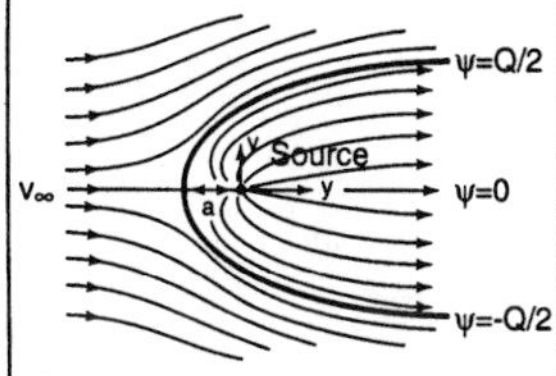 ψ=Q/2 Source ψ=0 v_∞ a ψ=-Q/2	Superposition of Uniform Flow and Source $$\psi = v_\infty r\sin\theta + \frac{Q\theta}{2\pi}$$	$$v_\theta = -v_\infty\sin\theta$$ $$v_r = +v_\infty\cos\theta + \frac{Q}{2\pi r}$$
D. Flow in a Corner 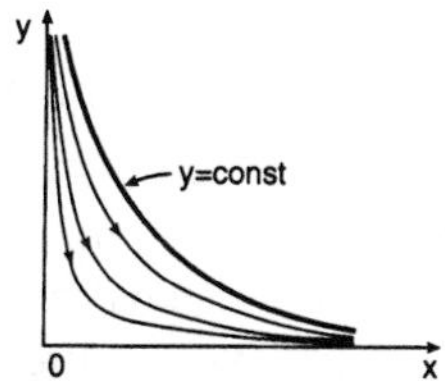 y y=const 0 x	No Superposition $$\psi = 2Axy$$ $$\psi = Ar^2\sin 2\theta$$	$$v_\theta = 2Ar\sin 2\theta$$ $$v_r = 2Ar\cos 2\theta$$

FIGURE 7.9 Flow fields resulting from the superposition of some simple flows.

Figure 7.9C shows the results of the superposition of uniform flow and a source. Plots of various value of ψ = constant leads to the appearance of a near-elliptical shape known as the Rankine half-body, with upper and lower streamlines equal to 1/2 Q, where Q is the strength of the source. An increase in Q thus will result in an increase of the body thickness. The maximum velocity occurs at $\theta = 63°$ and is given by $|v|_{Max} = 1.26\, v_\infty$.

The streamlines shown in Figure 7.9D cannot be obtained by superposition of simple flows. They represent rectangular hyperbolas which were deduced to represent flow in a right-angled corner. This example can be truly termed "a solution in search of a problem." A similar approach can be used to show that flow around corners of various angles can be represented by the general streamline:

$$\psi = Ar^n \sin n\,\theta \qquad (7.4.19)$$

The parameter n is related to the angle α of the corner as follows

n	1/2	2/3	3/2	2	3	4
a	360°	270°	135°	90°	60°	45°

The detailed deduction of the flow pattern from an assumed form of the stream function y is illustrated in the following example.

Illustration 7.4.3   Superposition of Uniform Flow and a Doublet: Flow Around an Infinite Cylinder or a Circle

A convenient method of analysis is to start with the simplest possible stream function $\psi = 0$, i.e., we set the sum of ψ for uniform flow and a doublet equal to zero:

$$\psi = \sin\theta\left(v_\infty r - \frac{K}{r}\right) = 0 \qquad (7.4.20)$$

This relation is satisfied for:

$$\theta = 0, -\pi, -2\pi, \ldots, \text{any } r \qquad (7.4.21)$$

and

$$r = (K/v_\infty)^{1/2}, \text{any } \theta \qquad (7.4.22)$$

These conditions represent the x-axis with an intervening circle (or infinitely long cylinder) of radius $R = (K/v_\infty)^{1/2}$. The size of the cylinder or circle thus can be manipulated by adjusting the strength K of the doublet. Note also that the stream functions with values other than zero, i.e., $\psi = C_1, C_2$, etc., represent flow around *humps* whose height diminishes with an increase in the constant C.

Let us now deduce velocities and pressures at various points of the flow field, using Table 7.6 as an aid.

Radial Velocity at the Cylinder Surface —

$$v_r = \frac{1}{r}\frac{\partial\psi}{\partial\theta} = \frac{1}{r}\cos\theta\left(v_\infty r - \frac{K}{r}\right) \qquad (7.4.23)$$

At the surface, $r = R = (K/v_\infty)^{1/2}$, so that:

$$v_r = \frac{\cos\theta}{(K/v_\infty)^{1/2}}[(v_\infty K)^{1/2} - (v_\infty K)^{1/2}] = 0 \qquad (7.4.24)$$

i.e., the radial velocity component vanishes at the surface everywhere, as required.

Tangential Velocity at the Cylinder Surface — Here we obtain from Table 7.6 and the relation $R = (K/v_\infty)^{1/2}$:

$$v_\theta = -\frac{\partial\psi}{\partial r} = -\sin\theta\left(v_\infty + \frac{K}{r^2}\right) = -2v_\infty\sin\theta \qquad (7.4.25)$$

Thus, at the stagnation points $\theta = 0$, $-\pi$, the tangential velocity vanishes, as required. The maximum velocity is attained at $\theta = -\pi/2$ and has the value $|v|_{Max} = v_\theta = 2v_\infty$, i.e., twice the velocity of approach v_∞. This is an important result and applies as well to flow just outside a viscous boundary layer.

Pressure Distribution at the Cylinder Surface — To calculate the pressure distribution in the flow field, we draw on Bernoulli's equation which for our present purposes assumes the form:

$$\frac{p}{\rho} + \frac{v_\theta^2}{2} = \frac{p_\infty}{\rho} + \frac{v_\infty^2}{2} \qquad (7.4.26)$$

Substitution of the Expression 7.4.24 into 7.4.25 yields the pressure distribution:

$$p = \frac{\rho v_\infty^2}{2}(1 - 4\sin^2\theta) + p_\infty \qquad (7.4.27)$$

For $\theta = 0$, $-\pi$ one obtains the stagnation pressure p_s:

$$p_s = \frac{\rho v_\infty^2}{2} + p_\infty \qquad (7.4.28)$$

Thus, p_s equals the pressure far from the cylinder, p_∞, augmented by the kinetic energy of the approaching fluid which is completely converted into what might be termed a volumetric pressure energy.

The minimum pressure p_{min} occurs at $\theta = -\pi/2$ and assumes the value:

$$p_{min} = p_\infty - 3\frac{\rho v_\infty^2}{2} \qquad (7.4.29)$$

i.e., the pressure here is diminished over the free stream pressure p_∞ by three times the kinetic energy of approach. The value closely approximates the actual value found in real flow around a cylinder. In fact, the Expression 7.4.26 is an accurate description of the pressure distribution in the upstream third of the cylinder. It is in the rear half that the relation breaks down due to viscous effects and separation. In particular, the pressure at $\theta = 0$ no longer equals that at $\theta = -\pi$, resulting in a net force or drag being exerted on the cylinder, while potential theory predicts zero drag due to the symmetry of the body. This is perhaps its most serious flaw, which is however amply compensated by the successful predictions in the upstream portion of the body. Considering the simple tools used in arriving at these results, this is no mean accomplishment.

7.4.2.2   Superposition by Multiplication: Product Solutions

The term *superposition by multiplication* is not commonly used in the literature which prefers to regard superposition as an additive process. We adopted it never-theless since it contains the same features as classical superposition, i.e., the solution of a complex problem by the process of patching together solutions to simpler problems. In the application we consider here the "simpler problems" are the solutions of the one-dimensional Fourier's or Fick's equation for unsteady conduction and diffusion, the complex counterpart being the two- and three-dimensional cases. The method is only applicable to linear PDEs which can be solved by the method of separation of variables. We provide below two examples which are based on Fourier's equation.

First consider the case of rectangular one-dimensional unsteady conduction in a finite domain $x_1 < x < x_2$. The system is described by:

$$\frac{\partial T_x}{\partial t} = \alpha \frac{\partial^2 T_x}{\partial x^2} \qquad (7.4.30)$$

with general Type III boundary conditions:

$$A_x \frac{\partial T_x}{\partial x} - B_x T_x = 0 \quad \text{at } x = x_1$$

$$\qquad (7.4.31)$$

$$C_x \frac{\partial T_x}{\partial x} - D_x T_x = 0 \quad \text{at } x = x_2$$

and initial condition:

$$T_x(x,0) = f_x(x) \qquad (7.4.32)$$

Its solution will be denoted by:

$$T_x(x,t) = g_x(x,t) \qquad (7.4.33)$$

Extend this case now to three dimensions in the rectangular domain $x_1 < x < x_2$, $y_1 < y < y_2$, and $z_1 < z < z_2$, and boundary conditions in those three dimensions identical in form to those described by Equation 7.4.34. The solution for these three-dimensional temperature distributions $T(x,y,z,t)$ can then be expressed as the *product* of three one-dimensional solutions, i.e.,

$$T(x,y,z,t) = g_x(x,t)g_y(y,t)g_z(z,t) \tag{7.4.34}$$

with initial conditions:

$$T(x,y,z,0) = f_x(x)f_y(y)f_z(z) \tag{7.4.35}$$

This is a useful and quite general result, except that the three-dimensional initial condition has to be of the separable form Equation 7.4.35.

Next consider the case of radial unsteady conduction in the domain $r_1 < r < r_2$ (infinitely long cylinder):

$$\frac{\partial T_r}{\partial t} = \alpha\left[\frac{\partial^2 T_r}{\partial r^2} + \frac{1}{r}\frac{\partial T_r}{\partial r}\right] \tag{7.4.36}$$

with general Type III boundary conditions:

$$A_r\frac{\partial T_r}{\partial r} - B_r T_r = 0 \quad \text{at } r = r_1$$
$$C_r\frac{\partial T_r}{\partial r} - D_r T_r = 0 \quad \text{at } r = r_2 \tag{7.4.37}$$

and initial condition:

$$T_r(r,0) = f_r(r) \tag{7.4.38}$$

The solution is denoted by:

$$T_r(r,t) = g_r(r,t) \tag{7.4.39}$$

We extend this case now to a *finite* cylinder in the domain $r_1 < r < r_2$ and $x_1 < x < x_2$, i.e., one described by the PDE:

$$\frac{\partial T}{\partial t} = \alpha\left[\frac{\partial^2 T}{\partial r^2} + \frac{1}{r}\frac{\partial T}{\partial r} + \frac{\partial^2 T}{\partial x^2}\right] \tag{7.4.40}$$

and with boundary conditions of Equations 7.4.31 and 7.4.37.

Its solution is then given by the *product* of the rectangular and radial solution Equations 7.4.33 and 7.4.39, i.e.,

$$T(r,x,t) = g_r(r,t)g_x(x,t) \qquad (7.4.41)$$

with initial condition:

$$T(r,x,0) = f_r(r)f_x(x) \qquad (7.4.42)$$

This is again a quite general result, except for the restriction of separability of the initial condition 7.4.42.

Validity of these solutions is proved by direct substitution of the solutions into the full PDEs and boundary conditions. The reader is urged to attempt other superpositions of this type. The Graetz problem appears to be a suitable candidate. We shall shortly present an interesting application of product solutions (Illustration 7.4.4).

7.4.2.3   Solution of Source Problems: Superposition by Integration

Problems involving sources of mass or energy, and the distributions in concentration and temperature associated with them arise in a wide variety of ways. A host of environmental problems involve sources of pollutants of one type or another. We had already encountered heat sources at the ODE, i.e., steady state level (Practice Problem 3.3.2 in Chapter 3) and in the formulations of the Poisson Equation 7.2.28 for distributed steady sources. The types we wish to consider here initially consist of instantaneous *point sources* which give rise to unsteady temperature and concentration distribution in infinite or semi-infinite space. The point source results can be integrated over space or time to arrive at distributions due to instantaneous line or area sources or those due to sources which are continuous over certain time intervals. This is the procedure referred to as *superposition by integration.*

In many of the solutions to source problems, an important new entity called the *error function* makes its appearance and therefore we shall devote a brief preamble to its description. The error function, denoted as erf(x), is defined as the integral:

$$\mathrm{erf}(x) = \frac{2}{\sqrt{\pi}} \int_0^x e^{-\lambda^2} d\lambda \qquad (7.4.43)$$

where the integrand will be recognized as the Gaussian error function $\frac{2}{\sqrt{\pi}} e^{-\lambda^2}$. It has the following properties shown in Table 7.7.

erf(x) cannot be determined analytically and numerical integration is required for its evaluation. A brief table of values appears in Table 7.8.

The error function also can be well approximated (max. error 8%) by the exponential expression:

$$\mathrm{erf}(\alpha) = 1 - \frac{e^{-x^2}}{1 + 1.248\,x} \qquad (7.4.44)$$

TABLE 7.7
Properties of the Error Function

1. $\text{erf}(0) = 0$
2. $\text{erf}(\infty) = 1$
3. $\text{erf}(-x) = -\text{erf}(x)$
4. $1 - \text{erf}(x) = \text{erfc}(x)$ (Complementary error function)
5. $\dfrac{d}{dx}\text{erf}\,x = \dfrac{2}{\sqrt{\pi}}e^{-x^2}$
6. $\displaystyle\int_x^\infty \text{erfc}\,x\,dx = \dfrac{1}{\sqrt{\pi}}e^{-x^2} - x\,\text{erfc}\,x$
7. Approximation for small x

   $\text{erf}\,x \cong 2\pi^{-1/2}x$
8. Approximation for large x

   $\text{erfc}\,x \cong \pi^{-1/2}e^{-x^2}\left[\dfrac{1}{x} - \dfrac{2}{x^3} + ...\right]$

TABLE 7.8
Values of the Error Function

x	erf(x)
0	0
0.05	0.05637
0.1	0.11246
0.15	0.16800
0.20	0.22270
0.25	0.27632
0.30	0.32863
0.35	0.37938
0.40	0.42839
0.50	0.52050
0.60	0.60386
0.70	0.67780
0.80	0.74210
0.90	0.79691
1.0	0.84270
1.2	0.91031
1.5	0.96611
2.0	0.99532
∞	1.00000

In the following illustrations we consider a number of interesting source problems in infinite and semi-infinite space which are arrived at by superposition of the simplex solution, that of an instantaneous source in one-dimensional infinite space. Both instantaneous and continuous sources are considered and the tools we use are superposition by multiplication as well as superposition by integration.

Illustration 7.4.4

The Instantaneous Infinite Plane Source — On occasion, simple solutions may be arrived at by inspired guesswork. The solution to the source problem in one-dimensional infinite space for Fourier's equation is a case in point. We consider the source to lie on the infinite y,z plane, with temperature variations taking place in the x-direction only. The solution then takes the form:

$$T = \frac{A}{t^{1/2}} \exp(-x^2 / 4\alpha t) \qquad (7.4.45)$$

where A is an arbitrary constant. It can be shown by direct substitution that this expression satisfies Fourier's equation:

$$\frac{\partial T}{\partial t} = \alpha \frac{\partial^2 T}{\partial x^2} \qquad (7.4.46)$$

More importantly, it also satisfies the following initial conditions:

$$T(x,0) = 0 \qquad (7.4.47)$$

and

$$T(0,0) = \infty \qquad (7.4.48)$$

Here Equations 7.4.47 and 7.4.48 express the fact that at time zero, the entire domain except for the origin is at zero temperature while at the origin it momentarily rises to infinity due to the instantaneous and concentrated nature of the source. The integration constant A is evaluated from the total heat released per unit area of an infinite plane, q_{Tot}, i.e.,

$$q_{Tot} = \rho Cp \int_{-\infty}^{\infty} T dx = A\rho Cp \int_{-\infty}^{\infty} \frac{\exp(-x^2 / 4\alpha t)}{t^{1/2}} dx = 2A\rho Cp(\pi\alpha t)^{1/2} \quad (7.4.49)$$

where the integral is obtained from tables of integrals. Thus, the temperature distribution in the infinite x-domain is given by:

$$T = \frac{q_{Tot}}{2\rho Cp(\pi\alpha t)^{1/2}} \exp(-x^2 / 4\alpha t) \qquad (7.4.50)$$

A. Infinite Plane Source

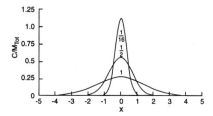

B. Point Source

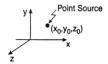

C. Finite Plane Source

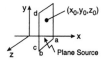

FIGURE 7.10 Configuration of some sources in infinite domains: (A) instantaneous infinite plane mass source emitting in the x-directions (numbers on the curves denote dimensionless time), (B) a point source emitting into three-dimensional infinite space, (C) a finite plane source emitting into three-dimensional infinite space. (Figure A from J. Crank, *Mathematics of Diffusion, 2nd ed.,* Oxford University Press, New York, 1975. With permission.)

An expression identical in form applies to mass diffusion, i.e., the solution of Fick's equation for this case is given by:

$$C = \frac{M_{Tot}}{2(\pi Dt)^{1/2}} \exp(-x^2/4Dt) \tag{7.4.51}$$

where M_{Tot} = total mass released.

The nature of the solution curves for Equation 7.4.51 is shown in Figure 7.10A, where the numbers on the curves indicate values of Dt.

We note that the quantity $q_{Tot}/\rho\,Cp$ is referred to as the strength Q of the heat source, so that Equation 7.4.50 can be written as:

$$T = \frac{Q}{2(\pi\alpha t)^{1/2}} \exp(-x^2/4\alpha t) \tag{7.4.52}$$

Since Q can also be expressed in the form:

$$Q = q_{Tot}/\rho \; Cp = TV \qquad (7.4.53)$$

a source of unit strength $Q = 1$ can be viewed as one which raises the temperature T of a unit volume $V = 1$ of the medium by one degree. This refinement is not required in the case of mass sources, where the total amount released per unit area also equals the strength of the source.

The Instantaneous Point Heat Source in Three-Dimensional Infinite Space — This situation is depicted in Figure 7.10B, where a point source of strength Q has been placed at some arbitrary coordinate point x_0, y_0, z_0. This merely requires a corresponding shift in the coordinates of the solution.

To solve this three-dimensional case, we invoke the principle of superposition by multiplication, described in Section 7.4.2.2. This involves extending the solution for the one-dimensional case, given by Equation 7.4.50 to the three-dimensional case, by multiplication in the three coordinate directions x, y, z. We obtain:

$$T(x,y,z,t) = \frac{Q}{8(\pi\alpha t)^{3/2}} \exp\left[\frac{-(x-x_0)^2 - (y-y_0)^2 - (z-z_0)^2}{4\alpha t}\right] \qquad (7.4.54)$$

If we shift the source to the origin and introduce the radial variable:

$$r = (x^2 + y^2 + z^2)^{1/2} \qquad (7.4.55)$$

we obtain the simple alternative formulation:

$$T(r,t) = \frac{Q}{8(\pi\alpha t)^{3/2}} \exp(-r^2/4\alpha t) \qquad (7.4.56)$$

The Instantaneous Finite Plane Source in Three-Dimensional Infinite Space — The situation considered here is depicted in Figure 7.10C. Since we already have in Equation 7.4.54 the solution of the *point* source in three-dimensional space, all we need to do is to extend that solution over the area of the plane source using superposition by integration. We obtain:

$$T(x,y,z,t) = \frac{Q'}{8(\pi\alpha t)^{3/2}} \int_{y_0=c}^{y_0=d} \int_{z_0=a}^{z_0=b} \exp\left[\frac{-(x-x_0)^2 - (y-y_0)^2 - (z-z_0)^2}{4\alpha t}\right] dy_0 dz_0$$

$$(7.4.57)$$

where $Q' = q'_{Tot}(J/m^2)/\rho C_p$.

Note that the integration variables are the coordinates of the point source, x_0, y_0, z_0, rather than the general space coordinates x, y, z. The plane source thus is seen to be made up of an infinite number of point sources which are summed or superposed by integration over the area of the plane.

The Continuous Point Source — Here our starting point is again the instantaneous point source, Equation 7.4.56, which now has to be integrated over the "life-time" t of the source. To do this, we introduce the integration variable t' and write the following integral of Equation 7.4.56:

$$T(r,t) = \frac{Q''}{8(\pi\alpha)^{3/2}} \int_0^t \frac{e^{-r^2/4\alpha(t-t')}}{(t-t')^{3/2}} \, dt' \tag{7.4.58}$$

Note that the argument of integration is $(t - t')$ rather than t'. Validation of this expression can be obtained by taking finite increments $\Delta(t - t')$ for a heat release of Δq_{Tot}, summing the increments, and letting $\Delta(t - t') \to 0$.

The form of the integral is similar to that of the error function, Equation 7.4.42, and the simple transformation $\tau = (t - t')^{1/2}$ reduces Equation 7.4.58 to the compact form:

$$T(r,t) = \frac{Q''}{4\pi\alpha r} \text{erfc} \frac{r}{(4\alpha t)^{1/2}} \tag{7.4.59}$$

where, as noted before:

$$\text{erfc}(x) = 1 - \text{erf}(x) = 1 - \int_0^x e^{-\lambda^2} d\lambda$$

The Expression 7.4.59 describes the transient temperature distribution in three-dimensional infinite space due to a continuous heat source of strength $Q''(J/m^3s)$.

The Point or Infinite Plane Source in the Semi-Infinite Domain: The Method of Images — With this example we wish to introduce the reader to a graphical technique termed the *method of images*. It consists of placing physical entities on either side of a boundary, here set at $x = 0$ of a semi-infinite domain, and proportion them in such a way that a prescribed boundary condition, e.g., $T = 0$, is satisfied. In heat conduction, this is done with the help of heat sources and heat "sinks." The latter can be viewed as "cryogenic" sources leading to temperatures below the datum of $T = 0$. In potential flow, a similar procedure applies in which images of the submerged object are placed on either side of a boundary which is required to have a prescribed value of the stream function, say $\psi = 0$. The method is most easily applied to a semi-infinite medium and becomes more complex in bounded geometries such as slabs, cylinders, or spheres. The latter cases are taken up in the specialized monographs dealing with heat conduction (see References).

In the problem considered here, a heat source of strength Q is placed at a distance of $x = x_0$ from the boundary, which is maintained at $T = 0$ by appropriate cooling. To solve for the resulting temperature distribution by the method of images, a heat "sink" of equal but opposite strength Q is placed at a distance $x = -x_0$ from the boundary. This "sink" gives rise to the temperature profile $T(x,t)$ shown in Figure 7.11A. Superposition of source and sink which is permitted because of the linearity of Fourier's equation then leads to the profile depicted in Figure 7.11B. Since the two entities are of equal but opposite strengths, temperatures at the boundary exactly

A. Cryogenic Sink

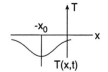

B. Superposition of Source and Sink

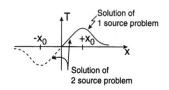

C. Superposition of Source and Source

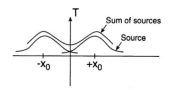

FIGURE 7.11   Superposition of sources and sinks by the method of images.

cancel each other to give the required value of T = 0. We note that the resulting distribution for x > 0 satisfies the posed problem, while the *entire* profile over the range $-\infty < x < \infty$ is to be regarded as a solution to the two source problem. The relevant equations are as follows:

For the cryogenic sink alone:

$$T = -\frac{Q}{(4\pi\alpha t)^{1/2}} \exp[-(x+x_0)^2 / 4\alpha t] \qquad (7.4.60)$$

For the heat source and cryogenic sink:

$$T(x,t) = \frac{Q}{(4\pi\alpha t)^{1/2}} \{\exp[-(x-x_0)^2 / 4\alpha t] - \exp[-(x+x_0)^2 / 4\alpha t]\} \quad (7.4.61)$$

Equation 7.4.61 represents the temperature distribution for the following two cases:

1. Heat source of strength Q at $x = x_0$ of a one-dimensional semi-infinite medium, with its surface x = 0 maintained at T = 0.

2. Heat source of strength Q at $x = x_0$ of a one-dimensional infinite domain and a source of strength $-Q$ at the position $x = -x_0$.

The latter is unlikely to arise in practice but is added for completeness. The following illustration contains yet another example of superposition by the method of images.

Illustration 7.4.5   Concentration Distributions from a Finite and Instantaneous Pollutant Source in Three-Dimensional Semi-Infinite Space

Pollution from point, line, and area sources is a frequent occurrence of environmental concern. The resulting concentration profiles are usually modeled by means of PDEs that combine convective transport due to air movement caused by wind and a diffusive mode of transport. A general formulation of the problem then leads to an extended form of Fick's equation given below:

$$D_x \frac{\partial^2 C}{\partial x} + D_y \frac{\partial^2 C}{\partial y^2} + D_z \frac{\partial^2 C}{\partial z^2} - v \frac{\partial C}{\partial x} = \frac{\partial C}{\partial t} \qquad (7.4.62)$$

where $D_{x,y,z}$ are empirical diffusion coefficients and v the wind velocity. Variations with time and in direction of v are not taken into account in this first model. Furthermore, we shall assume the dispersion coefficients in x and y to be equal D.

In the example considered here, an instantaneous plane source of strength $S(kg/m^2)$ and dimensions a,b is assumed located at ground level. This approximates conditions which arise due to brief periods of pollution from an industrial area. Material diffuses into the semi-infinite region depicted in Figure 7.12, and is further dispersed by air movement.

We present a solution that makes use of several of the devices and methods we described in previous sections.

First, we recognize the combination $v \frac{\partial C}{\partial x} + \frac{\partial C}{\partial t}$ as a convective derivative, Equation 7.3.76 which we were able to transform into a single derivative by iden-

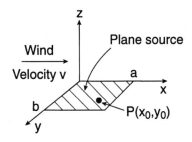

FIGURE 7.12   A finite plane mass source at ground level emitting into the atmosphere.

tifying new independent variables, Equations 7.3.70 and 7.3.71, and carrying out a reduction to canonical form. We choose the combination:

$$u = x - vt \quad \text{and} \quad \tau = t \tag{7.4.63}$$

and obtain the following relation between old and new derivatives using the formula of Table 7.5:

$$\frac{\partial C}{\partial t} = -v\frac{\partial C}{\partial x} + \frac{\partial C}{\partial \tau}$$

$$\frac{\partial C}{\partial x} = \frac{\partial C}{\partial u} \tag{7.4.64}$$

and

$$\frac{\partial^2 C}{\partial x^2} = \frac{\partial^2 C}{\partial u^2}$$

Introduction of these relations into the PDE 7.4.62 yields after cancellation of terms the following result:

$$D\left(\frac{\partial^2 C}{\partial u^2} + \frac{\partial^2 C}{\partial y^2}\right) + D_z\frac{\partial^2 C}{\partial z^2} = \frac{\partial C}{\partial \tau} \tag{7.4.65}$$

We thus have succeeded in reducing the model to Fick's equation which we can now proceed to treat by the various superposition techniques established in the previous section.

Second, we start by writing point source solutions for each coordinate direction. We obtain by adapting Equation 7.4.52 to the problem:

For the x-direction:

$$C(x,t) = \frac{1}{(4\pi Dt)^{1/2}} \exp[-(x - vt - x_0)^2 / 4Dt] \tag{7.4.66}$$

where we have introduced the new independent variable x-vt into the exponential term.

For the y-direction:

$$C(y,t) = \frac{1}{(4\pi Dt)^{1/2}} \exp[-(y - y_0)^2 / 4Dt] \tag{7.4.67}$$

For the z-direction ($z_0 = 0$):

Here we must recognize that the domain is a semi-infinite one, with a Type II (no flux) boundary condition at $z = 0$. The solution to that problem also can be obtained by the method of images, but this time by the addition of two sources. This results in a composite concentration distribution with a minimum at the origin (Figure 7.11C), thus satisfying the no flux condition. For mass diffusion this yields:

$$C(z,t) = \frac{2}{(4\pi D_z t)^{1/2}} \exp[-z/4D_z t] \tag{7.4.68}$$

Third, with the three uni-directional solutions on hand, we are in a position to solve the three-dimensional case using superposition by multiplication for a source of strengths. We obtain:

$$C(x,y,z,t) = \frac{2S}{(4\pi D_z t)^{1/2}} \exp[-z^2/4Dt]$$

$$\frac{1}{(4\pi Dt)} \exp[-(x - vt - x_0)^2/4Dt]\exp[-(y - y_0)^2/4Dt] \tag{7.4.69}$$

This is the solution to an instantaneous point source emitting into half-space. The result still needs to be converted to an area source, which is done in the next step.

Fourth, we adapt the method of superposition by integration applied to area sources in Illustration 7.4.4. This leads to the result:

$$C(x,y,z,t) = \frac{2S}{(4\pi D_z t)^{1/2}} \exp[-z_2/4Dt] \times$$

$$\frac{1}{(4\pi Dt)} \int_0^a \int_0^b \exp[-(x - vt - x_0)^2/4Dt]\exp[-(y - y_0)^2/4Dt]dx_0 dy_0 \tag{7.4.70}$$

It is left to the practice problems to show that the integrals can be converted into error functions. This yields the final result:

$$C(x,y,z,t) = \frac{S}{(\pi D_z t)^{1/2}} \exp[-z^2/4Dt] \times$$

$$\frac{1}{(4\pi Dt)} \left[\mathrm{erf}\,\frac{x - vt}{(4Dt)^{1/2}} - \mathrm{erf}\,\frac{x - vt - a}{(4Dt)^{1/2}} \right] \left[\mathrm{erf}\,\frac{y}{(4Dt)^{1/2}} - \mathrm{erf}\,\frac{y - b}{(4Dt)^{1/2}} \right] \tag{7.4.71}$$

Comments:

We have here a fairly impressive success story of the application of various superposition and reduction techniques. The original PDE, although linear, was nevertheless a complex expression in four dimensions (x, y, z, t). A numerical solution would present a fairly formidable task of discretization of four variables. The output would be copious and would lack the cohesiveness of Equation 7.4.71.

An additional advantage of the analytical result is its ability to reveal the dependence of the concentration C on various dimensionless parameters. We note in particular the incorporation of the wind velocity into the groups $(x - vt)/(4Dt)^{1/2}$ and $(x - vt - a)/(4Dt)^{1/2}$. Numerical solutions, unless properly nondimensionalized as above, would have to deal with a host of separate parameters.

Further obvious refinements can be added to the model. Continuous sources can be treated by integration over time as outlined in the previous illustration. Emissions from a smoke stack of height z_0 can be accommodated by the simple change in variable $z \to z_0$. Variations in diffusivities, particularly D_z, have been expressed in empirical terms described in specialized monographs. All these features and others not covered here have led to a substantial literature on the topic of atmospheric dispersion (see References at the end of the chapter).

7.4.2.4 More Superposition by Integration: Duhamel's Integral and the Superposition of Danckwerts

Duhamel's Integral — As originally conceived, Duhamel's integral was designed to express the solution of Fourier's equation for a time-varying surface temperature in terms of the solution to the simpler problem with a constant surface temperature. The formula was subsequently extended to Type II and III boundary conditions and to other Linear PDEs such as the wave equation with time varying forcing function. The general approach for Fourier's equation which applies equally to Fick's equation is as follows:

Suppose we wish to solve the following general problem:

$$\frac{\partial v}{\partial t} = \alpha \left[\frac{\partial^2 v}{\partial x^2} + \frac{\partial^2 v}{\partial y^2} + \frac{\partial^2 v}{\partial z^2} \right] \tag{7.4.72}$$

or equivalent forms in other coordinate systems, and one of the following boundary conditions applied to the surface S:

Type I $\qquad\qquad\qquad\qquad v(S) = f(t) \qquad\qquad\qquad\qquad (7.4.73)$

Type II $\qquad\qquad\qquad\qquad \frac{\partial v}{\partial n}(S) = g(t) \qquad\qquad\qquad\qquad (7.4.74)$

Type III $\qquad\qquad\qquad \frac{\partial v}{\partial n}(S) = K[v(S) - h(t)] \qquad\qquad\qquad (7.4.75)$

where n denotes the direction normal to the surface and f, g, h are arbitrary functions of t.

Suppose further that we have available the solution u to the reduced problem in which f, g, h are replaced by *unity*. Then the solution v to the general time-varying problem in the domain V is given by one of the following equivalent integrals:

$$v(V,t) = \frac{\partial}{\partial t} \int_0^t F(t-\tau)u(V,\tau)d\tau$$

$$= \frac{\partial}{\partial t} \int_0^t F(\tau)u(V,t-\tau)d\tau$$

(7.4.76)

and

$$v(V,t) = \int_0^t \frac{\partial}{\partial t} F(\tau)u(V,t-\tau)d\tau$$

$$= \int_0^t F(t-\tau)\frac{\partial}{\partial t} u(V,\tau)d\tau$$

(7.4.77)

where we have used the general symbol F to denote any one of the time varying surface functions f(t), g(t), or h(t).

In practice, the solution to the reduced problem u(v,t) is located in the literature, substituted into either Equation 7.4.76 or 7.4.77, whichever appears more convenient, and the indicated differentiation and integration carried. This certainly requires much less time than the full solution of one of the systems Equations 7.4.72 to 7.4.73 and can be applied to time varying surface conditions of arbitrary form. If the resulting integral cannot be evaluated analytically, a numerical determination is resorted to.

The following illustration demonstrates the application of Duhamel's integral.

Illustration 7.4.6   A Problem with the Design of Xerox Machines

The principle of electrostatic copying or xeroxing involves charging the copying paper in the image of the original — positive charge for dark areas, negative for light ones — and contacting the paper with negatively charged particles of carbon black encapsulated in a polymer film (Figure 7.13A). The particles adhere to the positive sites and have to be fixed to the paper by raising the temperature to 240°F (115.5°C). Failure to do so results in smudging of the copies.

An early problem which arose in the design of such copiers was the need to bring the paper to the required temperature in the short time stipulated by modern high-speed units. To overcome this difficulty, designers considered exposing the paper to a very intense and short heat flash of 10^{-3} s duration produced by a flash lamp-condenser combination. The power flux from this unit may be regarded as an isosceles triangle with base width $\tau_f = 10^{-3}$ s (see Figure 7.13B). For the design of the flash lamp-condenser unit, it was required to know the maximum heat flux q_{Max} that will give the required maximum surface temperature of 115.5°C. Note that the maximum lags behind that of the heat flux, and is to be found somewhere between $t_{1/2}$ and t_f.

To solve this rather intricate problem, we propose to proceed as follows:

A. Xerox Paper

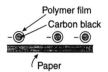

B. Heat Flash and Temperature

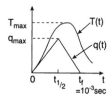

FIGURE 7.13 Heat conduction into Xerox paper: (A) composition of the paper, (B) surface heat flux and temperature as a function of time.

- Calculate the temperature profile that results from the time varying heat flash. This can be done using the known surface temperature which results from a constant heat flux of q = 1 and superposing that solution by means of Duhamel's integral to arrive at a solution for the variable heat flux case. Standard references on heat conduction provide the following temperature distribution $T_c(x,t)$ for constant unit flux q = 1 and a semi-infinite medium.

$$T_c(x,t) - T(x,0) = \frac{2}{k}\left[\left(\frac{\alpha t}{\pi}\right)^{1/2} \exp(-x^2/4\alpha t)\right] - \frac{x}{2}\,\mathrm{erfc}(x/2\sqrt{\alpha t})$$

The corresponding temperature at the surface is then given by:

$$T_c(0,t) - T(x,0) = \frac{2}{k}\left(\frac{\alpha t}{\pi}\right)^{1/2} \tag{7.4.78}$$

where $T_c(0,t)$ denotes the surface temperature for constant unit heat flux. This is the temperature which is used in the superposition integral to arrive at the solution $T_v(x,t)$ for *time varying flux*. We choose the Expression 7.4.76 to superpose and obtain:

$$T_v(0,t) - T(0,0) = \int_0^t \frac{\partial q(\tau)}{\partial t}[T(0,t-\tau) - T(0,0)]d\tau \tag{7.4.79}$$

where $T_v(0,t)$ is now the result of *variable* heat flux.

- The next step is to calculate $\partial q/\partial t$, using Figure 7.13B as a guide. Two expressions are obtained, one for the rising and one for the falling portion of the isosceles triangle.

- Substitute $\partial q/\partial t$ and Equation 7.4.78 into the integral of Equation 7.4.79. Integrate in two steps: from 0 to $t_{1/2}$ and from $t_{1/2}$ to t. The result contains q_{Max}, the parameter to be extracted:

$$T_v(0,t) = f(q_{Max}, t) \qquad (7.4.80)$$

- To obtain q_{Max} from this expression, we use the prescribed $T_{Max} = 115.5$ and the corresponding time t_{Max} obtained by differentiating Equation 7.4.79 and setting the derivative $= 0$. This is the time at which the maximum temperature shown in Figure 7.13B occurs.
- In the final step we substitute t_{Max} and $T_{Max} = 115.5°C$ into the evaluated Equation 7.4.80 and solve for q_{Max}. This is the desired result.

Let us see how this works out in practice.

Data for paper:
   Thermal conductivity $k = 0.1295$ J/msK
   Thermal diffusivity $\alpha = 6.65 \times 10^{-8}$ m²/s
   Thickness $L = 7.63 \times 10^{-5}$ m
   Initial temperature $T(x,0) = 20.1°C = 293.3$ K
   Absorption of incident heat $= 30\%$

We now proceed with a stepwise solution as outlined above.

- Substitution of Equation 7.4.78 into the Duhamel integral yields:

$$T_v(0,t) - T(0,0) = \int_0^t \frac{\partial q}{\partial t} \frac{2}{k} \left(\frac{\alpha}{\pi} \right)^{1/2} (t - \tau)^{1/2} d\tau \qquad (7.4.81)$$

which requires the determination of $\partial q/\partial t$ (second step below) and subsequent integration (Step III).

- From the slopes of the triangular heat pulse, Figure 7.13B, we obtain for the flux derivative:

$$\frac{\partial q}{\partial t} = \frac{q_{Max}}{t_{1/2}} \text{ for the interval } \quad 0 < \tau < t_{1/2} \qquad (7.4.82)$$

and

$$\frac{\partial q}{\partial t} = -\frac{q_{Max}}{t_{1/2}} \text{ for the interval } \quad t_{1/2} < \tau < t$$

- Substitution of Equation 7.4.82 into the integral Equation 7.4.81 and a two-step integration leads to the sum:

$$T_v(0,t) - T(0,0) = \frac{2}{k}\left(\frac{\alpha}{\pi}\right)^{1/2}\frac{q_{Max}}{t_{1/2}}\left[\int_0^{t_{1/2}}(t-\tau)^{1/2}d\tau - \int_{t_{1/2}}^t(t-\tau)^{1/2}d\tau\right] \quad (7.4.83)$$

and upon evaluation of the integrals to the expression:

$$T_v(0,t) - T(0,0) = \frac{2}{k}\left(\frac{\alpha}{\pi}\right)^{1/2}\frac{q_{Max}}{t_{1/2}}\left[\frac{2}{3}t^{3/2} - \frac{4}{3}(t-t_{1/2})^{3/2}\right] \quad (7.4.84)$$

- We now evaluate $\partial T_v/\partial t$, set it equal to zero, and solve for t_{Max}:

$$\frac{\partial T_v}{\partial t} = \frac{2}{k}\left(\frac{\alpha}{\pi}\right)^{1/2}\frac{q_{Max}}{t_{1/2}}[t_{Max}^{1/2} - 2(t_{Max}-t_{1/2})^{1/2}] = 0 \quad (7.4.85)$$

This leads to the result:

$$t_{Max} = \frac{4}{3}t_{1/2} \quad (7.4.86)$$

i.e., t_{Max} lies between $t_{1/2}$ and t_f, as expected.
- t_{Max} and the desired $(T_v)_{Max} = 115.5°C = 388.8$ K are substituted into Equation 7.4.84 and the result solved for q_{Max}. We obtain:

$$q_{Max} = \frac{k}{2}\left(\frac{\alpha}{\pi}\right)^{-1/2}\frac{[(T_v)_{Max} - T(0,0)]}{\left[\frac{2}{3}t_{Max}^{3/2} - \frac{4}{3}(t_{Max}-t_{1/2})^{3/2}\right]}t_{1/2} \quad (7.4.87)$$

or:

$$q_{Max} = \frac{0.1295}{2}\left(\frac{\pi}{6.65\times10^{-8}}\right)^{1/2}$$

$$\frac{[388.8-293.3]}{\frac{2}{3}\left(\frac{4}{3}0.5\times10^{-3}\right)^{3/2} - \frac{4}{3}\left[\frac{4}{3}0.5\times10^{-3}-0.5\times10^{-3}\right]^{3/2}} = 0.5\times10^{-3}$$

Hence,

$$q_{Max} = 2.47 \times 10^6 \text{ J/m}^2\text{s at 100\% efficiency}$$

and

$$q_{Max} = 8.22 \times 10^6 \text{ J/m}^2\text{s at 30\% efficiency}$$

This is the desired peak flux required for the design of the flash lamp-condenser unit.

Comments:

The reader will have noted that the literature solution for a semi-infinite medium was used in the calculations. This may appear surprising, given the small value of the thickness L of the paper. A quick calculation of the dimensionless time argument which appears in Equation 7.4.78, however, shows this to be justified. We obtain:

$$\frac{L^2}{4\alpha t} = \frac{(7.63 \times 10^{-5})^2}{4(6.65 \times 10^{-8})10^{-3}} = 21.8 \tag{7.4.88}$$

and

$$\frac{L}{2(\alpha t)^{1/2}} = 4.67$$

For these values of their respective arguments, both the exponential and the erfc in Equation 7.4.78 become vanishingly small, so that:

$$T_v(L,t) = T(L,0) \tag{7.4.89}$$

i.e., the bottom of the paper $x = L$, will, for the duration of the heat pulse, remain at the initial temperature of 20.1°C. This justifies the seemingly bizarre description of a sheet of paper as a semi-infinite medium. Had we chosen a finite geometry instead, the resulting solution would have been considerably more complex. We made effective use of the suggestions given under "Simplification of Geometry" in Section 7.3.5.

The Superposition of Danckwerts — Danckwerts considered the problem of Fickian diffusion with accompanying first order irreversible reaction. In one-dimensional Cartesian coordinates, the system is described by the PDE:

$$D\frac{\partial^2 C}{\partial x^2} - k_1 C = \frac{\partial C}{\partial t} \tag{7.4.90}$$

His proposal was to express the solution of Equation 7.4.89 in terms of the solution C of Fick's equation without a reaction term. He succeeded in developing the following superposition formula:

$$C = k_r D \int_0^t e^{-kD\tau} C'(\tau) d\tau + C' e^{-kDt} \tag{7.4.91}$$

where C' is the solution to Fick's equation:

$$D\frac{\partial^2 C'}{\partial x^2} = \frac{\partial C'}{\partial t} \tag{7.4.92}$$

Expressions of identical form were derived by Danckwerts for spheres and infinitely long cylinders for boundary conditions of Type I and Type III. For a semi-infinite medium, the following expression results:

$$C/C_0 = \frac{1}{2}\exp(-x\sqrt{k_r/D})\mathrm{erfc}\left[\frac{x}{2\sqrt{Dt}} - \sqrt{k_r t}\right]$$

$$+ \frac{1}{2}\exp(x\sqrt{k_r/D})\mathrm{erfc}\left[\frac{x}{2\sqrt{Dt}} + \sqrt{k_r t}\right]$$

(7.4.93)

It is left to the Practice Problems to derive this expression.

Practice Problems

7.1 Classification of PDEs: Oscillations of a Hanging Chain —

(a) Consider a heavy chain of uniform density suspended vertically from one end. If one takes the origin at the position of equilibrium of the lower, free end, and the x-axis along the equilibrium position of the chain, then small oscillations of the chain in the *horizontal* direction y are described by the following PDE:

$$\frac{\partial^2 y}{\partial t^2} = g\frac{\partial}{\partial x}\left(x\frac{\partial y}{\partial x}\right)$$

(P7.1)

where g = gravitational constant.

Give a complete classification of this equation as to linearity, homogeneity, type of coefficients, and whether it is elliptic, parabolic or hyperbolic.

(b) Classify the following PDE:

$$(ku_x)_x = u_y + ku$$

Consider the cases where (a) k = constant, (b) k = f(x), (c) k = g(u).

7.2 Boundary and Initial Conditions. Physical Interpretations —

(a) Consider the three-dimensional Laplace, Fourier, and Wave equations. How many boundary and initial conditions does each require?

(b) Classify the boundary and initial conditions and give a physical interpretation of the following Fourier system:

$$\frac{\partial T}{\partial t} = k\frac{\partial^2 T}{\partial x^2} + K_1 e^{-t} \quad 0 < x < L \quad t > 0$$

(P7.2)

$$\frac{\partial T}{\partial x}(0,t) = -K_2$$

$$T(L,t) = K_3$$

$$T(x,0) = f(x)$$

7.3 Derivation of Simple Partial Differential Equations —
(a) Using the procedures given in Illustration 7.2.1 for deriving the PDE for a vibrating string, derive Equation P7.1 for the oscillation of a suspended chain.

(b) Show that the temperature distribution in an electrical conductor of specific resistivity S and carrying an electrical current i is given by:

$$k\frac{\partial^2 T}{\partial x^2} + \frac{Si^2(t)}{(\pi R^2)^2} - \frac{2h}{R}(T - T_s) = \rho Cp\frac{\partial T}{\partial t} \qquad (P7.3)$$

where h is the convective heat loss to the surroundings of temperature T and R = wire radius.

(Hint: $q(J/s) = R_e i^2$ where R_e = electrical resistance = $SL/\pi R^2$.)

7.4 Transformation of Independent Variables —
(a) Starting with Laplace's equation in Cartesian coordinates (Equation 7.2.14), show that introduction of the cylindrical coordinates r, φ, z, defined by the relations:

$$x = r \cos \varphi, \; y = r \sin \varphi, \; z = z \qquad (P7.4)$$

leads to the form:

$$\frac{\partial^2 u}{\partial r^2} + \frac{1}{r}\frac{\partial u}{\partial r} + \frac{1}{r^2}\frac{\partial^2 u}{\partial \varphi^2} + \frac{\partial^2 u}{\partial z^2} = 0 \qquad (P7.5)$$

(b) Show that the three-dimensional polar coordinates r, θ, φ are related to the Cartesian coordinates by the relations:

$$x = r \sin \theta \cos \varphi, \; y = r \sin \theta \sin \varphi, \; z = r \cos \theta \qquad (P7.6)$$

Using these relations, derive Laplace's equation for a sphere in three dimensions:

Answer:

$$\frac{1}{r^2}\left(\frac{\partial}{\partial r}r^2\frac{\partial u}{\partial r}\right) + \frac{1}{r^2 \sin\theta}\frac{\partial}{\partial \theta}\left(\sin\theta\frac{\partial u}{\partial \theta}\right) + \frac{1}{r^2 \sin^2\theta}\frac{\partial^2 u}{\partial p^2} = 0 \qquad (P7.7)$$

7.5 Similarity Transformation for Non-Fickian Diffusion — Non-Fickian diffusion is the term used to describe diffusional transport in which the diffusion coefficient depends on concentration, $D = f(C)$. This case arises in the diffusion of solutes present in high concentrations, particularly in high density gases and in liquids, and in the gas and liquid phase diffusion of solutes through polymeric substances.

Consider non-Fickian diffusion in a one-dimensional semi-infinite medium with an initial concentration $c(x,0) = C_0$ and an imposed surface concentration of $C_s(0,t) = C_s$ at $t > 0$. Derive a similarity variable η for the system and show that the similarity transformation reduces the non-Fickian diffusion equation:

$$\frac{\partial}{\partial x} D(C) \frac{\partial C}{\partial x} = \frac{\partial C}{\partial t} \qquad (P7.8)$$

to the form:

$$\frac{d}{d\eta} D(C) \frac{dC}{d\eta} + 2\eta \frac{dC}{d\eta} = 0 \qquad (P7.9)$$

Describe a physical problem in heat conduction that can be solved by the same method.

7.6 Transformation of Nonhomogeneous Boundary Conditions to Homogeneous Form — The constant rate drying of a porous slab $0 < x < L$ can be described by the following system of equations:

$$D_{eff} \frac{\partial^2 C}{\partial x^2} = \frac{\partial C}{\partial t} \qquad (P7.10)$$

$$\left(\frac{\partial C}{\partial x}\right)_0 = -\left(\frac{\partial C}{\partial x}\right)_L = \frac{W}{D_{eff}}; \quad \left(\frac{\partial C}{\partial x}\right)_{L/2} = 0; \quad C(x,0) = C_0$$

where W = rate of drying.

Convert these expressions to a system with homogeneous boundary conditions without introducing nonhomogeneous terms into the PDE.

(Hint: Since four expressions have to be made or kept homogeneous, a third order polynomial with four undetermined coefficients suggests itself as a trial function for a new dependent variable C'. Show that if the polynomial is defined in x only, incompatible conditions arise. Remedy this by including time t in the trial function $C' = C + f(x,t)$.

7.7 Reduction to Canonical Form —

(a) Show that the two-dimensional wave equation is hyperbolic. Identify the characteristics and reduce the PDE to canonical form.

Answer: $\dfrac{\partial^2 u'}{\partial \bar{x} \partial \bar{y}} = 0$

(b) Reduce the following PDE to canonical form:

$$\frac{\partial^2 u}{\partial x^2} = x^2 \frac{\partial^2 u}{\partial y^2} \qquad (P7.11)$$

Answer: $\dfrac{\partial^2 u'}{\partial \bar{x} \partial \bar{y}} = \dfrac{1}{4(\bar{x} - \bar{y})} \left(\dfrac{\partial u'}{\partial \bar{x}} - \dfrac{\partial u'}{\partial \bar{y}} \right)$

Comment:
Although the new PDE is more complex in appearance, it has the virtue of having the same structure as the canonical form of a generalized wave equation.

7.8 Steady-State Temperature in a Quadrant: Solution of Laplace's Equation — Using Item 3 of the solutions to Laplace's equation shown in Figure 7.7, calculate the dimensionless temperature along the insulated portion at a position x = 0.5.

Answer: $u = \dfrac{1}{3}$

7.9 Wind Velocity and Pressure Near the Eye of a Tornado — The flow pattern in tornadoes is well represented by superposition a vortex and a sink (see Figure 7.9A). Given that at a distance of 1 km from the eye $v_\theta = v_r = -0.5$ m/s and p = 1 atm, calculate the absolute velocity and pressure at a distance of 15 m from the eye. Assume a constant density of air $\rho = 1.25$ kg/m^3.

Answers: v = 27.1 m/s; p = 0.986 atm

Comment:
Viscous effects usually start making themselves felt at a distance of 40 m from the eye. The above answers therefore are to be regarded as *maximum* values.

7.10 A Moving Source Problem — A moving point contact is pressed against the plane x = 0 with a constant force F per unit length. It moves with a speed v, producing a constant coefficient of friction μ (Figure 7.14). Obtain the temperature distribution T(x,y,z), assuming an initial temperature of zero and neglecting heat losses to the surroundings. This type of problem arises in milling and lathe operations.

(Hint: The problem is equivalent to a *stationary* continuous source of strength Fμv and a medium *moving* with velocity v. The PDE is then of the form 7.4.62, Illustration 7.4.5. Reduce it to Fourier's equation in line with what was done there, and follow this up with superposition by multiplication and by integration over time.)

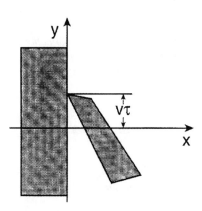

FIGURE 7.14   Configuration of a moving point source.

Answer:

$$T(x, y, z) = \frac{F\mu v}{8\rho Cp(\alpha\pi)^{3/2}} \int_0^t \frac{\exp-[x^2 + \{y - v(t - \tau)\}^2 + z^2]/4\alpha(t - \tau)}{(t - \tau)^{3/2}}$$

7.11 The Danckwerts Superposition — Derive the formula of Equation 7.4.93 using the Danckwerts superposition integral, Equation 7.4.91. The result describes the unsteady concentration distribution for diffusion, accompanied by a first-order irreversible reaction in a semi-infinite medium. Obtain the required concentration distribution $C'(x,t)$ for the case of no reaction from the pertinent literature and use the error function relations given in Table 7.6.

REFERENCES

The general topic of Partial Differential Equations is covered in a number of monographs of which we found the following particularly lucid and thorough:
R.L. Street. *The Analysis and Solution of Partial Differential Equations,* Brook/Cole, Monterey, CA, 1973.

The text covers all major analytical as well as numerical methods in understandable fashion. More profound treatments are found in:
P.D. Garabedian. *Partial Differential Equations,* John Wiley & Sons, New York, 1965.

And in the classic:
R. Courant and D. Hilbert. *Methods of Mathematical Physics, vol. I and II,* Interscience, New York, 1953, 1962.

The methods developed prior to 1970 for solving nonlinear partial differential equations by analytical, approximate, and numerical methods are covered in the definitive monographs:
W.F. Ames. *Non-Linear Partial Differential Equations in Engineering, Vol. I and II,* Academic Press, New York, 1965, 1972.
Classification and properties of PDEs are to be found in all texts on PDEs.

Background for a general approach to similarity transformation is to be found in monographs of Ames. More detailed accounts of the method are given in:
G.W. Bluman and J.D. Cole. *Similarity Methods for Differential Equations,* Springer, New York, 1974.

And in:
R. Sheshadri and T.Y. Na. *Group Invariance in Engineering Boundary Value Problems,* Springer, New York, 1985.

Reduction to canonical form is to be found in all texts on PDEs, including those of Street, Ames, and Garabedian. Conformal mapping and the underlying theory of complex variables is taken up in the excellent monograph:
R.V. Churchill and J.W. Brown. *Complex Variables and Applications, 5th ed.,* McGraw-Hill, New York, 1990.

This contains an Appendix of the more important conformal transformations and various solutions of Laplace's equation arrived at by conformal mapping.

Accounts on inviscid or potential flow and the superposition of simple flows are contained in intermediate level texts on Fluid Mechanics. Among those that stand out:
V.L. Streeter and E.B. Wylie. *Fluid Mechanics, 8th ed.,* McGraw-Hill, New York, 1985.
And in particular:
F.M. White. *Fluid Mechanics, 2nd ed.,* McGraw-Hill, New York, 1986.

The underlying potential theory is taken up in the classic:
O.D. Kellogg. *Foundations of Potential Theory,* Dover, New York, 1953.
See also:
L.M. Milne-Thomson. *Theoretical Hydrodynamics, 4th ed.,* McMillan, New York, 1960.
These monographs are fairly heavy reading for the uninitiated.

A large number of source problems in heat conduction are to be found in:
H.S. Carslaw and J.C. Jaeger. *Conduction of Heat in Solids,* Oxford University Press, New York, 1959.

Those pertaining to atmospheric pollution are treated in:
J.H. Seinfeld. *Atmospheric Pollution,* McGraw-Hill, New York, 1975.
And in the more recent version:
J.H. Seinfeld and S.N. Pandis. *Atmospheric Chemistry and Physics: From Air Pollution to Climate Change,* John Wiley & Sons, New York, 1997.

Derivations of Duhamel's integral, as well as applications, appear in Carslaw and Jaeger, and in:
R.V. Churchill. *Operational Mathematics, 3rd ed.,* McGraw-Hill, New York, 1972.

A description of the superposition of Danckwerts can be found in:
J. Crank. *Mathematics of Diffusion, 2nd ed.,* Oxford University Press, New York, 1978.
The text also contains a chapter on non-Fickian diffusion, encountered in Illustration 7.4.1 and in Practice Problem 7.5.

8 Vector Calculus: Generalized Transport Equations

Conscription if necessary, but not necessarily conscription.

William Lyon Mackenzie King
(speech during World War II Conscription Crisis)

PDEs if necessary, but not necessarily PDEs

Author's Adaptation

In the preceding chapter (7), we had presented an introduction to multidimensional models in time or space which took the form of partial differential equations. These were, for the most part, given in Cartesian coordinates for simplicity and confined to the classical equations of mathematical physics such as the Laplace and Fourier equations.

In the present chapter we undertake the derivation of the generalized, multidimensional equations for the transport of mass, energy, and momentum, based on their respective conservation laws. In other words, we will be dealing with mass, energy, and momentum balances in a most general way and at the PDE level. As before, momentum balances also may take the equivalent form of force balances or extensions of Newton's law.

The generalized approach we shall be taking calls for the use of vector notation and vector operations, principally within the framework of vector calculus. Therefore, we shall start our deliberations with an introduction to this difficult topic which is often viewed with misgivings by beginning students. We shall attempt to demystify the subject matter by placing it within the framework of physical reality, and justifying its use by means of illustrations. This is followed by individual sections dealing with mass, energy, and momentum balances that make use of the tools of vector calculus provided in the lead-in section. Solutions of PDEs, when they do occur, will make use only of the limited methods presented in Chapter 7 or those given at the ODE level. More elaborate and specialized solution methods will be presented and applied to the conservation laws, in the concluding chapter (9). The present chapter thus may be regarded as a bridge between introductory treatment of Chapter 7 and the elaborations that follow in Chapter 9.

8.1 VECTOR NOTATION AND VECTOR CALCULUS

We start this section by listing the principal features of vector operations and the uses to which they can be put.

A first point to note is that vector notation is, in essence, a convenient *shorthand* for a variety of algebraic, geometric, and differential operations and equations. Thus, the operational form $\nabla^2 u = 0$ is a shorthand version of Laplace's equation which in Cartesian coordinates has the "longhand" form $\partial^2 u/\partial x^2 + \partial^2 u/\partial y^2 + \partial^2 u/\partial z^2 = 0$. The symbol ∇^2, the so-called Laplacian, is to be regarded as an operator, symbolically represented by $\partial^2/\partial x^2 + \partial^2/\partial y^2 + \partial^2/\partial z^2$ in Cartesian coordinates. It resembles in this respect the D-operator which was encountered at the ODE level and symbolically expressed the operation d/dx.

A second important point is that the operational notation or shorthand is *independent of geometry*. Thus, the expression $\nabla^2 u = 0$ represents Laplace's equation in any arbitrary coordinate system, including Cartesian, spherical, and cylindrical coordinates. This shorthand form can be expanded into conventional notation by means of convenient dictionaries or conversion tables, an example of which appears in Table 8.1.

Any problem that can be treated vectorially can also, in principle, be solved by nonvectorial methods. However, the vectorial approach simplifies the manipulations and renders them less complex and much more elegant. The more complex a system, the greater the need for operational notation. Viscous flow, both Newtonian and non-Newtonian, and mechanical systems involving simultaneous translation and rotation are typical of processes that benefit from vectorial representations. The Maxwell equations of electromagnetics are invariably expressed and manipulated in vectorial form (see Practice Problem 8.1.8).

Merely putting a differential equation in vector form does not yield a solution. The vector equations must still be converted to scalar form using the appropriate dictionary and solved by scalar methods. However, vector transformations, undertaken prior to solution, are of considerable aid in simplifying the PDEs.

Some operators, such as the Laplacian mentioned above and the dot product **A** · **B** familiar from elementary vector algebra yield, on expansion, *single scalar equations*, in other words they are themselves scalar. Others, such as the cross product **A** × **B**, and the detested curl $\nabla \times$ **v**, are themselves vectors and, hence, decompose into an equivalent set of three scalar equations.

We mention these points as part of our endeavor to make vector notation more palatable to the reader. To further ease the transition, we present by way of an introduction to vector calculus, a brief summary of the principal relations pertaining to vector algebra. Most of these will be familiar from one course or another although they may have been conveniently forgotten.

8.1.1 SYNOPSIS OF VECTOR ALGEBRA

Defining relations and some other properties of the important entities and operations of vector algebra are listed in Table 8.2. We note the following:

TABLE 8.1
Differential Operators in Various Coordinate Systems

A. Gradient ∇u

(1) Cartesian

$$(\nabla u)_x = \frac{\partial u}{\partial x} \qquad (\nabla u)_y = \frac{\partial u}{\partial y} \qquad (\nabla u)_z = \frac{\partial u}{\partial z}$$

(2) Cylindrical

$$(\nabla u)_r = \frac{\partial u}{\partial r} \qquad (\nabla u)_\theta = \frac{1}{r}\frac{\partial u}{\partial \theta} \qquad (\nabla u)_z = \frac{\partial u}{\partial z}$$

(3) Spherical

$$(\nabla u)_r = \frac{\partial u}{\partial r} \qquad (\nabla u)_\theta = \frac{1}{r}\frac{\partial u}{\partial \theta} \qquad (\nabla u)_\varphi = \frac{1}{r\sin\theta}\frac{\partial u}{\partial \varphi}$$

B. Divergence $\nabla \cdot \mathbf{v}$

(1) Cartesian

$$\nabla \cdot \mathbf{v} = \frac{\partial v_x}{\partial x} + \frac{\partial v_y}{\partial y} + \frac{\partial v_z}{\partial z}$$

(2) Cylindrical

$$\nabla \cdot \mathbf{v} = \frac{1}{r}\frac{\partial}{\partial r}(rv_r) + \frac{1}{r}\frac{\partial v_\theta}{\partial \theta} + \frac{\partial v_z}{\partial z}$$

(3) Spherical

$$\nabla \cdot \mathbf{v} = \frac{1}{r^2}\frac{\partial}{\partial r}(r^2 v_r) + \frac{1}{r\sin\theta}\frac{\partial}{\partial \theta}(v_\theta \sin\theta) + \frac{1}{r\sin\theta}\frac{\partial v_\varphi}{\partial \varphi}$$

C. Curl $\nabla \times \mathbf{v}$

(1) Cartesian

$$(\nabla \times \mathbf{v})_x = \frac{\partial v_z}{\partial y} - \frac{\partial v_y}{\partial z} \qquad (\nabla \times \mathbf{v})_y = \frac{\partial v_x}{\partial z} - \frac{\partial v_z}{\partial x} \qquad (\nabla \times \mathbf{v})_z = \frac{\partial v_y}{\partial x} - \frac{\partial v_x}{\partial y}$$

(2) Cylindrical

$$(\nabla \times \mathbf{v})_r = \frac{1}{r}\frac{\partial v_z}{\partial \theta} - \frac{\partial v_\theta}{\partial z} \qquad (\nabla \times \mathbf{v})_\theta = \frac{\partial v_r}{\partial z} - \frac{\partial v_z}{\partial r} \qquad (\nabla \times \mathbf{v})_\tau = \frac{1}{r}\frac{\partial}{\partial r}(rv_\theta) - \frac{1}{r}\frac{\partial v_r}{\partial \theta}$$

(3) Spherical

$$(\nabla \times \mathbf{v})_r = \frac{1}{r\sin\theta}\frac{\partial}{\partial \theta}(v_\varphi \sin\theta) - \frac{1}{r\sin\theta}\frac{\partial v_\theta}{\partial \varphi}$$

$$(\nabla \times \mathbf{v})_\theta = \frac{1}{r\sin\theta}\frac{\partial v_r}{\partial \varphi} - \frac{1}{r}\frac{\partial}{\partial r}(rv_\varphi)$$

$$(\nabla \times \mathbf{v})_\varphi = \frac{1}{r}\frac{\partial}{\partial r}(rv_\theta) - \frac{1}{r}\frac{\partial v_r}{\partial \theta}$$

D. Laplacian $\nabla^2 u$

(1) Cartesian

$$\nabla^2 u = \frac{\partial^2 u}{\partial x^2} + \frac{\partial^2 u}{\partial y^2} + \frac{\partial^2 u}{\partial z^2}$$

TABLE 8.1 *(continued)*
Differential Operators in Various Coordinate Systems

(2) Cylindrical

$$\nabla^2 u = \frac{1}{r}\frac{\partial}{\partial r}\left(r\frac{\partial u}{\partial r}\right) + \frac{1}{r^2}\frac{\partial^2 u}{\partial \theta^2} + \frac{\partial^2 u}{\partial z^2}$$

(3) Spherical

$$\nabla^2 u = \frac{1}{r^2}\frac{\partial}{\partial r}\left(r^2\frac{\partial u}{\partial r}\right) + \frac{1}{r^2 \sin\theta}\frac{\partial}{\partial \theta}\left(\sin\theta\frac{\partial u}{\partial \theta}\right) + \frac{1}{r^2 \sin\theta}\frac{\partial^2 u}{\partial \varphi^2}$$

E. Convective Operator $(v \cdot \nabla)v = A$

(1) Cartesian

$$A_x = v_x\frac{\partial v_x}{\partial x} + v_y\frac{\partial v_x}{\partial y} + v_z\frac{\partial v_x}{\partial z} \qquad A_y = v_x\frac{\partial v_y}{\partial x} + v_y\frac{\partial v_y}{\partial y} + v_z\frac{\partial v_y}{\partial z}$$

$$A_z = v_x\frac{\partial v_z}{\partial x} + v_y\frac{\partial v_z}{\partial y} + v_z\frac{\partial v_z}{\partial z}$$

(2) Cylindrical

$$A_r = v_r\frac{\partial v_r}{\partial r} + \frac{v_\theta}{r}\frac{\partial v_r}{\partial \theta} - \frac{v_\theta^2}{r} + v_z\frac{\partial v_r}{\partial z}$$

$$A_\theta = v_r\frac{\partial v_\theta}{\partial r} + \frac{v_\theta}{r}\frac{\partial v_\theta}{\partial \theta} + \frac{v_r v_\theta}{r} + v_z\frac{\partial v_\theta}{\partial z}$$

$$A_z = v_r\frac{\partial v_z}{\partial r} + \frac{v_\theta}{r}\frac{\partial v_z}{\partial \theta} + v_z\frac{\partial v_z}{\partial z}$$

(3) Spherical

$$A_r = v_r\frac{\partial v_r}{\partial r} + \frac{v_\theta}{r}\frac{\partial v_r}{\partial \theta} - \frac{v_\theta^2 + v_\varphi^2}{r} + \frac{v_\varphi}{r\sin\theta}\frac{\partial v_r}{\partial \varphi}$$

$$A_\theta = v_r\frac{\partial v_\theta}{\partial r} + \frac{v_\theta}{r}\frac{\partial v_\theta}{\partial \theta} + \frac{v_r v_\theta}{r} - \frac{v_\varphi^2 \cot\theta}{r} + \frac{v_\varphi}{r\sin\theta}\frac{\partial v_\theta}{\partial \varphi}$$

$$A_\varphi = v_r\frac{\partial v_\varphi}{\partial r} + \frac{v_\theta}{r}\frac{\partial v_\varphi}{\partial \theta} + \frac{v_r v_\varphi}{r} + \frac{v_\theta v_\varphi \cot\theta}{r} + \frac{v_\varphi}{r\sin\theta}\frac{\partial v_\varphi}{\partial \varphi}$$

F. Laplacian of a Vector $\nabla^2 v$

(1) Cartesian

$$(\nabla^2 v)_x = \frac{\partial^2 v_x}{\partial x^2} + \frac{\partial^2 v_x}{\partial y^2} + \frac{\partial^2 v_x}{\partial z^2} \qquad (\nabla^2 v)_y = \frac{\partial^2 v_y}{\partial x^2} + \frac{\partial^2 v_y}{\partial y^2} + \frac{\partial^2 v_y}{\partial z^2}$$

$$(\nabla^2 v)_z = \frac{\partial^2 v_z}{\partial x^2} + \frac{\partial^2 v_z}{\partial y^2} + \frac{\partial^2 v_z}{\partial z^2}$$

(2) Cylindrical

$$(\nabla^2 v)_r = \frac{\partial}{\partial r}\left(\frac{1}{r}\frac{\partial}{\partial r}(rv_r)\right) + \frac{1}{r^2}\frac{\partial^2 v_r}{\partial \theta^2} - \frac{2}{r}\frac{\partial v_\theta}{\partial \theta} + \frac{\partial^2 v_r}{\partial z^2}$$

$$(\nabla^2 v)_\theta = \frac{\partial}{\partial r}\left(\frac{1}{r}\frac{\partial}{\partial r}(rv_\theta)\right) + \frac{1}{r^2}\frac{\partial^2 v_\theta}{\partial \theta^2} + \frac{2}{r}\frac{\partial v_r}{\partial \theta} + \frac{\partial^2 v_\theta}{\partial z^2}$$

TABLE 8.1 *(continued)*
Differential Operators in Various Coordinate Systems

$$(\nabla^2 \mathbf{v})_z = \frac{1}{r}\frac{\partial}{\partial r}\left(r\frac{\partial v_z}{\partial r}\right) + \frac{1}{r^2}\frac{\partial^2 v_z}{\partial \theta^2} + \frac{\partial^2 v_z}{\partial z^2}$$

(3) Spherical

$$(\nabla^2 \mathbf{v})_r = \nabla^2 v_r - \frac{2}{r^2}v_r - \frac{2}{r^2}\frac{\partial v_\theta}{\partial \theta} - \frac{2}{r^2}v_\theta\cot\theta - \frac{2}{r^2\sin\theta}\frac{\partial v_\varphi}{\partial \varphi}$$

$$(\nabla^2 \mathbf{v})_\theta = \nabla^2 v_\theta + \frac{2}{r^2}\frac{\partial v_r}{\partial \theta} - \frac{v_\theta}{\partial \theta} - \frac{v_\theta}{r^2\sin^2\theta} - \frac{2}{r^2}\frac{\cos\theta}{\sin^2\theta}\frac{\partial v_\varphi}{\partial \varphi}$$

$$(\nabla^2 \mathbf{v})_\varphi = \nabla^2 v_\varphi - \frac{v_\varphi}{r^2\sin^2\theta} + \frac{2}{r^2\sin\theta}\frac{\partial v_r}{\partial \varphi} + \frac{2\cos\theta}{r^2\sin^2\theta}\frac{\partial v_\theta}{\partial \varphi}$$

A Free Vector A is defined by its magnitude, i.e., length |A| and its direction, but not its location in space. An exception is the position vector **R** (Figure 8.1A) which always starts at the origin, extends to some point P(x,y,z) and, hence, has the components x, y, z. Thus,

$$\mathbf{R} = x\mathbf{i} + y\mathbf{j} + z\mathbf{k} \qquad (8.1.1)$$

Here **i, j, k** are unit vectors, i.e., have a length of 1 and are directed along the coordinate axes. Unit vectors, premultiplied by the components, provide a complete description of a vector.

Free Vectors are to be distinguished from line vectors which are defined by magnitude, direction, *and* line of action, i.e., two line vectors can only be equal if, in addition to having the same magnitude and direction, they lie on the same line. This type of vector is used mainly in solid mechanics. The presentation here is confined to free vectors.

The Normal Vector N (Figure 8.1B) passes through some point P(x,y,z) on the surface S and is orthogonal to two Vectors **u** and **v** which are themselves tangent to the surface at the same point P. Thus,

$$\mathbf{N} = \mathbf{u} \times \mathbf{v}$$

and

$$\mathbf{n} = \frac{\mathbf{N}}{|\mathbf{N}|} = \frac{\mathbf{u} \times \mathbf{v}}{|\mathbf{u} \times \mathbf{v}|} \qquad (8.1.2)$$

where **n** is the unit normal vector and the vertical bars denote absolute magnitude. We shall encounter **n** again in the definition of certain entities which arise in vector calculus.

TABLE 8.2
Relations of Vector Algebra

System/Operation	Defining Relation	Other Properties
Free vector **A**	$\mathbf{A} = A_x\mathbf{i} + A_y\mathbf{j} = A_z\mathbf{k}$ $\mathbf{A} = \|A\|[\cos(A,x)\mathbf{i} + \cos(A,y)\mathbf{j} + \cos(A,z)\mathbf{k}$ $\mathbf{A} = \|A\|\mathbf{a}$ Magnitude $\|A\| = A_x{}^2 + A_y{}^2 + A_z{}^2)^{1/2}$ Unit vectors **i, j, k**: Along x,y,z axes **a**: Along vector **A**	Two vectors **A**, **B** are equal if they have identical magnitude and direction, or $A_x = B_x$, $A_y = B_y$, $A_z = B_z$ $\mathbf{A} = -\mathbf{B}$ implies two parallel vectors of equal magnitude and opposite direction
Addition and substraction	$(\mathbf{A} \pm \mathbf{B}) = (A_x \pm B_x)\mathbf{i} + (A_y \pm B_y)\mathbf{j} + (A_z \pm B_z)\mathbf{k}$	For graphical construction see Figure 8.1C/D
Multiplication by scalar m	$m\mathbf{A} = mA_x + mA_y + mA_z$ $m\mathbf{A} = m\|A\|[\cos(A,x)\mathbf{i} + \cos(A,y)\mathbf{j} + \cos(A,z)\mathbf{k}$ $m\mathbf{A} = m\|A\|\mathbf{a}$	
Dot product $\mathbf{A} \cdot \mathbf{B}$ = a scalar	$\mathbf{A} \cdot \mathbf{B} = \|A\|\,\|B\|\cos(A,B)$ $\mathbf{A} \cdot \mathbf{B} = A_xB_x + A_yB_y + A_zB_z$ $\mathbf{A} \cdot \mathbf{B} = \|A\|$ projection of **B** on **A** $\mathbf{A} \cdot \mathbf{B} = \|B\|$ projection of **A** on **B** $\mathbf{A} \cdot \mathbf{B} = 0$ if **A**, **B** orthogonal $\mathbf{A} \cdot \mathbf{B} = \|A\|\,\|B\|$ if **A**, **B** parallel $\mathbf{i} \cdot \mathbf{j} = \mathbf{j} \cdot \mathbf{k} = \mathbf{i} \cdot \mathbf{k} = 0$ $\mathbf{i} \cdot \mathbf{i} = \mathbf{j} \cdot \mathbf{j} = \mathbf{k} \cdot \mathbf{k} = 1$	Dot product is: Distributive $\mathbf{A} \cdot (\mathbf{B} + \mathbf{C}) = \mathbf{A} \cdot \mathbf{B} + \mathbf{A} \cdot \mathbf{C}$ Commutative $\mathbf{A} \cdot \mathbf{B} = \mathbf{B} \cdot \mathbf{A}$ Associative $(t\mathbf{A}) \cdot \mathbf{B} = t(\mathbf{A} \cdot \mathbf{B})$
Cross product $\mathbf{A} \times \mathbf{B}$ = a vector	$\mathbf{A} \times \mathbf{B} = \mathbf{C}$ = vector normal to **A, B** $\mathbf{AB} = (A_yB_z - A_zB_y)\mathbf{i} + (A_zB_x - A_xB_z)\mathbf{j} + (A_xB_y - A_yB_x)\mathbf{k}$ $\|A \times B\| = \|A\|\,\|B\|\sin(A,B)$ = area of parallelogram $\mathbf{A} \times \mathbf{B} = 0$ if A, B, parallel	Cross product is: Distributive Associative It is NOT commutative $\mathbf{A} \times \mathbf{B} = -\mathbf{B} \times \mathbf{A}$

Addition and subtraction of vectors (Figure 8.1C/D) occasionally give rise to some confusion and it is helpful to remember the following rules — in addition, the two vectors to be added meet head-to-tail, in subtraction, tail-to-tail. The *direction* of the difference vector **B** – **A** must be such that **A** + (**B** – **A**) = **B**.

Both dot and cross products are used extensively in mechanics and in the solution of problems in geometry and analytical geometry, of which we give some examples in the next illustration. Both products also make their appearance in vector calculus.

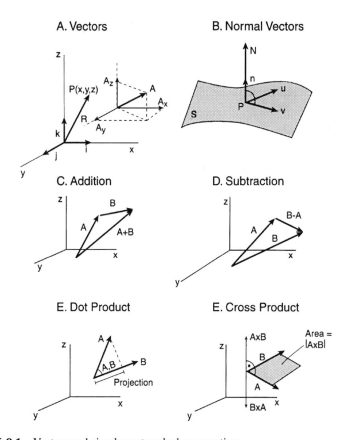

FIGURE 8.1   Vectors and simple vector algebra operations.

It is helpful to remember the following properties which are often used in applications of the two vector operations.

*The Dot Product **A** · **B*** is a scalar which is proportional to the projection of a vector, and is zero when **A**, **B** are orthogonal. Hence, it is frequently used to describe the component of a vector in a particular direction, i.e., its projection on a vector in a particular direction and when two lines intersect at a right angle (see Illustration 8.1.1 and definition of divergence, Section 8.1.2).

*The Cross Product **A** × **B*** is a vector which is orthogonal to **A**, **B** and becomes zero when **A**, **B** are parallel. Hence, it can be used to find the normal to two given lines (see Practice Problem 8.1.4 and definition of curl, Section 8.1.2).

Illustration 8.1.1   Two Geometry Problems

We consider in the first of these two examples an inscribed quadrilateral formed by joining the midpoints of any other arbitrary quadrilateral (Figure 8.2A). The task is to prove that the inscribed figure is always a parallelogram.

We start by noting that the vector sum of the four sides of the external quadrilateral equals zero:

A. Inscribed Parallelogram

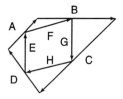

B. Inscribed Triangle

C. Distance Between Two Lines

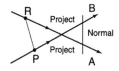

FIGURE 8.2   Three simple geometry problems expressed in terms of vector operations.

$$\mathbf{A} + \mathbf{B} + \mathbf{C} + \mathbf{D} = 0 \qquad (8.1.3)$$

This follows from the law of addition of vectors, which in this case yields ($\mathbf{A}$ + $\mathbf{B}$) = $-(\mathbf{C} + \mathbf{D})$ (see Figure 8.1C as a guide).

Since the sides of the inscribed figure join the midpoints of the external quadrilateral, we can write, using again the concepts of vector addition:

$$\mathbf{F} = \frac{1}{2}(\mathbf{A} + \mathbf{B}) \qquad (8.1.4)$$

$$\mathbf{H} = \frac{1}{2}(\mathbf{C} + \mathbf{D}) \qquad (8.1.5)$$

Substituting Equation 8.1.3 into Equation 8.1.4 and comparing with Equation 8.1.5 we obtain:

$$\mathbf{F} = -\mathbf{H} \qquad (8.1.6)$$

This relation implies that the sides $\mathbf{F}$, $\mathbf{H}$ are parallel and equal in magnitude (see statement in Table 8.1). The sides $\mathbf{E}$, $\mathbf{G}$ must then perforce also be parallel and of equal length, so that the inscribed figure is proven to be a parallelogram. Note that this proof required nothing more than concepts of vector equality and addition. The equivalent and purely geometrical proof is more cumbersome and far less elegant.

In a second example, we wish to prove that any angle inscribed in a semicircle is a right angle (Figure 8.2B). This is equivalent to proving that the dot product $\mathbf{C} \cdot \mathbf{D} = 0$. This product can be expressed in terms of the constituent vector sum,

$$\mathbf{C} \cdot \mathbf{D} = (\mathbf{P} + \mathbf{A}) \cdot (\mathbf{P} - \mathbf{A}) \tag{8.1.7}$$

Since dot products are distributive (see Table 8.1), the right side of Equation 8.1.7 can be "multiplied out" in the conventional algebraic sense to yield:

$$\mathbf{C} \cdot \mathbf{D} = \mathbf{P} \cdot \mathbf{P} - \mathbf{A} \cdot \mathbf{A} \tag{8.1.8}$$

As well, since $\cos(\mathbf{A},\mathbf{A}) = \cos(\mathbf{P},\mathbf{P}) = 1$, we obtain, by the defining formula for dot products (Table 8.1):

$$\mathbf{C} \cdot \mathbf{D} = |\mathbf{P}|^2 - |\mathbf{A}|^2 = 0 \tag{8.1.9}$$

$\mathbf{P}$ and $\mathbf{A}$ have the same length, i.e., the radius of the circle, hence, the right side vanishes and the proof is complete.

We hope, by this short preamble to have made the reader feel more comfortable with vectors in preparation for the somewhat more advanced concepts of vector calculus.

8.1.2 DIFFERENTIAL OPERATORS AND VECTOR CALCULUS

Differential operators represent, as we have noted, a shorthand for certain operations involving partial derivatives. The four principal ones that we wish to consider in more detail here are: the gradient, the divergence, the curl, and the Laplacian. Some operate on vectors or are themselves vectors, others are scalars or operate on scalars. When the result is a vector, there are three equivalent scalar equations to be considered. We summarize these features for the reader in Table 8.3.

Expressions for these operators in Cartesian, cylindrical, and spherical coordinates had previously been presented in Table 8.1 which also lists the convective operator $(\mathbf{v} \cdot \nabla)\mathbf{v}$ and the Laplacian of a vector $\nabla^2\mathbf{v}$. The latter appear principally in momentum balances (see Section 8.4).

There are several ways in which operators can be viewed. The simplest and perhaps most simplistic is to regard them as a shorthand for certain combinations of partial derivatives which appear in mathematical physics. Thus, the Laplacian $\nabla^2\mathbf{u}$ ($= \partial^2 u/\partial x^2 + \partial^2 u/\partial y^2 + \partial^2 u/\partial z$ in Cartesian coordinates) appears in a host of classical PDEs, including Laplace's and Fourier's equations, as well as those of Poisson and Helmholtz. The divergence of fluid velocity $\nabla \cdot \mathbf{v}$ ($= \partial v_x/\partial x + \partial v_y/\partial y + \partial v_z/\partial z$), makes its appearance in the continuity equation of fluid mechanics. Force, or momentum balances which arise in the same field contain the gradient of pressure ∇p that, being a force, is also a vector, with Cartesian components $\partial p/\partial x$, $\partial p/\partial y$ and $\partial p/\partial z$.

TABLE 8.3
The Differential Operators

Operator	Operates On	Is Itself
Gradient grad u = ∇u	A scalar	A vector
Divergence div $\mathbf{v} = \nabla \cdot \mathbf{v}$	A vector	A scalar
Curl curl $\mathbf{v} = \nabla \times \mathbf{v}$	A vector	A vector
Laplacian ∇^2u	A scalar	A scalar

A somewhat more elevated use of operators comes about by exploiting the properties of the "del" or ∇ notation. We have seen a variety of such dels in Table 8.2, a straight "del" which appears in the gradient, a "del dot" which appeared in the divergence, a "del cross" in the curl, and a "del square" associated with the Laplacian. Each of these operators can be expanded into forms which provide a better understanding of the mathematical operation involved. We have done this for Cartesian coordinates and summarize the results in Table 8.4. Some useful applications of this notation will be shown in Illustration 8.1.3.

A third way of viewing differential operators is to attribute some physical meaning to them. This is not always easy to accomplish, but we shall do our best.

Finally, we turn to the most important aspect of operational notation, its role as a powerful and compact tool to express complex physical problems in multidimensional space and to facilitate their solution. Once certain rules of the operational "game" have been laid down, as we have attempted to do here, manipulation, simplification, and ultimately solution of such physical problems becomes much more manageable. A certain sense of uneasiness will usually remain because of the

TABLE 8.4
The Del Notation (Cartesian)

Symbol	Expanded Form
∇	$\mathbf{i}\dfrac{\partial}{\partial x} + \mathbf{j}\dfrac{\partial}{\partial y} + \mathbf{k}\dfrac{\partial}{\partial z}$
$\nabla \cdot$	$\left(\mathbf{i}\dfrac{\partial}{\partial x} + \mathbf{j}\dfrac{\partial}{\partial y} + \mathbf{k}\dfrac{\partial}{\partial z}\right)\cdot$
$\nabla \times$	$\left(\mathbf{i}\dfrac{\partial}{\partial x} + \mathbf{j}\dfrac{\partial}{\partial y} + \mathbf{k}\dfrac{\partial}{\partial z}\right)\times$
∇^2	$\mathbf{i}\dfrac{\partial^2}{\partial x^2} + \mathbf{j}\dfrac{\partial^2}{\partial y^2} + \mathbf{k}\dfrac{\partial^2}{\partial z^2}$

A. Gradient

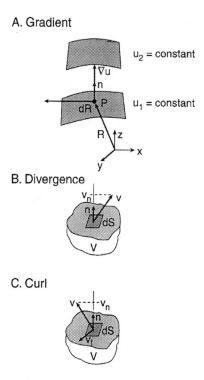

B. Divergence

C. Curl

FIGURE 8.3 The three principal operators of differential calculus: (A) the gradient ∇, (B) the divergence $\nabla \cdot$, (C) the curl $\nabla \times$.

unfamiliar nature of the symbolism but this is no different than other areas of mathematics. In time and if one persists, the benefits will outweigh the drawbacks.

8.1.2.1 The Gradient ∇

As seen from Table 8.3, the gradient operates on a scalar, such as pressure or temperature but it itself a vector. A *physical* definition of ∇u may be given by considering surfaces in three-dimensional space which have a constant value of the scalar u, for example isothermal surfaces in a temperature field (Figure 8.3A). One may then define the gradient as a vector which *points in the direction of maximum increase in u* (i.e., is normal to the isothermal plane) and *has a magnitude equal to the maximum increase per unit distance*. In mathematical terms, one obtains:

$$\nabla u \quad = \quad \frac{du}{dn} \quad \mathbf{n}$$

(8.1.10)

Gradient   Magnitude Unit normal

An alternative expression in terms of the vector *components* of ∇u is obtained by introducing the position vector $\mathbf{R}$ to the isothermal plane, as well as its differential $d\mathbf{R}$ which is tangent to the plane (see Figure 8.3A). We then obtain:

By virtue of orthogonality:

$$\nabla u \cdot d\mathbf{R} = 0 \qquad (8.1.11)$$

By virtue of constant u:

$$\frac{\partial u}{\partial x} dx + \frac{\partial u}{\partial y} dy + \frac{\partial u}{\partial z} dz = du = 0 \qquad (8.1.12)$$

Since dx, dy, dz are the components of $d\mathbf{R}$, it follows from the definition of the dot product that $\dfrac{\partial u}{\partial x}, \dfrac{\partial y}{\partial y}, \dfrac{\partial u}{\partial z}$ must be the components of the gradient. We, thus, obtain the following "working equation" for the gradient:

$$\nabla u = \mathbf{i} \frac{\partial u}{\partial x} + \mathbf{j} \frac{\partial u}{\partial y} + \mathbf{k} \frac{\partial u}{\partial z} \qquad (8.1.13)$$

Now Fick's and Fourier's laws postulate that mass and heat flux, N and q, are proportional to and in the direction of the largest *decrease* per unit distance of concentration and temperature, i.e., they must be proportional to the *negative* gradient of C and T. These laws, therefore, take the vectorial form

$$\mathbf{N} = -D\nabla C \qquad (8.1.14)$$

$$\mathbf{q} = -k\nabla T \qquad (8.1.15)$$

8.1.2.2 The Divergence $\nabla \cdot$

Here it is convenient to start with a mathematical definition which we make more palatable later by giving it some physical meaning. There are several such definitions available of which we choose the following:

$$\nabla \cdot \mathbf{v} = \lim_{V \to 0} \frac{\int_S \mathbf{n} \cdot \mathbf{v} \, dS}{V} \qquad (8.1.16)$$

This odd looking expression, sketched in Figure 8.3B, in essence states that the projection of a vector $\mathbf{v}$ onto the unit normal vector to the surface dS yields, upon integration over the surface, division by volume V and allowing V to shrink to a point the divergence of that vector. Let us attempt to make some physical sense of this expression and set $\mathbf{v}$ equal to the velocity of a flowing fluid. Its dot product with the unit normal yields:

$$\mathbf{n} \cdot \mathbf{v} = |\mathbf{n}| \text{ projection of } \mathbf{v} \text{ onto } \mathbf{n} \qquad (8.1.17)$$

so that

$$\mathbf{n} \cdot \mathbf{v} = (1)(v_n) = \text{normal component of } \mathbf{v}$$

We can then write the integral in the form:

$$\frac{\int_S \mathbf{n} \cdot \mathbf{v} \, dS}{V} = \frac{\rho \int v_n \, dS}{\rho V} \tag{8.1.18}$$

which shows that the integral represents the net outflow of fluid from the surface S per unit mass of enclosed fluid. By allowing V to shrink to a point, this becomes the net outflow per unit mass at a point of the flow field which is the divergence of the velocity.

Two items need to be noted in connection with the divergence.

1. Although we have arrived at some degree of understanding of the physical meaning of $\nabla \cdot \mathbf{v}$, we still lack a convenient mathematical representation of it. This requires evaluation of the awkward Expression 8.1.16 and will be undertaken in Illustration 8.1.2. Evidently the result will have to be a scalar, since the integrand $\mathbf{n} \cdot \mathbf{v}$ is a scalar and we shall find that the divergence is in fact represented by the sum of a set of first order partial derivatives.

2. A second point concerns the manipulation of the divergence to arrive at a general vectorial representation of the conservation of mass. This can be done by making use of the integral theorems of vector calculus. Specifically, we shall make use of the so-called divergence theorem to arrive at a vectorial representation of the continuity equation. This is taken up in Illustration 8.1.4. We now turn to the more difficult task of making some sense of the forbidding expression referred to as the *curl*.

8.1.2.3   The Curl $\nabla \times$

The mathematical definition of the curl we have chosen starts innocently enough by replacing the dot product of the divergence in Equation 8.1.16, by the cross product $\mathbf{n} \times \mathbf{v}$. We obtain:

$$\nabla \times \mathbf{v} = \lim_{V \to 0} \frac{\int_S \mathbf{n} \times \mathbf{v} \, dS}{V} \tag{8.1.19}$$

To make some physical sense of this expression we note that the magnitude of the cross product is given by:

$$|\mathbf{n} \times \mathbf{v}| = (1) \, |\mathbf{v}| \sin(\mathbf{n},\mathbf{v}) = v_t = \text{tangential velocity component} \tag{8.1.20}$$

With some imagination, the curl $\nabla \times \mathbf{v}$ therefore can be regarded as a "net" tangential velocity over the surface of an infinitesimally small domain. If non-zero, one could consider this to be the result of shear forces and, in fact, almost all viscous flow turns out to be "rotational," i.e., obeys $\nabla \times \mathbf{v} \neq 0$, and almost all inviscid flow ($\mu = 0$) is "irrotational," characterized by $\nabla \times \mathbf{v} = 0$. There are very few exceptions to these rules, of which three are mentioned.

1. Gas flow, although essentially inviscid because of its low viscosity, is invariably and strongly rotational in the rear of a submerged bluff body, as evidenced by the eddies formed there.
2. A rotating cylindrical vessel filled with a viscous fluid nevertheless is irrotational. This is a minor case which rarely arises in practice.
3. An inviscid fluid subjected to Coriolis forces due to the rotation of the Earth will be in rotational flow. This is again a highly specialized subject that will not be dealt with here.

Two further points need to be made.

What precisely is meant, in mathematical terms, by the statement $\nabla \times \mathbf{v} = 0$? The answer is that the *components* of the curl vector become zero. Inspection of Table 8.1 shows that this results, for Cartesian coordinates, in the following three relations:

$$\frac{\partial v_z}{\partial y} - \frac{\partial v_y}{\partial z} = 0 \quad \frac{\partial v_x}{\partial z} - \frac{\partial v_z}{\partial x} = 0 \quad \frac{\partial v_y}{\partial x} - \frac{\partial v_x}{\partial y} = 0 \qquad (8.1.21)$$

Derivation of these expressions from the integral (Equation 8.1.19) is a considerable task which we cunningly relegate to the practice problems. To ease the pain, some useful hints will be provided.

The second point to be made is, since inviscid and irrotational flow are essentially identical, why not confine ourselves to the former which is more easily formulated? The answer to this question is provided in detail in Section 8.4, but we summarize the results briefly here. The momentum balances for viscous flow are represented by the three scalar and nonlinear Navier-Stokes equations. By making the assumption of inviscid flow, the equations are shortened, but still remain nonlinear and three in number. Assuming irrotational flow, on the other hand, brings about a drastic reduction from three nonlinear PDEs to a single linear PDE, Laplace's equation. This is a dramatic simplification made all the more so by the fact that Laplace's equation has been extensively studied and numerous solutions to it by a variety of methods are known. Some of these were tabulated in Figure 7.7 of the preceding chapter.

Finally, in our consideration of differential operators, we turn our attention to the Laplacian operator ∇^2.

8.1.2.4 The Laplacian ∇^2

Here we dispense with a physical interpretation and confine ourselves to a derivation in mathematical terms. We had previously in Table 8.3 noted the following equivalence for the gradient operator:

$$\nabla = \mathbf{i}\frac{\partial}{\partial x} + \mathbf{j}\frac{\partial}{\partial y} + \mathbf{k}\frac{\partial}{\partial z} \tag{8.1.22}$$

Also noted in that table was the expanded form of the divergence operator:

$$\nabla \cdot \left(\mathbf{i}\frac{\partial}{\partial x} + \mathbf{j}\frac{\partial}{\partial y} + \mathbf{k}\frac{\partial}{\partial z} \right). \tag{8.1.23}$$

We now proceed to operate on the gradient operator ∇ with the divergence operator $\nabla \cdot$. This leads, in the first instance, to the following dot product:

$$\nabla \cdot \nabla = \left(\mathbf{i}\frac{\partial}{\partial x} + \mathbf{j}\frac{\partial}{\partial y} + \mathbf{k}\frac{\partial}{\partial z} \right) \cdot \left(\mathbf{i}\frac{\partial}{\partial x} + \mathbf{j}\frac{\partial}{\partial y} + \mathbf{k}\frac{\partial}{\partial z} \right) \tag{8.1.24}$$

If we further apply the rule given in Table 8.2 that a dot product equals the sum of the products of its components, we obtain formally:

$$\nabla \cdot \nabla = \frac{\partial}{\partial x}\frac{\partial}{\partial x} + \frac{\partial}{\partial y}\frac{\partial}{\partial y} + \frac{\partial}{\partial z}\frac{\partial}{\partial z} \tag{8.1.25}$$

The rules of operational notation call for these products of partial derivatives to be equivalent to second order derivatives. Thus, Equation 8.1.25 becomes:

$$\nabla \cdot \nabla = \frac{\partial^2}{\partial x^2} + \frac{\partial^2}{\partial y^2} + \frac{\partial^2}{\partial z^2} \tag{8.1.26}$$

This is no different from what was done with the D-operator at the ODE level where we postulated the equivalence:

$$DD = \frac{d}{dx}\frac{d}{dx} = \frac{d^2}{dx^2} \tag{8.1.27}$$

Readers may at first balk at these rules, seemingly introduced at a whim and with no more justification than that they may, well, "look right." We remind them, however, that if these rules are established with consistency and in a way which yields correct results, operator notation becomes an extremely powerful and compact tool for manipulating differential equations. We repeat that the crux is consistency and a regard for the results obtained.

A number of useful relations have resulted from these procedures which we summarize for the convenience of the reader in Table 8.5. Proofs for several of these expressions are given in the illustrations that follow. We note that some of these equations are scalar, others are vectorial PDEs. Thus, the equations involving the divergence $\nabla \cdot$ are all scalar PDEs, the remainder are vectorial, equivalent to a set of three scalar PDEs.

TABLE 8.5
Relations Involving ∇, $\nabla \cdot$, and $\nabla \times$

1. $\nabla(u + w) = \nabla u + \nabla w$
2. $\nabla(uw) = u\nabla w + w\nabla u$
3. $\nabla \cdot (\mathbf{A} + \mathbf{B}) = \nabla \cdot \mathbf{A} + \nabla \cdot \mathbf{B}$
4. $\nabla \cdot (u\mathbf{A}) = \nabla u \cdot \mathbf{A} + u\nabla \cdot \mathbf{A}$
5. $\nabla u \cdot d\mathbf{R} = du$
6. $\nabla \cdot (\nabla \times \mathbf{A}) = 0$
7. $\nabla \cdot (\nabla u \times \nabla w) = 0$
8. $\nabla \cdot (\mathbf{A} \times \mathbf{B}) = \mathbf{B} \cdot (\nabla \times \mathbf{A}) - (\mathbf{A} \cdot \nabla \times \mathbf{B})$
9. $\nabla \times (\mathbf{A} + \mathbf{B}) = \nabla \times \mathbf{A} + \nabla \times \mathbf{B}$
10. $\nabla \times (u\mathbf{A}) = u\nabla \times \mathbf{A} + \nabla u \times \mathbf{A}$
11. $\nabla \times \nabla u = 0$
12. $\nabla \times (\mathbf{A} \times \mathbf{B}) = (\mathbf{B} \cdot \nabla)\mathbf{A} - (\mathbf{A} \cdot \nabla)\mathbf{B} + \mathbf{A}(\nabla \cdot \mathbf{B}) - \mathbf{B}(\nabla \cdot \mathbf{A})$
13. $(\mathbf{A} \cdot \nabla)\mathbf{A} = \dfrac{1}{2}\nabla(\mathbf{A} \cdot \mathbf{A}) - \mathbf{A} \times (\nabla \times \mathbf{A})$
14. $\nabla^2\mathbf{A} = \nabla(\nabla \cdot \mathbf{A}) - \nabla \times (\nabla \times \mathbf{A})$
15. $\nabla \times \mathbf{R} = 0$

Illustration 8.1.2   Derivation of the Divergence

The task to be undertaken here is the conversion of the integral of Equation 8.1.16 into an equivalent PDE. To accomplish this, we consider a cube of magnitude $\Delta x \Delta y \Delta z$ and focus, in the first instance, on the two faces at the positions x and x + Δx. We obtain for the integrand

At position x:

$$\mathbf{n} \cdot \mathbf{v} \, \Delta S = (-1) \text{ projection of } \mathbf{v} \text{ on } \mathbf{n} = -|v|_x \, \Delta y \Delta z$$

At position x + Δx:

$$\mathbf{n} \cdot \mathbf{v} \, \Delta S = (1) \text{ projection of } \mathbf{v} \text{ on } \mathbf{n} = |v|_{x+\Delta x} \, \Delta y \Delta z$$

Note that at position x, the normal $\mathbf{n}$ is pointed in the *negative* x direction, hence its magnitude is -1.

Summing the two components and using the full Expression 8.1.16, we obtain:

$$\lim_{\Delta V \to 0} \frac{(v|_{x+\Delta x} - v_x)}{\Delta x} = \frac{\partial v_x}{\partial x} \tag{8.1.28}$$

Similar applications of this scheme to the faces in the y and z directions yields, in the limit, the terms $\partial v_y/\partial y$ and $\partial v_z/\partial z$, and the divergence becomes:

$$\nabla \cdot \mathbf{v} = \lim_{V \to 0} \frac{\int_S \mathbf{n} \cdot \mathbf{v}\, dS}{V} = \frac{\partial v_x}{\partial x} + \frac{\partial v_y}{\partial y} + \frac{\partial v_z}{\partial z} \qquad (8.1.29)$$

This is the expression we had reported in Table 8.1.

Illustration 8.1.3: Derivation of Some Relations Involving ∇, $\nabla \cdot$, and $\nabla \times$

In this example, we present the derivation of some of the relations we had previously given in Table 8.5 without proof. To do this, we use the expressions for the "del" notation shown in Table 8.3 and apply the usual rules of vector dot and cross multiplication.

Item 5: $\nabla u \cdot d\mathbf{R} = du$ — The expansion of $\nabla \cdot$ and $d\mathbf{R}$ leads in the first instance to the following expression:

$$\nabla u \cdot d\mathbf{R} = \left(\mathbf{i}\frac{\partial u}{\partial x} + \mathbf{j}\frac{\partial u}{\partial y} + \mathbf{k}\frac{\partial u}{\partial z} \right) \cdot (\mathbf{i}\, dx + \mathbf{j}\, dy + \mathbf{k}\, dz) \qquad (8.1.30)$$

Dot multiplying out, we obtain:

$$\nabla u \cdot d\mathbf{R} = \frac{\partial u}{\partial x}dx + \frac{\partial u}{\partial y}dy + \frac{\partial u}{\partial z}dz \qquad (8.1.31)$$

where the right side of the equation will be recognized as the total differential du of the scalar u. Hence,

$$\nabla u \cdot d\mathbf{R} = du \quad \text{Q.E.D.}$$

Item 6: $\nabla \cdot (\nabla \times A) = 0$ — Here the expansion of the component vectors becomes somewhat lengthier. We obtain in the first instance:

$$\nabla \cdot (\nabla \times \mathbf{A}) = \left(\mathbf{i}\frac{\partial}{\partial x} + \mathbf{j}\frac{\partial}{\partial y} + \mathbf{k}\frac{\partial}{\partial z} \right) \cdot$$
$$\left[\mathbf{i}\left(\frac{\partial A_z}{\partial y} - \frac{\partial A_y}{\partial z} \right) + \mathbf{j}\left(\frac{\partial A_x}{\partial z} - \frac{\partial A_z}{\partial x} \right) + \mathbf{k}\left(\frac{\partial A_y}{\partial x} - \frac{\partial A_x}{\partial y} \right) \right] \qquad (8.1.32)$$

We now expand the right side by the rules of dot multiplication, noting that the resulting component products of the type $\dfrac{\partial}{\partial x}\dfrac{\partial A_z}{\partial y}$ are to be regarded as *second derivatives*. There results the following scalar sum of mixed derivatives:

$$\left(\frac{\partial}{\partial x}\frac{\partial A_z}{\partial y}-\frac{\partial}{\partial x}\frac{\partial A_y}{\partial z}\right)+\left(\frac{\partial}{\partial y}\frac{\partial A_x}{\partial z}-\frac{\partial}{\partial y}\frac{\partial A_z}{\partial x}\right)+\left(\frac{\partial}{\partial z}\frac{\partial A_y}{\partial x}-\frac{\partial}{\partial z}\frac{\partial A_x}{\partial y}\right) \quad (8.1.33)$$

Upon inspection these derivatives are found to exactly cancel each other. We, therefore, obtain:

$$\nabla \cdot (\nabla \times \mathbf{A}) = 0 \quad \text{Q.E.D.}$$

Item 11: $\nabla \times \nabla u = 0$ — Proceeding as before we first expand the individual operators and obtain:

$$\nabla \times \nabla u = \left(\mathbf{i}\frac{\partial}{\partial x}+\mathbf{j}\frac{\partial}{\partial y}+\mathbf{k}\frac{\partial}{\partial z}\right)\times\left(\mathbf{i}\frac{\partial u}{\partial x}+\mathbf{j}\frac{\partial u}{\partial y}+\mathbf{k}\frac{\partial u}{\partial z}\right)$$

This is followed by cross multiplication of the right side using the rules of vector algebra. We do this for one vector component only, which yields:

$$\mathbf{i}\left(\frac{\partial}{\partial z}\frac{\partial u}{\partial x}-\frac{\partial}{\partial x}\frac{\partial u}{\partial z}\right) \quad (8.1.34)$$

Similar expressions result for other vector components. One notes immediately that the mixed derivatives appearing in each component cancel each other so that the vector $\nabla \times \nabla u$ becomes identically zero. This completes the required proof.

8.1.3 INTEGRAL THEOREMS OF VECTOR CALCULUS

We present in this section, a number of so-called integral theorems of vector calculus which can be proven by fairly elementary applications of the operations of vector algebra and vector calculus. They are somewhat forbidding in apperance but share the common feature that they all relate surface and volume integrals of certain vector entities to each other. They, therefore, provide a link between the interior of a domain which could, for example, be represented by the solution space, to surface conditions, for example, the boundary conditions. This is a useful relation to have.

The integral theorem are four in number and take the following form:

(1) *Divergence theorem:*

$$\int\int_S (\mathbf{A} \cdot \mathbf{n})dS = \int\int\int_V (\nabla \cdot \mathbf{A})dV \quad (8.1.35)$$

(2) *First form of Green's theorem (Green's first identity):*

$$\int\int_S \mathbf{n} \cdot (u\nabla w)dS = -\int\int\int_V [u\nabla^2 w + \nabla u \cdot \nabla w]dV \quad (8.1.36)$$

(3) *Second form of Green's theorem (Green's second identity):*

$$\iint_S \mathbf{n} \cdot (u\nabla w - w\nabla u)dS = -\iiint_V [u\nabla^2 w - w\nabla^2 u]dV \qquad (8.1.37)$$

Equation 8.1.37 is derived from the first form of Green's theorem by writing the latter twice with the scalars u and w interchanged, and subtracting the result.

(4) *Generalized transport theorem:*

$$\iint_S [X](\mathbf{v} \cdot \mathbf{n})dS = \frac{D}{Dt}\iiint_V [X]dV - \iiint_V \frac{\partial}{\partial t}[X]dV$$

| Rate of flux of [X] across the surface | Rate of change of [X] within flowing entity | Rate of change of [X] within volume V |

$$(8.1.38)$$

Here D/Dt is the so-called substantial or convective derivative that records changes within a flowing parcel of constant mass. It is related to the partial derivatives, fixed in space, via the expression:

$$\frac{D}{Dt}[\mathbf{X}] = \frac{\partial[\mathbf{X}]}{\partial t} + (\mathbf{v} \cdot \nabla)[\mathbf{X}] \qquad (8.1.39)$$

where $[\mathbf{X}]$ is an arbitrary entity (scalar vector or tensor) and $(\mathbf{v} \cdot \nabla)[\mathbf{X}]$, is the convective operator tabulated in Table 8.1. The process of recording changes within a moving entity is referred to as the *Lagrangian approach,* while the analysis in a fixed entity is termed *Eulrian.* Derivations of these expressions appear in standard texts on transport phenomena (see References). They are best understood by means of applications. We, therefore, proceed to use the theorems in the derivation of certain equations in vectorial form and introduce the reader as well to the concept and application of Green's functions, a much-dreaded topic. We shall attempt to ease the task by providing both physical and mathematical interpretations of these functions and demonstrate their use by means of practical illustrations.

Illustration 8.1.4 Derivation of the Continuity Equation

Here we start with the transport theorem and set [X] equal to density ρ. This causes the convective derivative $\frac{D}{Dt}$ to drop out since $\rho \, dV = dm = 0$ for a fluid packet of constant mass. There remains:

$$\iint_S \rho(\mathbf{v} \cdot \mathbf{n})dS = -\iiint_V \frac{\partial}{\partial t}\rho \, dV \qquad (8.1.40)$$

The surface integral is next converted into a volume integral using the divergence theorem (Equation 8.1.35) where we set $\mathbf{A} = \rho\mathbf{v}$. There results:

$$\iiint_V (\nabla \cdot \rho \mathbf{v}) dV = -\iiint_V \frac{\partial}{\partial t} \rho dV$$

or alternatively,

$$\iiint_V \left[(\nabla \cdot \rho \mathbf{v}) + \frac{\partial_\rho}{\partial t} \right] dV = 0 \qquad (8.1.41)$$

Since the volume V can assume any arbitrary value, the integral can only vanish if the integrand itself becomes zero. We obtain:

$$-(\nabla \cdot \rho \mathbf{v}) = \frac{\partial}{\partial t} \rho \qquad (8.1.42)$$

which is the generalized continuity equation in vector notation. For one-dimensional incompressible flow, the expression reduces to:

$$\rho \frac{dv_x}{\partial x} = 0$$

or

$$v_x \rho = \text{constant} \qquad (8.1.43)$$

which is equivalent to the continuity equation given in Chapter 3.

Illustration 8.1.5 Derivation of Fick's Equation

Fick's equation, which was first presented in Chapter 7, Equation 7.2.32, is to be distinguished from Fick's *law*, Equation 8.1.14. The latter is an *empiricism* which states that diffusional flux $\mathbf{N}$ is proportional to the (negative) concentration gradient, while the former is an equation to be derived here in general vectorial form. It also can be derived by the traditional "in – out = change" approach, as was done for the one-dimensional Fourier equation (Illustration 7.2.1), but that procedure is less general and has to be repeated for each new geometry. We start with Fick's law, Equation 8.1.14, and express it in the following dual form:

$$\mathbf{N} \text{ (moles/sm}^2) = -D\nabla C = C\mathbf{v} \qquad (8.1.44)$$

where C = molar concentration, and $\mathbf{v}$ = velocity vector of the diffusing species. This expression is then operated on by the divergence operator $\nabla \cdot$. We obtain:

$$\nabla \cdot C\mathbf{v} = -\nabla \cdot D\nabla C \qquad (8.1.45)$$

The left side of the equation is recognized from the continuity Equation 8.1.42 as equaling $-\partial C/\partial t$ so that one obtains:

$$\frac{\partial C}{\partial t} = \nabla \cdot D\nabla C \qquad (8.1.46)$$

This is the most general form of Fick's equation which accounts for variable diffusivities. A more easily recognized version is obtained by setting D = constant. This yields:

$$\frac{\partial C}{\partial t} = D\nabla \cdot \nabla C = D\nabla^2 C \qquad (8.1.47)$$

where $\nabla^2 C$ is seen to be the Laplacian of the concentration C. Note that in this derivation use was made of the continuity equation which itself sprang from two integral theorems, and of the divergence operator $\nabla \cdot$ which upon application to the gradient ∇C yielded the Laplacian $\nabla^2 C$. Thus, considerable use was made of vector notation and operations.

Illustration 8.1.6   Superposition Revisited:
Green's Functions and the Solution of PDEs by
Green's Functions

The purpose of this illustration is to introduce the reader to the concept of Green's functions and to their use in solving the classical linear Laplace, Poisson, and Fourier equations. We place this topic in this particular location since many manipulations involving Green's functions call for the use of the integral theorem presented in Section 8.1.3.

Let us start by defining these functions: Green's functions, also known as source, influence, or response functions, are solutions to linear homogeneous PDEs or ODEs with homogeneous (i.e., zero) boundary and initial conditions in which the underlying system has been subjected to a point, line, or plane forcing function or pulse of unit strength. That point function is typically an instantaneous or continuous heat or mass source, an instantaneous or continuous load in mechanical systems, or a point charge in electrical systems. Two applications of Green's functions are sketched in Figure 8.4.

Consider the case of an instantaneous heat source shown in Figure 8.4A. Here the Green's function is the solution to Fourier's equation in a two-dimensional domain with zero initial and boundary conditions (i.e., the BC and IC are homogeneous) and an instantaneous point source at $P(x_0,y_0)$. That Green's function or solution to the point source problem is given the symbol:

$$\text{Green's function} = G(x_0,y_0,x,y) \qquad (8.1.48)$$

where x_0, y_0 is the location of the point source in 2-D, and x, y are the general coordinates of the domain.

In Chapter 7, Section 7.4 we had given the solution to the instantaneous point source problem in one-dimensional infinite space that took the form:

A. Instantaneous Point Source

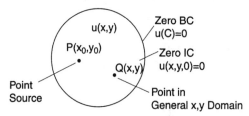

B. Point Load

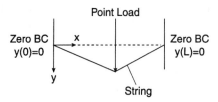

FIGURE 8.4 Physical systems involving: (A) a point source, (B) a point load. Green's functions are the solutions to these problems with homogeneous boundary conditions.

$$T = \frac{Q}{2(\pi\alpha t)^{1/2}} \exp(-x^2 / 4\alpha t) \qquad (7.4.52)$$

with the point source placed at the origin $x_0 = 0$. In Green's function nomenclature, the system is converted to an instantaneous point source of unit strength which releases its heat at time $t = \tau$.

The solution to that problem, i.e., the Green's function is then given by:

$$G(0, x, t - \tau) = \frac{1}{2[\pi\alpha(t - \tau)]^{1/2}} \exp[-x^2 / 4\alpha(t - \tau)] \qquad (8.1.49)$$

with the underlying PDE represented by:

$$\alpha \frac{\partial^2 G}{\partial x^2} + \delta(x - x_0)\delta(t - \tau) = \frac{\partial G}{\partial t} \qquad (8.1.50)$$

Here the Dirac delta functions $\delta(x - x_0)\delta(t - \tau)$ are used as a symbolism to denote the fact that G is zero everywhere except at the point x_0 and time τ where it has instantaneous unit strength 1.

We will not delve into the theory underlying the Dirac point function but merely use them as a symbolic way to denote the presence of a point source. To aid in the manipulations which may be needed, we summarize its more important properties in Table 8.6.

TABLE 8.6
Properties of the Dirac Delta Function

1. $\int_{-\infty}^{\infty} \delta(x)dx = 1$

2. $\int_{-\infty}^{\infty} \delta(x - x_0)dx = 1$

3. $\int_{x_0-a}^{x_0+a} \delta(x - x_0)dx = 1$

4. $\iiint_V \delta(P,Q)dV_Q = 1$

5. $\iiint_V u(Q)\delta(P,Q)dV_Q = u(P)$

Laplace Transforms
6. $L\{\delta(t)\} = 1$
7. $L\{\delta(t - t_0)\} = e^{-st_0}$

To further expand on the topic of Green's functions, we list the following important properties.

All solutions to unit point source problems with Homogeneous BCs and ICs are to be regarded as Green's functions. Some of these were presented in Chapter 7, Section 7.4. Additional tabulations of Green's functions appear in the accompanying Table 8.7.

Green's functions depend on (1) the underlying PDE which they solve, (2) the geometry, and (3) the associated boundary conditions. One speaks, for example, of a Green's function for Laplace's equation for a sphere with a Type I (homogeneous) boundary condition or, alternatively, of a "Green's function for the Dirichlet problem of the sphere."

Green's functions can be generated by the superposition procedures outlined in Chapter 7 and by other methods, principally the Laplace transformation. The References on heat conduction contain many examples of this type. The reader also is urged to reach into the literature on related topics such as electrostatics and potential theory for additional source material, even though this may appear to be a forbidding prospect.

The Green's functions carry the immense advantage of allowing us to express solutions of nonhomogeneous systems in closed form and in terms of integrals of the Green's functions and the nonhomogeneous terms of the system. In this they resemble the Duhamel integral discussed in Chapter 7, Section 7.4. We illustrate these integral formulations by deriving the solution to Poisson's equation for heat conduction in terms of Green's functions. Poisson's equation is itself nonhomogeneous but we will, in addition, impose nonhomogeneous boundary conditions of a general and arbitrary form. The task is then to solve the following set:

$$\nabla^2 u + \frac{A(Q)}{k} = 0 \quad u(S) = f(S) \qquad (8.1.51)$$

TABLE 8.7
Green's Functions for Type I BC

Domain	Green's Function (Unit Strength)

Fourier's equation

1. 1-D Cartesian

$$G(x_0, x, t - \tau) = \frac{1}{2[\pi\alpha(t-\tau)]^{1/2}} \exp[-(x-x_0)^2 / 4\alpha(t-\tau)]$$

2. 1-D Spherical

$$G(0, r, t - \tau) = \frac{1}{2[\pi\alpha(t-\tau)]^{1/2}} \exp[-r^2 / 4\alpha(t-\tau)]$$

3. 3-D Cartesian

$$G(P, Q, t - \tau) = \frac{1}{8[\pi\alpha(t-\tau)]^{3/2}} \times \exp[-(x-x_0)^2 / 4\alpha(t-\tau)]$$
$$\times \exp[-(y-y_0)^2 / 4\alpha(t-\tau)] \times \exp[-(z-z_0)^2 / 4\alpha(t-\tau)]$$

4. Semi-infinite 1-D Cartesian

$$G(x_0, x, t - \tau) = \frac{-}{2[\pi\alpha(t-\tau)]} \times$$
$$\{\exp[-x-x_0)^2 / 4\alpha(t-\tau)] - \exp[-(x+x_0)^2 / 4\alpha(t-\tau)]\}$$

Laplace's equation

5. Semi-infinite 2-D

$$G(x_0, y_0, x, y) = \frac{1}{4\pi} \ln \frac{(x+x_0)^2 + (y-y_0)^2}{(x-x_0)^2 + (y-y_0)^2}$$

6. Circle (r, θ), radius R

$$G(r_0, \theta_0, r, \theta) = \frac{1}{4\pi} \ln \frac{R^2 + r^2 r_0^2 / R^2 - 2r r_0 \cos(\theta_0 - \theta)}{r_0^2 + r^2 - 2r r_0 \cos(\theta_0 - \theta)}$$

7. Finite 1-D, $0 < x \le 1$

$$G(x_0, x) = (1 - x_0)x \qquad \text{for } x \ge x_0$$
$$= (1 - x)x_0 \qquad \text{for } x \le x_0$$

where Q denotes the coordinates of the domain, S its surface, and k the thermal conductivity. A solution of this model would yield the steady-state temperature in a three-dimensional domain containing a distribution of heat sources emitting at a rate $A(J/m^3s)$ and bounded by a surface S maintained at a position-dependent temperature f(S). The corresponding model for a *single* continuous point source is given by the set:

$$\nabla^2 G = -\delta(P, Q) \quad G(S) = 0 \qquad (8.1.52)$$

where G is the Green's function, i.e., the solution of Poisson's equation for a unit point source and zero surface temperature.

We start the derivation with Green's second identity, Equation 8.1.37, which relates the Laplacian of *two* scalar functions, here u and G, *within* a domain, to values of u and G prescribed on the surface:

$$\iiint_V (u\nabla^2 G - G\nabla^2 u)dV = \iint_S (u\nabla G - G\nabla u) \cdot \mathbf{n}dS \qquad (8.1.53)$$

This is a fairly formidable looking vector equation which does, however, simplify considerably by substitutions from the model equations and certain other relations. Thus, we have:

Within the domain V:
(From the model)

$$\nabla^2 u = -A / k \tag{8.1.54}$$

and from both the model and Item 5 of Table 8.6:

$$\iiint_V u\nabla^2 G dV = -\iiint u\delta(P, Q)dV = -u(P) \tag{8.1.55}$$

The latter expression is of particular significance since it gives us directly the solution we are seeking, i.e., u(P).

On the Surface S:
(From the model)

$$u = f(S) \tag{8.1.56}$$

and

$$G(S) = 0$$

(From vector calculus and algebra)

$$\nabla G = \frac{\partial G}{\partial n} \mathbf{n} \quad \text{(see definition of gradient)}$$

and consequently,

$$\nabla G \cdot \mathbf{n} = \frac{\partial G}{\partial n} \mathbf{n} \cdot \mathbf{n} = \frac{\partial G}{\partial n} \tag{8.1.57}$$

With these values in hand, Equation 8.1.53 reduces to the solution:

$$u(P) = -\iiint_V G(A / k)dV - \iint_S \frac{\partial G}{\partial n} f(S)dS \tag{8.1.58}$$

Comments:
The Expression 8.1.58 represents an explicit and general solution to Poisson's' equation for an arbitrary distribution of sources A(Q) in the interior of the domain and an equally arbitrary nonhomogeneous surface condition f(S). The latter can be,

it will be noted, of a discontinuous nature, a property which is not easily accommodated by other solution methods.

The expression also is a solution for Laplace's equation, as is easily seen by setting the source term $A(Q) = 0$. We obtain in this case the reduced formula:

$$u(P) = -\iint_S \frac{\partial G}{\partial n} \cdot f(S)dS \qquad (8.1.59)$$

where $f(S)$ is, as before, an arbitrary surface distribution of u. We can use this equation, for example, to calculate the steady-state temperature distribution in a rectangle whose sides are kept at four different temperature — $T(x,0)$, $T(x,a)$, $T(0,y)$, and $T(b,y)$.

The normal derivative of the Green's function, $\partial G/\partial n$, is easily evaluated for simple geometries. Thus, for the aforementioned rectangle, $(\partial G/\partial n)_{y=0} = (-\partial G/\partial y)_{y=0}$ since the normal points in the negative y-direction, and $(\partial G/\partial n)_{y=a} = (\partial G/\partial y)_{y=a}$. Similar expressions apply to the other two sides. For radial configurations, these expressions are replaced by the simple relation $\partial G/\partial n = \partial G/\partial r$.

There are some disadvantages to the method which need to be noted.

1. Green's functions vary, as we had noted, with the geometry of the system. This is also evident from the tabulations of Table 8.7. Thus, for a particular problem under consideration, the appropriate Green's function has to be either located in the literature or derived from the basic model.
2. Green's functions also vary with the type of boundary condition assigned to the surface of the domain. Thus, for a Type III boundary condition, the Green's function is the solution to the homogeneous point source problem with "radiation" or convective transport from the surface to a medium of zero value of the scalar function u. The solution then changes accordingly.
3. Green's functions do not always have the simple forms shown in Table 8.7. For finite geometries, in particular, they often consist of infinite series of complex functions whose manipulation becomes cumbersome.

Having noted some of the stumbling blocks, we must reiterate that the Green's functions remains an attractive and powerful tool for obtaining closed-form explicit solutions to linear nonhomogeneous PDEs. It is widely used particularly to obtain solutions to nonhomogeneous forms of Fourier's equations, of which we give an example below.

Illustration 8.1.7   The Use of Green's Functions in Solving Fourier's Equation

Green's functions also can be applied to obtain closed form solutions to Fourier's equation with distributed heat sources and with prescribed nonhomogeneous initial and boundary conditions. That system is described by the following set of equations:

$$\alpha \nabla^2 T + \frac{1}{\rho Cp} A(Q) = \frac{\partial T}{\partial t} \qquad (8.1.60)$$

with surface BC:

$$T(S) = g(S,t) \qquad (8.1.61)$$

and IC:

$$T(Q,0) = f(Q) \qquad (8.1.62)$$

where Q as before denoted the coordinates of the system, and k,α are the thermal conductivity and diffusivity respectively. This is clearly the most general form of Fourier's equation and poses a challenging problem even though the underlying equations are all linear.

We present the solution without proof which is fairly straightforward and makes use, as before, of Green's identities (see Reference). It takes the form:

$$T(P,t) = \iiint_V G(P,Q,t)f(Q)dV + \alpha \int_0^t \iiint_V G(P,Q,t=\tau)\frac{A}{k}(Q,\tau)dVd\tau$$

$$-\alpha \int_0^t \iint_S \frac{\partial}{\partial n}G(t-\tau)_S g(S,t)dSd\tau \qquad (8.1.63)$$

Let us try to make some sense of this equation by noting the following points.

$G(P,Q,t-\tau)$ is, as usual, a Green's function and, hence, describes the temperature distribution which results from an instantaneous heat source of unit strength releasing heat at $t = \tau$ and position P. For our purposes, Green's functions are obtained from tabulations such as Table 8.7 and other literature sources, i.e., we shall not attempt to derive them ourselves.

The three integrals on the right side of Equation 8.1.63 contain, in sequence, the nonhomogeneous initial condition $T(Q,0) = f(Q)$, a general distributed and time-dependent heat source $A(Q,\tau)$, and the nonhomogeneous surface boundary condition $T(S) = g(s,t)$. The latter is allowed to vary with position on the surface as well as in time. These are, then, the most general conditions one can expect to encounter in linear versions of Fourier's equation.

To obtain a better grasp of the uses of Equation 8.1.60, we consider the simple case of conduction in the semi-infinite one-dimensional domain $x \geq 0$, devoid of heat sources and subject to the following general conditions:

IC $\qquad\qquad\qquad\qquad T(x,0) = f(x) \qquad (8.1.64)$

BC $\qquad\qquad\qquad\qquad T(0,t) = g(t) \qquad (8.1.65)$

For these one-dimensional conditions, Equation 8.1.63 becomes:

$$T(x_0, t) = \int_0^\infty G(x_0, x, t) f(x) dx - \alpha \int_0^t \frac{\partial}{\partial n} G(x_0, x, t - \tau)|_{x=0} \, g(\tau) d\tau \quad (8.1.66)$$

where the Green's function, taken from Table 8.6, has the form:

$$G(x_0, x, t - \tau) = \frac{1}{4[\pi\alpha(t - \tau)]} \{\exp[-(x - x_0)^2 / 4\alpha(t - \tau)]$$

$$- \exp[-(x + x_0)^2 / 4\alpha(t - \tau)]\} \quad (8.1.67)$$

The only manipulation required here is the evaluation of the normal derivative of the Green's function $\partial G/\partial n$ which is given by:

$$\left[\frac{\partial G}{\partial n}\right]_{x=0} = -\left[\frac{\partial G}{\partial x}\right]_{x=0}$$

since the normal is taken in the negative x-direction. Hence,

$$\left[\frac{\partial G}{\partial n}\right]_{x=0} = \{4\pi\alpha(t - \tau)\}^{-1/2} - \{4\pi\alpha(t - \tau)\}^{-1} \times \{\exp[-x_0^2 / 4\alpha(t - \tau)]4x_0\} \quad (8.1.68)$$

The final solution then has the form:

$$T(x_0, t) = (4\pi\alpha t)^{-1/2} \int_0^\infty f(x) \{\exp[-(x - x_0)^2 / 4\alpha t] - \exp[-(x + x_0)^2 / 4\alpha t]\} dx$$

$$- x_0 (4\pi\alpha^3)^{-1/2} \int_0^t g(\tau)(t - \tau)^{-3/2} \exp\{-[x_0^2 / 4\alpha(t - \tau)]\} d\tau$$

$$(8.1.69)$$

Comments:

The solution is still a fairly intimidating expression but it should be recalled that it accommodates quite general and arbitrary initial and boundary conditions. Evaluation of the integrals, which in most cases has to be done numerically, poses no problem since convergence of the first integral is quite rapid.

One notes that the integration in space is with respect to x, not x_0. The latter then becomes the new distance variable in the solution.

The Expression 8.1.69, seemingly an incomprehensible glob of mathematics, does yield to a physical interpretation. We had previously in Chapter 7, Section 7.4 defined strength of a source as the temperature to which the amount of heat liberated would raise a unit volume of the medium, so that:

$$Q = TV \quad (7.4.53)$$

It follows from this definition that an initial distribution of temperature in a no source problem, here given by f(x) can be regarded as equivalent to a continuous distribution of instantaneous point sources of strength.

$$Q = TV = [f(x)]avg \, A\Delta x \qquad (8.1.70)$$

and in the limit:

$$q = f(x)A \, dx \qquad (8.1.71)$$

The first integral in our solution thus can be seen as representing the temperature at time t of a medium with zero surface temperature resulting from initial distribution of instantaneous heat sources of strength f(x). In other words, we have replaced the initial temperature distribution by an equivalent set of instantaneous heat sources which produce the prescribed initial condition. A physical interpretation of the second integral is a little less straightforward, involving a distribution of sources and sinks and is described in the literature (see References). This removes to some extent the sense of incomprehension upon being confronted with Equation 8.1.66.

Practice Problems

8.1.1 Angle Between Two Lines — Find the angle between two lines connecting the origin to the points A(1,2,-2) and B(2,2,1).

(Hint: Use the dot product.)
Answer: 63° 37′

8.1.2 Proof of Cosine Law — Use the relation $A + B + C = 0$ valid for the sides of a triangle to derive the Cosine law: $|A|^2 = |B|^2 + |C|^2 + 2|B| \, |C|\cos(B,C)$.

(Hint: Dot multiply the triangle equation $A = -(B + C)$ by itself.)

8.1.3 Distance of a Point from a Plane — Given a plane through the point A(2,4,1), B(-1,0,1), and C(-1,4,2). Find the distance of the point P(1,-2,1) from the plane.

(Hint: Find the unit normal to the plane, then project the vector connection P to one of the points A, B, C onto the unit normal.)
Answer: 14/13

8.1.4 Distance Between Two Lines —

(a) Using Figure 6.2C as a guide, show that the distance d between the two lines is given by:

$$d = \frac{\vec{RP} \cdot (A \times B)}{|A \times B|} \qquad (8.1.72)$$

where **R** and **P** are two arbitrary points on the respective lines.

(b) Let $\vec{AB}$ and $\vec{CD}$ represent the vectors along the centerlines of two pipes, each 10 cm in outside diameter. The coordinates in feet forming these lines are given by A(4,0,3), B(0,6,8), C(0,0,9), and D(5,9,4). Find the clearance between the two pipes.
Answer: 1.5 in.

8.1.5 Differential Operators — Prove the relations given by Items 7, 8, and 15 of the Table 8.5.

(Hint: If proof can be provided for *one* coordinate system, the relation is valid for *all* coordinate systems.)

8.1.6 Derivation of the Divergence Theorem — Give a derivation of the divergence theorem, Equation 8.1.35.

(Hint: Write $\iint_S (\mathbf{A} \cdot \mathbf{n}) dS$ in the equivalent form $\sum_{i=1}^{n} \left[\frac{1}{\Delta V_i} \iint_{S_i} \mathbf{A} \cdot \mathbf{n}\, dS \right] \Delta V_i$ and

let $n \to \infty$.)

8.1.7 Volume of a Cone — Use the divergence theorem to show that the volume of a cone is $V = \frac{1}{3} \pi r^2 h$.

(Hint: Use a position vector R with the apex of the cone as the origin and start by showing that $V = \frac{1}{3} \iint_S \mathbf{n} \cdot \mathbf{R}\, dS$. Note: Volumes of other shapes can be determined in similar but less easy fashion.)

8.1.8 Maxwell's Equations of Electromagnetic Theory — Maxwell's equations relate electric and magnetic fields to the charges and currents which produce them. They are four in number and are expressed as follows:

$$\nabla \cdot \mathbf{E} = 4\pi\rho \qquad\qquad (8.1.73)$$

$$\nabla \cdot \mathbf{B} = 0 \qquad\qquad (8.1.74)$$

$$\nabla \times \mathbf{E} = -\frac{1}{C} \frac{\partial \mathbf{B}}{\partial t} \qquad\qquad (8.1.75)$$

$$\nabla \times \mathbf{B} = \frac{1}{C} \frac{\partial \mathbf{E}}{\partial t} + \frac{4\pi}{C} \mathbf{J} \qquad\qquad (8.1.76)$$

where $\mathbf{E}$ = electric field, $\mathbf{B}$ = magnetic field, ρ = charge density (charge q per volume), $\mathbf{J}$ = current density (current i per unit cross-sectional area), and C = speed of light. Recall that by "field" is meant the force exerted on a unit charge q_0.

Equations 8.1.72 and 8.1.73 express the fact that time-varying magnetic fields produce electric fields (i.e., an electric current) while time-varying electric fields in turn produce magnetic fields. Equation 8.1.71 states that the total "flux" of magnetic forces over a closed surface is zero, i.e., "what goes in must come out" (recall the definition of divergence, Equation 8.1.16). Vectors fields with a zero divergence therefore are often referred to as *solenoidal*. Equation 8.1.70 finally relates the "flux" of electric forces to the charge density ρ. The answers sought are as follows.

1. Which of Maxwell's equations are scalar, which are vectorial? Choose one of the latter category and expand it into an equivalent set of three scalar equations in Cartesian coordinates.
2. Classify the PDEs which result from Maxwell's equations as to order, linearity, and homogeneity.

8.1.9 Conservation of Charge: The Continuity Equation of Electricity — Use the divergence and generalized transport theorems, Equations 8.1.35 and 8.1.38 to derive the following continuity equation of electricity:

$$\frac{\partial p}{\partial t} = -\nabla \cdot \mathbf{J} \tag{8.1.77}$$

where, as before, p and $\mathbf{J}$ are charge and current densities. Note the similarity to the continuity equation of fluid mechanics.

8.1.10 Deflection of a String Under Gravity — The deflection u of a string under its own weight is described by the ODE:

$$\frac{d^2u}{dx^2} = \frac{\rho g}{T} \tag{8.1.78}$$

where T = tension of the string.

This is a one-dimensional Poisson equation and can be solved by means of Green's functions as well as by direct integration. Use both methods.
(Hint: Consult Table 8.7.)

Answer: $u = \dfrac{\rho g}{2T} x(x-1)$ $\qquad\qquad$ (8.1.79)

8.1.11 The Interior Dirichlet Problem for a Circle — When an arbitrary potential $u(R,\theta)$ is imposed on the circumference of a circle or infinitely long cylinder of radius R, with u held at zero as $r \to \infty$, a steady-state distribution of the potential, $u(r,\theta)$, results both within and outside the circle. Derivation of the former is referred to as the *interior* Dirichlet problem for a circle, the latter as the *exterior* Dirichlet problem for a circle. The same language is applied to other geometries. Thus, one speaks of the Dirichlet problem for a half-plane (see problem 8.12) and the Dirichlet problem for a rectangle.

Using the Green's functions of Table 8.7 as a guide, show that the steady-state temperature within a circle which results from a prescribed boundary temperature distribution $T(R,\theta)$ is given by:

$$T(r,\theta) = \frac{R^2 - r^2}{2\pi} \int_0^{2\pi} \frac{T(R,\theta')d\theta'}{R^2 - 2Rr\cos(\theta' - \theta) + r^2} \tag{8.1.80}$$

8.1.12 Dirichlet's Problem for a Half-Plane — Derive the potential distribution that results from a distribution u = f(y) imposed along the positive x-axis x > 0, with u → 0 as x → ∞.

(Hint: Use the Green's Function of Table 8.7.)

Answer: $u(x,y) = \dfrac{x}{\pi} \displaystyle\int_{-\infty}^{\infty} \dfrac{f(y')dy'}{x^2 + (y-y')^2}$ 　　　　　　　　(8.1.80)

Note that in view of the arbitrary form of the imposed boundary condition, Equations 8.1.80 and 8.1.81 can be regarded as solutions to an infinite set of different problems. The method of Green's function allows us to derive these solutions in a terse, closed form.

8.2   TRANSPORT OF MASS

We had already, in Illustration 8.1.4, given consideration to the transport of *total mass* which culminated in the continuity Equation 8.1.42. To arrive at this result, we started with the generalized transport theorem, Equation 8.1.38, and substituted density ρ for the variable quantity X. This caused the convective term $\dfrac{D}{Dt}\displaystyle\iiint_V \rho\,dV$ to drop out. We then introduced the divergence theorem (Equation 8.1.35) to convert the surface integral $\displaystyle\iint_S \rho(\mathbf{v}\cdot\mathbf{n})dS$ into a volume integral $\displaystyle\iiint_V (\nabla\cdot\mathbf{v})dV$ which was combined with the remaining volume integral of the transport theorem into a single expression. It was then argued that the integrand must vanish for the integral to be identically zero for any arbitrary volume, as required. This finally led to the continuity Equation 8.1.42.

We now consider the transport of a particular *species* characterized for example by its molar concentration C_A, and apply the same scheme as before. The difference here is that the convective term no longer vanishes since the mass of the species A may change due to a chemical reaction. We have in fact:

$$\frac{D}{Dt}\iiint_V C_A\,dV = \pm\iiint_V r_A\,d\backslash \qquad (8.2.1)$$

since by definition $dC_A/dt = \pm r_A$. The transport theorem for the species A then reads:

$$\iint_S C_A(\mathbf{v}\cdot\mathbf{n})dS = \pm\iiint_V r_A\,dV - \iiint_V \frac{\partial}{\partial t}C_A\,dV \qquad (8.2.2)$$

Introducing the divergence theorem as before and setting the integrand of the resulting volume integral equal to zero yields:

$$-\nabla\cdot C_A\mathbf{v} = \pm r_A + \frac{\partial C_A}{\partial t} \qquad (8.2.3)$$

A number of points need to be noted in connection with this expression. Equation 8.2.3 represents a *single* (scalar) partial differential equation. This is in contrast to the vector PDE, equivalent to three scalar PDEs which arises in momentum balances to be taken up in Section 8.4, and which lead the Navier-Stokes equation. Solution of Equation 8.2.3 yields the distribution of C_A in three dimensions and in time.

The rate term r_A is to be taken as negative for species consumption, positive for species production. $\nabla \cdot C_A \mathbf{v}$ expresses concentration changes due to both convective flow and diffusion. $C_A \mathbf{v}$ will be recognized as the molar flux $\mathbf{N_A}$ (moles A per unit time and area) and is represented by the auxiliary relation seen in one-dimensional form in Chapter 3 (Equation 3.2.3). That relation now becomes, in vectorial form:

$$\mathbf{N_A} = x_A(\mathbf{N_A} + \mathbf{N_B}) - CD_{AB} \nabla x_A$$

$$\text{Flux} \qquad \text{Convection} \qquad \text{Diffusion}$$

(8.2.4)

where $\mathbf{N}$ is a molar flux *vector*. Equation 8.2.4 thus consists of three scalar PDEs. Upon substitution into the mass balance Equation 8.2.3, however, the operation $\nabla \cdot$ converts the expression into a single scalar PDE. We further note that for the special case of diffusion through a stagnant film, $\mathbf{N_B} = 0$, and for equimolar counter diffusion, $\mathbf{N_A} = -\mathbf{N_B}$. For the latter case, as well as for trace diffusion, Equation 8.2.4 reduces to the simple relation:

$$\mathbf{N_A} = -CD_{AB} \nabla x_A$$

(8.2.5)

and for constant molar concentration C:

$$\mathbf{N_A} = -D_{AB} \nabla C_A$$

(8.2.6)

This is the three-dimensional version of Fick's law which was seen in one-dimensional form in Chapter 3, Equation 3.2.1.

We now turn to some practical applications of these equations. We consider the following cases:

- Combined convection, reaction, and diffusion (Illustration 8.2.1)
- Combined reaction and diffusion (Illustration 8.2.2)
- Combined convection and diffusion (Illustration 8.2.3)
- Unsteady diffusion (Illustrations 8.2.4 and 8.2.5)
- Steady-state multidimensional diffusion (Illustration 8.2.6)

Illustration 8.2.1 Catalytic Conversion in a Coated Tubular Reactor: Locating Equivalent Solutions in the Literature

The system under consideration here consists of a tubular reactor whose wall is coated with a catalyst that could, for example, be an immobilized enzyme (bioreactor). The purpose of modeling is then usually confined to relating size of the reactor to conversion for a given flow and set of kinetic parameters (design problem). The device also has been occasionally used to investigate the kinetics of a catalytic reaction without the added complications of heat effects and diffusional resistance within a catalyst pellet (parameter estimation).

We assume laminar flow conditions and plug flow ($v \neq f(r)$) with an irreversible reaction $A \rightarrow B$, $r_A = k_r C_A$ taking place at the wall. This leads to the development of radial and axial concentration profiles described by a partial differential mass balance. The situation is then essentially equivalent to that of the Graetz problem, given in Chapter 7, Section 7.2.

The mass balance can be derived in classical fashion using the "in − out = change" scheme or from the generalized conservation Equations 8.2.3 and 8.2.4. Let us use the latter to gain some practice in vector manipulation. Assuming steady-state conditions and making the substitution $C_A \mathbf{v} = \mathbf{N}_A$, we obtain:

$$\nabla \cdot \mathbf{N}_A = 0 \tag{8.2.7}$$

Note that reaction is not included at this stage since none takes place in the bulk fluid. It makes its appearance instead as a wall boundary condition (see Equation 8.2.13).

We first proceed to decompose the divergence operator of Equation 8.2.3 using the "dictionary" provided in Table 8.1. We obtain, for cylindrical coordinates:

$$\nabla \cdot \mathbf{N}_A = \frac{1}{r}\frac{\partial}{\partial r}(rN_{Ar}) + \frac{1}{r}\frac{\partial N_{A\theta}}{\partial \theta} + \frac{\partial N_{Az}}{\partial z} \tag{8.2.8}$$

A first simplification results by noting that $N_{A\theta} = 0$ (no circumferential flux) and that the axial component N_{Az} of the vector $\mathbf{N}_A$ can be written as:

$$N_{Az} = C_A\left[\frac{N_{Az} + N_{Bz}}{C}\right] - CD_{AB}\frac{\partial}{\partial z}(C_A / C) \tag{8.2.9}$$

where the mole fractions of Equation 8.2.4 have been replaced by concentration.

Here the total molar concentration C is a constant and the expression $(N_{Az} + N_{Bz})/C$ equals fluid velocity v. If in addition we assume diffusion to be principally in the radial direction, the axial diffusion term in Equation 8.2.9 drops out and we obtain the simple expression:

$$N_{Az} = C_A v \tag{8.2.10}$$

To evaluate the radial flux N_{Ar}, we note that $N_{Ar} + N_{Br} = 0$ (equimolar counter diffusion) and from the dictionary of Table 8.1 the radial component $(\nabla N_A)_r = \partial N_A/\partial r$, so that from Equation 8.2.4:

$$N_{Ar} = -CD_{AB}\frac{\partial C_A / C}{\partial r} = -D_{AB}\frac{\partial C_A}{\partial r} \tag{8.2.11}$$

This is simply Fick's law applied to the radial direction. Substitution of Equations 8.2.10 and 8.2.11 into Equation 8.2.8 then yields the scalar second order linear PDE:

$$v\frac{\partial C_A}{\partial z} = D_{AB}\left[\frac{\partial^2 C_A}{\partial r^2} + \frac{1}{r}\frac{\partial C}{\partial r}\right] \qquad (8.2.12)$$

Three boundary conditions are required, which are as follows:

At the inlet: $\qquad\qquad\qquad C_A(r,0) = (C_A)^0$

At the axis: $\qquad\qquad\qquad \dfrac{\partial C_A}{\partial r}(0,z) = 0 \qquad\qquad (8.2.13)$

At the wall: $\qquad\qquad -D_{AB}\dfrac{\partial C_A}{\partial r}(R,z) = k_r C_A(R,z)$

These equations can be solved by standard analytical techniques, as will be shown in the next chapter. Our aim here is to avoid this complication and to locate the solution of an equivalent problem in the literature. The reader may already have noted the similarity between Equation 8.2.12 and that for unsteady radial conduction in a cylinder with convective heat loss to a medium at zero temperature. In fact, by making the following substitutions, one arrives at completely identical models:

$C_A \qquad \rightarrow \quad$ Temperature T
$z \qquad\ \ \rightarrow \quad$ Time t
$D_{AB}/v \ \rightarrow \quad$ Thermal diffusivity α
$D_{AB} \qquad \rightarrow \quad$ Thermal conductivity k
$k_r \qquad\ \ \rightarrow \quad$ Heat transfer coefficient h
$(C_A)_0 \quad\ \rightarrow \quad$ Initial temperature T_0

The solution to this problem is readily available in the heat transfer literature. Translated back to the original variables, it assumes the following forbidding form:

$$C_A(r,z) = 2(C_A)_0 \sum_1^\infty \frac{\lambda_j}{\lambda_j^2 + \beta^2}\frac{J_1(\lambda_j)}{J_0(\lambda_j)}J_0\left(\lambda_j\frac{r}{R}\right)\exp(-\lambda_j^2 z/\gamma^2) \quad (8.2.14)$$

where $\beta = k_r R/D_{AB}$
$\qquad \gamma = R(v/D_{AB})$
$\qquad \lambda_j = $ j-th root of the expression

$$\lambda J_1(\lambda) - \beta J_0(\lambda) = 0 \qquad\qquad (8.2.15)$$

$J_0 = $ Bessel function of first kind and order zero
$J_1 = $ Bessel function of first kind and order one

This infinite series represents the concentration profiles as they develop in the axial and radial directions.

The already panic-stricken will be further dismayed to learn that the result has to be converted to the more useful *average*, or mean integral concentration $(C_A)_{avg}$, i.e., we have to evaluate:

$$(C_A)_{avg} = \int_0^1 C_A 2\pi y dy / \int_0^1 2\pi y dy = 2\int C_A y dy \qquad (8.2.16)$$

where we have nondimensionalized the radial distance by setting $y = r/R$. In other words, we have to evaluate the integral of the y-dependent part of Equation 8.2.14, $\int_0^1 J_0(\lambda_j y) y dy$. This is not as formidable a task as it appears since we have ready-made formula for just such cases. We reach back to Table 4.8 of Chapter 4 and extract:

$$\alpha \int x^k J_{k-1}(\alpha x) dx = x^k(\alpha x) + C \qquad (8.2.17)$$

Some manipulations then result in the following expression:

$$(C_A)_{avg} /(C_A)_0 = 4\sum_1^\infty \frac{\beta^2}{\lambda_j^2(\lambda_j^2 + \beta^2)} \exp(-\lambda_j^2 z / \gamma^2) \qquad (8.2.18)$$

We may at this point be permitted a sigh of relief, since the Bessel functions, at least, have disappeared, although they do lurk in the roots λ_j of Equation 8.2.15. The following may also prove soothing.

Comments:

The model we have presented is a rather limited one since it does not address complex reaction mechanism or the effect of the parabolic velocity profile that prevails under laminar flow conditions. The main purpose of the exercise is to

TABLE 8.8
Roots of $\lambda J_1(\lambda) - \beta J_0(\lambda) = 0$

β	λ_1	λ_2	λ_3	λ_4	λ_5
0	0	3.8317	7.0156	10.1735	13.3237
0.01	0.1412	3.8343	7.0170	10.1745	13.3244
0.1	0.4417	3.8577	7.0298	10.1833	13.3312
1.0	1.2558	4.0795	7.1558	10.2710	13.3984
10.0	2.1795	5.0332	7.9569	10.9363	13.9580
100.0	2.3809	5.4652	8.5678	11.6747	14.7834
∞	2.4048	5.5201	8.6537	11.7915	14.9309

practice the art of recognizing the equivalence of models for dissimilar processes and reaching into the literature for quick convenient solutions.

The Bessel functions J_0 and J_1 are of a periodic type (see Table 4.8) and, hence, have an infinite number of roots singly or when they appear in combination as in Equation 8.2.15. That latter expression is a characteristic transcendental equation that arises in conduction and diffusion equation with a Type III boundary condition. Its frequent occurrence has led to numerous tabulations of its roots, of which we give an abbreviated version in Table 8.8.

The fact that an infinite series has to be evaluated may at first sight appear discouraging. Closer inspection of Equation 8.2.18 shows, however, that the axial profile decays rapidly with increasing values of the roots λ_j. Fast convergence of the series therefore may be expected in all but very slow reactions. To explore this feature, we consider the following numerical example, taken to apply to a liquid system:

Reactor radius R = 5 cm
Rector length z = 100 cm
Rate constant $k_r = 2 \times 10^{-5}$ s^{-1}
Diffusivity $D_{AB} = 10^{-3}$ cm^2/s
Flow velocity v = 20 cm/s

We obtain, for the parameters,

$$\beta = k_r R / D_{AB} = (2 \times 10^{-5})(5)/10^{-3} = 10^{-1}$$

$$\gamma = R v / D_{AB} = (5)(20)/10^{-3} = 10^5$$

and from Table 8.8:

$$\lambda_1 = 0.4417, \quad \lambda_2 = 3.8577$$

The rate constant here is quite low and the fluid velocity high, so that conversions are expected to be low.

Substitution of these values into Equation 8.2.18 yields, for the first two terms of the series:

$$(C_A)_{avg} / (C_A)_0 = 4 \sum_{1}^{2} \frac{\beta^2}{\lambda_j^2 (\lambda_j^2 + \beta^2)} \exp(-\lambda_j^2 z / \gamma^2)$$

$$= 4 \frac{0.1^2}{0.4417^2 (0.4417^2 + 0.1^2)} \exp(-0.4477^2 \, 100 / 10^2)$$

$$+ 4 \frac{0.1^2}{3.8577^2 (3.8577^2 + 0.1^2)} \exp(-3.8577^2 \, 100 / 10^2)$$

$$(C_A)_{avg} / (C_A)_0 = 0.822 + 6.23 \times 10^{-11}$$

and conversion X = [1 − $(C_A)_{avg}/(C_A)_0$]100 = 17.8%.

The second term is seen to be negligibly small compared to the first, due primarily to the rapid decay of the exponential term caused by the high value of $\lambda_2^2 = 14.88$. This fast convergence is the norm in many practical applications and enables us to express the conversion X in terms of the simple expression:

$$X \cong 1 - \frac{4\beta^2}{\lambda_1^2(\lambda_1^2 + \beta^2)} \exp(-\lambda_1^2 z / \gamma^2) \qquad (8.2.19)$$

The rate constant k_r contained in the parameter β is easily extracted from this expression and experiments run at different reactor lengths z or feed velocity v contained in γ.

Illustration 8.2.2 Diffusion and Reaction in a Semi-Infinite Medium: Another Literature Solution

We consider in this example the unsteady equimolar or trace diffusion of a species A into a semi-infinite medium initially free of solute and an imposed concentration C_A^0 at the surface $x = 0$. The solute undergoes an irreversible first order reaction within the medium, A → B, with the rate given by $r = k_r C$. The partial differential mass balance for this case becomes:

$$\frac{\partial C}{\partial t} = D \frac{\partial^2 C}{\partial x^2} - k_r C \qquad (8.2.20)$$

Derivation of this expression is left to the Practice Problems.

The equation can be solved by standard linear techniques, e.g., the Laplace transform without undue difficulty. We use instead the approach applied in the previous illustration and seek a literature solution in the related discipline of heat conduction. This requires some thought and perseverance, as well as a good knowledge of the pertinent literature.

An initial inspection of Equation 8.2.20 does not appear encouraging. The reaction term $k_r C$ would have to be matched by a corresponding "heat sink" term hT which describes heat loss in proportion to the prevailing temperature T at a given point. This is not a realistic physical process but becomes so if the domain is reduced to that of a thin rod with a uniform temperature T over its cross-section, subject to convective heat loss at a rate hT to a medium at zero temperature. This results in the following two equivalent models.

(a) Diffusion in semi-infinite medium with irreversible reaction	(b) Conduction in semi-infinite thin rod with convective heat loss	
$\dfrac{\partial C}{\partial t} = D \dfrac{\partial^2 C}{\partial x^2} - k_r C$	$\dfrac{\partial T}{\partial t} = \alpha \dfrac{\partial^2 T}{\partial x^2} - \beta T$	
$C(x,0) = 0$	$T(x,0) = 0$	
$C(0,t) = C_0$	$T(0,t) = T_0$	(8.2.21)
$C(\infty,t) = 0$	$T(\infty,t) = 0$	

where $\beta = \dfrac{hP}{\rho CpA_C}$

A_C = rod cross-sectional area

P = rod perimeter

Note that the heat loss does not enter the model as a surface boundary condition but resides instead in the PDE itself. This becomes apparent in the derivation of the PDE which is left to the Practice Problems.

The solution to the temperature problem is available in standard texts on heat conduction and takes the form:

$$\frac{T}{T_0} = \frac{1}{2}\exp(-x\sqrt{\alpha/\beta})\operatorname{erfc}[x/2\sqrt{\alpha t} - \sqrt{\beta t}]$$

$$+\frac{1}{2}\exp(x\sqrt{\alpha/\beta})\operatorname{erfc}[x/2\sqrt{\alpha t} + \sqrt{\beta t}]$$

(8.2.22)

Translation into the corresponding diffusion problem is easily accomplished by means of the "dictionary" provided by the Equations 8.2.21.

Illustration 8.2.3   The Graetz–Lévêque Problem in Mass Transfer: Transport Coefficients in the Entry Region

We had already, on several occasions, referred to the Graetz problem, and the Lévêque version of it. In Illustration 8.2.1, we had encountered a modified Graetz problem in which concentration took the place of temperature and conditions at the wall were described by a BC of Type III. The solution was given in terms of an infinite series, Equations 8.2.14 and 8.2.18, which showed fast convergence for high to moderate diffusivities and small diameters, long conduits, or low velocities. When this is no longer the case, an alternative method known as the Lévêque solution is resorted to. We had briefly alluded to it in Chapter 6, Section 6.1, Illustration 6.1.6, in the context of protein transport in flowing blood. Protein diffusivities are quite low, or the order $10^{-6} - 10^{-5}$ cm^2/s, and development of the concentration becomes exceedingly slow, leading to slow convergence of the infinite series solutions.

The Lévêque solution focused on the so-called entry region near the tube inlet where profile development is still in its initial stage. The following assumption can then be made.

Temperature or concentration changes are confined entirely to a thin boundary layer adjacent to the conduit wall. Within the bulk of the fluid, changes in both the radial and axial directions are negligible. The profiles that result for mass transport are depicted in Chapter 6, Figure 6.7.

Since the boundary layer typically occupies only a small fraction of the tube diameter, curvature can be neglected. We can unravel the conduit and treat it as a flat plate. A corollary of this approach is that the boundary layer and the neighboring bulk fluid can be regarded as a semi-finite medium, with $C \rightarrow C_{bulk}$ as y (or r) $\rightarrow$ ∞. See in this connection Chapter 7, Section 7.3.5.

The boundary layer lies entirely within the linear portion of the (parabolic) velocity profile. This is justified by its thinness. We had encountered a similar situation in Illustration 7.3.1, where the *thermal* boundary layer development along a flat plant was seen to lag behind the momentum layer development, with the result that temperature changes along the plate lay entirely within the linear portion of the velocity profile. We can, with some imagination, anticipate that the underlying models and their solutions therefore will be identical in form if not in detail. This is, in fact, the case as we shall see below.

We start by performing a differential mass balance over the element Δx, Δy, where x is the coordinate along what is now a flat plate, y the direction perpendicular to it. Diffusion in the x-direction is neglected and the concentration at the wall is assumed to be zero along the entire length of the plate. This can be brought about by a fast reaction at the wall or rapid permeation through it. We use the in − out = 0 scheme rather than the generalized mass balances Equations 8.2.3 and 8.2.4 and obtain at steady state:

$$\text{Rate of solute in} - \text{Rate of solute out} = 0$$

$$\left[\begin{array}{c} vC_A \, W\Delta y \, |_x \\ -DW\Delta x \dfrac{\partial C}{\partial y}\Big|_y \end{array} \right] - \left[\begin{array}{c} vC_A \, W\Delta y \, |_{x+\Delta x} \\ -DW\Delta x \dfrac{\partial C}{\partial y}\Big|_{y+\Delta y} \end{array} \right] = 0 \tag{8.2.23}$$

where W = width of the plate, equal to the perimeter of the unraveled tube.

Dividing by $\Delta x \Delta y W$ and letting the increments go to zero, we obtain the following linear second order PDE:

$$D\frac{\partial^2 C}{\partial y^2} - v\frac{\partial C}{\partial x} = 0 \tag{8.2.24}$$

We note that for the linear portion of the velocity profile we can write:

$$\text{Shear rate } \dot{\gamma} = \frac{dv}{dy} = \frac{v-0}{y-0} = \frac{v}{y} \tag{8.2.25}$$

so that the PDE 8.2.17 becomes:

$$D\frac{\partial^2 C}{\partial y^2} - \dot{\gamma}y\frac{\partial C}{\partial x} = 0 \tag{8.2.26}$$

with boundary conditions:

At the inlet: $\qquad C(0,y) = C_0$

At the wall: $\qquad C(x,0) = 0 \qquad\qquad$ (8.2.27)

In the bulk fluid: $\qquad C(x,\infty) = C_0$

The form of this model is precisely that of the development of the thermal boundary layer along a flat plate, Equations 7.3.14 and 7.3.15. Its solution was obtained by similarity transformation which can be applied to the present case as well. The details are left to the exercises (see Practice Problem 8.2.4). The final solution is of the same form as Equation 7.3.25 and is given by:

$$\frac{C}{C_0} = \frac{\int_0^{\eta} \exp(-\eta^3)dr}{\int_0^{\infty} \exp(-\eta^3)dr} \tag{8.2.28}$$

where the similarity variable η is given by:

$$\eta = y\left(\frac{\dot{\gamma}}{9Dx}\right)^{1/3} \tag{8.2.29}$$

We now turn to the task of deriving an effective mass transfer coefficient k_f from the concentration profile Equation 8.2.28. The key to the procedure is the equation:

$$D\left.\frac{\partial C}{\partial y}\right|_{y=0} = k_f(C_0 - 0) \tag{8.2.30}$$

which merely expresses the rate of arrival of solute in two equivalent forms, one involving Fick's law, the other an effective mass transfer coefficient k_f and its associated driving force. The crux then is the evaluation of the derivative $(\partial C/\partial y)_{y=0}$.

We start the procedure by first evaluating the integral in the denominator of Equation 8.2.28. To do this, the substitution $x = \eta^3$ is made, which yields:

$$\int_0^{\infty} \exp(-\eta^3)d\eta = \frac{1}{3}\int_0^{\infty} x^{-2/3}e^{-x}dx \tag{8.2.31}$$

The integral on the right is known as the Gamma function $\Gamma(n)$ and has the general definition:

$$\Gamma(n) = \int_0^\infty x^{n-1} e^{-x} dx \tag{8.2.32}$$

where n is any positive or negative number. It has to be evaluated numerically and is tabulated in most mathematical handbooks for the interval $1 \le n \le 2$. Some selected values are reproduced in Table 8.9. They are seen to be close to unity over the entire range. Other values of n are obtained from the following recursion formula:

$$\Gamma(n) = n\Gamma(n-1) = n(n-1)\Gamma(n-2) \text{ etc.} \tag{8.2.33}$$

The Gamma function can consequently be regarded as a generalized factorial n! applicable to *any* positive or negative number.

For the case in hand, we obtain from Equation 8.2.31 and the recursion formula Equation 8.2.33

$$\frac{1}{3} \int_0^\infty x^{-2/3} e^{-x} dx = \frac{1}{3} \int_0^\infty x^{1/3-1} e^{-x} dx$$

$$= \frac{1}{3}\Gamma(1/3) = \frac{1}{3}\frac{\Gamma(4/3)}{1/3} = \Gamma(4/3) = 0.89407 \tag{8.2.34}$$

where the numerical value is interpolated from Table 8.9.

To evaluate the derivative $(\partial C/\partial y)_{y=0}$ we apply the chain rule of partial differentiation (see Table 7.4) and write, using the profile Equation 8.2.28:

$$\left.\frac{\partial C}{\partial y}\right|_{y=0} = \left.\frac{\partial C}{\partial \eta}\frac{\partial \eta}{\partial y}\right|_{y=0} = \left.\frac{C_0}{0.89407}\exp(-\eta^3)\left(\frac{\dot{\gamma}}{9Dx}\right)^{1/3}\right|_{y=0} = \frac{C_0}{0.89407}\left(\frac{\dot{\gamma}}{9Dx}\right)^{1/3} \tag{8.2.35}$$

Substitution of this expression into Equation 8.2.30 finally yields the effective mass transfer coefficient:

$$k_f = 0.54\left(\frac{\dot{\gamma}D^2}{x}\right)^{1/3} \tag{8.2.36}$$

For boundary conditions of Type II and Type III, the coefficient on the right is some 10 to 15% higher. This leads us to propose an average coefficient of 0.6, applicable to all three types of BCs. Thus, we have:

$$k_f \cong 0.6\left(\frac{\dot{\gamma}D^2}{x}\right)^{1/3}$$

TABLE 8.9
Values of the Gamma Function

n	$\Gamma(n)$
1.000	1.00000
1.050	0.97350
1.100	0.95135
1.150	0.93304
1.200	0.91816
1.250	0.90640
1.300	0.89747
1.350	0.89115
1.400	0.88726
1.450	0.88566
1.500	0.88623
1.550	0.88887
1.600	0.89352
1.650	0.90011
1.700	0.90864
1.750	0.91906
1.800	0.93138
1.850	0.94561
1.900	0.96177
1.950	0.97988
2.000	1.0000

The reader will note that this is the expression we used in Chapter 6, Section 6.1 to analyze protein transport in flowing blood (Equation 6.1.42).

Comments:

Equation 8.2.36 has a number of noteworthy features. Foremost among them is the weak, one third power dependence of k_f on shear rate $\dot{\gamma}$ and distance x. Since $\dot{\gamma} = 8v/d$ for laminar flow in a cylindrical tube, k_f will be proportional to $v^{0.33}$. This contrasts with the much stronger dependence, $k_f \propto v^{0.8}$, found in turbulent flow (see Chapter 3, Table 3.5).

The Graetz-Lévêque problem for mass transfer has its origin and counterpart in heat transfer which will be discussed in some detail in Section 8.3. From the results given there, it can be deduced that the Lévêque (Entry) region extends over the following range:

$$0 < \frac{xD}{vd^2} < 10^{-3}$$

This relation serves as a quick means of establishing limits of velocity and tubular diameter and length beyond which the flow ceases to be in the entry region.

In blood flow, for example, with a typical protein diffusivity $D = 10^{-5}$ cm²/s, average flow velocity of $v = 10$ cm/s and near-inlet distance $x = 0.1$ cm, the critical vessel diameter which arises from the Condition 8.2.30 is given by:

$$d \geq \left(\frac{xD}{10^{-3} v}\right)^{1/2} = \left(\frac{(0.1)(10^{-5})}{(10^{-3})(10)}\right) = 10^{-2} \text{ cm} \tag{8.2.37}$$

In other words, for the Lévêque solution to be valid in blood flow, the vessel diameter cannot be less than 0.1 mm. This is the lower limit we had set on d in calculating coagulant concentrations at the vessel wall (Chapter 6, Illustration 6.1.6).

When the vessel geometry becomes more complex as in the case of branching conduits or bifurcations, numerical methods have to be resorted to both for entry and the fully developed regions. An alternative procedure is to measure local shear rates over a span of 0.1 to 1 mm, and use these values in an integrated version of Equation 6.1.42 to arrive at an average mass transfer coefficient. We obtain in this case:

$$\bar{k}_f = 0.8\left(\frac{\dot{\gamma}_{\text{Meas'd}} D^2}{L}\right)^{1/3} \tag{8.2.38}$$

where L is the length or resolution of the measuring device and $\dot{\gamma}_{\text{Meas'd}}$ the local shear-rate determined by experimental measurement. One such experimental technique is the elegant electrochemical method described in Practice Problem 8.2.3. Interpretation of the primary measurement, an electrical current i, requires the use of Equation 8.2.35 and thus shows a nice intertwining of modeling and experiment.

Illustration 8.2.4   Unsteady Diffusion in a Sphere: Sorption and Desorption Curves

In this classical problem which has its exact counterpart in the unsteady conduction of heat we consider diffusional uptake or release of a solute by a porous sphere. These processes are often referred to as sorption or desorption, although no actual sorptive retention on the solid matrix takes place.

We consider the general case of a Type III boundary condition, descriptive of a film resistance at the surface, and obtain the following model:

$$\frac{\partial C}{\partial t} = D\left(\frac{\partial^2 C}{\partial r^2} + \frac{2}{r}\frac{\partial C}{\partial r}\right) \tag{8.2.39}$$

with boundary conditions:

At the surface: $\pm D\dfrac{\partial C}{\partial r}\bigg|_{r=R} = k_f(C_{r=R} - C_0)$

At the center:
$$\frac{\partial C}{\partial r}\bigg|_{r=0} = 0 \qquad (8.2.40)$$

Initially:
$$C(0,r) = C^0$$

The PDE 8.2.39 can be obtained by performing a classical mass balance over the spherical increment Δr, or by substitution of the vector flux Equation 8.2.4 into the generalized mass balance Equation 8.2.3 and use of the dictionary Table 8.1.

Solution of the model is accomplished by standard linear techniques of which we shall give examples in Chapter 9. For our present purposes we note that the primary information consists of the unsteady concentration profiles $C(r,t)$, which are usually converted into the more useful fractional uptake or fractional release M_t/M_∞. Here M_t denotes the total amount taken up or released up to time t, M_∞ the same quantity at time infinity. M_t is obtained from the concentration profiles $C(r,t)$ by applying the relation:

$$M_t = -\int_0^t D\frac{\partial C}{\partial r}\bigg|_{r=R} dt \qquad (8.2.41)$$

Plots of M_t/M_∞ as a function of Dt/R^2, and the parameter $Sh = k_f R/D$ are displayed in Figure 8.5. Note that the limiting cases of $Sh = \infty$ and $Sh = 0$ correspond to the limiting boundary conditions $Cl_{r=R} = C_0$ (Type I) and $\dfrac{\partial C}{\partial r}\bigg|_{r=R} = 0$ (Type II). The latter case represents an impermeable sphere.

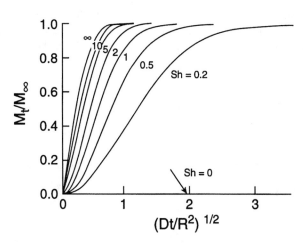

FIGURE 8.5 Fractional uptake and release as a function of dimensionless time for diffusion in and out of a sphere (BC Type III). (J. Crank, *Mathematics of Diffusion, 2nd ed.,* Oxford University Press, New York, 1975. With permission.)

Let us briefly demonstrate the use of the plots with a numerical example. We choose:

$$k_f = 10^{-4} \text{ cm/s}, \quad D = 10^{-4} \text{ cm}^2/\text{s}, \quad R = 1 \text{ cm}$$

representative of a liquid system and obtain $Sh = (10^{-4})(1)/10^{-4} = 1$. We use this value to calculate the time necessary to deplete a sphere to one half its original solute content. We obtain from Figure 8.5:

$$(Dt/R^2)^{1/2} = 0.5 \text{ at } M_t/M_\infty = 0.5, \quad Sh = 1$$

Hence,

$$t = \frac{0.5^2}{10^{-4}} 1^2 = 2500 \, s \approx 42 \, min$$

Note that the same time is required to achieve a fractional *uptake* of the same magnitude 0.5.

In this example, the exterior medium was assumed to be infinite in extent, resulting in a constant concentration C_0 of the surroundings. Of more frequent occurrence is the situation in which the surroundings consist of a finite volume of a well-stirred solution. This case is taken up below.

Illustration 8.2.5   The Sphere in a Well-Stirred Solution: Leaching of a Slurry

We assume in this example that a sphere, or an aggregate of spheres of volume V_{sphere}, is suspended in a well-stirred medium of limited volume V_{soln}. By "well-stirred" we wish to imply that the concentration in the fluid is uniform and equal to that at the sphere surface (i.e., film resistance is negligible). The model is similar to that of the previous illustration, differing from it only in the surface boundary condition. We have:

$$\frac{\partial C}{\partial t} = D\left(\frac{\partial^2 C}{\partial r^2} + \frac{2}{r}\frac{\partial C}{\partial r}\right) \qquad (8.2.42)$$

with boundary conditions:

At the surface:
$$DA\frac{\partial C}{\partial r}\bigg|_{r=R} = V_{soln}\frac{\partial C}{\partial t}\bigg|_{r=R}$$

At the center:
$$\frac{\partial C}{\partial r}\bigg|_{r=0} = 0 \qquad (8.2.43)$$

Initially:
$$C(0,r) = C^0$$

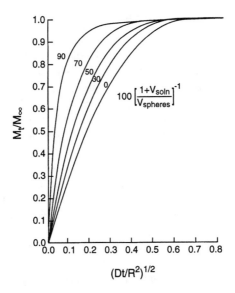

FIGURE 8.6 Fractional diffusional uptake and release as a function of dimensionless time for spheres in a well-stirred solution of limited volume. (J. Crank, *Mathematics of Diffusion, 2nd ed.,* Oxford University Press, New York, 1975. With permission.)

The concentration profiles initially obtained are again converted into fractional uptake or release M_t/M_∞, with the volume ratio $V_{soln}/V_{spheres}$ now appearing as a parameter. The results are displayed in Figure 8.6. We use the plots to calculate the following numerical example.

Suppose it is desired to calculate the time required to extract 90% of the oil contained in oil-bearing vegetable seeds assumed to be spherical. We set:

$$R = 0.5 \text{ cm}, \quad D = 10^{-4} \text{ cm}^2/\text{s} \quad \text{and} \quad V_{soln}/V_{spheres} = 1$$

so that $100 \ (1 + V_{soln}/V_{spheres})^{-1} = 50$.

From Figure 8.6 we obtain, for $M_t/M_\infty = 0.9$, $(Dt/R^2)^{1/2} = 0.34$, and $t = (0.34^2)(0.5^2)/10^{-4} = 289 \text{ s} \approx 5 \text{ min}$.

Comments:

One notes from Figure 8.6 that release time diminishes with decreasing solution volume, which also results in higher extract concentrations. It is advantageous to minimize solvent volume. One has to keep in mind, however, that efficient stirring requires a certain minimum ratio of solvent to solids volume. Furthermore, with decreasing amount of solvent there is a likelihood of a change in solution volume due to the volume of extracted oil. This would require a modification of the surface boundary condition that would complicate the model considerably.

A parameter value of zero corresponds to an infinitely large solution volume. This implies in turn a constant external concentration and the plot becomes identical to that of Figure 8.1 at $Sh = \infty$, i.e., under conditions of no film resistance.

Illustration 8.2.6   Steady-State Diffusion in
Several Dimensions

In the absence of convective flow and reactions, steady-state diffusional transport is described by Laplace's equation $\nabla^2 C = 0$. Some solutions to this PDE, principally arrived at by the technique of conformal mapping, has previously been given in Table 7.7. Additional solutions will be presented in Figure 8.11 of the next section in connection with steady-state multidimensional conduction which also is described by Laplace's equation. The latter are not given as distributions, as was the case in Table 7.7, but rather in terms of so-called shape factors S which allows the direct calculations of the rate of heat flow q between two bodies maintained at different temperatures. The compilations can evidently be used to calculate the analogous case of steady diffusional *mass* flow between two surfaces at different concentrations. The need for this might arise for example in connection with emanations from underground deposits or in connection with controlled release devices.

Let us then reach forward to Table 8.11 and consider the case of a cylinder (or circular hole) of length L and diameter d with a surface temperature of T_1, buried deep in a semi-infinite medium with surface temperature $T_2 < T$. The shape factor for this case, Item 8b, is given by:

$$S = 2\pi L \ln (2L/d) \qquad (8.2.44)$$

and is used directly in Newton's law of cooling to obtain the flux q'. Thus,

$$q' \ (J/s) = kS(T_1 - T_2) \qquad (8.2.45)$$

or

$$q' = 2\pi L \ln(2L/d)k(T_1 - T_2) \qquad (8.2.46)$$

The equivalent case of diffusive mass flow N_A is then given by:

$$N'(moles/s) = 2\pi L \ln(2L/d)D(C_1 - C_2) \qquad (8.2.47)$$

Suppose the solute is quickly removed from the surface of the semi-infinite medium, for example, by a flowing fluid, so that $C_2 \approx 0$. Let us further set L = 100 cm, d = 10 cm, $C_1 = 10^{-4}$ mol/cm^3, and D = 10^{-4} cm^2/s. Then the total amount diffusing will be given by:

$$N(moles/s) = 2\pi L \ln (2L/d)D \ C_1 = 2\pi 100 \ln [(2(100)/10)](10^{-4})(10^{-4})$$

$$N_A = 1.88 \ 10^{-5} \ mol/s$$

Practice Problems

8.2.1 Mass Balances for Reverse Osmosis and Ultrafiltration — In reverse osmosis (RO) and ultrafiltration (UF), pressure is applied to a flowing solution to force solvent, usually water, through the permeable wall of the duct, thus separating it from the dissolved solute. In RO, which is the term usually reserved for the membrane-based desalination of water, the solute molecules are small and the principal aim is to produce pure solvent. The term UF, on the other hand, is usually applied to solutions with large solute molecules such as proteins. The primary purpose there is to achieve a concentration of valuable or objectionable solutes and, less frequently, to recover solvents other than water.

(a) Show, using both the vectorial formulation and the classical "in – out" approach, that the total and component mass balances for steady laminar flow in a cylindrical tube are given by:

$$\frac{\partial}{\partial r}(r\,v_r) + \frac{\partial}{\partial z}(r\,v_z) = 0 \tag{8.2.48}$$

and

$$v_r\frac{\partial C}{\partial r} + v_z\frac{\partial C}{\partial z} = D\left[\frac{d^2C}{\partial r^2} + \frac{1}{r}\frac{\partial C}{\partial r} + \frac{\partial^2C}{\partial z^2}\right] \tag{8.2.49}$$

What and how many additional balances are needed to complete the model?

(b) Boundary conditions at the wall are required for both the solute concentration C and the radial fluid velocity v_r. Show that these are given by:

$$D\frac{\partial C}{\partial r}\bigg|_{r=R} = v_r\,C_A\,|_{r=R} \tag{8.2.50}$$

$$v_r\,|_{r=R} = K_1(p - p_{ext})_{r=R} - K_2\,C\,|_{r=R} \tag{8.2.51}$$

and provide a physical explanation for the parameters.

8.2.2 A Lévêque Problem — Consider steady laminar flow in a tubular "reactor," L = 100 cm and d = 1 cm, which releases solute from the wall at an unknown constant rate N(mol/cm²s). Velocity v of the fluid is 10 cm/s, diffusivity D of the solute 10^{-5} cm²/s.

(a) What is the concentration boundary layer thickness δ at the exit?
(Hint: Recall the definition of the mass transfer coefficient k_f and that $\dot\gamma = 8\,v/d$.)

(b) If the average outlet concentration is found to be 10^{-5} mol/L, what is the value of N?

(Hint: Use the ratio $(d/\delta)^2$ to find the wall concentration C_w, then apply $N = k_f C_w$.)

Answer: (a) 0.33 mm

8.2.3 The Electrochemical Method — Local or "spot" wall shear rates $\dot{\gamma}$ in complex tubular geometries can be determined experimentally by measuring the current which results from an induced electrochemical reaction at electrodes installed in the wall of the conduit. Typically in this method, an upstream section of a metallic tube serves as an anode. Tiny electrodes, 0.1 to 1 mm in diameter embedded in the wall at various locations of the downstream test section act as cathodes. The fluid carries a dissolved ionic solute, typically a ferric cyanide. A voltage is applied to the electrodes and the current from the resulting redox reaction (e.g., $Fe(CN)_6^{-3} \rightarrow Fe(CN)_6^{-2}$) is measured.

Show that the shear rate $\dot{\gamma}$ at a given anode is related to the measured current by the expression:

$$\dot{\gamma} = \frac{1.9\,L}{(LWFC_0)^3 D^2}\,i^3 \tag{8.2.52}$$

where L,W = length and width of a cathode
    F   = Faraday number
    C_0 = solute concentration in the bulk fluid
    D   = solute diffusivity
    i   = measured current

(Hint: Obtain the ion flow N (moles/s) by integrating Equation 8.2.35 from 0 to L, then substitute the result into the electrochemical relation $N = i/F$.)

Note that because of their cubic dependence, high precision measurements of cathode dimensions, solute concentration, and current are required.

8.2.4 Derivation of the Lévêque Relation — Apply a similarity transformation to Equations 8.2.26 and 8.2.27 to derive the Expression 8.2.28.

8.2.5 Diffusion and Reaction in a Semi-Infinite Medium — Make a differential mass balance to derive Equation 8.2.20.

8.2.6 Unsteady Conduction in a Thin Rod — Derive the set of Equations 8.2.21b by making an appropriate differential heat balance.

8.2.7 Batch Adsorption of a Trace Substance — When a diffusing solute partitions or adsorbs onto the solid matrix, one can often use standard solutions for non-sorbing solids to follow the course of adsorption by suitably modifying one of the solution parameters. For the case of adsorption by a sphere from a well-stirred solution, for example, $V_{soln}/V_{spheres}$ in Figure 8.6 is replaced by $V_{soln}/(KV_{spheres})$, where K is the partition coefficient or Henry's constant.

Assume the following parameter values: $K = 10$, $V_{soln}/V_{spheres} = 10$, $D = 10^{-5}$ cm^2/s, $R = 1$ cm.

(a) Show by making a cumulative mass balance that the modified parameter $100/(1 + V_{soln}/K V_{spheres})$ also represents the percentage of solute in the solution that is ultimately taken up by the solids at $t \to \infty$ (50% here).

(b) What is the fraction of solute content of the solution taken up from the solution after 1 h?

(Hint: Multiply the ordinate value by the parameter value.)

Answer: 37%

8.2.8 Solutions from Solutions — Suppose all you have available is a standard heat transfer text which only gives solutions to Fourier's equation for a plane sheet and a sphere with Type I boundary conditions. You need to find a solution to Fick's equation for a plane sheet with one face impermeable, the other exposed to a sinusoidally varying concentration. How would you proceed?

8.3   TRANSPORT OF ENERGY

Derivation of the generalized energy equation proceeds along the lines established for the transport of mass, with one or two extra items added. Briefly, the following steps are involved.

One starts with the general statement of the First Law of Thermodynamics

$$\begin{array}{c} \text{Change in energy} \\ \text{of the system} \end{array} = \begin{array}{c} \text{Energy added} \\ \text{to the system} \end{array} + \begin{array}{c} \text{Work done} \\ \text{on system} \end{array} \qquad (8.3.1)$$

Here energy includes transfer by conduction, radiation, or induction heating, as well heat produced by internal sources (e.g., nuclear reaction). Work encompasses the effects of gravity, buoyancy, electrical, and shear forces, as well as conventional piston work. Change in energy consists of two terms: internal and kinetic energy.

The resulting equation is combined with the generalized momentum balance and continuity equation. This results in the cancellation of all work terms due to body forces and of kinetic energy.

The surface integrals are converted to volume integrals via the divergence theorem and the total integrand set equal to zero, as was done in Section 8.2. The following expression, often referred to as the thermal energy balance, is then obtained:

$$\rho \frac{D}{Dt}(H) = \frac{DP}{Dt} + \nabla \cdot k\nabla T + \mu\phi + \rho q_b \qquad (8.3.2)$$

where $\mu\phi$ is a viscous dissipation term, and q_b represents the rate of heat transfer to the system by radiation, induction, and internal heat sources. This equation is of general validity and applies to compressible and incompressible flow, as well as reacting systems. Heat of reaction ΔH_r for the latter is contained in the enthalpy term DH/Dt but is somewhat cumbersome to extract. It is more convenient, in these cases, to formulate the model by the classical "in – out = change" approach (see Practice Problem 8.3.1).

In what follows we confine ourselves to nonreacting systems and address the following topics:

- Conduction with laminar convection (Illustration 8.3.1)
- Conduction with a moving boundary (Illustration 8.3.2)
- Heat transfer in a packed bed (Illustration 8.3.3)
- Unsteady conduction (Illustration 8.3.4)
- Steady-state multidimensional conduction (Illustration 8.3.5)

Illustration 8.3.1   The Graetz-Lévêque Problem (Yet Again!)

The PDEs pertinent to this problem have previously been derived in Chapter 7, Illustration 7.2.1 (the Graetz problem) for a cylindrical tube, using the classical in – out = 0 approach. Here we use the generalized energy balance, Equation 8.3.2, as a starting point, neglecting pressure and viscous dissipation terms which are insignificant compared to enthalpy and conduction, and omitting $\rho\, q_b$ which does not apply here. For constant thermal conductivity we then obtain the reduced form:

$$\rho \frac{D}{Dt} H = k\nabla^2 T \tag{8.3.3}$$

This equation applies to any arbitrary duct geometry. The convective derivative DH/Dt is next decomposed using the Relation 8.1.39 and we obtain:

$$\rho \frac{\partial H}{\partial t} + (\rho \mathbf{v} \cdot \nabla)H = k\nabla^2 T \tag{8.3.4}$$

As a further step, we introduce the auxiliary enthalpy relation:

$$H = C_p\, (T - T_0) + H_0$$

which reduces Equation 8.3.3 with no loss of generality (except k = const.) to the form:

$$\frac{\partial T}{\partial t} + \mathbf{v} \cdot \nabla T = \alpha \nabla^2 T \tag{8.3.5}$$

To apply this equation to a cylindrical tube with steady flow, we drop the time derivative and draw on our dictionary Table 8.1 to identify components of the

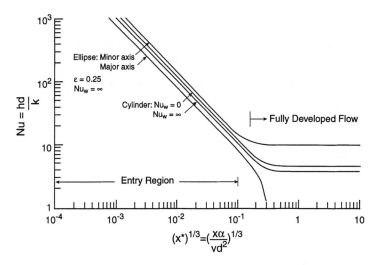

FIGURE 8.7 Local Nusselt numbers as a function of dimensionless distance for steady heat transfer in tubular flow.

differential operators. The final form obtained, neglecting axial conduction, is identical to that derived by classical means in Illustration 7.2.1:

$$v(r)\frac{\partial T}{\partial x} = \alpha\left[\frac{\partial^2 T}{\partial r^2} + \frac{1}{r}\frac{\partial T}{\partial r}\right] \qquad (7.2.44)$$

where the velocity will in general vary with radial distance.

The Graetz problem was previously alluded to on several occasions in the context of the corresponding mass transfer problem. Here we address it in its original form which deals with the steady radial and axial temperature profiles in tubular flow for different boundary conditions. The distributions initially obtained are converted into equivalent Nusselt numbers Nu = hd/k using the thermal equivalent of Equation 8.2.30. Plots of local Nusselt numbers, i.e., those which prevail at a particular axial position x are shown in Figure 8.7 for cylindrical and elliptical ducts as a function

of dimensionless distance $x^* = \dfrac{x\alpha}{vd^2}$. Several features are of note.

The functional form of the Nusselt number shows three distinct domains for ducts of all shapes.

1. The *entry region*, in which Nu varies with the negative 1/3 power of dimensionless distance and which prevails for values $x^* < 10^{-3}$. Here the principal resistance to heat transfer resides in a thin boundary layer near the wall.

TABLE 8.10
Nusselt Numbers for Laminar Tubular Flow and
Boundary Conditions of Type I

Duct Geometry	Entry Region	Fully Developed Region
Cylinder	$Nu = 1.08\left(\dfrac{x\alpha}{vd^2}\right)^{-1/3}$	$Nu = 3.66$
Parallel planes	$Nu = 1.23\left(\dfrac{x\alpha}{vd^2}\right)^{-1/3}$	$Nu = 7.54$
Annulus, $d_i/d_0 = 0.5$	$Nu = 1.29\left(\dfrac{x\alpha}{vd^2}\right)^{-1/3}$	—
Square	—	$Nu = 2.98$
Triangular	—	$Nu = 2.47$

2. The *fully developed region* that comes about with the penetration of the boundary layer to the center line of the duct. This domain starts at an approximate value of $x^* \approx 0.03$ and exhibits constant Nusselt numbers.
3. *A transition region* that falls between the two aforementioned domains and spans the approximate range $10^{-3} < x^* < 0.03$.

A compilation of Nusselt Numbers which apply to the entry and fully developed regions are given for some common tubular geometries in Table 8.10.

Variations of Nu with the type of wall boundary condition imposed are slight. The plots shown, which apply to a Type I boundary condition, have the lowest Nusselt numbers, with those for the other extreme of a Type II BC being generally 10 to 15% higher value for Type III BCs lie inbetween.

For noncircular tubular cross-sections, Nusselt numbers vary along the perimeter as well and these variations can be quite significant, as shown by the elliptical duct of Figure 8.7.

Nusselt numbers for laminar tubular flow also are often presented in so-called log-mean form, $(Nu)_{lm}$. These are values which have been averaged over the axial distance as well and cast in a form suitable for direct substitution into the heat exchanger design equation we had given in Chapter 3, Section 3.2:

$$q = UA(LMTD) \tag{3.3.17}$$

where $1/U = 1/h_{lm} + 1/h_{shell}$.

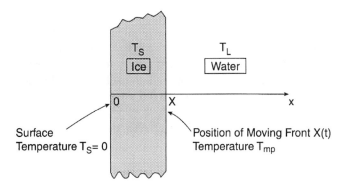

FIGURE 8.8   A moving boundary problem — freezing of water in a semi-infinite medium.

Illustration 8.3.2   A Moving Boundary Problem: Freezing in a Semi-Infinite Solid

We had previously encountered moving boundary problems on a number of occasions, principally in the context of freeze-drying of food (Chapter 3, Illustration 3.3.12) and burning fuel droplets (Chapter 4, Illustration 4.3.2). Additional examples were given in Practice Problem 3.3.5. The treatment used there was an approximate one, based on the assumption that (1) the front moved slowly so that the quasi-steady-state assumption could be applied to the exterior domain, and (2) that the interior domain could be considered "well-stirred," i.e., with a uniform state variable which changed with time only. This resulted in a reduction of the model to the ODE/AE level.

We now wish to take up a rigorous formulation of the problem, using freezing in a semi-infinite medium as an example. The situation is depicted in Figure 8.8, where x is the coordinate of the medium and X(t) that of the ice front. At time t = 0, a surface temperature T(0,t) = 0 < T_0 is imposed upon a liquid initially at T(x,0) = T_0. Conduction in the two phases obeys Fourier's equation, i.e., we have:

$$\frac{\partial T_L}{\partial t} = \alpha_L \frac{\partial^2 T_L}{\partial x^2} \tag{8.3.6}$$

with boundary condition:

$$T_L(\infty,t) = T_0 \tag{8.3.7}$$

and

$$\frac{\partial T_S}{\partial t} = \alpha_S \frac{\partial^2 T_S}{\partial x^2} \tag{8.3.8}$$

with boundary condition:

$$T_S(0,t) = 0 \tag{8.3.9}$$

where the subscripts $_S$ and $_L$ refer to solid and liquid respectively.

Solutions of these PDEs take a standard error function form found in the literature, but since they each have only one BC, the solutions will contain unknown integration constants. Thus, for Equations 8.3.6 and 8.3.7 we have the solution:

$$T_L = T_0 - B \text{ erfc}[x/2(\alpha_L t)^{1/2}] \tag{8.3.10}$$

and for Equations 8.3.8 and 8.3.9:

$$T_S = A \text{ erf }[x/2(\alpha_S t)^{1/2}] \tag{8.3.11}$$

The evaluation of A and B require additional BCs which must come from conditions at the ice front.

The first of these is a statement of temperature equality at the interface. Thus,

$$T_S(X,t) = T_L(X,t) = T_{mp} \tag{8.3.12}$$

where T_{mp} is the melting point. Equation 8.3.12 would ordinarily suffice to obtain A and B, but the new variable X requires an additional relation. This is given by an energy balance over the moving interface which takes account of the liberated heat of freezing. We consider in the first instance a finite domain of ± Δx on either side of the front and an associated time interval Δt. This leads to the balance.

Energy in over Δt − Energy out over Δt = Change over Δt

$$\left[--k_L A \frac{\partial T_L}{\partial X}\bigg|_{X+\Delta x}\right]\Delta t - \left[--k_L A \frac{\partial T_S}{\partial X}\bigg|_{X+\Delta x}\right]\Delta t = \Delta(H_L + H_S) \tag{8.3.13}$$

Note that Fourier's law takes a double negative sign here since conduction is in the negative x-direction.

If we now set $H_L = 0$ (for example), then H_S is given by:

$$H_S = \Delta H_p \, \rho A(-\Delta X) \tag{8.3.14}$$

where ΔH_f = heat of freezing (a negative quantity). Dividing by AΔt and going to the limit then yields:

$$k_S \frac{\partial T_S}{\partial X} - k_L \frac{\partial T_L}{\partial X} = \Delta H_f \, \rho \frac{dX}{dt} \tag{8.3.15}$$

It looks, at this stage, as if Equations 8.3.10 and 8.3.11 will have to be substituted into Equation 8.3.15 and integrated, and the resulting expression used in Equation

8.3.12 to evaluate the integration constants A and B. A clever and valid ploy is used to avoid this messy procedure. We note that substitution of the ice temperature into the boundary condition 8.3.12 yields:

$$A \, \text{erf} \, [X/2(\alpha_s t)^{1/2}] = T_{mp} \qquad (8.3.16)$$

and argue that since the melting point is a constant, the error function argument must also be a constant. This requires:

$$X = C2(\alpha_s)^{1/2} \qquad (8.3.17)$$

where the proportionality constant C is evaluated from the interface BC 8.3.12 and 8.3.15. The resulting nonlinear equation is somewhat unwieldy but its solution manageable by numerical means. With the value of C in hand, and the integration constants evaluated from Equation 8.3.12, the solutions become explicit. Thus, for the solid temperature we obtain the following simple expression:

$$T_s = \frac{T_{mp}}{\text{erf} \, C} \, \text{erf}[x / 2(\alpha_s t)^{1/2}] \qquad (8.3.18)$$

where C comes from the solution of the aforementioned nonlinear equation.

Comments:

The novel aspects in this problem are the formulation of the interface boundary conditions 8.3.12 and 8.3.15 which are characteristic of thermal moving boundary problems. Both melting and freezing are described in this fashion, as well as vaporization and condensation phenomena. For reacting systems, the heat of reaction ΔH_r replaces ΔH_f.

The Relation 8.3.17 which at first sight seems to appear out of nowhere, in fact, is based on solid arguments. It takes insight and some perseverance, however, to deduce it from Equation 8.3.16.

The nonlinear equation in the parameter C which results shows, albeit indirectly, that moving boundary problems are inherently nonlinear and generally require numerical methods of solution. The procedure outlined above, however, keeps the numerical work at a minimum and arrives at explicit expression for the state variables T_S and T_L.

Illustration 8.3.3   Heat Transfer in a Packed Bed:
Heat Regenerators

In heat regenerators, also termed heat recuperators, hot and cold fluids are passed in alternating fashion through a solid matrix which in turn absorbs and then releases the heat, the process being repeated cyclically. Beds packed with solid particles are often employed in this application (see Figure 8.9A) and we use this configuration to derive the equations applicable to the heat uptake step. We consider the heat regenerator to be initially at a uniform temperature T_0, with the inlet gas temperature

A. Through-Flow, Fixed Bed

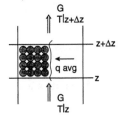

B. Cross-Flow, Moving Bed

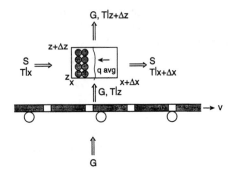

FIGURE 8.9 Heat transfer between a flowing medium and aggregates of solids. The through-flow process (A) is unsteady, the cross-flow process (B) is at steady-state.

at T_i. The heat transfer resistance is assumed to reside principally in the fluid because of its much lower thermal conductivity. Consequently, the solid phase temperature may be considered uniform at a particular position z in the bed and at time t. Axial conduction is neglected compared to lateral heat transfer.

This description evidently holds only during the initial step of the recuperative process which in subsequent cycles will have a nonuniform initial temperature. If, however, the heat transfer front is sharp, as is frequently the case, the degree of nonuniformity will not be severe and the solution will be a good first approximation of the actual process.

To model the process, we use a classical "in – out = change" approach and obtain for an incremental axial distance Δz.

Gas phase energy balance:

$$\text{Rate of energy in} - \text{Rate of energy out} = \frac{\text{Rate of change of}}{\text{energy content}}$$

$$v\rho_f A_C Cp_f (T_f - T_{ref})|_z - \left[\begin{array}{c} v\rho_f A_C Cp_f (T_f - T_{ref})|_{z+\Delta z} \\ +ha(T_f - T_s)_{avg} A_C \Delta z \end{array}\right] = \rho_f Cp_f \varepsilon A_C \Delta z \left(\frac{\partial T}{\partial t}\right)_{avg}$$

$$(8.3.19)$$

where the subscripts $_f$ and $_s$ refer to fluid and solid, A_C is the cross-sectional area of the regenerator, and a = heat transfer area in m^2/m^3 bed. Dividing by $A_C\rho_f Cp_f \Delta z$ and letting $\Delta z \to 0$ yields:

$$-v\frac{\partial T_f}{\partial z} - \frac{ha}{\rho_f Cp_f}(T_f - T_s) = \varepsilon\frac{\partial T_f}{\partial t} \qquad (8.3.20)$$

A similar procedure for the solid phase yields:

Solid phase energy balance:

$$\frac{ha}{\rho_f Cp_f}(T_f - T_s) = \frac{\rho_s Cp_s}{\rho_f Cp_f}\frac{\partial T_s}{\partial t} \qquad (8.3.21)$$

where division by $\rho_f Cp_f$ nondimensionalizes the coefficients.

The reader may have noticed the similarity to the chromatographic process mentioned in Chapter 7 which has an identical configuration, with convective transport of mass replacing the transport of heat being considered here. We reproduce the pertinent equations in rearranged form for comparison below for the case of a linear phase equilibrium $Y^* = q/H$.

$$-v\frac{\partial Y}{\partial z} - \frac{K_{0Y}a}{\rho_f}(Y - q/H) = \varepsilon\frac{\partial Y}{\partial t} \qquad (7.2.4)$$

and

$$\frac{K_{0Y}a}{\rho_f}(Y - q/H) = \frac{\rho_s}{\rho_f}\frac{\partial q}{\partial t} \qquad (7.2.5)$$

Equivalence of terms for the two processes is presented below in the form of a "dictionary." We have:

Heat Transfer	Mass Transfer
T_f	Y
T_s	q/H
1	H
v	v
$\rho_f Cp_f$	ρ_f
$\rho_s Cp_s$	ρ_s
$ha/\rho_f Cp_f$	$K_0 a$

(Hint to the reader: Table 3.6 on mass transfer coefficients can be used to show that $K_{0Y}a/\rho_f = K_0 a$ has units of reciprocal time, as does $ha/\rho_f Cp_f$.)

We now reach back to Chapter 6, Table 6.5, where we had presented values of two dimensionless parameters, $N = K_0 a\, z/v$ and $T = K_0 a (\rho_f t/\rho_b H)$ for 1 and 10% "breakthrough" attained in the adsorption of a solute in a fixed bed of solids. These solutions can be used directly for the prediction of temperature breakthrough, making appropriate use of the dictionary given above. Let us see how this works out for a particular numerical example. We choose the following parameter values, which are good averages for a typical heat recuperation process.

Inlet temperature	$T_i = 1000°C$
Initial bed temperature	$T_0 = 25°C$
Fluid heat capacity	$Cp_f = 1$ kJ/kg K
Solid heat capacity	$Cp_s = 0.5$ kJ/kg K
Fluid density	$\rho_f = 1.0$ kg/m^3
Solid density	$\rho_s = 3000$ kg/m^3
Heat transfer coefficient	ha $= 50$ kJ/sm^{3}K
Height of bed	$z = 10$ m
Velocity	$v = 10$ m/s

With the use of the dictionary one obtains:

$$N = \frac{ha}{\rho_f Cp_f} \cdot \frac{z}{v} = \frac{50}{(1)(1)} \frac{10}{10} = 50 \,(10\% \text{ breakthrough})$$

The time to 10% breakthrough is then given by:

$$t = \frac{\rho_s Cp_s}{ha} T_{sorption} = \frac{(3000)(0.5)}{50} 57 = 1710 \,s$$

or approximately half an hour. This also can be considered as an estimate of the half cycle time so that the full cycle would run for about an hour.

Illustration 8.3.4   Unsteady Conduction

We briefly allude to this case, described by Fourier's equation, in order to present two typical solutions, those for conduction in a sphere and radially in a cylinder with an imposed boundary condition of Type I (Figure 8.10). These solutions are usually given as temperature profiles, rather than in terms of cumulative uptake or release as was the case in mass diffusion (Figure 8.5 and 8.6). A host of other solutions to Fourier's equation in both graphical and analytical form, running literally into the hundreds, if not thousands, can be found in the literature (see references at end of chapter). The plots are given in terms of the fractional approach of the temperature to steady-state $(T - T_0)/T_s - T_0)$, where $T_0 =$ initial temperature, $T_s =$ imposed surface temperature, and the dimensionless Fourier number $Fo = \alpha t/R_0^2$ characteristic of unsteady conduction. Dimensionless radial distance r/R is a parameter. We note the following points in connection with these plots.

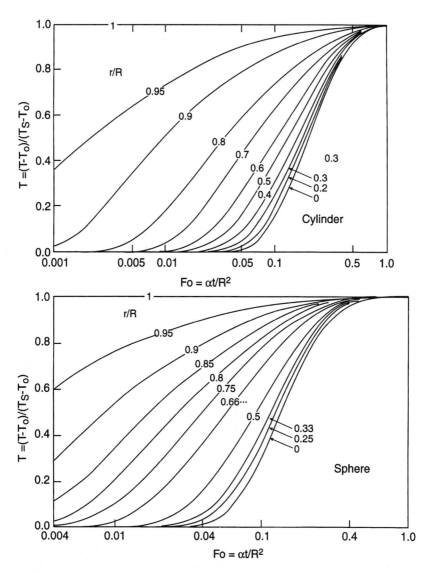

FIGURE 8.10 Dimensionless temperature as a function of the Fourier number in unsteady conduction in a cylinder and a sphere.

Uptake or release in a sphere is faster than in a cylinder, since the heat transfer area per unit volume is larger in the former case. Typically these plots are used to calculate temperatures attained, usually at the surface or center, after a prescribed time interval t. Conversely one can calculate the time required to attain a prescribed temperature. The solutions are not generally used to extract thermal diffusivities from measured temperature profiles since simpler steady-state methods can be applied.

For boundary conditions of Type II and Type III, additional parameters have to be inserted into the solutions and solution plots. For Type III BCs the dimensionless

Biot number $Bi = \dfrac{h_f d}{k_s}$ is used, where h_f is the external convective film coefficient and k_s is the conductivity of the solid. That number had previously been alluded to in Illustration 3.3.3. Note that the Nusselt number $Nu = h_f d/k_f$ is similar in appearance but contains the fluid rather than the solid thermal conductivity.

Illustration 8.3.5   Steady-State Temperatures and Heat Flux in Multidimensional Geometries: The Shape Factor

The topic of steady-state conduction between two isothermal surfaces was briefly taken up in Illustration 8.1.6 in connection with the corresponding case of steady mass diffusion between surfaces at constant concentration. Both these cases are described by Laplace's equation and both make use of the so-called shape factor S which is derived from its solution. S can then be used to calculate heat flux from the convenient linear relation:

$$q'(J/s) = kS(T_1 - T_2) \tag{8.2.45}$$

where S has the dimension of length. Table 8.10 gives a short tabulation of the more common geometries and their associated shape factors. Note that for items 1, 2, 5, 9, and 10, heat flux is given as $q''(J/sm)$, i.e., per unit length of the "buried" objects which extend into the paper to infinity.

The simple Expression 8.2.45 hides the fact that the underlying process is one of considerable complexity. To obtain the shape factor S, one must first solve Laplace's equation which for the complex geometries in question is usually done by conformal mapping. This results in temperature distributions of the type we had listed in Figure 7.7. To obtain the heat flux, the temperature gradient at the buried object has to be derived from the primary T-distribution, and that gradient integrated over the surface of the buried object. The result is then matched to the Expression 8.2.45 to yield the shape factor S which is tabulated in Figure 8.11.

Practice Problems

8.3.1 Temperature Transients in a Tubular Reactor — Consider a nonisothermal tubular reactor with an irreversible reaction A → products taking place in it. Show that for constant pressure operation, the temperature transients, occasioned for example by fluctuations in the feed, is given by:

$$Cp_v v \frac{\partial T}{\partial z} - \Delta H_r r_A - \frac{UP}{A}(T - T_{ext}) = Cp_v \frac{\partial T}{\partial t} \tag{8.3.22}$$

where Cp_v = volumetric heat capacity of the reaction mixture. Use the classical "in – out = change" approach.

8.3.2 Entry Length for Laminar Flow Heat Transfer — Entry length refers to the length of conduit necessary to establish fully developed temperature profiles,

Shape	Formula	Condition
1. Thin vertical strip in semi-infinite solid		
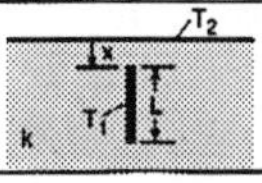	$S = 2.38/(x/L)^{0.24}$	$\frac{1}{2} < \frac{x}{L} < 12$
2. Thin horizontal strip in simi-infinite solid		
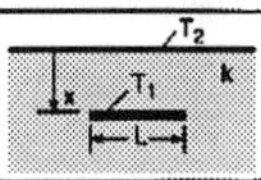	$2.94/(x/L)^{0.32}$	$\frac{1}{2} < \frac{x}{L} < 12$
3. Thin rectangular plate in semi-infinite solid		
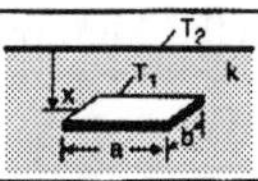	a) $\pi a \ln(4a/b)$ b) $2\pi a \ln(2\pi x/b)$ c) $2\pi a \ln(4a/b)$	$x = 0$ $a \gg b,\ x > 2b$ $x \gg a$
4. Thin circular disk in semi-infinite solid		
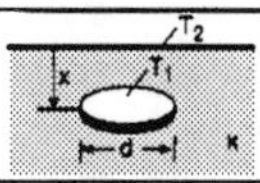	$2d$ $4d$	$x = 0$ $x \gg d$
5. Rectangular hole in semi-infinite solid		
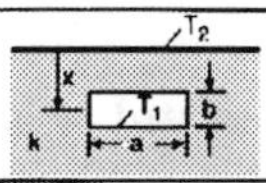	$(a/2b+5.7)/$ in $(3.5x/a^{1/4}b^{3/4})$	$a > b$
6. Spherical hole in semi-infinite solid		
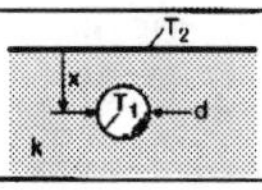	$2\pi d/(1-d/4x)$	$x > d/2$ $x \gg d$
7. Vertical circular surface hole in semi-infinite solid		
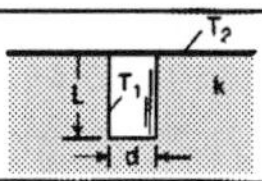	$2\pi L/(4L/d)$	$L > d$
8. Horizontal circular hole in semi-infinite solid		
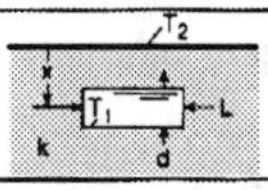	a) $2\pi L/\ln(4x/d)$ b) $2\pi L/\ln(2L/d)$	$d < x < L$ $x \gg d$
9. Circular hole in square solid		
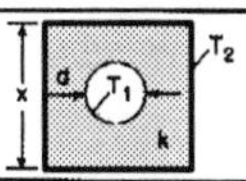	$2\pi/\ln(1.08x/d)$	$x > d$
10. Eccentric circular hole in cylindrical solid		
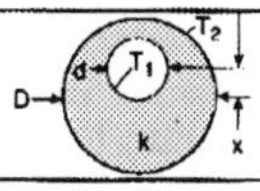	$2\pi/\cosh^{-1}[(D^2+d^2-4x^2)/2Dd]$	$D > d$

FIGURE 8.11 Shape factors.

i.e., the distance from the inlet required to allow the thermal boundary layer to penetrate to the tubular centerline. When that point is reached, the Nusselt number becomes constant (see Figure 8.7).

(a) Show that for laminar flow heat transfer in a cylindrical tube with a Type I boundary condition, the thermal entry length L is given by the approximate expression:

$$L/d \cong 0.03\ \text{Re Pr} \tag{8.3.23}$$

where the product Re Pr is also known as the Peclet Number Pe = vd/α.

(b) Derive the corresponding expression for laminar flow mass transfer.

8.3.3 Steam Heated Tube in the Entry Region (Laminar Flow) — Viscous fluids such as glycerol, which has a Prandtl number of the order 10^3 at room temperature, can have entry lengths of several meters (cf. Equation 8.3.23). Heating of such fluids in conventional heat exchangers will consequently lie entirely in the entry or Lévêque region. Consider the case of a viscous fluid being heated by isothermally condensing steam in a single-pass shell and tube heat exchanger. Show that the fluid temperature profile T(x) is given by the expression:

$$T_s - T = (T_s - T_i) \exp\left[-\frac{1.62\,\pi k}{FCp}\left(\frac{\alpha}{vd^2}\right)^{-1/3} x^{2/3}\right] \qquad (8.3.24)$$

(Hint: Consult Table 8.10.)

8.3.4 Temperature Rise in a Slit Due to Friction — The heat generated by laminar flow friction resides in the viscous dissipation term $\mu\phi$ of Equation 8.3.2, where ϕ is a function of the velocity components of the laminar flow field. For one-dimensional flow in a parallel plane channel, that dependence is given by the expression:

$$\phi = \left(\frac{\partial v_x}{\partial y}\right)^2 \qquad (8.3.25)$$

where x is the direction of flow, perpendicular to the coordination directly y.

Consider the case of steady liquid flow in a channel with both plates kept at the constant temperature T_w, with the heat generated by friction being lost by conduction to the walls. Show that the maximum temperature due to friction occurs at the centerline and is given by:

$$T_{Max} - T_w = \frac{1}{3}\mu\frac{v^2{}_{Max}}{k} \qquad (8.3.26)$$

(Hint: Use Equation 8.3.2 as a starting point and omit inapplicable terms. Use Equation 8.1.39 and Table 8.1 to convert to scalar form.)

Comment:

A similar case of conversion of mechanical energy into thermal energy occurs in Practice Problem 3.3.10 which considers the adiabatic temperature rise in turbulent flow caused by the pumping of a fluid in a closed loop.

8.3.5 Cross-Flow Heating of Solids — Loose granular solids can be heated by passing a hot gas through a perforated moving belt carrying the solids in cross-flow to the incoming gas (Figure 8.9B). Temperatures at any particular position x, z are then time-invariant, in contrast to the situation found in fixed-bed through-flow heating (Figure 8.9A and Illustration 8.3.3), which is an unsteady process.

Consider the differential element shown in Figure 8.9B and perform steady-state, "in − out = 0" energy balances in the gas and solid phases, with S kg/s of solids moving in the x-direction and G kg/s of gas in the z-direction. Show that the resulting PDEs are of exactly the same form as the through-flow Equations 8.3.20 and 8.3.21, when the unsteady term in Equation 8.3.20, which is of minor significance, is dropped. Solutions to the cross-flow problem can then be drawn from the same source as was used in Illustration 8.3.3, with the horizontal distance x replacing time t, and other parameters suitably changed. Make a small dictionary of the substitutions that have to be made.

Comments:

A similar problem, in which granular solids had to be cooled by air in cross-flow to the moving solids was encountered before in Chapter 6, Illustration 6.3.9. Because of the simple asymptotic approach used there, neither horizontal nor vertical temperature variations were considered. The more detailed treatment considered here does not involve an excessive amount of additional work since the answers can be obtained quickly from literature solution of similar problems or tabulations given in this text (Table 6.5).

Cross-flow processes of the type described are also extensively used in the drying of granular solid with heated air. The reader is invited to consider what additional terms would be needed in the heat transfer model to represent the drying process.

8.3.6 Heat Sealing of Plastic Sheets — Sheets of plastic and other materials are frequently bonded together by applying heated elements (platens) to the surfaces of the sheets. In order to establish the proper heating cycle, it is necessary to know the time required for the interface to reach a specified sealing temperature. Using literature solutions, calculate this quantity for the following three cases:

1. Both upper and lower platens are kept at a constant temperature T_p.
2. The upper platen is at T_p, the lower is "neutral," i.e., neither heated nor cooled. The thermal diffusivity of the platen is assumed to be approximately that of the plastic sheets and their dimensions are large compared to the thickness of the sheet. This is the most common situation.
3. The upper platen is at T_p, the lower platen is cooled to maintain its temperature at the initial value T_i.

Data:
   Initial temperature $T_i = 25°C$
   Upper platen temperature $T_p = 200°C$
   Required sealing temperature $T_s = 100°C$
   Thickness of each sheet L = 5 mm
   Thermal diffusivity $\alpha = 1.6 \cdot 10^{-7}$ m²/s

Contact resistance is to be neglected. Calculated values are consequently minimum times.

(Hint: Consult both the conduction and diffusion literature.)

Answer: (1) 51 s; (2) 124 s; (3) 141 s

8.3.7 Heat Losses from a Buried Steam Pipe — A steam pipe conveying 0.05 kg/s steam superheated to 125°C and a dew-point of 110°C is to be installed underground at a depth to the pipe centerline of 1 m. The question arises as to whether the pipe should be insulated to prevent condensation.

(a) Calculate the temperature to which the steam would be cooled without condensation, using Figure 8.11.
(b) What minimum thickness of insulation is needed to prevent condensation?

Data:
   Pipe diameter d = 10 cm
   Pipe length L = 50 m
   Soil thermal conductivity k = 0.5 W/mK
   Ground temperature T_2 = 25°C
   Steam heat capacity Cp = 2 kJ/kg K

Answer: (a) 105°C

Comment:
   Soil conductivities can vary considerably depending on moisture content, porosity, and composition. The cited value is an "average" conductivity and should be increased by an appropriate safety factor before proceeding to part (b). Note that k for dry solids is ~ 0.35 W/mK, for wet solid as high as 2.6 W/mK.

8.4 TRANSPORT OF MOMENTUM

We turn, in this last section of the chapter, to the task of establishing a generalized momentum or force balance to complement the generalized mass and energy balances of the preceding sections. Here it is convenient to dispense with the generalized transport theorem and start directly with a general statement of Newton's law, applied to a moving "packet" of fluid of fixed mass. The convective derivative then appears in a natural way and we obtain:

$$\rho \frac{D\vec{v}}{Dt} = \sum F_b + \sum F_s$$

$$\underbrace{\qquad}_{\substack{\text{Body forces} \\ \text{per unit volume}}} \quad \underbrace{\qquad}_{\substack{\text{Surface forces} \\ \text{per unit volume}}}$$

(8.4.1)

Here the body forces include gravitational, thermal, electrical, and magnetic forces, while the term $\sum F_s$ deals mainly with forces arising from viscous stresses on the fluid element. Those stresses depend on the nature of the fluid, i.e., whether Newtonian or non-Newtonian (Bingham, Viscoelastic, etc. fluids). The stresses for these various cases consist of nine component tensors which can in turn be related to the more convenient velocity gradients. One such relation based on linear or Hookean deformation, i.e., for so-called Newtonian fluids, was derived by Stokes and can be used directly in the force balance previously derived by Navier. We dispense with the details of this part of the development which can be found in standard texts on transport phenomena (see References) and present instead a first version of the generalized momentum balance, applicable to Newtonian flow of constant density and expressed in terms of velocity components. We have:

$$\rho \frac{D\mathbf{v}}{Dt} = -\nabla p + \rho \mathbf{g} + \mu \nabla^2 \mathbf{v} \qquad (8.4.2)$$

or alternatively,

$$\frac{\partial}{\partial t}\mathbf{v} \quad + \quad (\mathbf{v}\cdot\nabla)\mathbf{v} \quad = \quad -\frac{1}{\rho}\nabla p \quad + \quad \mathbf{g} \quad + \quad \nu\nabla^2 \mathbf{v}$$

$$(8.4.3)$$

| Unsteady term | Convective term | Pressure term | Gravitation | Viscous term |

where $(\mathbf{v}\cdot\nabla)\mathbf{v}$ is the convective operator, and $\nabla^2\mathbf{v}$ the Laplacian of the velocity vector, both of which we had tabulated in the "dictionary" Table 8.1. These expressions represent the vectorial formulations of the Navier-Stokes equations. The following points need to be noted.

Equations 8.4.2 and 8.4.3 represent three scalar PDEs that together with the continuity equation describe the velocity and pressure distributions in a viscous, Newtonian flow field. To obtain the scalar components, use is made of the "dictionary" shown in Table 8.1. Thus, for the x-component in Cartesian coordinates, the dictionary yields:

$$\frac{\partial v_x}{\partial t} \quad + \quad v_x \frac{\partial v_x}{\partial x} + v_y \frac{\partial v_x}{\partial y} + v_z \frac{\partial v_x}{\partial z} \quad = \quad -\frac{1}{\rho}\frac{\partial p}{\partial x} \quad + \quad \nu\left[\frac{\partial^2 v_x}{\partial x^2} + \frac{\partial^2 v_x}{\partial y^2} + \frac{\partial^2 v_s}{\partial z^2}\right]$$

| Unsteady | Intertial or convective | Pressure | Viscous term |

$$(8.4.4)$$

Note that the convective term is nonlinear.

The Navier-Stokes equations hold for viscous Newtonian flow with constant density and viscosity. For compressible and non-Newtonian flow, one has to return to the tensorial form of the shear stresses and convert them to velocity gradients through use of appropriate relations.

Consideration of body forces was limited to gravity only. Other body forces, such as the buoyancy forces which arise in free convection, have to be added to the Navier-Stokes equations. The gravity force itself is usually taken in the vertical direction z only and can be expressed by the equivalent terms:

$$\mathbf{g} = g\nabla z = g\mathbf{k} \tag{8.4.5}$$

where we have made use of the fact that $\nabla z = \dfrac{\partial z}{\partial x}\mathbf{i} + \dfrac{\partial z}{\partial y}\mathbf{j} + \dfrac{\partial z}{\partial z}\mathbf{k} = \mathbf{k}.$

In what follows, we present a number of illustrations, each one of which will deal with a particular reduced form of the Navier-Stokes equation. We take up in turn the following topics:

- Duct flow (Illustration 8.4.1)
- Creeping flow (Illustration 8.4.2)
- Boundary layer flow (Illustration 8.4.3)
- Inviscid flow (Illustration 8.4.4)
- Irrotational flow (Illustration 8.4.5)

Illustration 8.4.1   Steady, Fully Developed Incompressible Duct Flow

We consider flow in a duct of arbitrary cross-section and place it in a Cartesian framework. The aim here will be to develop working expressions like the Poiseuille or Fanning equations which will allow us to calculate pressure drop as a function of volumetric flow rate Q or average velocity v. The following simplifications apply:

$$v_y = v_z = 0 \text{ (Impermeable walls)} \tag{8.4.6a}$$

$$\frac{\partial \mathbf{v}}{\partial t} = 0 \text{ (Steady flow)} \tag{8.4.6b}$$

$$\frac{\partial v_x}{\partial x} = 0 \text{ (Continuity)} \tag{8.4.6c}$$

$$\frac{\partial p}{\partial x} = \Delta p / L \text{ (Constant pressure drop)} \tag{8.4.6d}$$

Condition 8.4.6a implies that only one velocity component, v_x, needs to be considered; hence, one component momentum balance, that in the x-direction, suffices. Introducing the simplifications (Equations 8.4.6), that equation becomes:

$$0 = \frac{\Delta P}{L} + \mu\left[\frac{\partial^2 v_x}{\partial y^2} + \frac{\partial^2 v_x}{\partial z^2}\right] \tag{8.4.7}$$

We note that Equation 8.4.7 is of the same form as the classical Poisson equation:

$$\nabla^2 u + f(x,y,z) = 0$$

which is linear and can be solved by a variety of standard methods. The fact that $\Delta P/L$ is a constant, albeit an unknown one, simplifies the solution, which takes the form:

$$v_x = f(y,z,\Delta p/L) \tag{8.4.8}$$

Note that solutions also are available from other disciplines which deal with Poisson's equation (see Practice Problem 8.4.7).

The question now arises as to how these two-dimensional velocity distributions are to be translated into expressions for engineering use. Usually one wishes to retain the form of the Fanning Equation 3.4.5 as a working expression, and this requires extracting an appropriate friction factor f_{avg}, properly averaged over the perimeter of the duct, from the primary solution Equation 8.4.8. To do this, we reach back to Chapter 1, Table 1.2, where we had cited a relation between friction factor f and wall shear stress τ_w. We obtain for the present case:

$$f_{avg} = \frac{2(\tau_w)_{avg}}{\rho v^2} = \frac{2}{\rho v^2 P}\int_P \tau_w \, dP \tag{8.4.9}$$

τ_w is related to the velocity gradients via extensions of Newton's viscosity law. Thus, for a square duct with side b, the average shear stress would be given by:

$$\tau_w = \frac{1}{P}\int_P \tau_w \, dP = \frac{1}{4b}\left[2\int_0^b \frac{\partial v_x}{\partial y}\,dy + 2\int_0^b \frac{\partial v_x}{\partial z}\,dz\right] \tag{8.4.10}$$

Values for f_{avg} have been computed for a large number of duct geometries and are available in the specialized literature (see References). A short compilation for rectangular and triangular ducts is given in Table 8.11 in terms of the product $f\,Re_{d_h}$ where Re_{d_h} is computed for the hydraulic diameter $d_h = 4$ cross-sectional area/wetted perimeter. The changes with b/a and α are seen to be relatively modest. To obtain a sense of the magnitude of the pressure losses involved, consider the rather academic example of water flow, $v = 1$ cm/s, through a square duct of width $b = 1$ cm and length $L = 1$ m. With a kinematic viscosity for water at 25° of $v = 10^{-6}$ m²/s, we obtain:

$$d_h = 4b^2 / 4b = b = 10^{-2} \text{ m}$$

$$Re = \frac{vd_h}{v} = \frac{10^{-2}\,10^{-2}}{10^{-6}} = 100$$

$$f(b/a) = 56.9 / Re_{d_h} = 56.9/100 = 0.569$$

The Fanning equation then yields the following pressure drop:

TABLE 8.11
Friction Factor for Laminar Flow in
Noncircular Ducts

Rectangular		Isosceles Triangular	
b/a	$f\,Re_{d_h}$	Apex angle α, deg	$f\,Re_{d_h}$
0.0	96.0	0	48.0
0.1	84.7	10	51.6
0.25	72.9	30	53.3
0.50	62.2	50	52.0
0.75	57.9	70	49.5
1.0	56.9	90	48.0

$$\Delta p = 4f\rho\frac{v^2}{2}\frac{L}{d} = (4)(0.569)(1000)\frac{(10^{-2})^2}{2}\frac{1}{10^{-2}}$$

$$\Delta p = 11.4 \text{ Pa}$$

Illustration 8.4.2   Creeping Flow

The principal difficulty in solving the Navier-Stokes equation, apart from its dimensionality, resides in the nonlinear convective term $(\mathbf{v} \cdot \nabla)\mathbf{v}$. That term was neatly eliminated in the previous illustration by virtue of the Conditions 8.4.6, leaving us with a single linear PDE of the Poisson type. A similar result can be achieved by assuming the flow to be very slow, so that the convective term becomes small in comparison to the viscous term. We then refer to the system as being in *creeping flow*. This approximation is used in a number of applications of practical importance.

Low Reynolds number external flow around submerged bodies ($Re_p < 1$). The celebrated Stokes law for the drag on a submerged sphere, Equation 3.4.8 is directly derived from the velocity and pressure distributions arrived at by the solution of the linearized Navier-Stokes equation.

Slow viscous flow in narrow passages of varying cross-section. This topic is usually treated under the heading *lubrication theory.*

Incompressible flow through porous media, a vast subject with a number of important subtopics: filtration, reservoir, and petroleum engineering, groundwater seepage, geohydrology, etc.

In most of these cases, except flow through porous media (see Practice Problem 8.4.3), gravity forces are neglected and one winds up with the following operative equations:

Continuity equation $\quad\quad\quad\quad \nabla \cdot \mathbf{v} = 0$ $\quad\quad\quad\quad\quad$ (8.4.11)

Reduced Navier-Stokes equation $\quad \nabla p = \nu\nabla^2\mathbf{v}$ $\quad\quad\quad\quad\quad$ (8.4.12)

This is still a fairly formidable system of four PDEs, albeit linear ones, with dependent variables pressure p and the three velocity components. We now proceed to simplify this system and, in doing so, make fruitful use of certain operations of vector calculus presented in Section 8.1.

We start by noting that one can quickly decouple pressure and velocity by forming the divergence of Equation 8.4.12, i.e., by dot multiplying both sides with $\nabla \cdot$. There results, by virtue of formula 14 of Table 8.5,

$$\nabla \cdot \nabla p = \mu[\nabla \cdot \nabla(\nabla \cdot \mathbf{v}) - \nabla \cdot \nabla x(\nabla x \mathbf{v})] \tag{8.4.13}$$

The left side is immediately seen to be the Laplacian of p. The first term on the right vanishes because of the continuity equation 8.4.11, the second term by virtue of the relation 6 in Table 8.5. We thus obtain:

$$\nabla^2 p = 0 \tag{8.4.14}$$

i.e., the pressure distribution in creeping flow is described by Laplace's equation.

We still have the three velocity components of Equation 8.4.12 to contend with but for the two-dimensional case, at least, a reduction to a single PDE is possible. To achieve this for the Cartesian case, we first differentiate the equation with the y-component with respect to x, the x-component with respect to y, and subtract the result to eliminate p. This gives us a third order PDE in v_x and v_y. These two dependent variables are then coalesced into a single variable, the stream function ψ using the relations given in Chapter 7, Table 7.6. A single fourth order PDE in ψ results which is the biharmonic equation:

$$\nabla^4 \psi = \frac{\partial^4 \psi}{\partial x^4} + 2\frac{\partial^4 \psi}{\partial x^2 \partial y^2} + \frac{\partial^4 \psi}{\partial y^4} = 0 \tag{8.4.15}$$

The full creeping flow solution can thus be obtained by solving, independently, Laplace's equation in pressure p, and the biharmonic equation in ψ. The latter is also the governing equation for two-dimensional elasticity problems and solutions found in that discipline are often applicable to creeping flow problems.

Illustration 8.4.3   The Prandtl Boundary Layer Equations

We had already on a number of occasions, referred to boundary layer theory that divides the external flow field around submerged bodies into a thin boundary layer adjacent to the body surface in which viscous effects predominate, while the bulk fluid further away was essentially in inviscid or irrotational flow (Chapter 7, Illustration 7.4.3 and Figure 7.3). This concept, due to Prandtl, has been particularly successful in gas flow and aerodynamics. We re-examine the underlying equations briefly in order to place them on a firmer foundation, limiting ourselves to steady, incompressible two-dimensional flow. The governing equations for this case are given by:

Continuity:

$$\frac{\partial v_x}{\partial x} + \frac{\partial v_y}{\partial y} = 0 \tag{8.4.16}$$

x-Momentum (Navier-Stokes):

$$v_x \frac{\partial v_x}{\partial x} + v_y \frac{\partial v_x}{\partial y} = -\frac{1}{\rho}\frac{\partial p}{\partial x} + \nu\left(\frac{\partial^2 v_x}{\partial x^2} + \frac{\partial^2 v_y}{\partial y^2}\right) \tag{8.4.17}$$

y-Momentum (Navier-Stokes):

$$v_x \frac{\partial v_y}{\partial x} + v_y \frac{\partial v_y}{\partial y} = -\frac{1}{\rho}\frac{\partial p}{\partial y} + \nu\left(\frac{\partial^2 v_y}{\partial x^2} + \frac{\partial^2 v_y}{\partial y^2}\right) \tag{8.4.18}$$

where x is the direction along the wall and y is normal to it.

Prandtl made two crucial assumptions:

1. The velocity component normal to the wall is much smaller than that along it:

$$v_y \ll v_x \tag{8.4.19}$$

2. Changes in the x-direction are much smaller than those in the y-direction, with the result that:

$$\frac{\partial}{\partial x} \ll \frac{\partial}{\partial y} \tag{8.4.20}$$

Applying these relations to the y-momentum equation, we find that all velocity terms disappear and, hence,

$$\frac{\partial p}{\partial y} \approx 0 \tag{8.4.21}$$

In other words, Equation 8.4.18 disappears entirely and pressure varies along the boundary layer only, not through it. This means that the pressure distribution can be recovered from the solution of the inviscid outer field via Bernoulli's equation and Laplace's Equation. The governing model thus has been reduced to the following four relations:

Continuity:

$$\frac{\partial v_x}{\partial x} + \frac{\partial v_y}{\partial y} = 0 \tag{8.4.22}$$

x-Momentum (boundary layer):

$$v_x \frac{\partial v_x}{\partial x} + v_y \frac{\partial v_x}{\partial y} = -\frac{1}{\rho}\frac{\partial p}{\partial x} + v \frac{\partial^2 v_x}{\partial y^2} \tag{8.4.23}$$

Bernoulli equation (inviscid field):

$$U \frac{dU}{dx} = -\frac{1}{\rho}\frac{dp}{dx} \tag{8.4.24}$$

Laplace's equation:

$$\frac{\partial^2 \psi}{\partial x^2} + \frac{\partial^2 \psi}{\partial y^2} = 0 \tag{8.4.25}$$

where the stream function ψ is related to the velocity components v_x, v_y via the expressions given in Chapter 7, Table 7.6 and U is the outer field velocity.

The normal solution procedure then consists of the following steps:

1. Solve Laplace's equation for the outer field and from the stream function ψ recover the corresponding velocity components v_x and v_y.
2. Compute the outer field velocity U from its components: $U = (v_x^2 + v_y^2)^{1/2}$.
3. Introduce the stream function ψ into Equations 8.4.22 and 8.4.23. This has the effect of collapsing the two variables and, hence, the two equations into a single entity. The resulting third order PDE is then reduced to an ODE by similarity transformation and the ODE usually solved numerically. For a flat plate, this ODE is the Blasius Equation 7.3.32.
4. The solutions for the inner and outer regions are "patched together" or matched at the edge of the boundary layer where we typically specify:

$$v/U = 0.99 \tag{8.4.26}$$

This admittedly brief sketch is meant to convey the main steps of the solution procedure which has led to a host of successful solutions. One will note in particular the ingenious simplifications of Prandtl and the use of various classical tools such as the use of the stream function and Laplace's equation to describe the velocity distributions. Evidently a good deal of detail was left out, for which the reader is referred to specialized texts (see References).

Illustration 8.4.4   Inviscid Flow: Euler's Equation of Motion

We describe here briefly the inviscid version of the momentum balance usually attributed to Euler. It takes the form:

$$\rho \frac{D\mathbf{v}}{Dt} = -\nabla p - \rho \mathbf{g} \tag{8.4.27}$$

or

$$\frac{\partial \mathbf{v}}{\partial t} + (\mathbf{v} \cdot \nabla)\mathbf{v} = -\frac{\Delta p}{\rho} - \mathbf{g} \qquad (8.4.28)$$

and is introduced here mainly to provide a stepping stone to the more powerful Bernoulli equation. It also has important applications in the study of waves and open channel flows when one can neglect viscous forces, including wind-induced stresses.

Although the Equations 8.4.27 and 8.4.28 seem to have arisen from the Navier-Stokes Equations 8.4.2 and 8.4.3 valid for incompressible flow, a direct derivation from the force balance Equation 8.4.1 shows that it applies to compressible flow as well. Thus, the Bernoulli equation which we derive below from Euler's equation of motion is quite generally applicable to both compressible and incompressible flow.

Illustration 8.4.5 Irrotational (Potential) Flow: Bernoulli's Equation

To derive Bernoulli's equation from Euler's equation of motion, we start by expanding the convective term $(\mathbf{v} \cdot \nabla)\mathbf{v}$ using the vector relation 13 given in Table 8.5. We obtain, for steady flow:

$$\nabla \frac{1}{2} |\mathbf{v}|^2 - \mathbf{v}x(\nabla x\mathbf{v}) + \frac{1}{\rho}\nabla p + g\nabla z = 0 \qquad (8.4.29)$$

where we also have made use of Equation 8.4.5 to convert the gravity vector $\mathbf{g}$ to the gradient of the vertical distance z. We now introduce the irrotational flow condition $\nabla x\mathbf{v} = 0$ which, as was pointed out in Section 8.1, is in most instances, equivalent to the inviscid condition. This relatively modest increase in the stringency of the conditions imposed leads to an enormous simplification of Euler's equation. We obtain, in the first instance:

$$\nabla\left(\frac{1}{2}|\mathbf{v}|^2\right) + \frac{1}{\rho}\nabla p + g\nabla z = 0 \qquad (8.4.30)$$

where $|\mathbf{v}|$ = magnitude of the velocity vector.

This is beginning to look very much like Bernoulli's equation and a final operation will lead us to that goal. We dot multiply each term of the equation by the differential position vector $d\mathbf{R}$ and invoke Relation 5 of Table 8.5: $\nabla u \cdot d\mathbf{R} = du$. This yields:

$$v\,dv + \frac{1}{\rho}dp + g\,dz = 0 \qquad (8.4.31)$$

which is recognized as the differential form of Bernoulli's equation, applicable to both compressible and incompressible flow.

Comments:

One notices here, as in the case of creeping flow, Illustration 8.4.2, the power of vector notation and the simplicity of the operations, once certain basic tenets have been accepted. Their absence would make the transformation of Euler's equation to Bernoulli's equation a fairly cumbersome task which would have to be repeated for each new coordinate system. The result obtained thus is quite general and not dependent on the geometry of the system.

A careful reading of the present derivation of Bernoulli's equation will reveal that it differs from that given in Chapter 3, Illustration 3.4.7. The latter relies on a force balance performed for inviscid flow on a section of a stream tube and, consequently, required any two positions to which the equation was applied to lie on the same streamline. No such restriction applies here. One can integrate Equation 8.4.31 between any two points of the flow field without violating its validity. The present version is for that reason often referred to as the *Strong Form* of Bernoulli's equation. It must be remembered, however, that this greater freedom was bought at the cost of imposing the somewhat more stringent condition of irrotational flow. In either its "weak" or "strong" form, Bernoulli's equation has become, apart perhaps from the continuity equation, the most frequently used relation in fluid mechanics.

Practice Problems

8.4.1 Radial Velocity Profiles for Small Leakages through a Tubular Wall — Consider a fluid in steady creeping flow through a cylindrical tube with a permeable wall. The leakage velocity v_w is taken to be small, so that we may assume $\dfrac{\partial p}{\partial t} \approx 0$ and $\dfrac{\partial^2 v_x}{\partial x^2} \approx 0$, i.e., axial velocity v_x diminishes linearly with distance x.

(a) Show that the profile of *axial* velocity $v_x(r)$ remains parabolic but is associated with the derivative of pressure dp/dx rather than a constant pressure drop $\Delta p/L$. (Hint: Integrate the x-momentum balance, having first dropped the convective term.)

(b) Show that the profile of the *radial* velocity $v_r(r)$ is given by the following expression:

$$\frac{v_r}{v_w} = 2\frac{r}{R} - \left(\frac{r}{R}\right)^3 \tag{8.4.32}$$

(Hint: Integrate the continuity equation for cylindrical coordinates from 0 to r and from 0 to R to eliminate the pressure gradient. Table 8.1 is of use.)

Comment:

A situation of this type arises in urine flow through the kidney where tubular Reynolds numbers are of the order 10^{-2}. Water and various solutes pass from the blood and through the permeable wall of the tubules into the urine for ultimate elimination from the body.

Equation 8.4.32 has been used to determine radial solute concentration profiles and the magnitude of the internal mass transfer resistance $1/k_f$. What equations would you draw upon for this task?

8.4.2 Velocity Profiles Near a Moving Boundary — Suppose that one of the retaining walls of a parallel plane channel is suddenly set in motion with a constant velocity v_0.

(a) Show that the relation describing the resultant time-dependent velocity profiles is given by the equation:

$$\frac{\partial \mathbf{v}}{\partial t} = \nu \nabla^2 \mathbf{v} \qquad (8.4.33)$$

(b) Indicate what disciplines might provide ready-made solutions to this problem where $\nabla^2 \mathbf{v}$ is the Laplacian of the velocity vector $\mathbf{v}$, and is tabulated in the dictionary Table 8.5.

8.4.3 Flow in Porous Media — Flow in a porous medium is customarily described by the empirical D'Arcy's law which in three dimensions and with gravity included, becomes:

$$\mathbf{v}_s = -\frac{K}{\mu}(\nabla p - \rho \mathbf{g}) \qquad (8.4.34)$$

where $\mathbf{v}_s$ is the superficial velocity vector and K is the permeability of the medium. Show that for incompressible flow with constant K/μ, D'Arcy's law leads to Laplace's equation in the pressure p. Back-substitution into Equation 8.4.34 then yields the velocity profiles which can be integrated to yield total volumetric flow rates. Note that the corresponding case of compressible flow was taken up in Illustration 7.4.1.

8.4.4 Tangential Velocity Distributions Between Rotating Cylinders —

(a) Show that for two concentric cylinders of radius R_i and R_0, with the latter rotating with an angular velocity ω, the tangential velocity v_θ is given by:

$$v_\theta = \omega R_0 \left(\frac{R_i}{r} - \frac{r}{R_i}\right) \Big/ \left(\frac{R_i}{R_0} - \frac{R_0}{R_i}\right) \qquad (8.4.35)$$

(Hint: Integrate the equation for θ momentum, using the BCs $v_\theta(R_i) = 0$, $v_\theta(R_0) = \omega R_0$.)

(b) Derive the corresponding expression for the case of the *inner* cylinder rotating with the outer cylinder held stationary.

8.4.5 Form Drag on a Sphere in Creeping Flow — The pressure distribution for creeping flow around a submerged sphere was derived by Stokes. Neglecting gravity effects (i.e., buoyancy), the relevant expression is given by:

$$p = p_\infty - \frac{3}{2}\frac{\mu v_\infty}{R}\left(\frac{R}{r}\right)^2 \cos\theta \qquad (8.4.36)$$

Integrate this relation over the surface of the sphere to obtain the so-called form drag F_f, i.e., the portion of the total drag due to pressure forces.

Answer: $F_f = 2\pi\mu R v_\infty$

8.4.6 Pressure Drop in Ducts of Different Geometries — Consider three types of ducts: cylindrical, square, and triangular with $\theta = 90°$, all of equal weight, i.e., equal thickness and perimeter. Establish the ratio of pressure drop per unit length for these configurations.

8.4.7 Solutions from Solutions — The steady-state temperature distribution in a rectangle with constant internal heat generation A (J/m³s) and the surfaces $x = \pm a$ and $y = \pm b$ kept at zero temperature is given by the formidable expression:

$$T = \frac{A(a^2 - x^2)}{2k} - \frac{16Aa^2}{k\pi^3} \sum_{n=a}^{\infty} \frac{(-1)^n \cos[(n+1)\pi x / 2a]\cosh(2n+1)\pi y k / 2a}{(2n+1)^3 \cosh(2n+1)\pi bk / 2a} \qquad (8.4.37)$$

What, if any problem discussed in this section, can be solved by this equation? What are the difficulties and how would you proceed?

REFERENCES

8.1 Vector Notation and Calculus: This topic is usually taken up in separate chapters in texts on applied mathematics, among them:

E. Kreyszyg. *Advanced Engineering Mathematics, 7th ed.,* John Wiley & Sons, New York, 1992.

Basics of vector calculus and their application to fluid mechanics can be found in intermediate level texts on the topic such as:

V.L. Streeter, E.B. Wylie, and K.W. Bedford. *Fluid Mechanics, 9th ed.,* McGraw-Hill, New York, 1998.

F.M. White. *Fluid Mechanics, 2nd ed.,* McGraw-Hill, New York, 1986.

J. Szekely. *Fluid Flow Phenomena in Metallurgical Processing,* Academic Press, New York, 1979.

Vector calculus is extensively used as well in monographs on transport phenomena in general. See:

R.B. Bird, W.F. Stewart, and E.N. Lightfoot. *Transport Phenomena,* John Wiley & Sons, New York, 1960.

J.C. Slattery. *Momentum, Energy and Mass Transfer in Continua,* McGraw-Hill, New York, 1972.
The latter gives a derivation of the generalized transport theories.

Texts exclusively devoted to vector analysis include:
H.F. Davis and A.D. Snider. *Introduction to Vector Analysis, 4th ed.,* Allyn and Bacon, Boston, 1979.

An attempt to demystify differential operators is made in the light-hearted:
H.M. Schey. *Div, Grad, Curl and All That,* Norton, New York, 1973.

Discussions of Green's functions, which rank with vector calculus as a topic strenuously avoided by students, is discussed with varying degrees of thoroughness in:
H.S. Carslaw and J.C. Jaeger. *Conduction of Heat in Solids,* Oxford University Press, New York, 1959.
P.R. Garabedian. *Partial Differential Equations,* John Wiley & Sons, New York, 1964.
G.F.D. Duff and D. Naylor. *Differential Equations of Applied Mathematics,* John Wiley & Sons, New York, 1966.
M.D. Weinberg. *Applications of Green's Functions in Science and Engineering,* Prentice-Hall, Upper Saddle River, NJ, 1971.
I. Stakgod. *Green's Functions and Boundary Value Problems,* 2nd ed. John Wiley & Sons, New York, 1998.
R.L. Street. *The Analysis and Solution of Partial Differential Equations,* Brook/Cole, Monterey, CA, 1973.

8.2 Transport of Mass: Mass balances, both in their vectorial and scalar forms are dealt with extensively in the texts on transport phenomena cited above. References for the Graetz-Lévêque problem are cited under Transport of Energy. The definitive monograph on diffusion, both with and without reaction, is by:
J. Crank. *Mathematics of Diffusion, 2nd ed.,* Oxford University Press, New York, 1979.
The text contains analytical as well as numerical solutions of Fick's equation for various geometries and boundary conditions, and for variable diffusion coefficients. References for the shape factor applicable to steady-state diffusion appear in the section on transport of energy. The electrochemical method is described in:
T. Mizushina. *The Electrochemical Method in Transport Phenomena, Advances in Heat Transfer, vol. 7,* Academic Press, New York, 1971, 87–161.

8.3 Transport of Energy: Detailed treatments of this topic are again found in the texts of Bird, Stewart, and Lightfoot, and of Slattery cited above. Solutions to the Graetz-Lévêque problem are given in the admirable compendium:
R.K. Shah and A.L. Loudon. *Source Book of Solutions for Compact Heat Exchangers, Advances in Heat Transfer Supplement I,* Academic Press, New York, 1978.

Moving boundary problems are encountered with such frequency that they have become the domain of specialized monographs. See:
J. Crank. *Free and Moving Boundary Problems,* Oxford Science Publications, Oxford, U.K., 1984.
V. Alexides and A.D. Solomon. *Mathematical Modeling of Melting and Freezing Processes,* Hemisphere, New York, 1993.
M. Zerrpukat and C.R. Chatwin. *Computational Moving Boundary Problems,* John Wiley & Sons, New York, 1994.

See also Carslaw and Jaeger, previously cited, which provides the background for Illustration 8.3.2.

Treatments of heat regenerators and recuperator are found in:
H. Hausen. *Heat Transfer in Counterflow, Parallel Flow and Cross Flow,* McGraw-Hill, New York, 1983.
W.M. Kays and A.L. Loudon. *Compact Heat Exchangers, 3rd ed.,* McGraw-Hill, New York, 1984.

The definitive compilation of solutions to Fourier's equation is the much cited:
H.S. Carslaw and J.C. Jaeger. *Conduction of Heat in Solids, 2nd ed.,* Oxford University Press, New York, 1959.
See also:
V. Arpacci. *Conduction Heat Transfer,* Addison Wesley, Reading, MA, 1966.

Compilations of shape factors for steady-state conduction in multidimensional media appear in:
W.M. Rohsenow, J.P. Hartnett, and E.N. Ganic (Eds.). *Handbook of Heat Transfer Applications, 2nd ed.,* McGraw-Hill, New York, 1985.

8.4 Transport of Momentum: This topic, like the two preceding ones, is dealt with in detail in the aforementioned treatises on transport phenomena. Laminar duct flow and the associated friction factors are taken up in:
R.K. Shah and A.L. London. Source Book of Solutions for Compact Heat Exchangers, *Advances in Heat Transfer, Sup. I,* Academic Press, New York, 1978.

Creeping flow in narrow passages is treated in:
W.E. Langlois. *Slow Viscous Flow,* McMillan, New York, 1964.

For external creeping flow around submerged bodies, see:
J. Happel and H. Brenner. *Low Reynolds Number Hydrodynamics, 2nd ed.,* Noordhoof, Leyden, The Netherlands, 1973.

A multitude of solutions to creeping flow problems can be found in the two classical monographs:
H. Lamb. *Hydrodynamics,* Dover, New York, 1945.
L.M. Milne-Thomson. *Theoretical Hydrodynamics, 4th ed.,* McMillan, New York, 1960.

The related topic of elasticity is taken up in:
S. Timoshenko and J.N. Goodier. *Theory of Elasticity,* McGraw-Hill, New York, 1970.
All three aforementioned monographs make fairly heavy reading.

The definitive treatise on external flows and associated boundary layers is by:
H. Schlichting. *Boundary Layer Theory, 7th ed.,* McGraw-Hill, New York, 1979.

Flow through porous media is taken up in a number of specialized monographs. An advanced level treatment with numerous PDE models and solutions is found in:
J. Baer. *Dynamics of Fluids in Porous Media,* Elsevier, New York, 1962.

9 Solution Methods for Partial Differential Equations

Never before have we had so little time to do so much.

Franklin Delano Roosevelt

In this final chapter, we present outlines of three important classical methods for the solution of partial differential equations. We start with the method of separation of variables which dates back to the 18th century and finds its principal application in the solution of second order homogeneous and linear PDEs. A host of solutions to Fourier's and Fick's equations are arrived at by this method, and we present several illustrations to explain and expand on the procedure. An opening preamble is devoted to the twin topics of Fourier series and orthogonal functions that play a key role in the application of the method of separation of variables.

The second section deals with the Laplace and other integral transform methods, this time in the context of solving partial differential equations. These methods again apply to linear PDEs only, but are capable of handling nonhomogeneous systems as well. They can be used to reach a wider range of the classical PDEs of mathematical physics. While the main focus is on the Laplace transformation, some time is spent in explaining and illustrating the use of the less common integral transforms. We also present an example of Laplace domain analysis that we had applied in Chapter 5 in the context of ordinary differential equations.

The final section introduces the reader to the method of characteristics. This elegant and powerful procedure extends our reach considerably and enables us to address First Order quasilinear, as well as linear PDEs. We limit ourselves to the treatment of single equations, but provide sufficient detail for the reader to grasp the general methodology of the procedure. The solution of systems of quasilinear PDEs, which is a much wider topic, can be pursued in one of the many excellent monographs listed at the end of the chapter.

9.1 SEPARATION OF VARIABLES

9.1.1 ORTHOGONAL FUNCTIONS AND FOURIER SERIES

We open this segment of the chapter with a preamble to introduce the reader to the concepts of orthogonal functions and of Fourier series expansion. Both of these topics make their appearance in the course of solving partial differential equations by separation of variables and it is, therefore, natural to introduce them within the framework of this important solution method. Both orthogonal functions and Fourier series have other important applications, such as the representation of arbitrary functions, but our focus here will be their role in the solution of partial differential equations. In the course of our narrative, we will present some of their general properties, thus preparing the ground for their use in other areas as well.

To demonstrate the genesis of these two concepts — or tools, as they become here — we outline in step-wise fashion the application of the method of separation of variables. We shall see that near the close of the procedure, we reach a seeming impasse which cannot be overcome by conventional means. It is at this point that we introduce the notion of orthogonal functions and Fourier series expansion. In what follows we develop the various steps that lead us to that point.

Step 1 — The essence of the method of separation of variables lies in the assumption that the solution can be expressed as the product of functions of a single variable. Thus, for a PDE in the dependent variable u and in Cartesian coordinates, the solution is assumed to have the general form

$$u = f(x)\ g(y)\ h(z)\ k(t) \qquad (9.1.1)$$

This assumption, the validity of which has to be ultimately proven, can be applied to any arbitrary PDE, but is usually successful only in the case of linear second order homogeneous PDE with constant or variable coefficients. The reasons for the restrictions will become apparent in the course of the development of the procedure.

At times it is possible to provide a physical rationale for the assumed solution form. If the reader will cast a glance back at Chapter 1, Figure 1.1 describing the quenching of a steel billet, it will become apparent that the temperature profiles which arise in this case can be viewed as *sine half waves with a time-dependent amplitude*. It seems reasonable to assume, therefore, that the solution might have the form:

$$T = \sum A(t) \sin bx \qquad (9.1.2)$$

where $A(t)$ is the time-varying amplitude. We have craftily included a summation sign since we surmise that a single sine function will not suffice to represent all profiles, in particular the discontinuous ones which appear at the start of the operation. This concept of using a *sum* of functions to represent another function will, as we shall see, ultimately lead to the notion of a Fourier series expansion.

Step 2 — We introduce the assumed form of Solution 8.1.1 into the PDE. We had previously indicated in Section 7.3 that when this is done for the case of the one-dimensional conduction (Fourier) equation, with an assumed solution form $u = T(t)X(x)$, slight rearrangement of the result led to the expression:

$$\frac{1}{\alpha}\frac{T'(t)}{T(t)} = \frac{X''(x)}{X(x)} \qquad (7.3.3)$$

It was then argued that the two sides, which are functions of different independent variables, can only be equal if they are constant. We, therefore, wrote:

$$\frac{1}{\alpha} \frac{T'(t)}{T(t)} = \frac{X''(x)}{X(x)} = \text{constant} = -\lambda^2 \qquad (7.3.4)$$

where the constant is set $= -\lambda^2$ rather than λ to avoid redundant solutions and square roots.

Note that by this procedure we had reduced the PDE to a set of equivalent ODEs. For PDEs in more than two independent variables, similar results are obtained. This is a major simplification which does, however, hinge on the validity of the assumed solution form. If the PDE had been nonhomogeneous, the product solution would have yielded:

$$\frac{1}{\alpha} T'X = TX'' + f(x,t) \qquad (9.1.3)$$

and the felicitous form Equation 7.3.4 would not have been obtained. This is the principal reason for restricting the method of separation of variables to homogeneous systems.

Step 3 — After this promising start, we turn to the relatively mundane task of solving the ODEs which can usually be accomplished by standard methods. It is to be noted, however, that since λ is arbitrary and yet to be defined, we must accommodate the possibility of λ being zero as well as non-zero. This will in general give rise to two different sets of solutions which we accommodate by invoking the superposition principle, i.e., we argue that since each set is presumed to be a solution to the PDE, their sum must also be a solution. Note that if the PDE had been nonlinear and, thus, ineligible for superposition procedures, the proceedings would have come to a halt at this point. This explains our restriction of the method of separation of variables to *linear PDEs*.

Step 4 — Solution of the ODEs is followed by an evaluation of the integration constants and of the eigenvalues λ. We use for this purpose the available boundary conditions, leaving the initial condition to the last for reasons which will become apparent later. After most of the integration constants have been evaluated and with one BC left over, we may have the following situation:

Solution to this point:

$$u = C \sin(\lambda x) \exp(-K\lambda^2 t) \qquad (9.1.4)$$

Remaining BC:

$$u(a,t) = 0 \qquad (9.1.5)$$

where the latter might represent a normalized temperature or concentration at $x = a$. One sees immediately that this condition can be used to evaluate λ, for with $u = 0$ at $x = a$, we must have $\sin(a\lambda) = 0$, and λ takes on the infinite set of values $\lambda =$

$n\pi/a$ (the so-called eigenvalues of the PDE), with $n = 1,2,3,...$. This neat result would not have come about if Equation 9.1.5 had been nonhomogeneous. We have a second good reason to require homogeneity of both the PDE and the boundary condition for a successful application of the method.

To accommodate this infinite set of solutions we invoke the superposition principle as before so that the solution now becomes:

$$u = \sum_{n=1}^{\infty} C \sin(n\pi x / a) \exp(-Kn^2\pi^2 t / a^2) \qquad (9.1.6)$$

We have here our second glimpse of the dreaded infinite series which crop up regularly in solutions of PDEs. At least now we know the culprit — it is *superposition*.

Step 5 — At this stage we are seemingly left with only one integration constant, C, to be determined, for which we have the initial condition available. This turns out to be the most difficult step and leads to an impasse. For suppose the initial condition were given as:

$$u(x,0) = f(x) = 1 \qquad (9.1.7)$$

representing, for example, a uniform and normalized initial temperature or concentration. Then substitution into the Solution 9.1.4 yields:

$$C = \left[\sum_{n=1}^{\infty} \sin(n\pi x / a) \right]^{-1} \qquad (9.1.8)$$

which is clearly unacceptable since the right side is a function of x and not a constant.

Suppose that we assigned a different constant to each sine term, hoping that by properly weighting them, the sine would converge to unity. This is legitimate as long as the initial condition is satisfied. We would then have:

$$f(x) = 1 = C_1 \sin (\pi x/a) + C_2 \sin (2\pi x/a) + ... C_n \sin (n\pi x/a) + ... \qquad (9.1.9)$$

This may lead to the desired result but compounds our difficulties since an infinite set of constants will now have to be evaluated. It speaks to the genius of the early workers in this field that they not only persisted in this line of attack but ultimately devised a way of evaluating the coefficients. To do this, they drew on two seemingly unrelated and innocuous expressions which are nowadays routinely found in all tables of integrals:

$$\int_0^a \sin(m\pi x / a) \sin(n\pi x / a) dx = 0 \qquad (9.1.10)$$

$$\int_0^a \sin^2(n\pi x / a) dx = a / 2 \qquad (9.1.11)$$

They then multiplied each term of Equation 9.1.9 by $\sin(n\pi x/a)dx$ and integrated from 0 to a. This causes all terms on the right side to vanish except the n-th coefficient which by virtue of Equation 9.1.11 becomes:

$$C_n = \frac{\int_0^a f(x)\sin(n\pi x/a)dx}{\int_0^a \sin^2(n\pi x/a)dx} = \frac{2}{a}\int_0^a 1\sin(n\pi x/a)dx \qquad (9.1.12)$$

or, upon evaluation of the last integral

$$C_n = \frac{2}{n\pi}[1-(-1)^n] \qquad (9.1.13)$$

Thus, we have obtained a general expression for the n-th integration constant and are now in a position to write the infinite series (Equation 9.1.6) in explicit form:

$$u = \frac{2}{\pi}\sum_{n=1}^{\infty}\frac{1}{n}[1-(-1)^n]\sin(n\pi x/a)\exp(-Kn^2\pi^2 t/a^2) \qquad (9.1.14)$$

Comments:
We note that the sequence in which we used the boundary and initial conditions is now justified, for it was the earlier evaluation of λ which led to the infinite series and ultimately the determination of its coefficients. Had the initial condition been introduced prior to that point we would have obtained:

$$C = [\sin(\lambda x)]^{-1} \qquad (9.1.15)$$

a self-contradictory result with no means of resolution.

The need to have a homogeneous PDE as well as homogeneous BCs was justified on several occasions. That requirement, however, does not extend to the initial condition since any nonhomogeneity $f(x)$ can be accommodated easily in the first integral of Equation 9.1.12. This is in agreement with what was stated in Section 7.3.3 of Chapter 7, dealing with the elimination of nonhomogeneous terms. The approach taken there was to accept even severe nonhomogeneities in the initial condition, provided the PDE and remaining BC could be rendered homogeneous. This has now been justified.

We use this occasion to introduce the reader to the terminology associated with these proceedings. We had already referred to λ as the eigenvalues of the PDE. Associated with them are the so-called eigenfunctions $f(\lambda)$, here $\sin\lambda x$. The infinite series (Equation 9.1.9) is referred to as the Fourier series expansion of $f(x) = 1$, the associated constants C_i as Fourier coefficients. Sequences of functions like $\sin(n\pi x/a)$ which obey the type of relations expressed by Equations 9.1.10 and 9.1.11 are referred to as *orthogonal functions*. The latter will be taken up in greater detail below.

The reader may have wondered whether there are other functions with the felicitous properties of sin(nπx/a) and, if so, whether they can be used in the solution of PDEs. The answer to both questions is yes. There are, in fact, a broad range of such orthogonal functions and what is more they arise as solutions of certain linear second order ODEs which in turn are generated in the course of applying the method of separation of variables. The conditions which the ODEs have to satisfy so as to yield an orthogonal set of functions is enshrined in the Sturm-Liouville theorem. We shall take a brief leave from PDEs and separation of variables in order to address these important concepts, as well as Fourier series in general, after which we shall return with further examples of PDE solutions.

9.1.1.1   Orthogonal and Orthonormal Functions

We start with a definition. A sequence of continuous functions $y_1(x)$, $y_2(x)$, ..., $y_n(x)$, ... are said to be orthogonal with respect to the weight function $p(x)$ in the interval $a \leq x \leq b$ if the following two conditions are met:

$$\int_a^b p(x) y_m(x) y_n(x) dx = 0 \tag{9.1.16a}$$

$$\int_a^b p(x) y_n^2(x) dx = C^2 \tag{9.1.16b}$$

where $C \neq 0$ is the so-called norm or normalizing factor. By dividing each y_j by the norm C, we obtain a new set of functions ϕ termed *orthonormal:*

$$\phi_j = y_j/C \tag{9.1.17}$$

and with it a modification of the Conditions 9.1.16:

$$\int_a^b p(x) \phi_m(x) \phi_n(x) dx = 0 \tag{9.1.18a}$$

$$\int_a^b p(x) \phi_n^2(x) dx = 1 \tag{9.1.18b}$$

These new terms are related to the functions of our previous discussion as follows:

Orthogonal functions: $y_m(x) \rightarrow \sin(m\pi x/a)$
$\qquad\qquad\qquad\qquad y_n(x) \rightarrow \sin(n\pi x/a)$
Weight function: $p(x) \rightarrow 1$
(Norm)^2: $C^2 \rightarrow a/2$
Orthonormal function: $\phi_j \rightarrow (2/a)^{1/2} \sin(j\pi x/a)$

TABLE 9.1
Sets of Orthogonal Functions

Set	Interval	Normalizing Factor C	Weight Function
1. $\sin nx$ $n = 0, 1, 2, \ldots$	$(-\pi, \pi)$	$\pi^{1/2}$	1
2. $\cos nx$ $n = 0, 1, 2, \ldots$	$(-\pi, \pi)$	$(\pi/2)^{1/2}, \pi^{1/2}$	1
3. $\sin(n\pi x/a)$ $n = 0, 1, 2, \ldots$	$(0, a)$	$(a/2)^{1/2}$	1
4. $\cos(n\pi x/a)$ $n = 0, 1, 2$	$(0, a)$	$(a/2)^{1/2}, a^{1/2}$	1
5. $(\sin \lambda_j x)/x$ $\lambda_j = $ roots of $\tan a\lambda = a\lambda$	$(0, a)$	$\dfrac{\sin a\lambda}{2^{1/2}}$	x_2
6. $\cos(\lambda_j x)$ $\lambda_j = $ roots of $\tan \lambda = h/\lambda$	$(0, 1)$	$\left(\dfrac{h + \sin^2 \lambda_j}{2h}\right)^{1/2}$	1
7. $J_k(\lambda_j x)$ $\lambda_j = $ roots of $J_k(\lambda a) = 0$	$(0, a)$	$\dfrac{a}{\sqrt{2}}[J_{k+1}(\lambda_j a)]$	x
8. $J_k(\lambda_j x)$ $\lambda_j = $ roots of $\lambda a\, J_{k+1}(\lambda a) -$ $hJ_k(\lambda a) = 0$	$(0, a)$	$\left[\dfrac{\lambda_j^2 a^2 + h^2 - k^2}{2}\right]^{1/2} \dfrac{J_k(\lambda_j a)}{\lambda_j}$	x

A number of sets of orthogonal functions which are of frequent occurrence in the solution of PDEs by separation of variables are listed in the accompanying Table 9.1. We note some of the implications of this table and follow this up with an illustration.

We start by pointing out that the weight function p(x) of Equation 9.1.16 is in some instances unity, in others a simple function of x. This does not complicate unduly the evaluation of the Integrals 9.1.16. A second noticeable feature is that the running index of the sequence, n or λ, is not necessarily composed of positive integers. This is so for certain trigonometric functions, Items 1 to 4, but in other cases, Items 5 to 8, λ_j are the roots of certain transcendental equations. We had previously, in Table 8.8, Chapter 8, given a short list of the roots of Item 8. Roots of the equations contained in Items 5 to 7 can be found in standard texts on diffusion and conduction, and in mathematical handbooks (see References). Using the table entries for Item 7, for example, the orthogonality relations 9.1.16 now become:

$$\int_0^a xJ_k(\lambda_m x)J_k(\lambda_n x)dx = 0 \tag{9.1.16c}$$

$$\int_0^a xJ_k^2(\lambda_n x)dx = C^2 = \frac{a^2}{2}J_{k+1}^2(\lambda_n a) \tag{9.1.16d}$$

These somewhat abstract-looking relations have, in fact, their uses. One may anticipate that Bessel functions of this type will arise in solving PDEs in cylindrical coordinates, and that the Relations 9.1.16c and 9.1.16d would then be very handy in evaluating Fourier coefficients in much the same way as the simpler Relations 9.1.10 and 9.1.11.

Illustration 9.1.1   The Cosine Set

It will be of further comfort to the uninitiated to have a particular set of entries in Table 9.1 derived in detail. We choose for this purpose the cosine sequence, Item 2, and set out to prove orthogonality and to derive the norm C.

$$m \neq n \neq 1$$

We use the trigonometric formula:

$$\cos mx \cos nx = \frac{1}{2}[\cos(n-m)x + \cos(m+n)x] \qquad (9.1.19)$$

and obtain from integral tables, using a weight function $p(x) = 1$ in Equation 9.1.16a:

$$\int_{-\pi}^{\pi} (1)(\cos mx)(\cos nx)dx = \frac{1}{2}\left[\frac{\sin(n-m)x}{m-m} + \frac{\sin(m+n)x}{m+n}\right]_{-\pi}^{\pi} = 0 \quad (9.1.20)$$

We repeat this for the first term and obtain:

m = 1:

$$\int_{-\pi}^{\pi} (1)(1)\cos nx\, dx = -\frac{1}{2}\sin y\Big|_{-n\pi}^{n\pi} = 0 \qquad (9.1.21)$$

To fulfill the second Condition 9.1.6b and obtain the norm we show, using the appropriate formula from integral tables:

m = n ≠ 0:

$$\int_{-\pi}^{\pi} (1)\cos^2 nx\, dx = \frac{1}{2}\left[x + \frac{\sin 2nx}{2n}\right]_{=\pi}^{\pi} = \pi = C_1^{\,2} \qquad (9.1.22)$$

m = n = 0:

$$\int_{-\pi}^{\pi} (1)1^2 dx = 2\pi = C_2^{\,2} \qquad (9.1.23)$$

This shows, as was indicated in Table 9.1 that, for the cosine sequence only, we have two norms, a general one C_1 for the case $n \neq 0$, and a special one, C_2, for n =

0. This does not, however, invalidate the Condition 9.1.16b and the set can still be considered orthogonal.

9.1.1.2   The Sturm-Liouville Theorem

We have seen that orthogonal functions are highly useful tools, not only in the solution of PDEs by the method of separation of variables, but also in the representation of both continuous and discontinuous functions. To find these functions by choosing them at random and *guessing* both the weight function p(x) and the interval of orthogonality (a,b) is evidently an unrewarding task. Fortunately a theorem is available which *generates* these functions and the associated weight functions and intervals from a general linear second order ODE with variable coefficients of the form:

$$[r(x)y']^1 + [q(x) + \lambda p(x)]y = 0 \qquad (9.1.24)$$

with the following boundary conditions of Type III:

$$A_1 y(a) + A_2 y'(a) = 0 \qquad (9.1.25)$$

$$B_1 y(b) + B_2 y'(b) = 0$$

Such second order systems arise, as we have seen, in the course of applying the method of separation of variables. They are referred to as *Sturm-Liouville systems*. The theorem may be phrased as follows.

Provided that over the interval $a \le x \le b$, p(x), q(x), r(x), and r'(x) are real and continuous, the solutions of the Sturm-Liouville system will be a set of functions $y_n(x)$ which are orthogonal with respect to the weight function p(x) over the interval $a \le x \le b$. Furthermore, any function f(x) which is sectionally continuous in this interval (translation: $f(x) \ne \infty$) can be expanded in terms of the orthogonal set:

$$f(x) = \sum_{n=0}^{\infty} C_n y_n(x) \qquad (9.1.26)$$

The following are to be noted. If p(x) or r(x) should vanish at the end points, the theorem will still hold provided y(x) remains finite at those points. The theorem also applies if the interval is replaced by an unbounded one.

This is a powerful statement which will ease our task considerably. It merely requires an inspection of an ODE and its boundary conditions to establish orthogonality and the validity of a series expansion of arbitrary functions. We shall use it in subsequent illustrations to solve PDEs by the method of separation of variables.

9.1.1.3   Fourier Series

We had seen in Table 9.1 that sequence of both sine and cosine functions form an orthogonal set. They can be combined into a more general form known as a Fourier series:

$$\frac{1}{2}a_0 + \sum_{n=1}^{\infty} (a_n \cos nx + b_n \sin nx) \tag{9.1.27}$$

where the Fourier coefficients are given by:

$$a_n = \frac{1}{\pi} \int_{-\pi}^{\pi} f(x) \cos nx \, dx \tag{9.1.28a}$$

$$b_n = \frac{1}{\pi} \int_{-\pi}^{\pi} f(x) \sin nx \, dx \tag{9.1.28b}$$

f(x) is an arbitrary function over $(-\pi, \pi)$ and π in the denominator is recognized as the square of the norm C^2 (see Table 8.1).

We note the following properties of this series. Any function defined arbitrarily over the interval $(-\pi,\pi)$ and outside it by the equation $f(x + 2\pi) = f(x)$, and which has a *finite* number of discontinuities and extrema over that interval, can be represented by a Fourier series. Thus, the Fourier series can be used to represent both a function f(x) over $(-\pi,\pi)$ for values of x in that interval, or a *periodic* function with period 2π for *all* values of x.

The Fourier series can be extended to an arbitrary interval $(-a,a)$ and then becomes:

$$\frac{a_0}{2} + \sum_{n=1}^{\infty} [a_n \cos(n\pi x/a) + b_n \sin(n\pi x/a)] \tag{9.1.29}$$

with the Fourier coefficients given by:

$$a_n = \frac{1}{a} \int_{-a}^{a} f(x) \cos(n\pi x/a)dx \tag{9.1.30a}$$

$$b_n = \frac{1}{a} \int_{-a}^{a} f(x) \sin(n\pi x/a)dx \tag{9.1.30b}$$

If f(x) is an even function $f(x) = f(-x)$, all the sine terms vanish. For odd functions $f(x) = -f(-x)$, on the other hand, the cosine terms drop out. The coefficient a_0(n = 0) carries a factor $\frac{1}{2}$ designed to accommodate the differences in norms for cos nx and cos 0 (see Equations 9.1.22 and 9.1.23). With this factor in place, a *single* norm $C = (\pi)^{1/2}$ can be used for the entire series. Let us illustrate the use of Fourier series with a particular example.

A. The Function

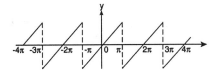

B. Convergence

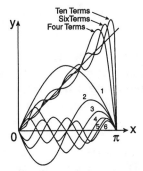

FIGURE 9.1 Expansion of a saw-tooth function (A) by means of a Fourier sine series (B). Lower curves in (B) represent individual sine terms, the upper curves their sum.

Illustration 9.1.2 Fourier Series Expansion of a Function f(x)

We set out to represent the function $f(x) = x$, i.e., a straight line of slope 1 in the interval $(-\pi,\pi)$ by means of a Fourier series expansion. The form of the function, and its periodic extension, is shown in Figure 9.1A. Using Equations 9.1.28a/b to evaluate the Fourier coefficients, and making appropriate use of tables of integrals, we find:

$$a_n = \frac{1}{\pi} \int_{-\pi}^{\pi} x \cos nx \, dx = 0 \qquad (9.1.31)$$

$$b_n = \frac{1}{\pi} \int_{-\pi}^{\pi} x \sin nx \, dx = -\frac{2}{n} \cos n\pi \qquad (9.1.32)$$

Only the sine terms remain, and we obtain:

$$x = \sum_{n=1}^{\infty} b_n \sin nx$$

that is

$$x = 2\left[\left(-\frac{1}{1}\cos\pi\right)\sin x + \left(-\frac{1}{2}\cos 2\pi\right)\sin 2x + \ldots\right]$$ (9.1.33)

or

$$f(x) = x = 2\left[\sin x - \frac{\sin 2x}{2} + \frac{\sin 3x}{3} - \ldots\right]$$

This is the desired expansion of x over the interval $(-\pi,\pi)$.

Comments:

The disappearance of the cosine terms was to be expected since the function in question is an odd one, with $f(x) = -f(-x)$. Since the series (Equation 9.1.33) has the period 2π, it also represents the periodic extension of $f(x) = x(-\pi,\pi)$, shown as a graph of discontinuous parallel lines in Figure 9.1A. Note that at the points of discontinuity, the series converges to zero which is one half of the sum of the right-hand and left-hand limits.

Convergence of the Fourier series to $f(x) = x$ over the interval $(0,\pi)$ is graphically depicted in Figure 9.1B. The lower terms represent the individual sine terms, the upper curves their sum. The degree of convergence is marked but will evidently require a considerable number of terms to achieve acceptable agreement.

This completes our intermezzo on orthogonal functions and Fourier series. We return to the topic of separation of variables and illustrate its use in the solution of linear second order PDEs with a number of examples.

Illustration 9.1.3   The Quenched Steel Billet Revisited

This example considers the temperature transients which arise when a hot steel billet is exposed, at time $t = 0$, to an external temperature T_s. We assume a uniform initial temperature T_0 and neglect external heat transfer resistance. The system and its boundary and initial conditions are depicted in Figure 9.2.

Prior to proceeding to a solution, we nondimensionalize and normalize the temperature variable by setting:

$$\theta = \frac{T - T_s}{T_1 - T_s}$$ (9.1.34)

The following set of equations and conditions is obtained:

Fourier's equation $$\frac{\partial\theta}{\partial t} = \alpha\frac{\partial^2\theta}{\partial x^2}$$ (9.1.35)

A. Billet

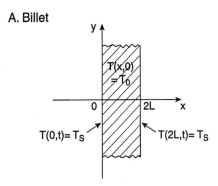

B. Initial Condition

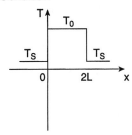

FIGURE 9.2   Geometry, BCs, and IC for a quenched steel billet.

This eases the representation of the results and as a bonus yields homogeneous boundary conditions.

At the two surfaces $\qquad\qquad \theta(0,t) = 0$ $\hfill$ (9.1.36a)

$$\theta(2L,t) = 0 \qquad\qquad (9.1.36b)$$

Initially $\qquad\qquad\qquad \theta(x,0) = 1$ $\hfill$ (9.1.36c)

Although these three conditions are sufficient in principle, two additional conditions are given which are helpful in evaluating integration constants. They must at any rate also be satisfied by the solution.

Steady-state $\qquad\qquad\qquad \theta(x,\infty) = 0$ $\hfill$ (9.1.36d)

Symmetry $\qquad\qquad\qquad \dfrac{\partial \theta}{\partial x}(L,t) = 0$ $\hfill$ (9.1.36e)

We now introduce the assumption of separation of variables and substitute the resulting expression into Fourier's Equation 9.1.35 (Steps 1 and 2 of our preamble). After some rearrangement there results:

$$\frac{1}{\alpha}\frac{T'(t)}{T(t)} = \frac{X''(x)}{X(x)} = -\lambda^2 \qquad (9.1.37)$$

The constant value on the right which can be positive, negative, or zero has already been justified, but squaring it and assigning it a negative sign need to be explained. Both moves are taken on anticipatory grounds: We expect the temperature $\theta = T(t)X(x)$ to decay exponentially with time, hence the negative sign. To ensure that this feature is not wiped out by negative values of λ, the latter is squared. This also eliminates square roots which we expect will arise in the solution of the ODEs in $X(x)$.

Step 3: Solution of ODEs — We apply separation of variables to the ODE in t, and the standard D-operator method to the ODE in x. There results:

For $\lambda^2 \neq 0$ $\qquad\qquad T_1 = C_1 \exp(-\alpha\lambda^2 t) \qquad\qquad (9.1.38a)$

$$X_1 = C_2 \cos \lambda x + C_3 \sin \lambda x$$

For $\lambda^2 = 0$ $\qquad\qquad\qquad T_2 = C_4 \qquad\qquad\qquad (9.1.38b)$

$$X_2 = C_5 + C_6 x$$

We now invoke the superposition principle by adding the two solutions and obtain:

$$\theta = T_1 X_1 + T_2 X_2 = C_7 + C_8 x + (C_9 \cos (x + C_{10} \sin \lambda x)\exp(-\alpha\lambda^2 t) \quad (9.1.39)$$

Step 4: Evaluation of Constants — We note that there are five constants to be evaluated, hence it becomes convenient to draw on the auxiliary boundary condition (Equation 9.1.36d). The reader also is reminded of the necessity to leave the initial condition unused for the time being. We obtain the following results:

BC (9.1.36d): $\theta(x,\infty) = 0$ — This results in the exponential term vanishing. The remaining terms must also vanish and we obtain $C_7 = C_8 = 0$.

BC (9.1.36a): $\theta(0,t) = 0$ — Here the sine terms vanish, hence to obtain $\theta = 0$, the cosine terms must also drop out. This requires $C_9 = 0$.

BC (9.1.36b): $\theta(2L,t) = 0$ — This condition is used to determine the Eigenvalues λ. At this stage the solution is composed of:

$$\theta = C_{10} \sin \lambda x \exp(-\alpha\lambda^2 t) \qquad (9.1.40)$$

To satisfy to the BC, the sine terms must vanish, which is accomplished by setting $\lambda = n\pi/2L$, $n = 1, 2, 3, \ldots$. We obtain:

$$\lambda = n\pi / 2L \qquad \text{Eigenvalues}$$

$$f(x) = \sin \lambda x \qquad \text{Eigenfunctions}$$

Linear superposition of this result now gives us the following infinite series:

$$\theta = \sum_{n=1}^{\infty} C_{10} \sin(n\pi x / 2L) \exp(-\alpha n^2 \pi^2 t / 4L^2) \qquad (9.1.41)$$

Step 5: Evaluation of Fourier Coefficients — The problem which faces us at this stage has already been noted. To satisfy the initial condition (Equation 9.1.36c), we must decompose C_{10} into an infinite set of coefficients C_n and hope for a valid Fourier expansion in terms of orthogonal functions. We had previously shown orthogonality of the sine sequence by making use of certain integrals of that function. We will not repeat that near-miraculous solution but make use instead of the Sturm-Liouville theorem which proves orthogonality and guarantees a Fourier expansion. Scrutiny of our ODEs 9.1.37 shows that the Sturm-Liouville System associated with our model is given by the ODE in x:

$$X'' + \lambda^2 X = 0 \qquad (9.1.42)$$

with associated boundary conditions:

$$X(0) = 0 \qquad (9.1.43a)$$

$$X(2L) = 0 \qquad (9.1.43b)$$

Comparison of these equations with the general Sturm-Liouville system (Equations 9.1.24 and 9.1.25) shows that the weighting function here is $p(x) = 1$, and that the interval of orthogonality is given by the physical boundaries of the system, $(0,2L)$. Expansion of some function $f(x)$ (here $f(x) = 1$) in terms of the eigenfunction which result from Equation 9.1.42, i.e., $\sin(n\pi x/2L)$, is also guaranteed. We have a valid representation of the initial condition:

$$1 = C_1 \sin(\pi x/2L) + C_2 \sin 2\pi x/2L + \dots + C_n \sin(n\pi x/L) + \dots \quad (9.1.44)$$

The Fourier coefficients are now evaluated by multiplying each term by $p(x)\sin(n\pi x/2L)dx$ and integrating over the interval $(0,2L)$, where $p(x) = 1$ here. We obtain:

$$\int_0^{2L} (1)(1)\sin(n\pi x / 2L)dx = \int_0^{2L} C_1(1)\sin(\pi x / 2L)\sin(n\pi x / 2Ldx = 0$$

$$+\int_0^{2L} C_2(1)\sin(2\pi x / 2L)\sin(n\pi x / 2L)dx + \dots + \int_0^{2L} C_n(1)\sin^2(n\pi x / 2L)dx + \dots = 0$$

$$(9.1.45)$$

All terms on the right side except the n-th one drop out by virtue of orthogonality and we obtain the following result for the n-th Fourier coefficient:

$$C_n = \frac{\int_0^{2L} \sin(n\pi x/2L)dx}{\int_0^{2L} \sin^2(n\pi x/2L)dx} \qquad (9.1.46)$$

The integral in the denominator is the square of the norm, and tabulated in the Table 9.1: $C^2 = 2L/2 = L$. The integral in the numerator yields:

$$\int_0^{2L} \sin(n\pi x/2L)dx = -\frac{2L}{n\pi}\cos(n\pi x/2L)\Big|_0^{2L} = \frac{2}{n\pi}[1-(-1)^n] \qquad (9.1.47)$$

Our solution then takes the final form of the following infinite series:

$$\theta(x,t) = \frac{2}{\pi}\sum_{n=1}^{\infty}\frac{1}{n}[1-(-1)^n]\sin(n\pi x/2L)\exp(-\alpha n^2\pi^2 t/4L^2) \qquad (9.1.48)$$

Comments:

One notes that for even values of n, $[1-(-1)^n] = 0$ so that only odd terms remain in Equation 9.1.48. This has led to an alternative formulation, frequently found in the literature, which takes form:

$$\theta(x,t) = \frac{4}{\pi}\sum_{n=1}^{\infty}\frac{1}{2n-1}\sin\left(\frac{2n-1}{2L}x\right)\exp(-\alpha n^2\pi^2 t/4L^2) \qquad (9.1.49)$$

In this formulation, none of the terms vanish.

It is of some interest to verify whether the unused symmetry condition $\partial\theta/\partial x|_{x=L} = 0$ is indeed satisfied. This is done by a term-by-term differentiation of the Fourier series and yields the result:

$$\frac{\partial\theta}{\partial x}\Big|_{x=L} = \sum_{n=1}^{\infty}\frac{1}{L}\underbrace{[1-(-1)^n]}_{0\,\text{for}\atop\text{even terms}}\underbrace{\cos(n\pi/2)}_{0\,\text{for}\atop\text{odd terms}}\exp(-\alpha n^2\pi^2 t/4L^2) \qquad (9.1.50)$$

Thus all terms of the series vanish and the BC is consequently satisfied.

For small times t and low values of thermal diffusivity α, convergence of the series Equation 9.1.48 is quite slow since representation close to the initial rectangular temperature distribution (Figure 9.2B) requires a considerable number of terms. In these cases use is made of an alternative solution, arrived at by Laplace transformation which takes the form of an infinite series of complementary error function. This solution has fast convergence for low values of α and t. Its derivation is taken up in Section 9.2, Illustration 9.2.3.

Illustration 9.1.4 Conduction in a Cylinder with External Resistance: Arbitrary Initial Distribution

In Illustration 8.2.1 of the preceding chapter, the unsuspecting reader was confronted with an infinite series of Bessel functions which was used to describe concentration profiles in a tubular reactor undergoing a first order irreversible reaction at the wall. It was shown there that provided radial velocity gradients were neglected, the underlying model was identical to that describing unsteady conduction in an infinitely long cylinder with an external heat transfer resistance and constant initial temperature.

In the present illustration, we consider the same problem under the somewhat broader condition of an arbitrary initial temperature distribution $T(r,0) = f(r)$, otherwise retaining the same features as before. The model is then comprised of the following equations and boundary or initial conditions:

Fourier equation:
$$\frac{\partial T}{\partial t} = \alpha \left[\frac{\partial^2 T}{\partial r^2} + \frac{1}{r} \frac{\partial T}{\partial r} \right] \tag{9.1.51}$$

At steady-state:
$$T(r, \infty) = T_e \tag{9.1.52a}$$

Symmetry:
$$\left. \frac{\partial T}{\partial r} \right|_{r=0} = 0 \tag{9.1.52b}$$

$$\text{or} \quad T|_{r=0} = \text{finite}$$

At the surface:
$$-k \left. \frac{\partial T}{\partial r} \right|_{r=R} = h(T|_{r=R} - T_e) \tag{9.1.52c}$$

Initially:
$$T(r,0) = f(r) \tag{9.1.52d}$$

where T_e = temperature of external medium.

The solution proceeds over the same steps as those of the previous illustration.

Step 1: Separate Variables — This is done by assuming the following form of solution

$$T = F(r)G(t) \tag{9.1.53}$$

Step 2: Substitution into the PDE — This step, followed by some rearrangement, yields the separated expression:

$$\frac{1}{\alpha} \frac{G'(t)}{G(t)} = \frac{1}{F} \left[F'' + \frac{1}{r} F' \right] = -\lambda^2 \tag{9.1.54}$$

Justification of the constant term $-\lambda^2$ follows along the lines given in the previous illustration.

Step 3: Solution of ODEs — We apply separation of variables to the ODE in t, p-substitution for the ODE in r when $\lambda^2 = 0$, and for $\lambda^2 \neq 0$ the generalized solution for second order ODEs with variable coefficients, Equation 4.3.66 of Chapter 4. This yields:

For $\lambda^2 \neq 0$

$$F_1 = C_1 J_0(\lambda r) + C_2 Y_0(\lambda r) \tag{9.1.55a}$$

$$G_1 = C_3 \exp(-\alpha\lambda^2 t)$$

For $\lambda^2 = 0$

$$F_2 = C_4 + C_5 \ln r \tag{9.1.55b}$$

$$G_2 = C_6$$

Superposition of these two solutions leads to the expression:

$$T = F_1 G_1 + F_2 G_2 = [C_7 J_0(\lambda r) + C_8 Y_0(\lambda r)]\exp(-\alpha\lambda^2 t) + C_9 + C_{10} \ln r \tag{9.1.56}$$

Step 4: Evaluation of Constants — It is best here to start with the symmetry condition 9.1.52b and follow this up with the conditions (a) and (c). The initial condition is as usual left to the last. We obtain the following results:

BC (9.1.52b) $T|_{r=0}$ = finite (i.e., bounded) — Here we note that the Bessel function $Y_0(\lambda r)$ goes to minus infinity for zero values of the argument (see Figure 4.4) as does the logarithmic term. For the solution to remain finite we must therefore set $C_8 = C_{10} = 0$.

BC (9.1.52a) $T(r,\infty) = T_e$ — This condition causes the exponential term in Equation 9.1.56 to vanish so that $C_9 = T_e$. At this point the solution has been reduced to the form:

$$T - T_e = C_7 J_0(\lambda r)\exp(-\alpha\lambda^2 t) \tag{9.1.57}$$

BC (9.1.52c) $-k\left.\dfrac{\partial T}{\partial r}\right|_{r=R} = h(T|_{r=R} - T_e)$ — This relation is used to determine the eigenvalues λ and requires evaluation of the derivative of the Bessel function $J_0(\lambda r)$. This can be done using the formulas given in Table 4.8 of Chapter 4 and yields:

$$\left.\frac{\partial T}{\partial r}\right|_{r=R} = C_7[-\lambda J_1(\lambda R)]\exp(-\alpha\lambda^2 t) \tag{9.1.58}$$

Back-substitution into the boundary condition yields the transcendental equation:

$$\lambda R J_1(\lambda R) = K J_0(\lambda R) \tag{9.1.59}$$

where $K = \dfrac{hR}{k}$. This is seen to be identical in form to the expression given in Item 8 of Table 9.1. We can consequently expect $J_0(\lambda_j r)$ to be an orthogonal set over the interval $(0,R)$ with weight function $p(r) = r$ and λ_j given by the roots of Equation 9.1.58 which we had previously tabulated in Table 8.8. We note that the solution has now become, by virtue of superposition:

$$T - T_e = \sum_{n=1}^{\infty} C_n J_0(\lambda_n r) \exp(-\alpha \lambda_n^2 t / R^2) \qquad (9.1.60)$$

The same result also can be obtained by a Sturm-Liouville Analysis.

Step 5: Evaluation of Fourier Coefficients — We follow the procedure outlined in the previous illustration, i.e., after introducing the initial condition, we multiply each term of the infinite series by $[rJ_0(\lambda_m r)dr]$ and integrate from 0 to R. Dropping all terms but the n-th, we arrive at the following formula for C_n:

$$C_n = \frac{\int_0^R r[f(r) - T_1]J_0(\lambda_n r)dr}{(\text{Norm})^2} \qquad (9.1.61)$$

Using the expression for the norm given in Table 9.1, with k set $= 0$, we finally obtain:

$$T - T_e = 2 \sum_{n=1}^{\infty} \frac{\lambda_n \int_0^R r[f(r) - T_e]J_0(\lambda_n r)dr}{(\lambda_n^2 R^2 + K^2)J_0^2(\lambda_n R)} J_0(\lambda_n r) \exp(-\alpha \lambda_n^2 t / R^2) \qquad (9.1.62)$$

Comments:

Before being overwhelmed by the complexity of this expression, the reader is reminded that such series often converge quite fast, as was seen in Illustration 8.2.1. The integral will in general have to be evaluated numerically but this poses no great problem since J_0 is a well-behaved periodic function.

Equation 9.1.62 is of the same form as Equation 8.2.14 of Illustration 8.2.1, but has slightly different boundary and initial conditions.

Illustration 9.1.5   Steady-State Conduction in a Hollow Cylinder

So far in our illustrations we were able to apply the method of separation of variables in a rather mechanical way once the principles of orthogonality had been established. This is not always the case. Even modest changes in the underlying model may require rather substantial changes in our approach, although the basic step-wise procedure we had established previously still applies. We show this with the following example.

Consider an infinitely long *hollow* cylinder with the interior and exterior surfaces maintained at the *angle-dependent* temperature $f_i(\theta)$ and $f_0(\theta)$. We wish to establish the resultant steady-state temperature distribution $T(r,\theta)$ in the interior of the cylinder. The underlying model is Laplace's equation:

$$\nabla^2 T = 0 \qquad (9.1.63)$$

which we translate with the help of our dictionary Table 8.1 into radial and angular coordinates. There results:

$$\frac{\partial^2 T}{\partial r^2} + \frac{1}{r}\frac{\partial T}{\partial r} + \frac{1}{r^2}\frac{\partial^2 T}{\partial \theta^2} = 0 \qquad (9.1.64)$$

So far we have merely traded the angular derivative $(1/r^2)(\partial^2\theta)/\partial r^2)$ for the time derivative $\partial T/\partial t$ of the previous illustration. The first difficulty arises when we attempt to formulate boundary conditions. We appear to require at least four BCs, two for each second derivative, but seem to have only two available:

At the outer surface: $T(R_0,\theta) = f_0(\theta)$ (9.1.65a)

At the inner surface: $T(R_i,\theta) = f_i(\theta)$ (9.1.65b)

With some imagination one might add a third condition expressing periodicity of the temperature:

Periodicity: $T(r,\theta) = T(r,\theta+2n\pi)$ (9.1.65c)

or $T(r,\theta - \pi) = T(r,\theta + \pi)$

but this exhausts the possible condition. One hopes that a single BC will be capable of evaluating more than one constant, as was the case with the Fourier coefficients. Let us proceed with the solution.

Steps 1 and 2 — We assume the solution to be of the form:

$$T = R(r)S(\theta) \qquad (9.1.66)$$

and obtain after substitution into the PDE:

$$r^2\frac{R''}{R} = r\frac{R'}{R} = -\frac{S''}{S} = +\lambda^2 \qquad (9.1.67)$$

Note that we have postulated positive real eigenvalues since we require the solution of $S(\theta)$ to be periodic, not exponential. This is the first departure from convention.

Step 3 — We proceed with the solution of the ODEs for the two cases $\lambda^2 \neq 0$ and $\lambda^2 = 0$ which is accomplished by standard D-operator and p-substitution methods.

A second departure from the routine occurs in the solution of the ODE $r^2R'' + rR' - \lambda^2R = 0$ which is of the Euler-Cauchy type (see Table 4.3) and requires the substitution $r = e^z$ to reduce to D-operator form. We obtain:

For $\lambda^2 = 0$: $$S_1 = C_1' + C_2'\,\theta \qquad\qquad (9.1.68a)$$

$$R_1 = C_3' + C_4'\ln r$$

For $\lambda^2 \neq 0$: $$S_2 = C_5'\cos \lambda\theta + C_6'\sin\, '\lambda\theta \qquad\qquad (9.1.68b)$$

$$R_2 = C_7'\,r^\lambda + C_8'\,r^{-\lambda}$$

Adding the solutions by superposition yields:

$$T = C_1 + C_2\ln r + C_3\theta + C_4\theta\ln r$$

$$+ (C_5r^\lambda + C_6r^{-\lambda})\cos\lambda\theta + (C_7r^\lambda + C_8r^{-\lambda})\sin\lambda\theta \qquad (9.1.69)$$

Step 4 — To evaluate the integration constants, we start by utilizing the periodicity condition Equation 8.1.64c, which in the first instance leads to the condition $C_3 = C_4 = 0$ since $\theta \neq \theta \pm \pi$. We then use the same condition to argue that since the solution, including the surface condition is periodic and has a finite number of discontinuities and extrema, it can be represented in terms of the Fourier series, Equation 9.1.27. In other words, we have equivalence of the following expressions:

$$f_{i,0}(R_{i,0}) = \frac{a_0}{2} + \sum_{n=1}^{\infty}[a_n\cos n\theta + b_n\sin n\theta]$$

$$\qquad\qquad\qquad\qquad\qquad\qquad (9.1.70)$$

$$f_{i,0}(R_{i,0}) = C_1 + C_2\ln R_{i,0} + \sum_{\lambda=1}^{\infty}[C_5R_{i,0}{}^\lambda + C_6R_{i,0}{}^{-\lambda}]\cos\lambda\theta$$

$$+ \sum_{\lambda=1}^{\infty}[C_7R_{i,0}{}^\lambda + C_8R_{i,0}{}^{-\lambda}]\sin\lambda\theta \qquad (9.1.71)$$

where we use $R_{i,0}$ to denote either the inner or outer radius. The Fourier coefficients a_n, b_n are equivalent to four infinite sets of coefficients C_5 to C_8 and are evaluated from Equations 9.1.28 and 9.1.29. The anomaly here is that each term in the Series has *two* Fourier coefficients associated with it due to the appearance of the sets of two constants (C_5, C_6) and (C_7, C_8) in Equation 9.1.71. This causes no difficulty, however, since we have *two* boundary conditions available in Equations 9.1.65a/b. Application of the Equation 9.1.28 then yields the following set of relations:

For $a_0/2$:

$$C_1 + C_2 \ln R_0 = \frac{1}{2\pi} \int_{-\pi}^{\pi} f_0(\theta) d\theta \qquad (9.1.72a)$$

$$C_1 + C_2 \ln R_i = \frac{1}{2\pi} \int_{-\pi}^{\pi} f_0(\theta) d\theta \qquad (9.1.72b)$$

For a_n:

$$C_5 R_0^{\lambda} + C_6 R_0^{-\lambda} = \frac{1}{\pi} \int_{-\pi}^{\pi} f_0(\theta) \cos \lambda\theta \, d\theta \qquad (9.1.72c)$$

$$C_5 R_i^{\lambda} + C_6 R_i^{-\lambda} = \frac{1}{\pi} \int_{-\pi}^{\pi} f_i(\theta) \cos \lambda\theta \, d\theta \qquad (9.1.72d)$$

For b_n:

$$C_7 R_0^{\lambda} + C_8 R_0^{-\lambda} = \frac{1}{\pi} \int_{-\pi}^{\pi} f_0(\theta) \sin \lambda\theta \, d\theta \qquad (9.1.72e)$$

$$C_7 R_i^{\lambda} + C_8 R_i^{-\lambda} = \frac{1}{\pi} \int_{-\pi}^{\pi} f_i(\theta) \sin \lambda\theta \, d\theta \qquad (9.1.72f)$$

with $\lambda = 1, 2, 3, \ldots$.

These linear algebraic relation in the constants can be solved to yield explicit relations for $C_1 \ldots C_8$.

Comments:

This is clearly a fairly complex problem of mainly academic interest. Its principal purpose was to induce the reader to "stretch" known principles and theorems to accommodate unusual circumstances. Mathematicians would want to provide more formal proof of the validity of the solution but we prefer to content ourselves with the somewhat intuitive procedure used here.

Evaluation of the solution does not present overwhelming difficulties. The integrals in Equations 9.1.70 can be determined numerically, and the result substituted into the final solution which now has the form:

$$T(r, \theta) = C_1 + C_2 \ln r + \sum_{\lambda=1}^{\infty} (C_5 r^{\lambda} + C_6 r^{-\lambda}) \cos \lambda x + \sum_{\lambda=1}^{\infty} (C_7 r^{\lambda} + C_8 r^{-\lambda}) \sin \lambda x \quad (9.1.73)$$

This form can be further compressed into Equation 9.1.77 (see Practice Problem 9.1.5).

Historical Note:

Early steps in the development of the method of separation of variables were taken in the 18th century and are associated with the names of the English mathematician, Brook Taylor of Taylor Series fame (1685–1731), Daniel Bernoulli (1700–1782), and Leonhard Euler (1707–1783), in Switzerland, and Jean d'Alembert (1717–1783) in France. Given the pre-eminence of music in the social life of the times, these scientists were drawn to the study of the mathematical theory of musical vibrations. By the 1750s, the wave equation was known and a solution of the boundary value problem of a vibrating string had been found. The twin notions of superposition and representation of arbitrary functions by trigonometric series made their first appearance and somewhat later Euler gave the formulas for the constants, which are now popularly known as Fourier Coefficients. It was left to Jean Baptiste Joseph Fourier (1768–1830) to illustrate the basic procedure of separation of variables and superposition and help popularize trigonometric series representation. His book, *Théorie Analytique de la Chaleur,* published in 1822, provides many examples of expansions in trigonometric series which arise in the conduction of heat. Although a relative latecomer to the field, his contributions were such that many of the tools used in separation of variables are now associated with his name.

Practice Problems

9.1.1 A Fourier Series Expansion of a Square Wave — Develop f(x) in Fourier series in the interval (–2,2) if $f(x) = 0$ for $-2 < x < 0$ and $f(x) = 1$ for $0 < x < 2$.

Answer: $f(x) = \dfrac{1}{2} + \dfrac{2}{\pi}\left[\sin(\pi x/2) + \dfrac{1}{3}\sin(3\pi x/2) + \dfrac{1}{5}\sin(5\pi x/2) + ...\right]$

9.1.2 Cosine Expansion of a Sine — Write the cosine series for $f(x) = \sin x$ in the interval $(0,\pi)$, and sketch the periodic extension of the result.

Answer: $\sin x = \dfrac{2}{\pi} + \dfrac{2}{\pi}\displaystyle\sum_{n=2}^{\infty}\dfrac{1+(-1)^n}{1-n^2}\cos nx$

9.1.3 Drying a Porous Slab — A slab of porous material is to be dried from both faces at a constant rate $W(kg/sm^2)$, (dielectric, microwave, or inducting heating), i.e., under conditions of constant heat supply. The initial moisture content is C_0 (kg/m^3) and the movement of moisture is described by Fick's law $N = -D_{eff}A(\partial C/\partial x)$. If the slab is of thickness L, determine the moisture concentration profile $C(x,t)$.

(Hint: Make the boundary conditions homogeneous by the methods outlined in Illustration 7.3.3.)

Answer: $C(x,t) - C_0 = \dfrac{W}{L D_{eff}}(Lx - x^2 - L^2/6 - 2D_{eff}t) + \dfrac{2W}{L D_{eff}}\displaystyle\sum_{n=1}^{\infty}\dfrac{(-1)^n + 1}{n^2}$

$\cdot \cos(n\pi x/L)\exp(-D_{eff}n^2\pi^2 t/L^2)$

Comments:

The solution yields $C = -\infty$ for $t \to \infty$. It thus is valid only for small finite values of time. This stands to reason since the surface gradient cannot stay constant indefinitely but must eventually diminish as the slab dries out. The homogeneous problem also represents a slab with sealed or insulated faces and an initial parabolic concentration or temperature distribution which spreads out through the solid with time.

9.1.4 The Vibrating String — Consider a string fixed at both ends and subjected to an initial arbitrary displacement $u = f(x)$. The model consists of the following set of equations:

$$C^2 \frac{\partial^2 u}{\partial x^2} = \frac{\partial^2 u}{\partial t^2} \tag{9.1.74}$$

$$u(0,t) = 0 \tag{9.1.75a}$$

$$u(L,t) = 0 \tag{9.1.75b}$$

$$u_t(x,0) = 0 \tag{9.1.75c}$$

$$u(x,0) = f(x) \tag{9.1.75d}$$

Use the method of separation of variables to show that the variations in amplitude $u(x,t)$ are given by the expression:

$$u(x,t) = \frac{2}{L} \sum_{n=1}^{\infty} \left[\int_0^L f(x) \sin(n\pi x / L) dx \right] \sin(n\pi x / L) \cos(n\pi ct / L) \tag{9.1.76}$$

9.1.5 Conduction in a Hollow Cylinder Revisited —
  (a) Derive the solutions Equation 9.1.67 to the separated ODEs applicable to angle-dependent steady-state conduction in a hollow cylinder.
  (b) Show that for $f_0 = 0$ upon solving for the constants C_1 to C_8 in Equation 9.1.72, Equation 9.1.73 can be reduced to the form:

$$T(r,\theta) = \frac{1}{2} \frac{\ln(R_0 / r)}{\ln(R_0 / R_i)} a_0 + \sum_{\lambda=1}^{\infty} \frac{(R_0 / r)^\lambda - (r / R_0)^\lambda}{(R_0 / R_i)^\lambda - (R_i / R_0)^\lambda} [a_n \cos \lambda\theta + b_n \sin \lambda\theta] \tag{9.1.77}$$

where the coefficients a_n, b_n are given by the integrals of Equation 9.1.72.

9.1.6 Cooling of a Solid Sphere — Consider a solid insulated sphere of unit radius and an initial temperature distribution $T(r,0) = f(r)$. Show that this distribution spreads out with time according to the expression:

$$T(r,t) = 3 \int_0^1 s^2 f(s) ds + \sum_{n=1}^{\infty} C_n \frac{\sin(\lambda r)}{r} \exp(-\lambda^2 kt) \tag{9.1.78}$$

and identify the eigenvalues, the Fourier coefficients, and the constant k. Verify that the steady-state condition is satisfied.

9.1.7 Double Fourier Series: Vibrations of a Membrane — Solve the following boundary value problem describing the vibrations of a square membrane of length π subjected to an initial displacement $u(x,y,0) = f(x)$.

$$\frac{\partial^2 u}{\partial t^2} = c^2 \left(\frac{\partial^2 u}{\partial x^2} + \frac{\partial^2 u}{\partial y^2} \right) \qquad (9.1.79)$$

$$u(0,y,t) = u(T,y,t) = u(x,0,t)u(x,\pi) = \frac{\partial u}{\partial t}(x,y,0) = 0 \qquad (9.1.80a)$$

$$u(x,y,0) = f(x,y) \qquad (9.1.80b)$$

Procedure: Start by showing that separation of variables leads to *three* Sturm-Liouville systems with solutions:

$$X = \sin mx \quad m = 1, 2, 3, \dots$$
$$Y = \sin ny \quad n = 1, 2, 3, \dots \qquad (9.1.81)$$
$$T = \cos\left[ct\sqrt{m^2 + n^2} \right]$$

Combine these results to arrive at the formal solution:

$$u(x,y,t) = \sum_{m=1}^{\infty} \sum_{n=1}^{\infty} C_{mn} \sin mx \sin nx \cos\left[ct\sqrt{m^2 + n^2} \right] \qquad (9.1.82)$$

and show that a Fourier expansion of the initial condition $f(x,y)$ yields the following expression for the Fourier coefficients:

$$C_{mn} = \frac{4}{\pi^2} \int_0^\pi \sin ny \int_0^\pi f(x,y) \sin mx \, dx \, dy \qquad (9.1.83)$$

Note that this problem requires an imaginative use of the principles learned in this section.

9.2 LAPLACE TRANSFORMATION AND OTHER INTEGRAL TRANSFORMS

9.2.1 General Properties

We had already pointed out in Chapter 5 that the Laplace transform is an important but special case of a larger class of operations termed integral transformations. We formalize this operation in the following expression:

$$T\{F(x_j)\} = \int_a^b f(x_j)K(s, x_j)dx_j = f(s) \tag{9.2.1}$$

where T is the operational symbol for the transformation, $F(x_j)$ is the function to be transformed, $K(s,x_j)$ is the so-called Kernel, $f(s)$ is the transformed function, and s a free parameter. Let us note a number of features of this operation, some of which had already been mentioned in Chapter 5.

$F(x_j)$ is a general function of the independent variable x_j and can take the form of an *explicit* function such as $\sin x_j$, $\exp(-x_j)$, 1, or can consist of *implicit* function, such as the dependent variable itself, $y(x_j)$ and its derivatives $y'(x_j)$, $y''(x_j)$, etc. $F(x_j)$ also can depend on several independent variables, only one of which, x_j, is "transformed," i.e., eliminated by integration. One can then write Equation 9.2.1 in the form:

$$T\{F(x_1 \ldots x_n)\} = \int_0^a F(x_1 \ldots x_n)K(s, x_1 \ldots x_n)dx_j = f(s, x_1 \ldots x_{j-1}x_{j+1} \ldots x_n) \tag{9.2.2}$$

Transformation of *explicit* functions of x_j result in *explicit* functions of s. Thus, the Laplace transform of 1 is $1/s$, and of $\exp(x_j)$, $1/(s-1)$. When implicit functions are transformed, a different result is obtained. The dependent variable $y(x_j)$ becomes $y(s)$, often written as $\bar{y}(s)$, i.e., it remains an unknown. Ordinary derivatives become algebraic expressions which incorporate boundary or initial conditions. Thus, the Laplace transform of a first derivative becomes, as we had seen:

$$L\{dy/dt\} = \int_0^\infty (dy/dt)e^{-st}dt = sy(s) - y(0) \tag{9.2.3}$$

where $y(0)$ is the initial condition. Transforms of *partial* derivatives in two independent variables can yield two different results. Let us demonstrate this by applying the Laplace transform to the derivatives $\partial y/\partial t$ and $\partial y/\partial x$ of the variable $y(x,t)$. For the former case we obtain:

$$L\{\partial y/\partial t\} = \int_0^\infty (\partial y/\partial t)e^{-st}dt = sy(x,s) - y(x,0) \tag{9.2.4}$$

i.e., the result is the same as for an ordinary derivative, except that the transformed variable and the initial condition are still functions of x. For $\partial y/\partial x$ on the other hand, we obtain:

$$L\{\partial y/\partial t\} = \int_0^\infty (\partial y/\partial x)e^{-st}dt = \frac{d}{dx}\int_0^\infty y\,e^{-st}\,dt = \frac{dy(x,s)}{dx} \tag{9.2.5}$$

i.e., by reversing the order of differentiation and integration we have shown that the partial derivative with respect to the *untransformed* variable x becomes an ordinary derivative in x. These results apply to integral transforms in general and can be summarized as follows:

(A) The transform of a derivative with respect to the independent variable being eliminated yields an *algebraic* expression which contains boundary and initial conditions.

(B) The transform of a derivative with respect to the other independent variable which is *not* being eliminated, yields an ordinary derivative. When there are more than two independent variables, the result (A) still holds, but the ordinary derivative of (B) is replaced by a new partial derivative:

$$T\{\partial y / \partial x_j\} = \int_a^b \partial y / \partial x_j \, K(s, x_i, x_j, x_n) dx_i = \frac{\partial \overline{y}}{\partial x_j}(x_1 \ldots s_n \ldots x) \quad (9.2.6)$$

Integral transforms are in essence a tool to reduce the number of independent variables. In the case of an ODE, the result is an algebraic equation, in the case of a PDE in two independent variables, the result is an ODE. Finally, when there are n independent variables, a new PDE in $(n-1)$ variables is obtained.

9.2.2 THE ROLE OF THE KERNEL

The *kernel* can assume various functional forms, the more common ones being exponential, trigonometric, and Bessel functions. Each of these kernels is capable of transforming a particular derivative, or set of derivatives, to algebraic expressions that incorporate specific boundary and initial conditions. The Laplace transform, for example, transforms partial derivatives of any order to algebraic equations in the *initial values* of the dependent variables and its derivatives. Thus, it is the preferred tool for initial value problems. Trigonometric kernels preferentially transform *second derivatives* to algebraic form, but incorporate boundary values of the dependent variable and its derivative. They are consequently used in boundary value situations. Kernels in various types of Bessel functions transform the *group* of derivatives $[\partial^2 y/\partial r^2 + (1/r)\partial y/\partial r]$ into algebraic forms containing boundary values. This group is associated with radial diffusion or conduction problems and its transform, termed a *Hankel transform,* finds its principal application in such processes.

We have summarized these and other properties of some common integral transforms in Table 9.2. To help in deciphering the various expressions we note that the defining equations for the sine and cosine transforms are identical in form to the Fourier coefficients given by Equations 9.1.30. The defining equations for the Hankel transforms likewise are identical in form to the Fourier coefficients which arise in the corresponding cylinder problems. One may surmise, therefore, that classes of integral transforms can be generated by examining Fourier coefficients and the underlying Sturm-Liouville systems from which they arise. This can in fact be done, as shown in the specialized literature (see References at the end of the chapter).

TABLE 9.2
Integral Transforms

1. Laplace Transform

Defining equation

$$L\{F(t)\} = \int_0^\infty F(t)e^{-st}dt = f(s)$$

Inversion formula

$$L^{-1}\{f(s)\} = \frac{1}{2\pi i}\int_c f(s)e^{st}ds$$

Transform of derivative

$$L\{F'(t)\} = sf - F(0)$$
$$L\{F''(t)\} = s^2f - sF(0) - F'(0)$$

Application   Initial value problems

2. Finite Fourier Sine Transform

Defining equation

$$S\{F(x)\} = \int_0^a F(x)\sin(n\pi x/a)dx = f_s(n)$$

Inversion formula

$$S^{-1}\{f(n)\} = \frac{2}{a}\sum_{n=1}^\infty f_s(n)\sin n\pi x/a$$

Transform of derivative

$$S\{F''(x)\} = -\frac{n^2\pi^2}{a^2}f_s(n) + \frac{n\pi}{a}[F(0) - (-1)^n F(a)]$$

Application   Type I BCs on slab surfaces

3. Finite Fourier Cosine Transform

Defining equation

$$C\{F(x)\} = \int_0^a f(x)\cos(n\pi x/a)dx = f_c(n$$

Inversion formula

$$C^{-1}\{f_c(n)\}_c = \frac{1}{a}f_c(0) + \frac{2}{a}\sum_{n=1}^\infty f_c(n)\cos(n\pi x/a)$$

Transform of derivative

$$C\{F''(x)\} = -\frac{n^2\pi^2}{a^2}f_c(n) + (-1)^n F'(a) - F'(0)$$

Application   Type II BCs on slab surfaces

4. Finite Hankel Transform

Defining equation

$$H\{F(y)\} = \int_0^1 F(y)yJ_0(\lambda_j y)dy = f_\pi(\lambda_j)$$

where λ_j = roots of $J_0(\lambda) = 0$

Inversion formula

$$H^{-1}\{f_H(\lambda_j)\} = 2\sum_{j=1}^\infty \frac{f_H(\lambda_j)J_0(\lambda_j y)}{J_1^2(\lambda_j)}$$

Transform of derivative

$$H\left\{F'' + \frac{1}{y}F'\right\} = -\lambda_j^2 f_H(\lambda_j) + \lambda_j J_1(\lambda_j)F(1)$$

Application   Type I BC on cylinder surface

5. Modified Hankel Transform

Defining equation

$$H_M\{F(y)\} = \int_0^1 F(y)yJ_0(\lambda_j y)dy = f_{MH}(\lambda_j)$$

where λ_j = roots of $\lambda J_1(\lambda) - \beta J_0(\lambda) = 0$

TABLE 9.2 *(continued)*
Integral Transforms

Inversion formula	$$H_M^{-1}\{f_{MH}(\lambda_j)\} = 2\sum_{j=1}^{\infty} \frac{f_{MH}(\lambda_j)\lambda_j^2 J_0(\lambda_j y)}{(\lambda_j^2 + \beta^2)J_0^2(\lambda_j)}$$
Transform of derivatives	$$H\left\{F'' + \frac{1}{y}F'\right\} = -\lambda_j^2 f_{MH}(\lambda_j) + J_0(\lambda_j)[\beta F(1) + F'(1)]$$
Application	Type III BC on cylinder surface

The inversion formula for both trigonometric and Hankel transforms are given in explicit form in terms of an infinite series. These series look suspiciously like the Fourier series we obtained by separation of variables and in fact are identical to them in many cases (see Illustrations 9.1.3 and 9.1.4). In the case of the Laplace transformation, no such simple inversion formula exists, and the general procedure requires evaluation of the contour integral in the complex plane shown in Table 9.2. This procedure is rarely followed, however, and use is made instead of the extensive tabulations of Laplace transforms available in the literature. A condensed version applicable to PDE problems is shown in Table 9.3, to be used in conjunction with the previous listings of Table 5.1.

TABLE 9.3
Laplace Transforms for PDEs

f(s)	F(t)	
1. $p(s)/q(s)$ where a_i = distinct real roots of $q(s)$ and $\varphi_i = (s - a_i)[p(s)/q(s)]$	$$\sum_{j=1}^{\infty} \lim_{s \to a_i} \varphi_i(s)e^{st}$$	(a)
	or	
	$$\sum_{j=1}^{\infty} \lim_{s \to a_i} [p(s)/q'(s)]e^{st}$$	(b)
2. $\exp(-k\sqrt{s})$	$\dfrac{k}{2\sqrt{\pi t^3}}\exp[-k^2/4t]$	
3. $[\exp(-k\sqrt{s})]/s$	$\operatorname{erfc}[k/2\sqrt{t}]$	
4. $[\exp(-k\sqrt{s})]/\sqrt{s}$	$\dfrac{1}{\sqrt{\pi t}}\exp[-k^2/4t]$	
5. $[\exp(-k\sqrt{s})]/s\sqrt{s}$	$2\sqrt{t/\pi}\exp[-k^2/4t] - k\operatorname{erfc}(k/2\sqrt{t})$	
6. $[\exp(-k/s)]/s$	$J_0(2\sqrt{kt})$	
7. $[\exp(k/s)]/s^n$	$\left(\dfrac{t}{k}\right)^{(n-1)/2} I_{n-1}(2\sqrt{kt})$	

The transforms of derivatives given in Table 9.2 dictate the type of transform appropriate to a particular problem. Suppose, for example, that one wishes to solve the unsteady conduction problem for an infinitely long cylinder with a prescribed surface temperature. This is described by the Fourier equation:

$$\frac{\partial T}{\partial t} = \frac{\alpha}{R^2}\left[\frac{\partial^2 T}{\partial y^2} + \frac{1}{y}\frac{\partial T}{\partial y}\right] \tag{9.2.7}$$

where the radial variable has been normalized to $y = r/R$.

If we use separation of variables, a second order ODE with variable coefficients results which leads to a rather lengthy solution procedure. The use of Hankel transforms, on the other hand, leads to a simple first order ODE as can be shown by using Item 4 of Table 9.2 and the rules for transform of derivatives previously described. We obtain the following ODE in the transformed temperature f_H $(= \overline{T})$:

$$\frac{R^2}{\alpha}\frac{df_H}{dt} = -\lambda_j f_H + \lambda_j J_1(\lambda_j)T(1) \tag{9.2.8}$$

where $T(1)$ is the prescribed surface temperature, Equation 9.2.8, although somewhat complex in appearance, can be immediately integrated by separation of variables to give a simple-exponential expression for $f_H(t)$. That result is then directly substituted into the inversion formula of Table 9.2 to arrive at the solution of the PDE, i.e., $T(y,t)$, where y is, as mentioned, the normalized radial variable. The integral transform thus is quite rapid and straightforward in its application. It has other advantages, as well as disadvantages, which are taken up below.

9.2.3   PROS AND CONS OF INTEGRAL TRANSFORMS

9.2.3.1   Advantages

The method is applicable to a large class of linear, nonhomogeneous first and second order partial differential equations, in particular (using a Cartesian description):

$$\nabla^2 u + ku + f(x, y, z, t) = \frac{\partial u}{\partial t} \tag{9.2.9}$$

which includes the Helmholtz, Poisson, Laplace, Fourier, and Fick's equations as subcases:

$$\nabla^2 u + ku + f(x, y, z, t) = \frac{\partial^2 u}{\partial t^2} \tag{9.2.10}$$

which includes the Wave Equation as a subcase:

$$\frac{\partial u}{\partial x} + k_1 u + k_2 v = k_3 \frac{\partial u}{\partial t}$$

$$\frac{\partial v}{\partial x} + k_3 u + k_4 v = k_5 \frac{\partial v}{\partial t}$$

(9.2.11)

which includes the linear chromatographic equations as a subcase. Integral transforms thus are in principle capable of handling nonhomogeneous terms of any description, in contrast to the method of separation of variables which required homogeneity in both the PDEs as well as the boundary conditions. The restriction to linear systems in both cases arises from the need to apply superposition and can be traced to their common foundation of Strum-Liouville systems.

Application of the method is quite mechanical in many instances, made so by the use of Tables of transforms and explicit inversion formula. Most boundary and initial conditions are automatically included in the transforms, thus reducing the necessity to evaluate integration constants.

9.2.3.2 Disadvantages

The Laplace transform is generally restricted to initial value situations and is mainly applied to the transformation of first order derivatives. The transformed PDE then is often a second order ODE which has to be solved and the solution inverted. This can lead to cumbersome procedures. The transforms based on trigonometric and Bessel functions, on the other hand, are limited to very specific geometries and boundary conditions. Note that Item 2 in Table 9.2, for example, is restricted to a slab configuration with Type I BCs. To handle Type III BCs for the same geometry, a completely new transform has to be developed with the help of the Sturm-Liouville Theorem.

Nonhomogeneous terms in the PDE cannot be processed unless the relevant integrals have analytical forms. The Hankel transform of a sine forcing function, for example, would require evaluation of the integral:

$$H\{\sin ay\} = \int_0^1 (\sin ay) y J_0(\lambda_j y) dy$$

(9.2.12)

which may not easily yield an analytical form. Because of this difficulty, tabulated expressions of the more unusual transforms, and their uses, are rather limited. The Laplace transform has remained the most frequently used integral transformation, exactly because of the extensive tabulations available (about 2000). The reader, nevertheless is, encouraged to explore the use of other transforms when confronted with boundary value situations involving nonhomogeneous linear PDEs.

9.2.4 THE LAPLACE TRANSFORMATION OF PDEs

Our main attention in Section 9.2 will be on applications of the Laplace transform, although the use of other transforms also will be illustrated. To aid in this task we present a short compilation of Laplace transforms which find frequent use in the solution of PDEs (Table 9.3). Some brief comments will be of help.

- Item 1 may be viewed as an extension of the Heaviside expansion given in Chapter 5, Table 5.1. p(s) and q(s) are now *arbitrary functions* in lieu of the more restricted polynomials used in the original definition, with q(s) having an infinite number of real or imaginary roots. Typically q(s) is composed of trigonometric, hyperbolic, or Bessel functions. An application of this inversion formula will be given in Illustration 9.2.1.
- Items 2 to 5 make their appearance in solutions of Fick's and Fourier's equations, among others, as does Item 1.
- Item 7 is typically encountered in the solution of the first order PDEs 9.2.11 where they lead to convolution integrals.
- Much more extensive tabulations, of course, are available for which the reader is referred to in the References.

Illustration 9.2.1   Inversion of a Ratio of Hyperbolic Functions

We illustrate here the inversion of the ratio $\sinh(x\sqrt{s})/\sinh(\sqrt{s})$ by the extended Heaviside expansion, Item 1b of Table 9.3. This requirement arises in the solution of certain diffusion and conduction problems.

We start by noting that a direct application of the inversion formula is not possible since the roots of the denominator are all imaginary. We craftily circumvent this difficulty by converting the hyperbolic function to a trigonometric one making use of the relations we had given in Table 4.6. We obtain:

$$\sinh\sqrt{s} = \frac{1}{i}\sin i\sqrt{s} \tag{9.2.13}$$

which has an infinite number of roots at:

$$i\sqrt{s} = \pm n\pi$$

or

$$s = -n^2\pi^2 \tag{9.2.14}$$

$$n = 1, 2, 3, \ldots$$

Having obtained these equivalent real roots, we are in a position to apply the inversion formula. We write:

$$L^{-1}\left\{\frac{(s)}{q(s)}\right\} = \sum_{n=1}^{\infty} \lim_{s \to -n^2\pi^2} \frac{\sinh x\sqrt{s}}{(\sinh\sqrt{s})'} e^{st} \tag{9.2.15a}$$

$$= \sum_{n=1}^{\infty} \frac{\frac{1}{i}\sin i\, x(-i)n\pi \exp(-n^2\pi^2 t)}{-\frac{n\pi i}{2}\cos i(-i)n\pi} \qquad (9.2.15b)$$

$$= \sum_{n=1}^{\infty} \frac{2}{n\pi} \frac{\sin n\pi x}{\cos n\pi} \exp(-n^2\pi^2 t) \qquad (9.2.15c)$$

and hence,

$$L^{-1}\left\{\frac{\sinh x\sqrt{s}}{\sinh \sqrt{s}}\right\} = \frac{2}{\pi} \sum_{n=1}^{\infty} \frac{(-1)^n}{n} \sin n\pi x \exp(-n^2\pi^2 t) \qquad (9.2.15d)$$

One notes the similarity to the Fourier series solution (Equation 9.1.48) which confirms that such inversions arise in conduction and diffusion problems.

Illustration 9.2.2   Conduction in a Semi-Infinite Medium

To give a simple illustration of the use of the Laplace transform and its short Table 9.3, we consider a semi-infinite medium initially at T_0 with its surface at $x = 0$ subjected to a lower temperature T_s. The model consists of the following equation:

$$\alpha \frac{\partial^2 T}{\partial x^2} = \frac{\partial T}{\partial t} \qquad (9.2.16)$$

with boundary and initial temperatures given by:

At the surface $\qquad\qquad\qquad T(0,t) = T_s \qquad\qquad\qquad (9.2.17a)$

At infinity $\qquad\qquad\qquad T(\infty,t) = \text{bounded} \qquad\qquad (9.2.17b)$

Initially $\qquad\qquad\qquad\qquad T(x,0) = T_0 \qquad\qquad\qquad (9.2.17c)$

We normalize the temperature using a new variable:

$$\Theta = \frac{T - T_s}{T_0 - T_s} \qquad (9.2.18)$$

and obtain the revised model:

$$\alpha \frac{\partial^2 \Theta}{\partial x^2} = \frac{\partial \Theta}{\partial t} \qquad (9.2.19)$$

$$\Theta(0,t) = 0 \tag{9.2.20a}$$

$$\Theta(\infty,t) = \text{bounded} \tag{9.2.20b}$$

$$\Theta(x,0) = 1 \tag{9.2.20c}$$

We now Laplace transform with respect to time t, noting that the left side of Equation 9.2.18 becomes an ordinary derivative in the transformed variable $\bar{\theta}(x,s)$, while the right side reduces to an algebraic expression. We obtain:

$$\alpha\bar{\theta}''(x,s) = s\bar{\theta}(x,s) - 1$$

or equivalently,

$$\bar{\theta}'' - (s/\alpha)\bar{\theta} = -1/\alpha \tag{9.2.21}$$

This is a second order linear, nonhomogeneous ODE with constant coefficients and can be solved by the standard D-operator method and the use of a particular integral for the nonhomogeneous term. There results:

$$\bar{\theta}(x,s) = A\exp(-x\sqrt{s/\alpha}) + B\exp(x\sqrt{s/\alpha}) + \frac{1}{s} \tag{9.2.22}$$

Since $\bar{\theta}(x,s)$ has to remain finite for $x \to \infty$, we obtain B = 0, and from the transformed surface condition Equation 9.2.19a, A = −1/s. Hence,

$$\bar{\theta}(x,s) = \frac{1}{s} - \exp\frac{\exp(-x\sqrt{s/\alpha})}{s} \tag{9.2.23}$$

The first term is inverted by Item 3 of our old Table 5.1, the second term by Item 3 of the new Table 9.3. We obtain:

$$\theta = \frac{T - T_s}{T_0 - T_s} = 1 - \text{erfc}(x/2\sqrt{\alpha t}) = \text{erf}(x/2\sqrt{\alpha t}) \tag{9.2.24}$$

We have here a particularly simple use of the transform tables as well as a simple, terse solution that is a characteristic of conduction or diffusion problems in a semi-infinite medium. The proceedings are somewhat more complex for finite geometries, as shown in the next illustration.

9.2.3   Conduction in a Slab: Solution for Small Time Constants

It had previously been pointed out that the classical Fourier series solution of the type represented by Equation 9.1.48 shows slow convergence for low values of the time constant appearing in the exponential term. The Laplace transform provides a means of expressing the solution in terms of an equivalent series of error functions, which shows *fast* convergence under these same conditions but is conversely less suitable for *large* values of the time. This equivalent series is obtained by means of an ingenious expansion of the transformed variable, undertaken midway through the solution procedure and prior to the inversion. We illustrate this with the following example.

Consider a slab $-a < x < +a$ initially at $T = 0$, subjected to a surface temperature T_s at time zero. The model for the transients is given by:

$$\alpha \frac{\partial^2 T}{\partial x^2} = \frac{\partial T}{\partial t} \tag{9.2.25}$$

$$T(a,t) = T_s \tag{9.2.26a}$$

$$\frac{\partial \overline{T}}{\partial x}(0,t) = 0 \tag{9.2.26b}$$

$$T(x,0) = 0 \tag{9.2.26c}$$

and in its Laplace transformed form by:

$$\frac{d^2 \overline{T}}{dx^2} - q^2 \overline{T} = 0 \tag{9.2.27}$$

$$\overline{T}(a,s) = T_s/s \tag{9.2.28a}$$

$$\frac{\partial \overline{T}}{\partial x}(0,s) = 0 \tag{9.2.28b}$$

where $q^2 = s/\alpha$, α = thermal diffusivity.

Note that the transform of T_s is T_s/s, not T_s as is often erroneously assumed. Note also that the symmetry condition Equation 9.2.26b is used in place of the second surface condition $T(-a,t) = T_s$ for greater convenience. This is not a requirement but avoids functions with negative arguments.

Solution of Equation 9.2.27 by the D-operator method and evaluation of the integration constants yields the transformed temperature:

$$\overline{T}(x,s) = \frac{T_s}{s}\frac{\cosh q\,x}{\cosh qa} \tag{9.2.29}$$

We could at this stage proceed to invert, using the technique of expressing cosh in terms of equivalent cosines, outlined in the previous illustration. This would yield a Fourier series similar to Equation 9.2.15d which converged well for large values of the exponential arguments. To obtain a form suitable for small values, we first rewrite Equation 9.2.29 in exponential form:

$$\overline{T} = \frac{T_s}{s\exp(qa)}\frac{\exp(qx)+\exp(-qx)}{[1+\exp(-2qa)]} \tag{9.2.30}$$

and expand the bracketed term by means of the binomial theorem. We obtain:

$$\overline{T}(x,s) = \frac{T_s}{s}\{\exp[-q(a-x)]+\exp[-q(a+x)]\}\sum_{n=0}^{\infty}(-1)^n\exp(-2naq) \tag{9.2.31}$$

or alternatively,

$$\overline{T}(x,s) = \frac{T_s}{s}\sum_{n=0}^{\infty}(-1)^n\exp\{-9[(2n+1)a-x]\}\sum_{n=0}^{\infty}(-1)^n\{-9[(2n+a)+x]\} \tag{9.2.32}$$

Since $q = (s/\alpha)^{1/2}$, each term in the two series has the form $[-\exp(-k\sqrt{s})]/s$, and therefore can be inverted by Item 3 of our Table 9.3. We obtain upon inversion:

$$\frac{T(x,t)}{T_s} = \sum_{n=0}^{\infty}(-1)^n\operatorname{erfc}\frac{(2n+1)a-x}{2\sqrt{\alpha t}} + \sum_{n=0}^{\infty}(-1)^n\operatorname{erfc}\frac{(2n+1)a+x}{2\sqrt{\alpha t}} \tag{9.2.33}$$

Had we proceeded directly with the inversion of Equation 9.2.28, the result would have been:

$$\frac{T(x,t)}{T_s} = 1 - \frac{4}{\pi}\sum_{n=0}^{\infty}\frac{(-1)^n}{2n+1}\cos\frac{(2n+1)\pi x}{2a}\exp\{-\alpha(2n+1)^2\pi^2/4a^2\} \tag{9.2.34}$$

Proof of this is left to the Exercises.

The reader may at this stage conclude that we have merely replaced an already complex expression by an even more complex one, Equation 9.2.32. A numerical example may help dispel this notion.

We choose a low value for the time constant $\alpha t/a^2 = 10^{-2}$, and evaluate T/T_s from both Equations 9.2.32 and 9.2.33 for the midpoint of the slab, $x = 0$. We obtain in the first case:

$$\frac{T}{T_s} = 2\{\text{erfc } 5 - \text{erfc } 15 + \text{erfc } 25 - ...\} \tag{9.2.35}$$

Since these small values of erfc are not tabulated, we use the expansion for large values of the argument given in Table 7.7:

$$\text{erfc } x \cong \pi^{-1/2}\left[\frac{1}{x} - \frac{1}{2x^3} + ...\right] \tag{9.2.36}$$

This yields:

$$\frac{T}{T_s} = 3.1 \times 10^{-12} - 1.5 \times 10^{-98} + ... \tag{9.2.37}$$

i.e., the temperature at the midpoint is for all practical purposes still at the initial temperature of zero. Convergence of the series is very rapid and practically complete after the first term.

Let us next look at the predictions of Equation 9.2.34. Here the result obtained is

$$\frac{T}{T_s} = 1 - \frac{4}{\pi}\left[\exp(-10^{-2}\pi^2/4) - \frac{1}{3}\exp(-9 \times 10^{-2}\pi^2/4) + ...\right]$$

or

$$\frac{T}{T_s} = 1 - [1.2422 - 0.3390 + 0.1374 - 0.0426 + ...] \tag{9.2.38}$$

One sees that convergence is painfully slow. In addition, the terms would have to be evaluated to at least *14* decimal places to match the result given by the error function series. This demonstrates the power and convenience of the latter and the total inadequacy of the exponential series for small values of the time constant.

Illustration 9.2.4   Conduction in a Cylinder Revisited: Use of Hankel Transforms

We had previously in Illustration 8.2.1 used the solution for unsteady radial conduction in a cylinder with surface resistance and zero external temperature to mimic radial diffusion in a tubular reactor with a first order reaction at the wall. The solution given there was taken from the literature and given without proof. We undertake that solution now, using the modified Hankel transform listed in Table 9.3, and examine its advantages compared to other methods.

Using a normalized radial variable $y = r/R$, the model is given by the following equations:

PDE
$$\frac{\alpha}{R^2}\left[\frac{\partial^2 T}{\partial y^2} + \frac{1}{y}\frac{\partial T}{\partial y}\right] = \frac{\partial T}{\partial t} \qquad (9.2.39)$$

At the centerline
$$T(0,t) = \text{bounded} \qquad (9.3.40a)$$

or
$$\frac{\partial T}{\partial y}(0,t) = 0$$

At the surface
$$-\frac{\partial T}{\partial y}\bigg|_{y=1} = \beta T\,|_{y=1} \qquad (9.2.40b)$$

where $\beta = hR/k$.

Initially
$$T(y,0) = T_0 \qquad (9.2.40c)$$

Application of the modified Hankel transform implies that each term in the model is transformed into the integral:

$$H_{M\pi}\{\text{Term}\} = \int_0^1 (\text{Term})y J_0(\lambda_j y)dy \qquad (9.2.41)$$

where λ_j are the roots of:

$$\lambda J_1(\lambda) - \beta J_0(\lambda) = 0$$

tabulated in Table 8.8. In particular, the left side of the PDE becomes an algebraic expression:

$$H_M\left\{\frac{\partial^2 T}{\partial y^2} + \frac{1}{y}\frac{\partial T}{\partial y}\right\} = -\lambda_j^{\,2}\overline{T}(\lambda_j) + J_0(\lambda_j)\left[\beta T + \frac{\partial T}{\partial y}\right]_{y=1} \qquad (9.2.42)$$

where the bracketed term vanishes because of the boundary condition Equation 9.2.40b. The right side of the PDE 9.2.39 is transformed into the total derivative $d\overline{T}/dt$, where we denote the transformed temperature by $\overline{T}$. The entire PDE thus is reduced to the simple first order ODE in $\overline{T}$.

$$-\lambda_j^2(\alpha/R^2)\overline{T} \doteq \frac{d\overline{T}}{dt} \qquad (9.2.43)$$

with the solution:

$$\overline{T} = \overline{T}_0 \exp(-\alpha\lambda_j^2 t/R^2) \qquad (9.2.44)$$

Here $\overline{T}_0$ is the transformed initial condition:

$$\overline{T}_0 = \int_0^1 T_0 y J_0(\lambda_j)dy = (T_0/\lambda_j)J_1(\lambda_j) \qquad (9.2.45)$$

in which we have used the tabulations of Bessel function integrals given in Table 4.8 of Chapter 4 to evaluate the integral. The transformed temperature $\overline{T}$ therefore is given by:

$$\overline{T}(\lambda_j, t) = (T_0/\lambda_j)J_1(\lambda_j)\exp(-\alpha\lambda_j^2 t/R^2) \qquad (9.2.46)$$

We are now ready to invert and introduce $\overline{T} = f_{MH}$ into the inversion formula given in Table 9.2. The result is

$$T(y,t) = 2T_0 \sum_{j=1}^{\infty} \frac{\lambda_j}{\lambda_j^2+\beta^2} \frac{J_1(\lambda_j)}{J_0^2(\lambda_j)} J_0(\lambda_j y)\exp(-\lambda_j^2 \alpha t/R^2) \qquad (9.2.47)$$

This expression is identical in form to Equation 8.2.18 used in the derivation of concentration profiles in the tubular reactor of Illustration 8.2.1.

Comments:

The method evidently requires some getting used to given the wealth of new symbols. Once these are accepted and understood, however, the transform reveals itself as a compact tool for solving problems in cylindrical coordinates with a Type III boundary condition. Application becomes quite mechanical, but one still has to keep a watchful eye on potential pitfalls. There is a temptation for example, to set the transform of the initial condition equal to the condition itself: $\overline{T}_0 = T_0$ instead of evaluating the full integral (9.2.45). With some care, such errors can be avoided.

The Hankel transform was shown capable of reducing a second order PDE with variable coefficients into a simple, separable first order ODE 9.2.43. The Laplace transform, by contrast, would only succeed in reducing the PDE to a second order ODE with variable coefficients which has to be solved and, more importantly, inverted. This is a cumbersome process. The method of separation of variables is similarly unwieldy, as shown in Illustration 9.1.4. Both methods lead to valid results, however, and are attractive because of their greater range of applications.

The reader who is overwhelmed by the appearance of the final result, Equation 9.2.45, is reminded that such series often converge after one term and that convenient tabulations of both Bessel functions and the eigenvalues λ_j are available.

Illustration 9.2.5   Analysis in the Laplace Domain: The Method of Moments

We had seen in Chapter 5 on Laplace transformation that a good deal of information about system behavior can be obtained from the transformed differential equations without going through the process of inversion. We termed this procedure *Laplace domain analysis* and were able to use it in particular to predict system stability.

We introduce the reader here to a similar analysis applied to PDEs that is designed specifically for use in parameter estimation from experimental data. The example we use to illustrate the procedure is that of linear chromatography, previously described by the fluid and solid mass balances, Equations 7.2.4 and 7.2.5. For our present purposes, we combine the two equations into a single two-phase mass balance and retain the solid-phase balance as a second relation. Thus,

Two-phase mass balance:

$$G_s \frac{\partial Y}{\partial z} + \varepsilon \rho_g \frac{\partial Y}{\partial t} + \rho_b \frac{\partial q}{\partial t} = 0 \tag{9.2.48}$$

Solid phase mass balance:

$$K_{os}a(q* - q) = \rho_b \frac{\partial q}{\partial t} \tag{9.2.49}$$

Equilibrium relation:

$$q* = HY \tag{9.2.50}$$

We note that the fluid phase driving force $(Y - Y*)$ of Equation 7.2.5 has been replaced by a solid driving force $(q* - q)$ which is better suited for the extraction of parameters of interest.

Let us look at both the experimental and mathematical sides of the procedure. The experiment consists of introducing a solute pulse $Y(0,t)$ into a chromatographic column (Figure 9.3A and B). The column is initially clean, i.e., $q(z,0) = Y(z,0) = 0$. The solute at first becomes adsorbed near the inlet of the column and subsequently is eluted by continued purge with carrier gas, making its appearance at the outlet as an attenuated pulse $Y(L,t)$, Figure 9.3C. Attenuation is due to the interphase mass transfer resistance residing in the transfer coefficient K_{os}.

On the mathematical side, we introduce the equilibrium Relation 9.2.48 into the solid-phase mass balance, and then Laplace transform Equations 9.2.46 and 9.2.47 with respect to time t. We obtain:

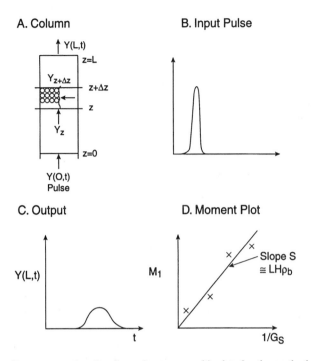

FIGURE 9.3 Parameter estimation from chromatographic data by the method of moments.

$$G_s \frac{d\overline{Y}}{dz} + \varepsilon\rho_g s\overline{Y}\rho_b s\overline{q} = 0 \qquad (9.2.51)$$

$$K_{0s}a(H\overline{Y} - \overline{q}) = \rho_b s\overline{q} \qquad (9.2.52)$$

where $\overline{Y}, \overline{q}$ denote the transformed fluid and solid phase concentration. Note that no initial conditions appear in these expressions since the column is clean at time $t = 0$. Eliminating $\overline{q}$ algebraically, we obtain the first order ODE in $\overline{Y}$:

$$G_s \frac{d\overline{Y}}{dz} + P(s)\overline{Y} = 0 \qquad (9.2.53)$$

which is integrated by separation of variables to yield:

$$\overline{Y} = \overline{Y}(0,s)\exp(-Pz/G_s) \qquad (9.2.54)$$

Here $P(s) = s\left[\varepsilon\rho_g + \dfrac{H K_{0s}a}{s + K_{0s}a/\rho_b}\right]$ and $\overline{Y}(0,s)$ is the transformed input pulse at $z = 0$, i.e., the boundary condition for the ODE 9.2.53. When that pulse is instantaneous, that is a Dirac function $\sigma(o)$, its Laplace transform is 1 (see Item 6 in Table 8.6), i.e., we can set $\overline{Y}(0,s) = 1$.

The question now arises how we can relate the measured output $Y(L,t)$ to the parameters contained in our transformed PDE, Equation 9.2.54. An ingenious method has been developed to achieve this. We reach back to our Table 5.1 of Laplace transforms and extract Item 9 which relates the derivative of the transformed variable to the time integral of the variable itself. We have:

$$\frac{d^n\overline{Y}}{ds^n} = (-1)^n \int_0^\infty t^n Y(t)e^{-st}dt \qquad (9.2.55)$$

and in particular:

$$\left.\frac{d^n\overline{Y}}{ds^n}\right|_{s=0} = (-1)^n \int_0^\infty t^n Y(t)dt \qquad (9.2.56)$$

where the integral on the right is referred to as the n-th moment of $Y(t)$.

The reader will note that this expression establishes the desired link between experiment and model. The left side can be established by differentiating the transformed PDE Equation 9.2.54 with respect to s and contains the physical parameters of the system such as the partition coefficient or Henry's constant H, and the mass transfer coefficient K_{0s} a. The right side represents various time integrals of the measured outlet concentration $Y(L,t)$. For $n = 0$, for example, the integral represents the area under the curve of Figure 9.3C. For higher order moments, the output concentration is multiplied by t^n and then integrated. The existence of n such moments gives us the ability in principle, to extract n physical parameters. The precision of the moments, however, quickly diminishes with increasing n, and in practice one therefore is confined to two or three such parameter determinations.

Suppose we wish to extract the Henry constant H from experimental output data. We proceed as follows. We normalize the moments by dividing them by the zeroth moment. This leads to simpler expressions and a cancellation of errors. We obtain, for the first normalized moment M_1

$$M_1 = -\frac{\int_0^\infty tY(t)dt}{\int_0^\infty Y(t)dt} = \left[\frac{d\overline{Y}}{ds}\bigg/\overline{Y}\right]_{s=0} = \frac{L}{G_s}(\varepsilon\rho_g + H\rho_b) \approx \frac{L}{G_s}H\rho_b \quad (9.2.57)$$

Similar expressions containing additional parameters can be obtained from the higher moments. Note again that the left side of Equation 9.2.55 represents the experiment, the right side represents the model. The first term of the latter is usually small compared to the product $H\rho_b$ and can be neglected.

In practice it will be desirable to perform a series of experiments to obtain the best parameter value by a least square fit. This can be done by running the column at different carrier flow rates G_s, or by using columns of different length. In the former case, a plot of the first moment M_1 against $1/G_s$ should yield a straight line with a slope $S \cong LH\rho_b$ from which the Henry constant H can be extracted (Figure 9.3D).

Comments:

We have here an example of the intertwining of imaginative modeling and experimentation. The accurate determination of Henry's constant by conventional equilibration involves a considerable expenditure in time and equipment. The procedure described here uses standard equipment available in most laboratories and can be carried out rapidly with relatively little effort. Electronic integrators are available for the evaluation of moments from the experimental output.

Extraction of the parameters from the data and model in principle can also be achieved by equating the theoretical transform $\overline{Y}$ to the Laplace transform integral of the experimental output, i.e., we write:

$$\overline{Y} = \overline{Y}(0,s)\exp(-P_z/G_s) = \int_0^\infty Y(L,t)e^{-st}dt \qquad (9.2.58)$$

and evaluate the integral for various values of the Laplace parameters, using the results to evaluate the parameters contained in P(s). This is evidently much more cumbersome than the method of moments which ultimately leads to a simple linear plot from which the parameters are extracted with ease.

Historical Note:

Early work on matters related to the Laplace transform was undertaken by the French mathematician Pierre Simon de Laplace (1749–1827) who investigated the properties of integrals of the form $\int_0^\infty F(t)e^{-st}dt$. Its application to the solution of differential equations had to await the work of the English electrical engineer Oliver Heaviside (1850–1925). He invented for that purpose what is now known as the Heaviside Operational Calculus and used it to solve a host of practical problems related particularly to electrical systems. His work was not immediately accepted, partly because of the difficult nature of his operational calculus, and also because of his lack of rigor for which he was much derided by the mathematical community. It was left to other workers to replace his calculus by the simple procedures which are now everyday tools used in the solution of differential equations. It was felt appropriate to name the method after Laplace for his early investigations of the relevant integral. Heaviside himself died a bitter recluse.

Practice Problems

9.2.1 Inversions from Other Inversions — Once certain inversion formulas are established, they can often be used to invert similarly structured functions by means of the convolution integral, Item 7 of Table 5.1. Consider the two related transforms, Items 2 and 3 of Table 9.3:

$$\exp(-k\sqrt{s}) \text{ and } [\exp(-k\sqrt{s})/s]$$

Derive the inverse of the latter by applying the convolution integral and using the known inverse of $\exp(-k\sqrt{s})$.

(Hint: Make the substitution $\lambda = k/2\sqrt{t}$.)

9.2.2 Inversion to Fourier Series — Invert the Expression 9.2.29, using the extended Heaviside expansion, Item 1 of Table 9.3 and converting the hyperbolic functions to trigonometric functions as shown in Illustration 9.2.1. Show that this leads to the solution (Equation 9.2.34) which is the alternative to the error function series (Equation 9.2.33).

9.2.3 Use of the Finite Cosine Transform — Consider a slab with an initial temperature distribution $T(x,0) = f(x)$ and both faces at $x = 0$ and $x = a$ insulated. This is a problem particularly well-suited for the finite Fourier cosine transform (Item 3, Table 9.2) which has the property of transforming second derivatives to boundary conditions of Type II. Show that its application yields the solution:

$$T = \frac{1}{a}\int_0^a f(x)dx + \frac{2}{a}\sum_{n=1}^{\infty}\left[\int_0^a f(x)\cos\frac{n\pi x}{a}dx\right]\cos\frac{n\pi x}{a}\exp(-\alpha n^2\pi^2 t/a^2)$$

The expression confirms that at steady-state ($t \to \infty$), the temperature in the slab becomes uniform and equal to the mean integral of the initial distribution $f(x)$.

9.2.4 Fourier Transforms in Infinite Media — Integral transforms also exist for semi-infinite domains. The definitions and inversions are similar in form to those for finite domains, with the exception that the summations in the inversion formulas are replaced by integrals with a continuous integrating variable r taking the place of the integers n. The Fourier sine transform, for example, is described by the following relations:

$$\text{Definition: } S_r\{F(x)\} = \int_0^{\infty} F(x)\sin rx\,dx = f(r) \qquad (9.2.59)$$

$$\text{Inversion: } S_r^{-1}\{f(r)\} = \frac{2}{\pi}\int_0^{\infty} f(r)\sin rx\,dx \qquad (9.2.60)$$

$$\text{Transform or derivative: } S_r\{F''(x)\} = -r^2 f(r) + rF(0) \qquad (9.2.61)$$

Devise a problem suitable for the application of this transform and by making use of Fourier sine transform tables in the literature, arrive at a solution of the problem. Compare the result with existing solutions.

9.2.5 Diffusion and Reaction — Consider the system of equations:

$$K_1 \frac{\partial^2 u}{\partial x^2} - K_2 u = \frac{\partial u}{\partial t} \tag{9.2.62}$$

$$u(0,t) = u_0 \tag{9.2.63a}$$

$$u(\infty,t) = 0 \tag{9.2.63b}$$

$$u(x,0) = 0 \tag{9.2.63c}$$

The model describes unsteady diffusion and reaction in a semi-infinite medium as well as conduction in a thin rod with convective heat exchange with the surroundings (see in this connection Illustration 8.2.2). Using Laplace transformation, show that the solution is given by:

$$u(x,t) = \frac{2u_0}{\sqrt{\pi}} \int_{x/2\sqrt{K_1 t}}^{\infty} \exp\left[-\lambda^2 - \frac{K_2 x^2}{4K_1 \lambda^2} \right] d\lambda \tag{9.2.64}$$

Use of special formulas reduces this expression to error function form.

9.2.6 Collision Frequency in the Coagulation of Aerosols — The theory of coagulation by Brownian motion postulates that any collision between two particles of radius R constitutes a coagulation event, and that the movement of the particles itself is described by Fick's equation.

(a) Show that the model for this process in a field with an initially uniform concentration C_0 is given by:

$$D \frac{1}{r^2} \frac{\partial}{\partial r}\left(r^2 \frac{\partial C}{\partial r} \right) = \frac{\partial C}{\partial t} \tag{9.2.65}$$

$$C(R,t) = 0 \tag{9.2.66a}$$

$$C(\infty,t) = C_0 \tag{9.2.66b}$$

$$C(r,0) = C_0 \tag{9.2.66c}$$

(b) Solve the system by Laplace Transformation to obtain the concentration distribution.

Answer: $C(r,t) = C_0\left[1 - \frac{R}{r} \text{erfc}\left(\frac{r-R}{2\sqrt{Dt}} \right) \right]$

(c) Show that the flux at $r = R$, i.e., the collision frequency, is given by:

$$N = 4\pi R^2 DC_0 \left[\frac{1}{R} + \frac{1}{\sqrt{\pi Dt}} \right]$$ (9.2.67)

9.2.7 Determination of Liquid Diffusivities — Liquid diffusivities can be determined by passing a solvent over the open end of a capillary sealed at the bottom and containing a solution of the solute whose diffusivity is to be measured (see Illustration 7.1.2 and the accompanying Figure 7.1B). The average solute concentration in the capillary is determined at various time intervals and the results used to extract values of D from the solution of an appropriate model. Show that the model leads to the following expression for the percentage of solute E_t remaining in the capillary:

$$E\% = \frac{800}{\pi^2} \sum_{n=1}^{\infty} \frac{1}{(2n-1)^2} \exp[-(2n-1)^2 \pi^2 Dt / 4L^2]$$

9.2.8 Integration of the Chromatographic Equation — A particularly simple form of the linear chromatographic equations is given by their nondimensionalized version, Equation 7.3.72. Consider the situation where the column is initially clean and is subjected at time $t = 0$ to a step change in concentration $Y(0,t) = Y_0$.

(a) Apply the Laplace transformation to both equations, and eliminate the transformed concentration Y*.
(b) Solve the resulting first order ODE in the transformed fluid phase concentration.
(c) Invert by using the convolution theorem and Item 7 of Table 9.3.

The result is given by:

$$\frac{Y}{Y_0} = 1 - \int_0^N \exp(-T - N') I_0(2\sqrt{TN'}) dN'$$ (9.2.68)

The right side is known as the J-Function $J(N,T)$ and is tabulated in the literature (see References at the end of the chapter). This solution was used to compile the Table 6.5 in Chapter 6.

9.3 THE METHOD OF CHARACTERISTICS

9.3.1 GENERAL PROPERTIES

Like the two preceding methods of separation of variables and integral transforms, the method of characteristics achieves its goal of simplification by reducing the PDE or system of PDEs to an equivalent set of ODEs. This is the only common feature of the three methods. In all other respects they differ both in concept as well as details of applications. In the following, we summarize the principal features and properties of the method.

The principal area of application of the method of characteristics is the solution of:

- Single first order PDEs of arbitrary form
- Systems of *hyperbolic* PDEs of otherwise arbitrary form
- Single second order *hyperbolic* PDEs, e.g., the Wave equation

The term *arbitrary form* encompasses both linear, quasilinear, and fully nonlinear PDEs. We note, however, that full theories have been developed only for systems of quasilinear PDEs and, to a lesser extent, single nonlinear PDEs. Sets of fully nonlinear PDEs still elude complete treatment, as they do at the ODE level.

A particularly rich area of application is that of certain homogeneous quasilinear first order PDEs in which one or more partial differential equations are combined with one or more auxiliary algebraic equations, i.e., those of the form:

$$\frac{\partial u}{\partial x} + \frac{\partial v}{\partial y} = 0 \tag{9.3.1}$$

$$v = f(u) \tag{9.3.2}$$

The PDE is in this instance termed *reducible* since it lacks algebraic terms in the dependent variables. It is homogeneous because it lacks isolated terms $f(x,y)$ and quasilinear by virtue of the linear appearance of its highest derivative.

We know from previous examples that the combination (Equation 9.3.1) arises in a natural way in all unsteady, convective transport processes, i.e., those lacking second order diffusive terms. We noted its appearance in equilibrium chromatography (see Equation 7.1.19):

$$G_s \frac{\partial Y}{\partial x} + [\epsilon \rho_g + \rho_b f'(Y)] \frac{\partial Y}{\partial t} = 0 \tag{9.3.3}$$

$$q = f(Y) \tag{9.3.4}$$

in traffic problems:

$$\frac{\partial q'}{\partial x} + \frac{\partial C}{\partial t} = 0 \tag{9.3.5}$$

$$q' = vC = g(C) \tag{9.3.6}$$

and in sedimentation:

$$\frac{\partial(vC)}{\partial z} + \frac{\partial C}{\partial t} = 0 \qquad\qquad (9.3.7)$$

$$v = h(C) \qquad\qquad (9.3.8)$$

Note that when a mass transfer resistance is included in Equation 9.3.1, the equation is no longer reducible and its analysis becomes correspondingly more complex. The treatment given in this chapter will principally deal with *single* quasilinear first order PDEs of the reducible form.

The reduction of the PDEs to ODE form is achieved by adopting a Lagrangian approach, i.e., instead of using a fixed Eulerian reference framework, we move with the physical entity such as concentration, temperature, or a vehicle and establish its trajectory or path of propagation. In other words we replace the previous variables, e.g., x, y, z, t by a *single* independent variable s, taken along the path of propagation. This concept, and the consequences which flow from it, require some getting used to, but provides us with rich benefits.

To provide the reader with a tangible example of the application of the method, we consider the unidirectional movement of vehicular traffic, depicted in the diagrams of Figure 9.4. Both normal traffic as well as conditions leading to rear-end collision are examined. The Eulerian representation is shown in the Figure (IA, IIA) as the "velocity profiles" of the cars, i.e., the velocity as a function of distance. The Lagrangian representation on the other hand, Figure 9.4 (IB, IIB), utilizes the z-t plane to trace the trajectory of each car, i.e., its position z at a particular time t. The top figures describe the movement of three cars all traveling at constant but different velocities, the car with the highest velocity being the farthest advanced. The bottom diagrams depict the reverse situation in which the slower car ② is ahead of the faster moving vehicle ①. If no evasive action is taken by either car, i.e., if we limit ourselves to a single coordinate direction z, the slower car will undergo a rear-end collision with the approaching faster car and the velocity will drop essentially to zero. There consequently will be a discontinuity in the velocity, a condition which we shall refer to as a *shock*. The Eulerian representation depicts this situation, as well as that for normal traffic in terms we are accustomed to, i.e., profiles of a state variable, here the vehicle velocity v. The Lagrangian representation on the other hand utilizes the velocity as a *parameter* which equals the inverse of the slope of each trajectory, termed a *characteristic*. Slow cars have steep characteristics, fast cars have shallower trajectories. If the vehicle velocity is constant, these trajectories will be straight lines of slope v^{-1}.

Let us now examine the mathematical formulation of these characteristics and present a summary of the various types encountered in practice.

9.3.2 THE CHARACTERISTICS

If we consider two independent variables only, for example, distance z and time t, and limit ourselves to a single state variable u, a first order quaslinear PDE takes on the general form:

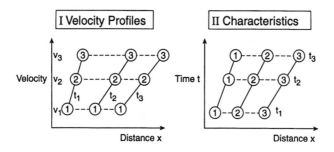

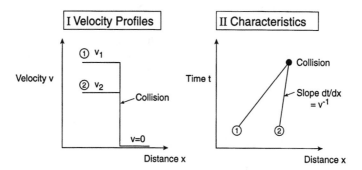

FIGURE 9.4   Vehicle movement represented in the v-x and the t-x (characterstic) planes.

$$A(x, t, u)\frac{\partial u}{\partial x} + B(x, t, u)\frac{\partial u}{\partial t} = C(x, t, u) \qquad (9.3.9)$$

Since quasilinearity is assumed here, this requires that A, B, and C be free of derivatives of u, but does permit the presence of nonlinear terms in u in these coefficients.

The transformation of this PDE into an equivalent set of ODEs is often based on the notion of a directional derivative, encountered in basic calculus. To arrive at an expression for this derivative, we start with the total differential of u:

$$dx\frac{\partial u}{\partial x} + dt\frac{\partial u}{\partial t} = du \qquad (9.3.10)$$

and, after dividing by ds, obtain:

$$\frac{dx}{ds}\frac{\partial u}{\partial x} + \frac{dt}{ds}\frac{\partial u}{\partial t} = \frac{du}{ds} \qquad (9.3.11)$$

where ds may be viewed as the differential arc along a characteristic. Comparing Equations 9.3.9 and 9.3.11 we see that the two expressions will be equivalent provided the following ODEs are satisfied:

$$\frac{dx}{ds} = A(x, t, u) \tag{9.3.12a}$$

$$\frac{dt}{ds} = B(x, t, u) \tag{9.3.12b}$$

$$\frac{du}{ds} = C(x, t, u) \tag{9.3.12c}$$

Many textbooks use more sophisticated arguments to arrive at these expressions, but the net result in each case is that the original PDE 9.3.9 has been transformed into an equivalent system of three ODEs in what are now the dependent variables x, t, and u. Since the arc length s is ultimately redundant to the solution, we may, as an alternative, eliminate ds by division, reducing the system to *two* simultaneous ODEs in the independent variables x and u:

Velocity of propagation $$\qquad \left(\frac{dx}{dt}\right)_c = \frac{A(x, t, u)}{B(x, t, u)} \tag{9.3.13a}$$

State variable $$\qquad \left(\frac{du}{dt}\right)_c = \frac{C(x, t, u)}{B(x, t, u)} \tag{9.3.13b}$$

The subscript $_c$ is used as a reminder that the derivatives are taken along a characteristic. Either set Equation 9.3.12 or Equation 9.3.13 may be integrated by standard ODE solution methods. The numerical procedure used in these cases is referred to as the *method of lines.*

When C = 0, the PDE 9.3.9 becomes reducible. If, in addition, the coefficients A and B are functions of the state variable u only, we obtain as a special case:

Velocity of propagation $$\qquad \left(\frac{dx}{dt}\right)_c = f(u) \tag{9.3.14}$$

This case arises in many applications of equilibrium chromatography, traffic theory, sedimentation, and other processes and can be analyzed in a particular fruitful manner. This will be shown in several of the illustrations which follow.

We end this section by summarizing certain important categories of characteristics which arise in practice. They are displayed in Figure 9.5.

Figure 9.5A consists of parallel characteristics of equal slope, i.e., of equal velocities of propagation. This is representative of all vehicles in a traffic problem

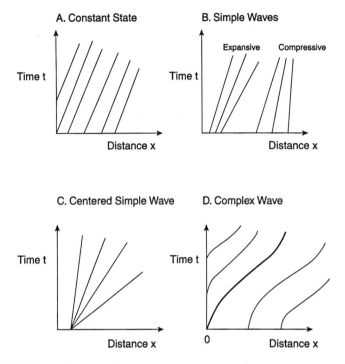

FIGURE 9.5   Types of characteristics.

moving at the same speed, or a fixed constant concentration being fed to a chromatographic column and is termed a *constant state*.

In Figure 9.5B, the velocity along a characteristic is constant but varies among different entities. This state is referred to as a *simple wave*. An important subcategory is the so-called *centered simple wave*, shown in Figure 9.5C. It may be thought of, for example, as representing a range of concentrations or temperatures emanating from a particular point in time and space.

Figure 9.5D, finally, represents the most general case of velocities of propagation which vary among physical entities or with time. This state is referred to as a *complex wave* and leads to curved characteristics.

Let us start our illustrations with a simple example which admits a closed form solution of the state variable.

Illustration 9.3.1   The Heat Exchanger with a Time-Varying Fluid Velocity

The case considered here is that of a single-pass, steam-heated shell and tube heat exchanger. The fluid being heated, assumed to be on the tube side, has a time varying inlet velocity v(t) that also will affect the heat transfer coefficient u(t) as the latter generally depends on Reynolds number.

The relevant model is given by the following first order linear PDE:

$$v(t)\rho Cp(\pi d^2 / 4)\frac{\partial T}{\partial x} + U(t)\pi d)[T_s - T] = \rho Cp\frac{\pi d^2}{4}\frac{\partial T}{\partial t} \qquad (9.3.15a)$$

or alternatively:

$$-v(t)\frac{\partial T}{\partial t} = K(t)[T_s - T] = \frac{\partial T}{\partial t} \qquad (9.3.15b)$$

where $K(t) = 4/d\rho Cp$.

By casting the PDE in the form of Equation 9.3.9 and applying the Relations 9.3.12, we obtain the following characteristic equations:

$$\frac{dt}{ds} = 1 \qquad (9.3.16a)$$

$$\frac{dx}{ds} = v(t) \qquad (9.3.16b)$$

$$\frac{dT}{ds} = K(t)[T_s - T] \qquad (9.3.16c)$$

These ODEs can be solved numerically to obtain a relation between T, x, and t at a particular point s along the characteristic. Alternatively, we can arrive at analytical forms by eliminating ds by division and integrating the result. We obtain in the first instance:

Velocity of propagation $\qquad \dfrac{dx}{dt} = v(t) \qquad (9.3.17a)$

State variable $\qquad \dfrac{dT}{dt} = K(t)[T_s - T] \qquad (9.3.17b)$

The first equation can be formally integrated by separation of variables. The solution to the second ODE is given by Item 6 of our listing of ODE solutions, Table 4.4. The result is given by the two expressions:

$$x = x_0 + \int_{t_0}^{t} v(t')dt' \qquad (9.3.18)$$

and

$$T(t, t_0) = T(t_0) \exp(-\overline{K}) + \int_{t_0}^{t} T_s K(t') \exp[-\overline{K}(t')] dt'' \qquad (9.3.19)$$

where $\overline{K} = \int_{t_0}^{t} K(t') dt'$.

Note that the resultant characteristics form a complex wave, shown in Figure 9.5D, since the slope $dt/dx = 1/v(t)$, i.e., varies with time. A distinction is now made between the characteristics emanating from the x-axis and those originating on the t-axis. The former describe the propagation of the temperature distribution $T(x,0) = f(x)$ initially present in the heat exchanger while the latter represent the pathways of the incoming feed temperature. For the characteristics emanating from the abscissa, Equations 9.3.18 and 9.3.19 become:

$$x_0 = x - \int_0^t v(t') dt' \qquad (9.3.20)$$

$$T(x, t) = f\left[x - \int_0^t v(t') dt' \right] \exp(-\overline{K}) + \int_0^t T_s K(t') \exp[-\overline{K}(t')] dt' \qquad (9.3.21)$$

It is left to the exercises to derive the corresponding expressions for the characteristics emanating from the *ordinate*.

Comments:

Equation 9.3.21, although somewhat cumbersome, represents a closed form expression for the unsteady temperature distribution of the fluid initially present in the exchanger. These solutions therefore are valid only during the initial period of displacement, $t_d = L/\overline{v}$, where L = heat exchanger length, and $\overline{v}$ = mean integral inlet velocity over the period t_d.

The reader should note that the deviations from the usual steady-state profiles products by this model are to be viewed as *maximum values*. In actual practice, the temperature peaks and valleys produced by the velocity fluctuations will be attenuated due to the heat capacity of the tubular wall. To take account of this effect, however, would require a second energy balance, thus complicating the model considerably.

Illustration 9.3.2   Saturation of a Chromatographic Column

The present illustration and that which follows deals with the two simplest and most common chromatographic or sorption operations. We consider, in the first instance, the saturation of a clean bed with a feed of constant solute concentration, and follow this up with the purge of a uniformly loaded column with pure carrier fluid or solvent. The latter process is alternatively termed *elution* or *desorption*.

The saturation step which appears to be the simpler of the two does, in fact, require special treatment when one applies the method of characteristics. We had already introduced the reader to the intuitive notion that in the absence of an interphase transport resistance, instantaneous equilibrium is established between the fluid and solid phases and the solute penetrates the bed in the form of a rectangular discontinuity. We now re-examine this phenomenon in more thorough fashion within the framework of the method of characteristics. The operative model is represented by Equations 9.3.3 and 9.3.4, which upon elimination of the solid phase concentration q lead to the single expression:

$$\frac{\partial Y}{\partial x} + [\varepsilon \rho_g / G_s + (\rho_b / G_s)f'(Y)]\frac{\partial Y}{\partial t} = 0 \qquad (9.3.22)$$

with boundary and initial conditions:

$$\text{Feed} \quad Y(0,t) = Y_F \qquad (9.3.23a)$$

$$\text{Clean bed} \quad Y(x,0) = 0 \qquad (9.3.23b)$$

Here $f'(Y)$ is the derivative or slope of the equilibrium relation $q = f(Y)$. Comparison of this expression with Equation 9.3.13a shows that the bracketed term equals the inverse of the propagation velocity, i.e.,

$$[\text{Propagation Velocity}]^{-1} = \left(\frac{dt}{dx}\right)_c = \varepsilon \rho_g / G_x + (\rho_b / G_s)f'(Y) \qquad (9.3.24)$$

We note that in practice the fluid phase accumulation term ρ_g can be neglected compared to its solid phase counterpart so that:

$$\left(\frac{dt}{dx}\right)_c \doteq \frac{\rho_b}{G_s}f'(Y) \qquad (9.3.25)$$

where $(dt/dx)_c$ = slope of the characteristics, shown in Figure 9.6. For Langmuir type equilibria, also termed Type I isotherms, the slope of the equilibrium curve $f'(Y)$ decreases with increasing values of Y. Consequently the slopes of the characteristics themselves will be *high* for *low* solute concentrations and decrease with an increase in concentration. This is reflected in the plots shown in Figure 9.6. Note that all characteristics are straight lines for a given solute concentration Y, i.e., for constant values of $f'(Y)$. We termed this situation a *constant state*.

Let us now examine these diagrams in more detail. Figure 9.6 (AI) shows straight lines emanating from the abscissa which describe the propagation of the initial (clean) bed condition. Similarly, the characteristics starting from the ordinate represent the pathways of the incoming feed concentration Y_F. The latter has the lower slope because of the higher value of $Y_F > 0$.

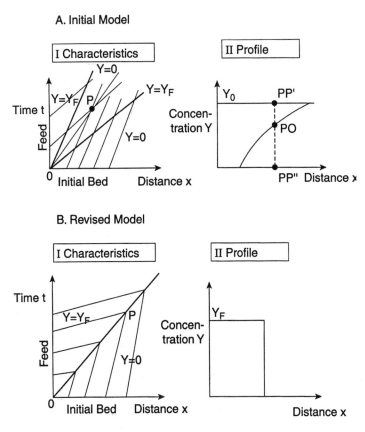

FIGURE 9.6 Characteristic diagrams and the resulting concentration profiles for the saturation of a clean chromatographic column or adsorber. (H.K. Rhee, R. Aris, and N.R. Amundson, *First Order Partial Differential Equations, vol. 1, Theory and Application of Single Equations,* Prentice-Hall, Upper Saddle River, NJ, 1986. With permission.)

A special situation arises at the origin representing the inlet at time $t = 0$. Here characteristics for both $Y = Y_F$ and $Y = 0$ must perforce emanate, and since the space between them cannot be left void, we must have a continuous spectrum of concentrations between those two limits, propagating at different but constant velocities. This produces a simple wave centered at the origin.

The structure of these three sets of characteristics leads to anomalies which are depicted in the initial model of Figure 9.6A. Since the higher concentrations of the simple centered have the lower slope, they propagate faster then their lower concentration cousins. This leads to an "overhanging profile" of the type shown in Figure 9.6 (IB) and is unacceptable on physical grounds. A second anomaly arises from the intersection of *three* characteristics at a *single* point P in the single wave region. This, in turn, implies the co-existence of three distinct concentrations carried by these characteristics at the same point in time and space. We have represented this situation by the three concentration levels PO, PP′, and PP″ in Figure 9.6 (IB).

Clearly, such a multiplicity of solutions is as unacceptable on physical grounds as the overhanging profile. The only way to overcome these twin anomalies is to introduce the notion of a discontinuous front which disposes of the overhang and eliminates the multiplicities at one and the same time. The characteristics through the origin are then reduced to a single pathway OP termed the *shock path.*

A consequence of the model revision is that the movement of the discontinuity is no longer described by the PDE 9.3.22. We must abandon that equation and replace it instead by a cumulative algebraic mass balance. This had already been done in Chapter 6, Section 6.2 and we repeat the result which was obtained there:

$$\frac{x}{t} = \frac{\rho_g v}{\rho_b (q/Y)_F} \qquad (6.2.44)$$

where q_F is the solid phase concentration in equilibrium with the feed Y_F.

Comments:

We start by noting that the development given here benefits considerably from the fact that the mass transfer resistance was neglected. This enabled us to combine the two differential balances which would otherwise have arisen (cf. Equations 7.2.4 and 7.2.5) into the single PDE 9.3.22. That equation, furthermore, is of the reducible type that leads to the immediate conversion into a single ODE, Equation 9.2.24.

The fact that the original PDE had to be abandoned in favor of an algebraic balance merely confirms that in modeling, as in other endeavors, dogma often has to yield to physical reality. Acceptance of this fact is part of the *Art of Modeling.*

Equation 6.2.44 can be applied in a variety of ways. In its most frequently used application, it allows us to calculate the minimum bed requirement per unit of feed treatment (cf. Equation 6.2.46). In the present case this becomes:

$$W_m \text{ [kg bed/kg carrier]} = Y_F / q_F \qquad (9.3.26)$$

Conversely, one can use Equation 6.2.46 to calculate the time a column can remain on stream before breakthrough occurs. That value is perforce a maximum one since mass transfer resistance will inevitably erode the discontinuity into an S-shaped front (see Figure 6.14) resulting in shorter breakthrough times.

Illustration 9.3.3   Elution of a Chromatographic Column

We turn here to the counterpart of the previous illustration and consider the elution or desorption of a uniformly loaded column with a clean purge. The same PDE as before, Equation 9.3.22, applies and it reduces to the same characteristic, Equations 9.3.23 or 9.3.24. What has changed are the boundary and initial conditions which are now reversed, i.e., we have:

Clean purge $Y(0,t) = 0$ (9.3.27a)

Uniform initial bed $Y(x,0) = Y_0$ (9.3.27b)

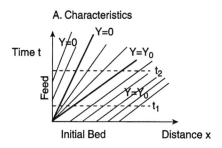

B. Profiles

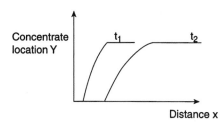

FIGURE 9.7   Characteristic diagram and concentration profiles for the desorption of a uniformly loaded chromatographic column or adsorber. (H.K. Rhee, R. Aris, and N.R. Amundson, *First Order Partial Differential Equations, vol. 1, Theory and Application of Single Equations,* Prentice-Hall, Upper Saddle River, NJ, 1986. With permission.)

Both of these conditions are again represented by straight line characteristics emanating from the ordinate and abscissa, respectively. The special case of $t = x = 0$ likewise leads to the same simple wave centered on the origin that we had seen before. There is, however, an important difference. None of the characteristics intersect, since they are either parallel or fan away from each other. This is shown in Figure 9.7A. As a consequence, no shocks arise and the PDE and its characteristics are retained as the underlying model.

To derive the corresponding profiles, we intersect the characteristics with constant time lines, for example, t_1 and t_2. Note that the slope of the characteristics increases and the propagation velocity of a particular concentration diminishes as we move from right to left. Low concentrations will consequently lag behind higher ones, leading to the type of expanding profiles shown in Figure 9.7B.

Suppose now, that we wish to establish the time required to purge a loaded column *completely* from adsorbed solute. We apply the characteristic (Equation 9.3.25) to the final concentration of the desorption process, i.e., $Y = 0$. Noting that the characteristics have a constant slope, we obtain:

$$\frac{dt}{dx} = \frac{t}{x} = \frac{\rho_b f'(Y)}{G_s} = \frac{\rho_b H}{\rho_g v} \qquad (9.3.28a)$$

or

$$t_{des} = \frac{\rho_b H}{\rho_g v} L \qquad (9.3.28b)$$

where H = Henry's constant, L = length of the column.

Comments:

One notes that the Equations 9.3.28 are identical in form to that describing the saturation step, Equation 6.2.44, with Henry's constant H taking the place of the ratio q_F/Y_F. A comparison of the two expressions also reveals that desorption is a slow, drawn out process compared to saturation since the slope at the origin of the equilibrium, the Henry constant H, is always larger than the ratio q_F/Y_F. This fact, long known to practitioners in the field, has led to the use of a hot purge to speed up the desorption process and bring it in line with the saturation step. This becomes necessary when operating a dual bed system, with one bed being on stream, while the other being regenerated.

The reader is reminded that the purge time calculated from Equation 9.3.26b is a *minimum* value, since the presence of transport resistance which was neglected here will slow down the desorption process.

Illustration 9.3.4   Development of a Chromatographic Pulse

Hitherto in our illustrations of chromatographic processes we had confined ourselves to uniform boundary and initial conditions. We now consider a slightly different situation in which the initial concentration is still uniform ($Y = 0$), but the feed is introduced as a rectangular solute pulse of duration t_0, followed by elution with clean purge. We have, for the BC and IC:

$$Y(x,0) = 0 \qquad (9.3.29a)$$

$$Y(0,t) = \begin{matrix} Y_F & 0 \le t \le t_0 \\ 0 & t > t_0 \end{matrix} \qquad (9.3.29b)$$

The characteristic diagram, shown in Figure 9.8A now consists of *four* sets of linear characteristics, some of which intersect and others which do not. Let us examine each set in turn.

The initial bed concentration $Y = 0$ emanates, as usual, from the abscissa. An identical set of characteristics also originates from the t-axis for $t > t_0$ since the concentration in the clean purge is also $Y = 0$. Between these two sets lies the region of pulse introduction during $0 \le t \le t_0$, for which the characteristics also are linear but of a lower slope, since $Y_F > 0$. The fourth set, comprising a simple wave centered at $t = t_0$, was anticipated since our previous deliberations had shown that two constant states of different velocities will always be separated by a simple wave.

A. Characteristics

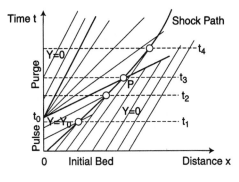

B. Profiles

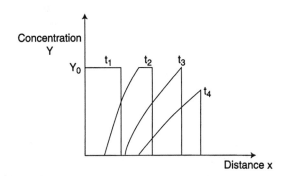

FIGURE 9.8 Deposition of a chromatographic pulse and subsequent elution with clean carrier gas. Note erosion of the plateau and diminishing shock strength with the passage of time. (H.K. Rhee, R. Aris, and N.R. Amundson, *First Order Partial Differential Equations, vol. 1, Theory and Application of Single Equations,* Prentice-Hall, Upper Saddle River, NJ, 1986. With permission.)

Let us now examine the interactions of these characteristics. The initial bed characteristics interact with those of the pulse in much the same way as was seen in bed saturation (Illustration 9.3.2). The two sets intersect and in fact give rise to a *fifth set* which is not shown here for clarity, consisting of a simple wave centered on the origin. The arguments we use in the saturation case lead us to the conclusion that the three sets merge into a single straight shock path OB, identical to the shock path OP seen in Figure 9.6 (BI). These shocks propagate, for the time being, with a constant velocity given by the inverse of the slope of OP. At t_1, this gives the rectangular profile shown in Figure 9.8B.

When $t > t_0$, for example $t = t_2$, the simple wave centered on t_0 comes into play. As we move horizontally we enter a region of diminishing solute concentrations, with ever-decreasing propagation velocities. This leads to a slow, expanding rear zone desorption whose concentrations increasingly lag behind the movement of the shock front. At $t = t_3$, this phase of profile development comes to an end. The plateau of $Y = Y_0$ has been completely eaten away and the expanding rear joins up directly with the shock front.

What happens beyond $t = t_3$? Here we see an intersection of the initial bed characteristics with those of the centered simple wave. Concentrations in that wave diminish with increasing values of t and result in a decrease of the height, or strength of the shock, as shown by the profile for $t = t_4$. Note that the shock path now curves upward resulting in a lower propagation velocity of the shock front.

We do not derive quantitative relations here which require the use of an actual equilibrium relation $q = f(Y)$, but note that the construction of the characteristic diagram is, by itself, capable of revealing all the qualitative features of a chromatographic process.

Illustration 9.3.5   A Traffic Problem

We turn here to the application of the method of characteristics to traffic movement as described by Equations 9.3.5 and 9.3.6. We had previously noted (see Section 7.2.1) that the relation between vehicle velocity v and concentration C in its simplest form is described by the expression:

$$v = v_m\left(1 - \frac{C}{C_m}\right) \tag{9.3.30}$$

Equation 9.3.30 satisfies the elementary conditions that velocity is at its maximum v_m on an empty highway where $C = 0$, and in turn drops to zero when vehicle density reaches its own maximum value of C_m. That maximum is representative of stalled, bumper-to-bumper traffic.

Substitution of 9.3.30 into Equation 9.3.6 and introduction of the result into Equation 9.3.5 yields the characteristic:

$$\frac{dt}{dx} = \frac{1}{1 - 2\overline{C}} \tag{9.3.31}$$

where $\overline{C}$ is the normalized vehicle concentration C/C_m.

Let us consider the situation where traffic has temporarily come to a halt in front of a red light, represented by the origin of the characteristic diagram shown in Figure 9.9A. Vehicle density to the left of the light is $\overline{C} = 1$ (bumper-to-bumper). To the right of it, $\overline{C} = 0$, representative of a road devoid of traffic. We wish to trace the vehicle movement when the light turns green.

We start by noting that the characteristics for $\overline{C} = 1$ all emanate from the negative x-axis and have a slope of -1, deduced from Equation 9.3.31. Those bearing the density $\overline{C} = 0$ (no traffic), originate on the positive x-axis and all have a slope of $+1$. These two constants states must be separated by a simple wave, which is here centered on the origin and encompasses all vehicle concentration between the two lines $\overline{C} = 1$ and $\overline{C} = 0$.

A. Characteristics

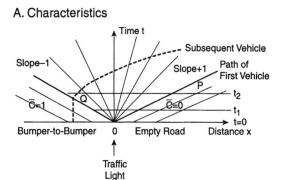

B. Profiles

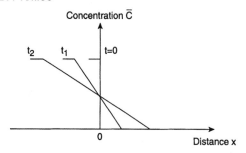

FIGURE 9.9 Traffic concentration at a red traffic light and subsequent vehicle movement when the light turns green. (H.K. Rhee, R. Aris, and N.R. Amundson, *First Order Partial Differential Equations, vol. 1, Theory and Application of Single Equations,* Prentice-Hall, Upper Saddle River, NJ, 1986. With permission.)

Movement starts when the light turns green. The resulting vehicle density "profiles" can be sketched by intersecting various horizontal lines for t = constant with the characteristics. The results are shown in Figure 9.9B and indicate that the initial discontinuous distribution at t = 0 quickly converts into a continuous profile that becomes increasingly drawn out with the passage of time.

It is important to note that the characteristics shown in Figure 9.9A describe the propagation pathways of various concentration levels, *not* those of the vehicles themselves. An exception occurs in the case of the first vehicle which, facing an empty road, immediately accelerates to the maximum velocity v_m and continues its trajectory along the characteristic OP. To trace the movement of subsequent vehicles in the t-x plane, one must eliminate vehicle density C between Equations 9.3.29 and 9.3.30 and integrate the result. An example of a typical pathway which is obtained in this fashion, is shown in Figure 9.9A. It is left to the Exercises to work out the details of the solution (see Practice Problem 9.3.6). Note that the vehicle remains stalled until it reaches the line 0Q and, thereafter, gradually accelerates.

Comments:

Once the application of the method of characteristics has been demonstrated by example, one is inclined to regard its relevance to traffic problems as self-evident.

This is certainly not the attitude one has on first being confronted with such problems. Here is a system composed of discrete entities (the vehicles), each entity subject to the whims of the driver. Traffic lights and other control mechanisms introduce some order into the proceedings, but the flow is still intermittent and has an air of unpredictability. To describe a system so at odds with our usual transport processes by a partial differential equation certainly required a leap of imagination and attests to the genius of the early workers in the field. As we have noted before, such departures from conventional thinking are one of the ingredients of successful modeling.

Practice Problems

9.3.1 The Unsteady Heat Exchanger — Show that the characteristics emanating from a point t_0 of the τ axis of the heat exchanger model given in Illustration 6.3.1 are described by the relations:

$$x = \int_{t_0}^{t} v(t')dt \qquad (9.3.32)$$

$$T(x,t) = T(0,t_0)\exp(-\overline{K}) + \int_{t_0}^{t} T_s K(t')\exp(-\overline{K}(t))dt' \qquad (9.3.33)$$

9.3.2 Linear Chromatography — Show that for systems with linear equilibria, $q = HY$, adsorption and desorption times are identical.

9.3.3 Linear Chromatography Again — Apply the problem discussed in Illustration 6.3.4 to a system with a linear isotherm, $q = HY$, and show that:

(a) The rectangular pulse moves through the column unchanged and undiminished.
(b) Its velocity of propagation v_p of the pulse is given by:

$$v_p = \frac{\rho_g v}{\rho_b H} \qquad (9.3.34)$$

9.3.4 The Type III Isotherm — Adsorption equilibria are often classified according to the *shape* of the equilibrium isotherm. The classical Langmuir equilibrium curve, for example, which is *concave* to the Y-axis, is termed a Type I isotherm. Its inverse, i.e., a curve which is *convex* to the Y-axis, is referred to as a Type III isotherm. Type II, IV, and V have inflection points and are generally known as BET isotherms. Show that the saturation step for a Type III Isotherm yields an elongated adsorption profile, while desorption leads to a shock front. Sketch the resulting profiles.

9.3.5 The Freundlich Isotherm — Freundlich isotherms are described by the relation:

$$q = kY^{1/n} \qquad (9.3.35)$$

where n is a positive integer $\neq 1$.

Consider the equilibrium elution of a column uniformly saturated with a solute obeying Equation 9.3.33. Show that the concentration at the outlet of the column (x = L) is given by the relation:

$$Y(L, t) = \left[\frac{1}{k} \left(\frac{vt}{L} - 1 \right) \right]^{n/(1-n)} \qquad (9.3.36)$$

9.3.6 Vehicle Pathway — Analyze the general vehicle pathway for Illustration 9.3.5. Show that the vehicle is at first stationary over a time interval $0 < t < t_0$ and, subsequently, follows a parabolic path, as shown in Figure 9.9A.

REFERENCES

9.1 Separation of Variables: Treatments of the method of separation of variables for solving PDEs are to be found in most texts dealing with advanced applied mathematics, including:
E. Kreyszig. *Advanced Engineering Mathematics, 7th ed.,* John Wiley & Sons, New York, 1991.
A more profound analysis of the method can be found in:
P.R. Garabedian. *Partial Differential Equations,* John Wiley & Sons, New York, 1964.
and in:
R.L. Street. *The Analysis and Solution of Partial Differential Equations,* Brock/Cole, Monterey, CA, 1973.

A text which provides a host of solved problems without sacrificing mathematical rigor is by:
R.V. Churchill and J.W. Brown. *Fourier Series and Boundary-Values Problems, 3rd ed.,* McGraw-Hill, New York, 1978. *See also the 2nd edition (R.V. Churchill, 1963). Which is somewhat more explicit in its applications. Both texts devote separate chapters to the twin topics of Fourier Series and Orthogonal Functions.*

A host of solutions to conduction and diffusion problems, arrived at by the method of separation of variables are to be found as usual in:
H.S. Carslaw and J.C. Jaeger. *Conduction of Heat in Solids, 2nd ed.,* Oxford University Press, New York, 1959.
J. Crank. *Mathematics of Diffusion, 2nd ed.,* Oxford University Press, New York, 1978.

Appendices in both texts provide listings of the roots of transcendental equations relevant to the method. These are also to be found in:
M. Abramowitz and I.A. Stegun. *Handbook of Mathematical Functions,* Dover, New York, 1965.
9.2 Laplace Transformation and Other Integral Transforms: This topic, like that of the method of separation of variables, is treated with varying degrees of thoroughness in the aforementioned monographs by Kreyszig, Street, and Garabedian. Solutions of Fourier's and Fick's equations by various integral transform methods can be found in Carlsaw and Jaeger, and in Crank previously cited.

A text which displays mathematical rigor as well as a host of solutions to practical problems, presented in eminently readable form, is by:

R.V. Churchill. *Operational Mathematics, 3rd ed.,* McGraw-Hill, New York, 1972.

The book covers all integral transform methods, with emphasis on the Laplace transform, and contains short tabulations of all major transforms. More extensive listings are to be found in:

A. Erdelyi (Ed.). *Tables of Integral Transforms, vols. 1 & 2,* McGraw-Hill, New York, 1954.

Tabulations of the J-function, Equation 9.2.68, can be found in the chapter on Adsorption and Ion-Exchange of recent editions of Perry's Handbook of Chemical Engineers.

9.3 Method of Characteristics: Although various developments connected with this method took place in the 19th and early 20th centuries, it was only in 1948 that it came to the attention of the scientific and engineering communities with the publication of:

R. Courant and K.A. Friedrichs. *Supersonic Flow and Shock Waves,* Wiley-Interscience, New York, 1948.

The text reflects war-time developments in aerodynamics and its focus is on pairs and systems of quasilinear first order PDEs. A lucid explanation of the method of characteristics precedes the core material. Various texts on wave phenomena have since made use of the method and expanded on it, among them:

A. Jeffrey and T. Taniuti. *Non-Linear Wave Propagation,* Academic Press, New York, 1964.

G.B. Whitman. *Linear and Non-Linear Waves,* John Wiley & Sons, New York, 1974.

A. Jeffrey. *Quasilinear Hyperbolic Systems and Waves,* Pitman, Marshall, MA, 1976.

N. Bleistein. *Mathematical Methods for Wave Phenomena,* Academic Press, New York, 1984.

All these texts make fairly heavy reading. A more readable account displaying both mathematical rigor and numerous interesting practical applications, appears in the two-volume treatise:

H.K. Rhee, R. Aris, and N.R. Amundson. *First Order Partial Differential Equations, vol. 1; Theory and Application of Single Equations, Vol. 2, Coupled Systems of Equations,* Prentice-Hall, Upper Saddle River, NJ, 1986, 1989.

Volume 1, which is of relevance here, contains many chromatographic and traffic problems from which the author has drawn.

Index

A

Absolute humidity, 151, 156
Acetone vapor, cracking of, 198
Adiabatic compression work, 100
Adiabatic saturation temperature, 154
Aerosols, coagulation of, 619
AEs, see Algebraic equations
Air
    adiabatic saturation of, 169
    properties of, 54
Airy equation, 214, 269
Aldrin, 357
Algebraic equations (AEs), 1, 10
Alkanes, 352
Alloys, tensile strength of, 117
Aminophylline, 315
Anastrophe, 259
Angle-dependent temperature, 593
Annular condensation, in vertical tube, 198
Annular flow regime, 185
Antoine equation, 187
Apparent distribution volume, 317
Apparent elimination rate constant, 316
Apparent flow rate, 317
Applesauce, 139
Arbitrary initial distribution, 591
Arbitrary surfaces, 115
Archimede's law, 114, 115, 116
Arrhenius equation, 167, 195
Asbestos, 73
Aspirators, 131
Augmented Jacobian, 261
Auxiliary relations, 2, 4, 15
Avogadro's number, 335
Axial component, 528
Axial flow, 226

B

Balance(s), see also Momentum balances, mass,
        energy, and
    categories of, 6
    chemical reaction mass, 57
    cumulative, 42
    differential component, 66
    energy, see Energy balance
    force, 189

    integral component, 67
    liquid phase, 24
    mass, 45
    ODE, 19
    PDE, 27
    shell side, 77
    steady-state
        differential, 22, 216
        integral, 10
        one-dimensional differential, 11
    unsteady differential, 12
    variables for, 6
Balances, properties and categories of, 3–7
    dependence on time and space, 7
    dependent and independent variables, 5
    integral and differential balances, 5
    steady-state balances, 7
    unsteady-state balances, 5–7
Balances, setting up of, 19–43
    batch filtration, 32–35
    decontamination of nuclear reactor coolant,
        26–29
    design of gas scrubber, 24–26
    diffusion through wall of high-pressure
        hydrogenation vessel, 42
    discharge of ladle of molten steel, 38–39
    drying of nonporous plastic sheet, 35–38
    ground penetration from oil spills, 41–42
    propagation of rectangular pulse in
        adsorber, 41
    responses of theoretical tray to
        disturbances, 40
    simplified leaching process, 39–40
    steam-heated tube, 22–24
    surge tank, 19–22
    thermal treatment of steel strapping, 29–32
Barbecue propane cylinder, 139
Basic laws, 2
Batch
    adsorption, 544
    distillation, of binary mixture, 16
    filter, diagram of, 33
    filtration, of slurry, 32
BCs, see Boundary conditions
Benzene, 352
Bernoulli equation, 128, 173, 269, 568
Bessel functions, 235, 273, 531, 582, 613
    properties of, 236
    zero order, 237

Bicycle tire, pumping up of, 109
Bifurcation, 259
    Hopf, 260, 261, 267
    points, 262, 270
    simple, 261
Bingham model, 136
Bingham plastic fluids, 136
Binomial theorem, 610
Biochemical reaction, 347
Biology, 314
Biomass formation, 345
Biomedical engineering, 314
Bioreactors, steady-state analysis of, 344
Biotechnology, 314, 341
Biot number, 83
Biphenyl, 357
Block diagrams, 298, 299
Blood
    dialysis, 324
    outlet concentration, 328, 329
    –tissue interaction, as pseudo one-
        compartment model, 319, 320
    vessels, 330
Boiling
    convective, 94, 95
    film, 95
    forced convection, 184
    heat transfer, 94
    pot, 94
Boundary
    conditions (BCs), 85, 209, 210, 583, 615
        homogeneous, 579
        limiting, 539
        transformation of nonhomogeneous,
            490
        Type II, 481, 548
        Type III, 470, 471, 555
        types of, 212
        useful hints on, 211
    layer flow, 562
    value problem (BVP), 210, 246
Bumper-to-bumper traffic, 634
Buoyancy, 14
Burk plot, 343
Burning fuel droplet, 218
BVP, see Boundary value problem

C

Capacity ratio, 80, 88
Capillary
    length, 56
    rise, 117, 119
Carbon tetrachloride, 118, 352

Carrier
    gas, 40
    units, 24
Cartesian coordinates, 487, 496, 561, 576
Catalyst pellet, heat effects in, 145
Catalytic conversion, in coated tubular reactor,
        527
Catastrophe, 253, 259
Cauchy-Euler equation, 214
Cell(s)
    deposition of from flowing medium, 350
    growth, 344
Cellular process, simple, 333
Centered simple wave, 625
Centrifugal pumps, 27
Chaos, 265, 266, 267
Characteristics
    equations, 305
    interactions of, 633
    method of, 620
Charge flow, damping effect on, 286
Chebyshev polynomials, 235
Chemical
    engineering, 313
    reaction
        mass balance, 57
        rates, 4
Chlorobenzenes, 352
Chloroform, 353
Choking flow, region of, 180
Chromatographic column
    desorption of uniformly loaded, 631
    elution of, 630
    saturation of, 627, 629
Chromatographic equation, integration of, 620
Chromatographic pulse, development of, 632
Chromatography, linear, 636
Civil engineering, 2, 313
Claude process, 171
Clausius-Clapeyron equations, 187
Coagulant concentration, 333
Coefficient
    matrix, 223, 304
    of thermal expansion, 31
Collision frequency, in coagulation of aerosols,
        619
Column
    of infinite height, 26
    variables, 161
Complementary function, 230
Complex functions, inversion of, 307
Component
    force, 116
    mass balance, 354
Composite cylinder, 90

Compressible flow
 charts, 179
 model equations, 182
 in variable area ducts, 181
Concentration
 fronts, 41
 profile, of cylindrical catalyst pellet, 239
Condenser, design of partial, 170
Conduction
 problem, boundary conditions in, 212
 rate, finite, 84
 in semi-infinite medium, 607
 in slab, 609
Conservation
 of charge, 525
 laws, 2, 3
Constants
 evaluation of, 592
 integration, 595
Consumption rate, 322
Contaminant, flushing-out of, 16
Continuity equation, 2, 175, 513
Continuous flow stirred tank reactor, 57, 58
Continuous point source, 476
Continuous stirred tank reactor (CSTR), 8, 148
Controlled release devices, 68
Controller gain, 306
Convective boiling, 94, 95, 184
Convective heat transfer, 76
Converging-diverging nozzle, 183
Convolution
 integral, 277, 281
 theorem, 278
Coordinate systems, differential operators in,
  497–499
Core
 energy balance, 218
 mass balance, 103, 218
Correction factor, 62
Cosine
 expansion of sine, 597
 law, 523
 set, 582
 transform, use of finite, 618
Countercurrent heat exchanger, 268
Creeping flow, 562, 564, 571
Critical damping, 294
Critical heat flux, 186
Critical points, 254, 256
Critical radius, 91
Cross products, 500, 501
Cryogenic liquefaction, 170
Cryogenic sink, 478
CSTR, see Continuous stirred tank reactor
Cumene, 357

Cumulative balance, 37, 42
Cylinder, 598, 611

D

D'Arcy's law, 34
D-operator method, 228, 588, 608
Danckwerts, 268, 488, 492
Decay ratio, 292
Dehumidification, 76, 142, 149
Del notation, 504
Dependent variables, 253
Desorption, 538, 627
Deviation variables, 286
Dew point, 11
Dialysate solution, 324
Difference
 element, 31, 59
 equation, 251
 formulation, 23
Differential
 balance, 78
 component balance, 66
 energy balance, 87
 equations, 280
 operators, 503, 504, 524
Diffusion, 619
 Fickian, 339
 isothermal, 60
 non-Fickian, 489
 problem, 239
 through stagnant film, 47
 steady-state, 542
 unsteady, 538
Diffusive flux, 47
Diffusive mass flow, 542
Diffusive transport, 61
Diffusivities
 measurement of, 55
 values of, 50
Dilatant model, 138
Dilution rate, 346
Dimensionless temperature, 555
Dirac delta functions, 288, 516, 517
Dirichlet problem
 for half-plane, 526
 interior, 525
Dissociation constant, 336
Distillation, 66, 81
Distributed model, 321, 351
Divergence, 506
 derivation of, 510
 operator, 509
 theorem, 507, 512

Dot product, 501
Double Fourier series, 599
Drag
coefficients, 113
force, 123
Dropwise condensation, 188
Duct flow, 562
Duhamel integral, 482, 485
Dye dilution, flow rate by, 349

E

Effective therapeutic concentration (ETC), 315, 316
Effectiveness factor(s), 57, 60, 62, 147
of cylindrical catalyst pellet, 239
determination of, 240
isothermal catalyst pellet, 63
nonisothermal, 146
Electrical circuits, equivalence of mechanical systems and, 284
Electrical heat supply, 300
Electrical heater, 299
Electrical RLC circuit, oscillation of, 309
Electricity, equation of, 525
Electrochemical method, 544
Electromagnetic theory, Maxwell's equations of, 524
Electronic integrators, 617
Elution, 627, 630
Emission radiation, 96
Energy, see also Momentum balances, mass, energy, and
balance(s), 45, 71, 144, 163, 186
core, 103, 218
differential, 87
gas phase, 157, 552
integral, 88
liquid phase, 158
mechanical, 132, 187, 193
quasi-steady-state differential, 219
shell, 145
solid phase, 553
change(s)
kinetic, 109
potential, 101
equation, alternative forms of, 196
flux, 71
rate of, 84, 143, 155
thermal, 99
transport of, 20, 545
Engineering problems, 162
Enthalpy, 154, 156
Environmental science, 313

Enzyme kinetics, 341, 343
Equilibrium
concentration, 336
gas solubilities, 161
points, 254
reaction, 320
relation, 159, 164, 187, 614
Equimolar counterdiffusion, 47
Error
function, 590, 609
properties of, 473
values of, 473
time derivative of, 302
ETC, see Effective therapeutic concentration
Euler
-Cauchy type solution, 595
equation of motion, 567
formula, 223
method, 247, 250
Evaporative cooling, 36
Evaporators, 184
Exchanger effectiveness, 81
Exothermic reactions, 167
Experimental measurements, importance of, 38
Explicit functions, transformation of, 600
External film coefficient, 104
External resistance, conduction in cylinder with, 591
Extraction ratio, 327

F

Fanning equation, 111, 134, 563
Fast convergence, 609
Fick's equation, 487, 515
derivation of, 514
solution of, 475
Film
boiling, 95
coefficient, 105
condensation, 188, 189
resistance, 9, 91
theory, 49–50
Filter
cake, permeability of, 33
medium, resistance of, 34
Fin
effectiveness, 224
efficiency, 84, 86
heat exchanger, 223
temperature, 224
Finite cylinder, 471
First law of thermodynamics, 2, 3, 99, 545

First order
    differential equations, 1
    ODEs, 209
    reactions, 318, 332
    systems, response of, 286
Fish, bioconcentration in, 357
Flakice, production of, 108
Flame temperature, unknown, 220
Flash lamp-condenser unit, 483, 486
Flash vaporization, 162
Flat plate catalyst, diffusion and reaction in, 70
Flexural rigidity, 296
Flow
    boundary layer, 562
    charts, compressible, 179
    creeping, 562, 564, 571
    duct, 562
    irrotational, 568
    Newtonian, 225
    in porous media, 570
    rate
        to heat exchanger, 14
        ratio, 327
    velocity, 531
    viscous, 496
Flowing fluid, momentum changes in, 121
Flowing systems, steady-state energy balance for, 101
Fluid(s)
    density, 554
    particle movement in, 123
    resistance, 327, 329
    statics, fundamental equation of, 114
    time-dependent, 138
    velocity, 528, 625
    viscoelastic, 138
Fluidization, of particle, 14, 141
Food products, 137
Force balances, 2, 45, 189
Forced vibration frequency, 283
Forcing functions, 83, 208, 290, 298
Form drag, on sphere in creeping flow, 571
Fourier
    coefficients, 579, 584, 601
    cosine transform, finite, 602
    equation, 91, 474, 587
    law, 15, 550
    series, 575, 583, 586
        double, 599
        expansion, 576, 585, 597
        inversion to, 618
        solution, 607
    sine
        series, 585
        transform, finite, 602

        transforms, 273, 618
Free vectors, 499
Freeze-drying
    of food, 102
    rate data, 103
Freezing
    heat of, 550
    of liquid, 107
    in semi-infinite solid, 549
Freundlich isotherm, 636
Friction, 187
    factor, 113, 173
    losses, 133
    pendulum with, 257
    temperature rise due to, 558
Frictionless flow, 180
Frictionless pendulum, 257
Frobenius, method of, 234
Furnace
    emissivity, 97
    walls, heat losses from, 108
Fuzziness, 267

G

Gamma function, 535, 536, 537
Gas(es)
    absorption, 60, 81
    compositional changes in, 105
    diffusivities of, 49
    film energy balance, steady-state, 220
    flow, 508
        rates, 178
        reactor, 191
    ideal, 99, 175, 177
    phase energy balance, 552
    scrubber, design of, 13, 24, 160
Gate valve, 133
Generalized transport theorem, 513
Geometry problems, 501
Globe valve, 133
Glycerin, 176
Glycerol, 73, 111
Graetz problem, 325, 332, 547
Graetz-Lévêque problem, 533, 546
Grashof number, 30, 92, 93
Gravity force, 231
Gravity, 14, 128, 190
Greases, 137
Green's function, 515, 521, 522
    first form of, 512
    use of in solving Fourier's equation, 520
Ground penetration, from oil spills, 41
Growth kinetics, 345

ized

H

Hagen-Poiseuille law, for circular pipes, 112
Hairpin heat exchanger, 107
Hanging chain, oscillations of, 488
Hankel transform(s), 611, 613
    finite, 602
    modified, 602
    of sine forcing function, 605
Heart
    –lung machines, 324
    muscle, blood flow rate to, 348
Heat
    capacity
        nitrogen, 87
        of steel strapping, 32
    emission, radiation, 96
    exchange, analogy between dialysis and, 349
    exchanger, 81
        countercurrent, 268
        effectiveness, 77
        extended surface, 85
        fin, longitudinal, 223
        flow rate to, 14
        hairpin, 107
        moving bed solid-gas, 86
        nonlinear countercurrent, 270
        with time-varying fluid velocity, 625
        unsteady, 636
    flux
        critical, 186
        variable, 484
    of freezing, 550
    humid, 154
    loss(es)
        from buried steam pipe, 17, 560
        from furnace walls, 108
        maximum possible, 213
    of reaction, 194
    regenerators, 551
    sensible, 143
    source, 478, 545
    supply, electrical, 300
    transfer, 143, 553
        actual, 86
        convective, 23, 76
        laminar flow, 556, 557
        by natural convection, 32
        negligible, 224
        in packed bed, 546, 551
        process, 92
        radiative, 98
        rate of, 149

    transfer coefficient(s), 104, 191, 529
        approximate values of, 74
        correlations for, 74
        estimating of, 89
        in packed bed of metallic particles, 75
        in steam-heated jacketed vessels, 75
Heaviside expansion, 275, 277, 289, 606
    inversion by, 291
    sum of, 279
Heavy water, 28
Hemodialyzers, 324
Henry's constant, 40, 616, 632
Hermite polynomials, 235
Holding tank
    containing solid waste, 63
    with variable holdup, 64
Hollow cylinder, 598
Hollow fiber, 324
Hooke's law, 231
Hoop-stress formula, 116
Hopf bifurcation, 260, 263, 264, 267
Horizontal beam, 296
    deflection of, 269
    point load on, 309
Horizontal plate, 191
Hot-wire anemometer, design of, 105
Hougen-Watson rate laws, 344
HTU-NTU relation, 160
Humid heat, 154
Humidification, 5, 76, 142
Humidity
    absolute, 156
    charts, 150, 152, 153, 155
    relative, 156
Hydrocarbon, thermal cracking of, 192
Hydrogenation vessel, high-pressure, 42
Hydrolases, 341
Hyperbolic functions, 226, 228, 606
Hypergeometric functions, 235
Hypsometric formula, 120, 140
Hysteresis effect, 147

I

ICs, see Initial conditions
Ideal gas(es), 48, 175
    adiabatic compression of, 99
    law, 177
Ignition temperature, 168
Images, method of, 477
Imposed voltage, 285
Impulse input, 294
Incompressible flow, 176

Industrial problems, complexity of, 28
Inertia, moment of, 269
Infection rates, 266
Infinite plane source, 477
Initial conditions (ICs), 209
Input transform, 301
Instantaneous infinite plane source, 474
Insulation thickness, optimum, 89, 91
Integral
    component balance, 67
    energy balance, 88
    mass balances, 326
    transforms, 602
Integrating factors, 241
Integration
    constant, 234, 242, 595
    methods, numerical, 248
Interface temperature, 54
Interphase heat, 46
Inverse transform, 275
Inversion(s), 276
    formula, 602
    inversions from, 617
    methods, 295
    by partial fractions, 291
    of transforms, 278
Inviscid flow, 567
Irrotational flow, 568
Isothermal compression work, 101
Isothermal diffusion, 60
Isothermal fluid, 29
Isothermal tubular reactor, 59
Isotope separation factors, 39

J

Jacobian
    augmented, 261
    determinant, 264
    matrix, 255
Jet
    pumps, 131
    velocity, 140

K

Kernel, role of, 601
Kerosene, napalm in, 139
Kinetic energy, 109, 187
Kirchoff's law, 2
Krogh cylinder, 322

L

Lagrangian approach, 513
Laguerre
    equation, 214
    polynomials, 235
Laminar convection, conduction with, 546
Laminar flow, 69, 110
    conditions, 528
    heat transfer, 556, 557
Laminar region, 124
Laplace
    domain analysis, 281, 295, 614
    equations, 118, 495, 518
    operator, 508
    transform(s), 602, 616
        of functions, 276
        general properties of, 275
        use of to solve integral equations,
            310
Laplace transformation, 273–311, 590, 599
    application to differential equations,
        280–298
        equivalence of mechanical systems
            and electrical circuits, 284–286
        horizontal beam, 296–298
        mass-spring system, 282–284
        response of first order systems,
            286–290
        response of second order systems,
            290–296
    block diagrams, 298–302
        controller and control element, 302
        measuring element, 301–302
        water heater, 301
    general properties of Laplace transform,
        274–280
    overall transfer function, 302–310
        Laplace domain stability analysis,
            305–307
        practice problems, 307–310
Law of conservation of mass, 19
Leaching process, simplified, 39
Leakage velocity, 569
Legendre functions, 61
Lewis relation, 155, 159
Ligand
    binding, to solution receptor, 350
    concentration, 334, 338
    molecules, binding of, 333
    -receptor complex, 337
Ligases, 341
Linde process, 171, 172
Linear chromatography, 636
Lines, method of, 624

Lineweaver-Burk plots, 344, 345
Liquefaction processes, contemporary industrial, 170
Liquid
    diffusivities, 49, 620
    enthalpy, 219
    freezing of, 107
    phase energy balance, 158
    vaporized pure, 186
    water, properties of, 53
LMTD, see Log mean temperature difference
Load, 300
Loading dose, 315
Log mean temperature difference (LMTD), 79
Longitudinal heat exchanger fin, 223
Lorenz
    attractor, 214
    equations, 265
Lubrication theory, 564

M

Mach number, 174, 178, 182, 183
Marker particle, design of, 16
Mass, see also Momentum balances, mass, energy and momentum
    balance(s), 45, 144, 241
        core, 103, 218
        difference element for, 227
        reactant, 193
        solid phase, 614
        two-phase, 614
        types of ODE and AE, 9–10
    flux, from concentration gradients, 12
    -spring system, 282
    transfer, 553
        effects, 41
        law, 21
    transfer coefficient, 49, 351
        estimation of, 52
        local, 331
        overall, 51
        relations among, 53
    transport of, 526
Mathematical methodology, 313
Matrix thermal conductivity, 104
Maxwell equations, 496, 524
Mean integral concentration, 530
Measuring element, 301
Mechanical energy balance, 132, 193
Membrane
    associated molecules, coupling with, 334
    processes, 324

resistance predominant, 325, 329
Mercury
    solubility, 355
    volatilization, from water, 353
Metals, tensile strength of, 117
Meteorology, 169
Method
    of characteristics, 620
    of Frobenius, 234
    of lines, 624
    of undetermined coefficients, 233
Methylene chloride, 352
Michaelis Menten
    equation, 344, 345
    kinetics, 350
    rate, 343
Mirror, design of curved, 244
Mixed-suspension mixed-product removal crystallizer (MSMPRC), 8
Model(s)
    Bingham, 136
    Dilatant, 138
    distributed, 5, 321, 351
    fin, 84
    Ostwald-de Wael, 137
    PDE, 13, 299
    pseudo one-compartment, 319
    shrinking-core, 268
    two-component, 349
Model solutions, information obtained from, 10–17
    design of gas scrubber, 13–14
    evaporation of water from open trough, 15
    flow rate to heat exchanger, 14
    fluidization of particle, 14–15
    pressure drop in rectangular duct, 16–17
    sealing of plastic sheets, 15–16
    steady multidimensional differential balances, 12–13
    steady-state integral balances, 10–11
    steady-state one-dimensional differential balances, 11
    unsteady cumulative integral balances, 11–12
    unsteady differential balances, 12
    unsteady instantaneous integral balances, 11
Modulus of elasticity, 269
Molar flow rates, 192, 194
Molar flux vector, 527
Molar mass flow, in binary mixtures, 46
Mollier diagrams, 170
Molten steel, discharge of ladle of, 38
Moment of inertia, 269

Momentum balances, mass, energy, and, 45–201
combined mass and energy balances,
142–172
design of gas scrubber, 160–162
flash vaporization, 162–165
heat effects in catalyst pellet,
145–149
humidity charts, 151–157
nonisothermal CSTR with second
order homogenous reaction,
142–143
nonisothermal tubular reactions,
143–145
operation of water cooling tower,
157–160
practice problems, 167–172
steam distillation, 165–166
wet-bulb temperature, 149–150
combined mass, energy, and momentum
balances, 172–198
adiabatic compressible flow in pipe,
177–179
compressible flow charts, 179–181
compressible flow in variable area
ducts with friction and heat
transfer, 181–183
converging-diverging nozzle,
183–184
film condensation on vertical plate,
188–191
forced convection boiling, 184–188
isothermal compressible flow in
pipe, 173–174
nonisothermal, nonisobaric tubular
gas flow reactor, 191–196
practice problems, 196–198
propagation of pressure wave,
velocity of sound, Mach number,
174–177
energy balances, 71–109
energy flux, 71–72
transport coefficients, 72–109
force and momentum balances, 110–142
momentum flux and equivalent
forces, 110
transport coefficients, 110–142
mass balances, 46–71
chemical reaction mass balance,
57–62
molar mass flow in binary mixtures,
46–48
tank mass balances, 62–65
transport coefficients, 48–56
tubular mass balances, 65–71

terms in various balances, 45–46
Monod
chemostat model, 346
kinetics, 344
Morphogenesis, Turning's paper on, 338
Morphogens, 339
Moving-bed
ore heater, 17
solid-gas heat exchanger, 86
Moving boundary problem, 102, 549
Moving source problem, 491
MSMPRC, see Mixed-suspension mixed-product
removal crystallizer
Multicompartment models, 318
Myocardium, 348

N

Napalm, 139
Natural frequency, 293
Natural vibration frequency, 283
Navier-Stokes equation, 3, 128, 229, 508
Negative feedback, 300
Newton's law, 22, 110, 230
of cooling, 542
extensions of, 495
flow, 225
viscosity law, 46
Nitrogen heat capacity, 87
Non-Fickian diffusion, 489
Nonisothermal tubular reactors, 143, 144
Nonlinear algebraic equations, 262
Nonlinear analysis, 252
Nonlinear behavior, in parameter space, 259
Nonlinear countercurrent heat exchanger, 270
Nonlinear terms, sources of, 206
Non-Newtonian behavior, 229
Non-Newtonian fluids, 136
Nonviscous liquid, 127
Normal vector, 499
nth order reaction, half-life for, 70
NTU, see Number of transfer units
Nuclear reactor
coolant, 26
fuel element, maximum temperature in,
107
purification of organic coolant for, 27
Nucleate boiling range, 95
Number of transfer units (MTU), 80
Numerical integration methods, 248
Nusselt number, 30, 92, 547

O

OC, see Organic carbon
ODEs, see Ordinary differential equations
Oil
    -bearing vegetable seeds, 541
    spills, 41
    viscosity of, 134
Open-loop transfer function, 303
Operating diagram, 25
Ordinary differential equations (ODEs), 1, 104,
    203–272
    analytical solutions of ODEs, 213–245
        D-operator method, 221–230
        nonhomogenous linear second order
            ODEs with constant coefficients,
            230–232
        other methods, 240–245
        separation of variables, 216–221
        series solutions of linear ODEs with
            variable coefficients, 232–240
    autonomous, 208
    balances, 19
    boundary and initial conditions, 209–213
        boundary conditions in conduction
            problem, 212–213
        useful hints on boundary conditions,
            211–212
    classification of, 268
    coupled, 340
    definitions and classifications, 203–209
        autonomous ODEs, 208–209
        homogenous and nonhomogenous
            ODEs, 207–208
        linear and nonlinear ODEs, 205–206
        ODEs with variable coefficients,
            206–207
        order of ODE, 203–204
    energy balances, solution of, 14
    first order, 62, 209, 217, 615
    homogenous, 207
    independent, 145
    initial value, 249
    Laplace transformation of, 297
    linear, 205, 232, 274
    liquid phase, 25
    nonautonomous, 208
    nonhomogenous, 207, 323
    nonlinear analysis, 252–270
        analysis in parameter space,
            258–264
        chaos, 265–270
        phase plane analysis, 253–258
    numerical methods, 245–252
        boundary value problems, 246

        initial value problems, 246–248
        potential difficulties, 249–252
        sets of simultaneous initial value
            ODEs, 249
    procedure for solving, 281
    second order, 85, 222, 231, 285, 339
    simultaneous, 281
    solution of, 577, 588, 592
    solver packages, 204, 245
    stability of, 249
    variable coefficient, 206, 274
Organic carbon (OC), 352
Organic solvent, high-boiling, 165
Orthogonal functions, 575, 579, 581
Orthonormal functions, 580
Oscillating temperature fluctuation, 309
Oscillation period, 292
Ostwald-de Wael model, 137
Outlet pressure, reduction of, 179
Output signal, attenuated, 290
Output transform, 301
Overshoot, 292
Oxido reductases, 341

P

Packed column, 25
Paper pulp, 139
Parabolic mirror, design of, 244
Parabolic velocity profile, 530
Parallel plate channel, 135
Parallel reactions, 167
Parameter
    estimation, 528
    space, 258, 259
Parasitic solutions, 250
Partial derivatives, transforms of, 600
Partial differential equations (PDEs), 1, 203,
    407–493
    balance, 27
    classification of, 488
    derivation of simple, 489
    PDEs of major importance, 418–435
        first order partial differential
            equations, 419–422
        second order partial differential
            equations, 422–435
    PDEs PDQ, 459–492
        in search of literature solution,
            460–464
        simple solutions by superposition,
            464–488
    practice problems, 488–492

properties and classes of PDEs, 409–418
    boundary and initial conditions, 413–418
    elliptic, parabolic, and hyperbolic PDEs, 412–413
    higher order PDEs, 410–411
    linear and nonlinear PDEs, 411–412
    order of PDE, 409–410
    PDEs with variable coefficients, 411
second order, 613
solution methods for, 575–638
    Laplace transformation and other integral transforms, 599–620
    method of characteristics, 620–637
    separation of variables, 575–599
transformation of, 623
useful simplifications and transformations, 435–459
    change in independent variables, 447–454
    elimination of dependent variables, 443–444
    elimination of independent variables, 435–443
    elimination of nonhomogenous terms, 445–447
    nondimensionalization, 457–459
    simplification of geometry, 454–457
Particle
    catalyst, 141
    falling, 124
    fluidization of, 14
    marker, 16, 126
    rising, 124
    in suspension, 124
Path of pursuit, 243, 270
PDEs, see Partial differential equations
Pendulum, 269
    analysis of, 255
    oscillating, 291
Percentage humidity, 151
Permeability, of medium, 42
Pharmacokinetics, one-compartment, 314
Phase
    equilibria, 351
    plane
        analysis, 253
        portrait, 266
        representation, of critical points, 256
    space analysis, 253
Physical configurations, 7–9
    one-dimensional pipe, 8–9
    quenched steel billet, 9
    stirred tank, 7–8

Pipe(s)
    adiabatic compressible flow in, 172, 177
    buried steam, 17
    one-dimensional, 1, 8
    steel, 127
Pitot tube, 197
Plastic sheets
    drying of, 35, 52
    heat sealing of, 559
Point
    load, on horizontal beam, 309
    source, 516
        continuous, 476
        solutions, 480
Poiseuille' law, 229
Poisson equation, 472, 517, 518, 519
Polymer sheet extrusion, 225, 227
Polynomial(s)
    approximation, method of, 246
    ratio of, 277, 279
Porous slab, drying of, 597
Potassium, 111
Power law fluids, 137
Prandtl
    boundary layer equations, 565
    number, 30, 72, 73, 92
Pressure
    distribution, at cylinder surface, 469
    drop
        in ducts of different geometries, 571
        relation, 135
    force, 119
    wave, propagation of, 174
Prey, 243
Primary information, 10
Product
    distribution, 241
    solutions, 470
Propagation velocity, 624, 626, 628
Proportional control, 300
Protein
    molecules, 333
    reaction, 349
p-substitution, 240, 243, 323, 594
Psychrometric charts, 150, 152, 153, 160
Psychrometric ratio, 155

Q

Quasi-steady state, 55
    assumption, 55, 56, 342
    differential energy balance, 219
Quenched steel billet, 7, 9, 586, 587

R

Radial fluid velocity, 543
Radial velocity profiles, 569
Radiation, 96
    heat emission, rate of, 96
    losses, 83
Radioactive decay series, 308
Rankine-Huguenot relation, 197
Raoult's law, 67, 166
Rate laws, 241
Rayleigh
    distillation, 30, 65, 149
    line, 184, 196
Reactant
    mass balance, 193
    species, 59
Reaction problem, 239
Reactive event, 330
Reactor
    radius, 531
    theory, 28
Recirculating pump, 26, 109
Rectangular pulse, propagation of in adsorber, 41
Recursion formula, 236
Redox reaction, 544
Reduction techniques, 481
Regular attractors, 260
Regulator problem, 300
Relative humidity, 151, 156
Required infusion rate, 317
Response time, 292
Reverse osmosis, 543
Reversible reaction, optimum temperature for, 167
Reynolds number, 51, 112, 133, 180
Riccati equation, 214
Rise time, 292
Runge-Kutta
    method, solution of ODEs by, 251
    routines, 204
Ruth equations, 32, 33, 34

S

Saddle points, 254
Saturation humidity, 149
Schmidt number, 54, 72
Sea anemone, 341
Second derivatives, 511
Second order
    differential equations, 2
    reaction, irreversible, 69
    systems, 83, 308

Sedimentation, 621
Semi-infinite medium, diffusion and reaction in, 532
Semi-infinite space, three-dimensional, 479
Sensible heat transfer, 158
Separation factor, 40
Separation of variables, 37, 216, 575
Servo-problem, 300
Set-point, 300
Settling tank, solids removal in, 140
Sewage sludge, 137
Shape factor, 556
Shear stress, from velocity gradients, 12
Shell-side mass balance, 325
Sherwood number, 51, 328, 329
Shock path, 633
Shooting method, 246
Shrinking-core model, 268
Silver
    melting point of, 97
    sample, melting of, 96
Simple bifurcation, 261
Sine
    half waves, with time-dependent amplitude, 576
    terms, 585
Singularity, 259
Sinusoidal input, 289, 295
Slug flow, 185
Slurry, leaching of, 540
Solid(s)
    cross-flow heating of, 558
    density, 554
    mass balance, 64
    phase
        concentration, 630
        energy balance, 553
        mass balance, 614
    removal, in settling tank, 140
    sphere, cooling of, 598
    stationary, 30
    volume, ratio of solvent to, 541
Solute(s)
    concentration, 628
    rates of volatilization of, 356
    release, in small blood vessel, 350
Solution(s)
    bracketing, 28
    curves, 475
    solutions from, 545
Solvent
    flow rate, 26
    storage tank, breathing losses in, 169
    vapor, evaporation of, 71
Sonic flow, 178

Sound, velocity of, 175
Source problems, solution of, 472
Special topics, 313–405
  biomedical engineering, biology and
      biotechnology, 314–351
    biotechnology, 341–344
    blood–tissue interaction as pseudo
        one-compartment model,
        319–321
    cell growth, Monod kinetics, steady-
        state analysis of bioreactors,
        344–348
    Krogh cylinder, 322–324
    membrane processes, 324–329
    one-compartment
        pharmacokinetics, 314–319
    practice problems, 348–351
    release of substances at blood vessel
        wall, 330–333
    simple cellular process, 333–338
    transport between flowing blood and
        muscle tissue, 321–322
    Turing's paper on morphogenesis,
        338–341
  real world, 373–404
    clumping of coal transported in
        freight cars, 377–378
    coating of pipe, 389–392
    debugging of vinyl chloride
        recovery unit, 379–383
    design of marker particle, 396–398
    failure of heat pipes, 387–389
    potential freezing of water pipeline,
        385–387
    practice problems, 398–403
    process vessel, 378–379, 383–384
    production of heavy water by
        methane distillation, 373–377
    release of potentially harmful
        chemicals to atmosphere,
        392–396
  visit to environment, 351–372
    actual bed requirements for
        adsorptive water purification,
        368–371
    bioconcentration in fish, 357–359
    cleansing of lake bottom sediment,
        359–360
    clearance of contaminated river bed,
        366
    contamination of river bed, 364–365
    mercury volatilization from water,
        353–356

      minimum bed requirements for
          adsorptive water purification,
          367–368
      practice problems, 371–372
      rates of volatilization of solutes
          from aqueous solutions, 356–357
      Streeter-Phelps river pollution
          model, 361–363
Sphere
    unsteady diffusion in, 538
    in well-stirred solution, 540
Stability
    analysis, Laplace domain, 305
    criterion, 302
Stagnation pressure, 469
Stanton number, 51, 52
Stationary points, 254
Stationary solid, 30
Stationary vane, forces on, 121
Steady state(s)
    algebraic mass, 170
    approach to, 125
    assumption, 220
    conduction, in hollow cylinder, 593
    diffusion, 542
    humidity profile, 36
    integral balances, 10
    mass balances, 347
    model equations, 304
    multiple, 168
    steam balance, 165
Steam
    consumption, 165, 166
    distillation, 165
    -heated tube, 22, 209, 558
    superheated, 196
    temperature, 93
Steel
    density, 38
    discharge of ladle of molten, 38
    flow rate, 87
    pipes, 127
    strapping, heat capacity of, 32
    surface, velocity at, 39
Stefan-Boltzmann law, 96
Stirred tank, 7
    assumption, 56
    dilution of solute in, 70
    problems, 216
    reactor, 7
Stresses, wind-induced, 568
Sturm-Liouville
    analysis, 593
    system, 589, 601
    theorem, 580, 583, 605

Submerged hinged gate, force on, 139
Submerged surfaces, forces on, 114
Subsonic flow, 1756
Substrate S, 341
Sulfuric acid, 73, 111
Superheated steam, 196
Superposition, 515, 578
Superposition
    of Danckwerts, 482, 487
    by integration, 472
    by multiplication, 470
    principle, 205
Surface tension, effects of, 117
Surge tank, 19, 20, 71, 209
System(s)
    critically damped, 293
    representation in complex plane of, 304

T

Tangential velocity
    at cylinder surface, 469
    distributions, between rotating cylinders, 570
Tank
    discharge from, 131
    mass balances, 62
Taylor series expansion, 337
Temperature
    bounded, 213
    difference, 78
    distribution, 90
    transients, in tubular reactor, 556
Tensile force, 119
Theorems, stretching known, 596
Theoretical tray, response of to disturbances, 40
Thermal boundary layer development, 534
Thermal conductivity, 30, 485, 529
Thermal diffusivity, 485, 529
Thermal energy, 99
Thermal radiation, 96
Thermocouple, response of to temperature change, 82
Thermodynamics, first law of, 545
Thiele modulus, 146, 258
Three-dimensional infinite space, 476
Time
    derivative, of error, 302
    integral, of error, 302
    varying flux, 484
Toluene, 352
Toothpaste, 137
Tornado, wind velocity near eye of, 491

Total mass balance, 354
Total mole balance, 163
Total reflux, 66
Traffic
    concentration, at red traffic light, 635
    problem, 621, 634
Trafficking, 334
Transfer
    function, 302
        open-loop, 303
        of system, 287
    unit, height of, 25
Transferases, 341
Transform tables, 608
Transonic flow, 176
Transport
    coefficients, 48, 72
    theorem, 526
Tube heat exchanger, , 76
Tubular fixed-bed catalytic reactor, 57
Tubular flow, 68
Tubular mass balances, 65
Tubular plug flow reactor, 58
Tubular reactor, 268, 351, 543
    with axial diffusion, 70
    types of, 65
Turbulent flow, 69, 110
Turning point, 259, 260
Two-bulb method, 55
Two-compartment model, 318, 349
Two-film theory, 50
Two-phase mass balance, 614

U

Ultimate periodic solution, 289
Ultrafiltration, 349, 543
Undetermined coefficients, method of, 233
Uniformity index, 225, 228
Unit
    impulse input, 288, 293
    step input, 290
Unsteady state, 125
Unsteady-state balances, 5
Unstirred tank, heat-up time of, 92

V

van der Pol equation, 214, 270
van Heerden diagram, 168
Vapor
    –liquid equilibria, 39
    lock, 141

pressure, 21
quality, 186
Vaporizers, 184
Variable(s)
coefficients, linear ODEs with, 232
dependent, 102, 253
deviation, 286
normalized radial, 612
separation of, 37, 82, 216, 575
similarity, 535
untransformed, 601
Vector(s)
addition of, 502
algebra, 496, 500
components, 505
expansion of component, 511
flux, 539
molar flux, 527
velocity, 514
Vector calculus, 495–573
transport of energy, 545–560
Graetz-Lévêque problem, 546–548
heat transfer in packed bed, 551–554
moving boundary problem, 549–551
steady-state temperatures and heat
flux in multidimensional
geometries, 556–560
unsteady conduction, 554–556
transport of mass, 526–545
catalytic conversion in coated tubular
reactor, 527–532
diffusion and reaction in semi-
infinite medium, 532–533
Graetz-Lévêque problem in mass
transfer, 533–538
practice problems, 543–545
sphere in well-stirred solution,
540–541
steady-state diffusion in several
dimensions, 542
unsteady diffusion in sphere, 538–540
transport of momentum, 560–571
creeping flow, 564–565
inviscid flow, 567–568
irrotational flow, 568–569
practice problems, 569–571
Prandtl boundary layer equations,
565–567
steady, fully developed
incompressible duct flow, 562–563
vector notation and vector calculus,
496–526
differential operators and vector
calculus, 503–512

integral theorems of vector calculus,
512–523
practice problems, 523–526
synopsis of vector algebra, 496–503
Vegetable seeds, oil-bearing, 541
Vehicle
density profiles, 635
pathway, 637
Velocity
average, 136
components, 561, 565, 567
distribution, 135, 189
fluctuations, 106
fluid, 528
gradients, 563
profile(s), 622
near moving boundary, 570
parabolic, 530
radial, 569
of propagation, 624, 626, 628
vector, 514
Ventricle, 348
Venturi meter, design of, 141
Vertical plate, 191
Vertical vaporizer, 185
Vibrating mass, velocity of, 284
Vibrating spring, with forcing function, 230
Vibration frequency, 283
Viscoelastic fluids, 138
Viscosity changes, 195
Viscous dissipation term, 545
Viscous flow, 496
drag and friction in, 4
flow rates in, 137
Viscous fluids, 558
Viscous force, 190

W

Wall shear stress, 563
Washout, 346
Waste-disposal holding tank, 63
Water
balance
over gas phase, 157
over water phase, 157
boiler length, 197
cooling, 142
operations, 149
tower, 157, 158
evaporation of, 69
heater, 301
mass balance, 64
properties of liquid, 53

purge, 65
removal load, 156
vapor pressure, 21, 355
Weight function, 581
Wet-bulb
depression, 150
humidity, 36
temperature, 36, 149
Wheatstone Bridge, 105
Wind
-induced stresses, 568
velocity, near eye of tornado, 491

X

Xerox machines, design of, 483

Y

y-momentum equation, 566